GUN TRADER'S GUIDE

SEVENTH EDITION

PAUL WAHL

Stoeger Publishing Company

Second Printing — April, 1976

Published by the Stoeger Publishing Company,
55 Ruta Court, South Hackensack, N. J. 07606

ISBN: 0-88317-020-5

Manufactured in the United States of America

Distributed to the book trade by Follett Publishing Company,
1010 West Washington Boulevard, Chicago, Illinois 60607 and
to the sporting goods trade by Stoeger Industries, 55 Ruta
Court, South Hackensack, New Jersey 07606

In Canada, distributed to the book trade by Nelson, Foster and
Scott, Ltd., 299 Yorkland Boulevard, Willowdale, Ontario
M2J 1S9 and to the sporting goods trade by Stoeger Trading
Company, 900 Ontario Street East, Montreal, Quebec H2L 1P4

CONTENTS

Introduction

Back in 1953, I wrote in the Introduction to the first edition of *Gun Trader's Guide:* "This is a book which the compiler—to whom guns are both business and pleasure—often wished someone would produce. Almost daily searches through shelves of arms books and files of manufacturers' literature, too frequent pangs of regret for having discarded some now invaluable old gun catalogue —these experiences suggested the need for a one-volume source of specification and price data on modern small arms: a gun trader's *vade mecum.* It is earnestly hoped that this book will fill that need." Twenty-two years later, it is gratifying to me that *Gun Trader's Guide* has indeed filled that need. Hundreds of thousands of gun buffs have made it their standard reference on the identification and evaluation of semi-modern and modern rifles, shotguns, pistols, and revolvers. *Gun Trader's Guide* is widely used not only by gun traders, amateur and professional, but also by shooters, collectors, students of firearms, military personnel, and law enforcement agencies. Well-worn copies will be found in the hands of many appraisers, insurance adjusters, pawnbrokers, etc.

In 1964, *Gun Trader's Guide* became the companion volume to the world's greatest gun annual, *Shooter's Bible.* Since the latter, a "must" for anyone interested in guns, provides complete information on current models, these—in general—are not to be found listed in *Gun Trader's Guide.*

Included in this new 7th Edition are rifles, shotguns, pistols and revolvers in either of these categories: (1) now-discontinued models which were in production in 1900 and/or subsequent years to date, (2) currently-produced models on the market for more than 5 years. To compile an all-inclusive work of this type would be an impossible task and no pretense is made that this is a complete listing. With few exceptions, however, all qualifying American firearms are included. Omitted are those foreign weapons which are rarely encountered in the United States.

For easy reference, the book is divided into three sections: *Rifles, Shotguns,* and *Handguns;* listings in each are arranged alphabetically by maker's name or brand name, whichever is better known.

Descriptions are limited to major specifications together with such additional data as may be useful in identification and evaluation. Frequently, dates of manufacture are given; some few of these are approximations because of lack of definite information. To aid in identification, most major types are illustrated.

While it is believed that the prices indicated herein, being based upon an exhaustive survey, are close to current *national average* market values, because of the many variables which enter into the evaluation of a used firearm, no price guide can be truly definitive. Geographical location—involving regional economic conditions, local preferences for certain models and calibers, etc. —has a serious effect on values. Ordinarily, the prices of used modern arms are tied closely to those of similar new guns; therefore, in areas where discount sales of the latter are prevalent, values of the former will be depressed accordingly.

As antique weapons become more and more scarce while the number of collectors multiplies, these gun hobbyists are turning to semi-modern—even modern—firearms. Often referred to as "classic guns" to distinguish them from antiques, this arms collecting category may soon include most of the rifles, shotguns, and handguns of the 1900-1941 period. Craftsmanship found in products of that era of gunmaking is rarely equalled nowadays —hence, the growing collector demand for these classic guns.

The Gun Control Act of 1968 ended the importation of surplus military firearms—a major factor in the post-World-War-II gun market and an area of considerable interest to arms collectors. Also banned as imports are virtually all small pocket handguns. Consequently, prices of these popular items have been rising sharply as they become scarcer on the U.S. market.

When a semi-modern or modern firearm achieves "collector's item" status, especially if it's quite rare, the market price often skyrockets. Incidentally, this is why values of many items, as quoted in this new edition, are considerably higher than in the 1973 *Gun Trader's Guide.* Collector interest in a particular model, it should be noted, is frequently regional and the value in one section of the country may be far greater than it is in others.

With the exception of some which have been on the market for more than 5 years, current models are not included in this volume. For specification and price data on these, the reader is referred to the last edition of the *Shooter's Bible.* Applying the arms trade's standard "rule of thumb", a used gun of current model, in excellent condition, is worth at retail level from 60% to 70% of the price at which the item is sold new. Where discounting is common, the basis for such evaluation would not, of course, be the manufacturer's list price; use the average price charged by local retailers.

The values indicated in *Gun Trader's Guide* are at retail level and a dealer buying for resale cannot be expected to pay these prices.

For the purpose of assigning comparative values, all arms listed are considered as being in "Excellent" used condition by National Rifle Association standards, as published in *The American Rifleman* magazine: "NEW—not previously sold at retail, in same condition as current factory production; NEW—DISCONTINUED—same as NEW, but discontinued model. The following definitions will apply to all SECOND-HAND articles: PERFECT—in new condition, in every respect; EXCELLENT—new condition, used but little, no noticeable marring of wood or metal, bluing perfect (except at muzzle or sharp edges); VERY GOOD—in perfect working condition, no appreciable wear on working surfaces, no corrosion or pitting, only minor surface dents or scratches; GOOD—in safe working condition, minor wear on working surfaces, no broken parts, no corrosion or pitting that will interfere with proper functioning; FAIR—in safe working condition but well worn, perhaps requiring replacement of minor parts or adjustments which should be indicated in advertisement, no rust but may have corrosion pits which do not render article unsafe or inoperable; POOR—badly worn, rusty and battered, perhaps requiring major adjustments or repairs to place in operating condition." Generally, an arm in "Good" condition is worth about 40% less than if it were in "Excellent" condition; other degrees of condition affect values proportionately.

This latest *Gun Trader's Guide* incorporates numerous changes required to bring it up to date. Reflecting the effects of inflation and increased demand, virtually every price is revised upwards. I hope that you will find it even more useful and interesting than its well-received predecessors.

—PAUL WAHL

Section I

RIFLES

Anschutz Model 1411

Anschutz Model 1413

Argentine Model 1891 Carbine

ArmaLite AR-7

ArmaLite Custom AR-7

Austrian Model 95 Rifle

British S.M.L.E. No. 1 Mark III*

J. G. Anschutz G. M. B. H. Jagd-und Sportwaffenfabrik, Ulm, West Germany

Anschutz Model 1411 Match 54 Rifle $275

Bolt action single shot. Caliber, 22 Long Rifle. 28-inch extra heavy barrel. Precision micrometer rear sight and globe front sight, both detachable. Scope bases. Target stock with checkered pistol grip, thumb rest, cheekpiece, beavertail fore-end, adjustable swivel. Weight, about 12½ pounds. Currently manufactured.

Anschutz Model 1413 Super Match 54 Rifle $425

Bolt action single shot "free-rifle." Specifications similar to Model 54, except has special stock with thumbhole, adjustable butt plate, palm rest. Weight, about 15½ pounds. Currently manufactured.

Argentine Military Rifles manufactured in Germany by D.W.M. and Ludwig Loewe & Co., Berlin

Argentine Model 1891 Mauser Military Rifle $75

Bolt action. Caliber, 7.65mm Mauser. 5-shot semi-fixed box magazine, clip-loaded. 29-inch barrel. Weight, about 8¾ pounds. Open rear sight, inverted "V" front sight. Military–type full stock. (Adopted 1891 by Argentina, also Bolivia, Colombia, Ecuador, Paraguay, Peru, and Uruguay).

Argentine Model 1891 Carbine $85

Same as Model 1891 Rifle, except has 17.6-inch barrel, is stocked to muzzle, has no bayonet stud.

ArmaLite Inc., Costa Mesa, California

Armalite AR-7 "Explorer" Survival Rifle $50

Takedown. Semi-automatic. Caliber, 22 Long Rifle. 8-shot box magazine. 16-inch cast aluminum barrel with steel liner. Peep rear sight, blade front sight. Molded plastic stock, recessed to stow barrel, action, and magazine. Weight, 2¾ pounds. Will float, either stowed or assembled. Made from 1959 to 1973. *Note:* Now manufactured by Charter Arms Corp., Stratford, Conn.

Armalite Custom AR-7 Rifle $75

Same as AR-7 Survival Rifle, except has deluxe walnut stock with cheekpiece and pistol grip. Weight, 3½ pounds. Made from 1964 to 1970.

Austrian Military Rifles manufactured at Steyr Armory, Steyr, Austria

Austrian Model 95 Steyr-Mannlicher Service Rifle.. $75

Straight-pull bolt action. Caliber, 8X50R Mannlicher (many of these rifles were altered during World War II to use the 7.9mm German service ammunition). 5-shot Mannlicher-type box magazine, 30-inch barrel. Weight about 8½ pounds. Blade front sight, rear sight adjustable for elevation. Military-type full stock.

Austrian Model 90 Steyr-Mannlicher Carbine $75

Same general specifications as Model 95 Rifle, except has 19½-inch barrel, weighs about 7 pounds.

Belgian Military Rifles manufactured by Fabrique Nationale D'Armes de Guerre, Herstal, Belgium; Fabrique D'Armes de l'Etat, Luttich, Belgium, Hopkins & Allen Arms Co. of Norwich, Connecticut, as well as contractors in Birmingham, England, also produced these arms during World War I

Belgian Model 1889 Mauser Military Rifle $75

Caliber, 7.65mm Belgian Service (7.65mm Mauser). 5-shot projecting box magazine. 30¾–inch barrel with jacket. Weight, about 8½ pounds. Adjustable rear sight, blade front sight. Straight-grip military stock. Made from 1889 to about 1935; this and the carbine model of the same type were the principal weapons of the Belgian Army at the start of World War II.

Belgian Model 1889 Mauser Carbine $75

Same as Model 1889 Rifle except has 20¾-inch barrel, weighs about 8 pounds. The Model 1916 Carbine is virtually the same except for minor difference in the rear sight graduations, the lower band which is closer to the muzzle and the swivel plate located on the side of the butt-tock.

Belgian Military Rifles manufactured by Fabrique Nationale D'Armes de Guerre, Herstal, Belgium

Belgian Model 1935 Mauser Military Rifle $95

Same general specifications as F. N. Model 1924; differences are minor. Caliber, 7.65mm Belgian Service.

Belgian Model 1936 Mauser Military Rifle $75

An adaptation of the Model 1889 with German M/98–type bolt, Belgian M/89 protruding box magazine. Caliber 7.65mm Belgian Service.

British Military Rifles manufactured at Royal Small Arms Factory, Enfield Lock, Middlesex, England, as well as private contractors

British Army Rifle No. 1 Mark III* $90

Short Magazine Lee-Enfield (S.M.L.E.). Bolt Action. Caliber, 303 British Service. 10-shot box magazine. 25¼-inch barrel. Weight, about 8¾ pounds. Adjustable rear sight, blade front sight with guards. Two-piece, full length military stock. *Note:* The earlier Mark III (approved 1907) is virtually the same as the Mark III* (adopted 1918) except for sights and different magazine cut-off which was eliminated on the latter.

British Army Rifle No. 3 Mark I* (Pattern '14) $90

Modified Mauser–type bolt action. Except for caliber, 303 British Service, and long range sights, this rifle is the same as U.S. Model 1917 Enfield. See listing of the latter for general specifications.

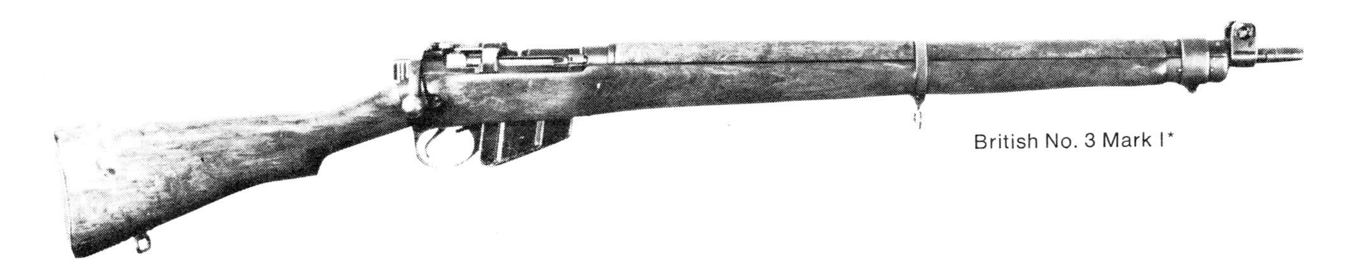

British No. 3 Mark I*

British Army Rifle No. 4 Mark I* $75

Post World War I modification of the S.M.L.E. intended to simplify mass production. General specifications same as Rifle No. 1 Mark III* except weighs 9¼ pounds, has aperture rear sight, minor differences in construction.

British Army Light Rifle No. 4 Mark I* $75

Modification of the S.M.L.E. Caliber, 303 British Service, 10-shot box magazine. 23-inch barrel. Weight, about 6¾ pounds. Micrometer click rear peep sight, blade front sight. One-piece military-type stock with recoil pad. Made during World War II.

British Army Rifle No. 5 Mark I* $75

Jungle Carbine. Modification of the S.M.L.E. similar to Light Rifle No. 4 Mark I* except has 20½-inch barrel with flash hider, carbine-type stock. Made during World War II, originally designed for use in the Pacific Theater.

Brno Sporting Rifles manufactured by Ceska Zbrojovka, Brno, Czechoslovakia

Brno Hornet Bolt Action Sporting Rifle $400

Miniature Mauser action. Caliber, 22 Hornet. 5-shot detachable box magazine. 23-inch barrel. Double set trigger. Weight, about 6¼ pounds. Three-leaf open rear sight, hooded ramp front sight. Sporting stock with checkered pistol grip and forearm, swivels. *Note:* This rifle was also marketed in the U.S. as the "Z-B Mauser."

Brno Model 21H Bolt Action Sporting Rifle $400

Mauser-type action. Calibers: 6.5X57, 7X57, 8X57mm. 5-shot box magazine. 20½-inch barrel. Double set trigger. Weight, about 6¾ pounds. Two-leaf open rear sight, hooded ramp front sight. Half-length sporting stock with cheekpiece, checkered pistol grip and forearm, swivels.

Brno Model 22F $400

Same as Model 21H except has full-length Mannlicher-type stock, weighs about 6 pounds 14 ounces.

Brno Model I Bolt Action Sporting Rifle $200

Caliber, 22 Long Rifle, 5-shot detachable magazine. 22¾-inch barrel. Weight, about 6 pounds. Three-leaf open rear sight, hooded ramp front sight. Sporting stock with checkered pistol grip, swivels.

Brno Model II $225

Same as Model I except with de luxe grade stock.

Browning Rifles manufactured by Fabrique Nationale d'Armes de Guerre, Herstal, Belgium, also by Miroku Firearms Mfg. Co., Tokyo, Japan; distributed in the U.S. by Browning, Morgan, Utah.

Browning 22 Automatic Rifle Grade I $95

Similar to discontinued Remington Model 241A. Autoloading. Takedown. Calibers: 22 Long Rifle, 22 Short (not interchangeably). Tubular magazine in butt-stock holds 11 Long Rifle, 16 Short. Barrel lengths: 19¼-inch in 22 L.R., 22¼-inch in 22 Short. Weight, about 4¾ pounds in L.R., 5 pounds in Short. Receiver scroll engraved. Open rear sight, bead front sight. Pistol-grip buttstock, semi-beavertail forearm, both checkered. Made from 1958 to date. *Note:* Since May 1972, this model has been manufactured by Miroku.

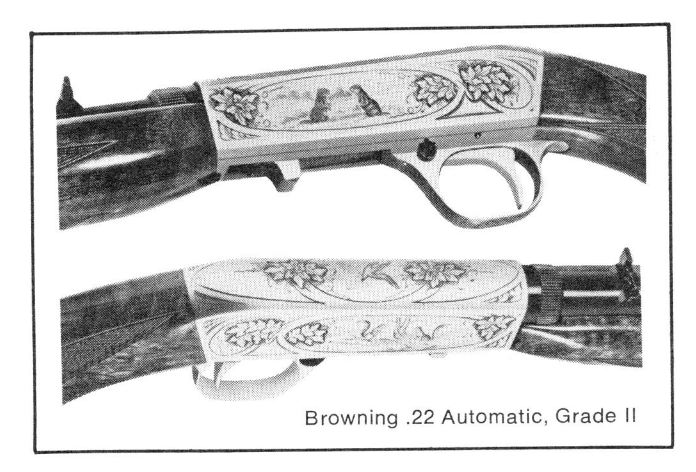

Browning .22 Automatic, Grade II

Browning 22 Automatic Rifle, Grade II $140

Same as Grade I, except satin chrome-plated receiver engraved with small game animal scenes, gold-plated trigger, select walnut stock and forearm. 22 Long Rifle only.

Browning 22 Automatic Rifle, Grade III $295

Same as Grade I, except satin chrome-plated receiver elaborately hand-carved and engraved with dog and gamebird scenes, scrolls and leaf clusters; gold-plated trigger, extra fancy walnut stock and forearm, skip-checkered. 22 Long Rifle only.

Brno Hornet

Brno Model 21H

Brno Model 22F

Brno Model II

Browning .22 Automatic, Grade I

Browning .22 Automatic, Grade III

Browning High-Power, Safari Grade

Browning High-Power, Medallion Grade

Browning High-Power, Olympian Grade

Browning T-Bolt, T-1

Browning High-Power Bolt Action Rifle, Safari Grade, Standard Action $315

Mauser-type action. Calibers: 270 Win., 30-06, 7mm Rem. Mag., 300 Win. Mag., 308 Norma Mag., 338 Win. Mag., 375 H&H Mag., 458 Win. Mag. Cartridge capacity: 6 rounds in 270, 30-06; 4 in magnum calibers. Barrel length: 22" in 270, 30-06; 24" in magnum calibers. Weight: 7 lbs. 2 oz. in 270, 30-06; 8¼ lbs. in magnum calibers. Folding leaf rear sight, hooded ramp front sight. Checkered stock with pistol grip, Monte Carlo cheekpiece, QD swivels; recoil pad on magnum models. Made from 1960 to 1974.

Browning High-Power Bolt Action Rifle, Safari Grade, Short Action $290

Same as Standard, except short action. Calibers: 222 Rem., 222 Rem. Mag. 22-inch lightweight barrel or 24" heavy barrel. No sights. Weight: 6 lbs. 2 oz. with lightweight barrel, 7½ lbs. with heavy barrel.

Browning High-Power Bolt Action Rifle, Safari Grade, Medium Action $300

Same as Standard, except medium action. Calibers: 22/250, 243 Win., 284 Win., 308 Win. Barrel: 22-inch lightweight barrel; 22/250 and 243 also available with 24" heavy barrel. Weight: 6 lbs. 12 oz. with lightweight barrel; 7 lbs. 13 oz. with heavy barrel.

Browning High-Power Bolt Action Rifle, Medallion Grade $490

Same as Safari Grade, except: receiver and barrel scroll engraved, ram's head engraved on floorplate; select walnut stock with rosewood forearm tip and grip cap.

Browning High-Power Bolt Action Rifle, Olympian Grade $850

Same as Safari Grade, except: barrel engraved; receiver, trigger guard and floor plate satin-chrome-plated and engraved with game scenes appropriate to caliber; finest figured walnut stock with rosewood forearm tip and grip cap, latter with 18K gold medallion.

Browning "T-Bolt" 22 Repeating Rifle, T-1 .... $45

Straight-pull bolt action. Caliber, 22 Long Rifle. 5-shot clip magazine. 24-inch barrel. Peep rear sight, blade/ramp front sight. Plain walnut stock with pistol grip. Weight, 6 lbs. Also available in left-hand model. Made from 1965 to 1973.

Browning "T-Bolt", T-2 .... $65

Same as T-1, except fancy figured walnut stock, checkered. Discontinued.

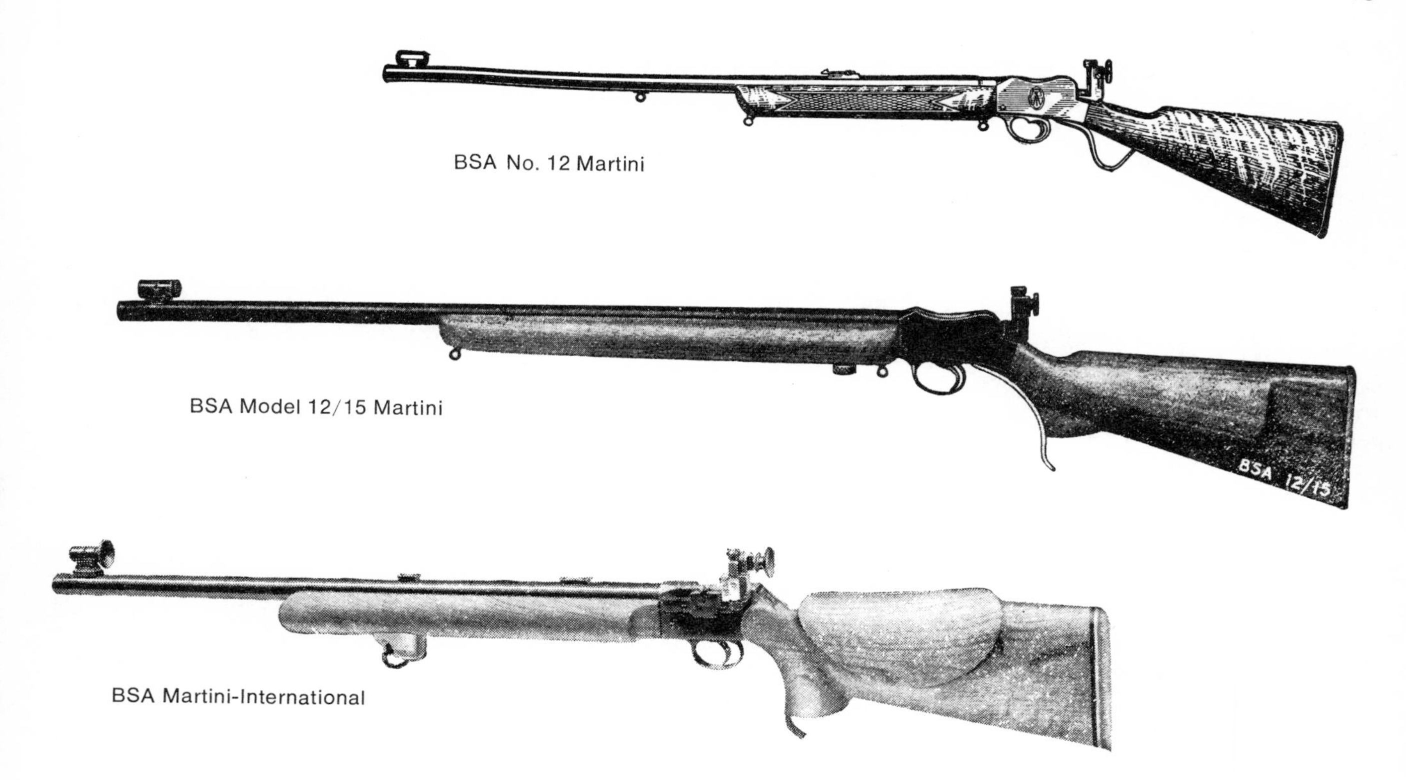

BSA No. 12 Martini

BSA Model 12/15 Martini

BSA Martini-International

BSA Guns Ltd., Birmingham, England

BSA No. 12 Martini Single Shot Target Rifle $150

Caliber, 22 Long Rifle. 29-inch barrel. Weight, about 8¾ pounds. Parker-Hale Model 7 rear sight and Model 2 front sight. Straight-grip stock, checkered forearm. *Note:* This model was also available with open sights or with BSA No. 30 and 20 sights.

BSA Model 15 Martini Single Shot Target Rifle . . . $175

Caliber, 22 Long Rifle. 29-inch barrel. Weight, about 9½ pounds. BSA No. 30 rear sight and No. 20 front sight. Target stock with cheekpiece and pistol grip, long semi-beavertail forearm.

BSA Centurian Model Match Rifle $200

Same general specifications as Model 15 except has "Centurion" match barrel, 1½″ groups at 100 yards guaranteed.

BSA Model 12/15 Martini Single Shot Target Rifle $175

Caliber, 22 Long Rifle. 29-inch barrel. Weight, about 9 pounds. Parker-Hale No. PH-7A rear sight and No. FS-22 front sight. Target stock with high comb and cheekpiece, beavertail forearm. *Note:* This is a post World War II model; however, a similar rifle, the BSA-Parker Model 12/15 was produced about 1938.

BSA Heavy Model 12/15 . . . . $200

Same as Standard Model 12/15 except has extra heavy barrel, weighs about 11 pounds.

BSA No. 13 Martini Single Shot Target Rifle $175

Caliber, 22 Long Rifle. Lighter version of the No. 12 with same general specifications, except has 25-inch barrel, weighs 6½ pounds.

BSA No. 13 Sporting Rifle

Same as No. 13 Target except fitted with Parker-Hale "Sportarget" rear sight and bead front sight. Also available in caliber 22 Hornet.

22 Long Rifle **$175**
22 Hornet **$200**

BSA Martini-International Single Shot Match Rifle — Heavy Pattern $200

Caliber, 22 Long Rifle. 29-inch heavy barrel. Weight, about 14 pounds. Parker-Hale "International" front and rear sights. Target stock with full cheekpiece and pistol grip, broad beavertail forearm, handstop, swivels. Available in Right Hand and Left Hand Models. Manufactured from 1950 to 1953.

BSA Martini-International—Light Pattern $200

Same general specifications as Heavy Pattern, except has 26-inch lighter weight barrel. Weight, about 11 pounds.

BSA Martini-International MK II Match Rifle $225

Same general specifications as original model. Heavy and Light Pattern. Improved trigger mechanism and ejection system. Redesigned stock and forearm. Made from 1953 to 1959.

BSA Martini-International MK III Match Rifle $250

Same general specifications as MK II Heavy Pattern. Longer action frame with I-section alloy strut to which forearm is attached; barrel is fully floating. Redesigned stock and forearm. Made from 1959 to 1967.

BSA Majestic Deluxe Featherweight Bolt Action Hunting Rifle

Mauser-type action. Calibers: 243 Win., 270 Win., 308 Win., 30-06, 458 Win. Mag. 4-shot magazine. 22-inch barrel with BESA recoil reducer. Weight, 6¼ lbs., except 8¾ lbs. in 458. Folding leaf rear right, hooded ramp front sight. European-style walnut stock, checkered, with cheekpiece, pistol grip, schnabel forend, swivels, recoil pad. Made from 1959 to 1965.

458 Win. Mag. caliber $175
Other calibers $140

BSA Majestic Deluxe Standard Weight $140

Same as Featherweight Model, except heavier barrel without recoil reducer. Calibers: 22 Hornet, 222 Rem., 243 Win., 7x57mm, 308 Win., 30-06. Weight, 7¼ to 7¾ pounds.

BSA Monarch Deluxe Bolt Action Hunting Rifle . . $140

Same as Majestic Deluxe Standard Weight Model, except has redesigned stock of U.S. style with contrasting hardwood fore-end tip and grip cap. Calibers: 222 Rem., 243 Win., 270 Win., 7mm Rem. Mag., 308 Win., 30-06. 22-inch barrel. Weight, 7 to 7¼ pounds. Made from 1965 to date.

BSA Monarch Deluxe Varmint Rifle $150

Same as Monarch Deluxe, except has 24-inch heavy barrel and weighs 9 pounds. Calibers: 222 Rem., 243 Win.

Canadian Military Rifles manufactured by Ross Rifle Co., Quebec, Canada

Canadian Model 1907 Mark II Ross Military Rifle . . $125

Straight pull bolt action. Caliber, 303 British. 5-shot box magazine. 28-inch barrel. Weight, about 8½ pounds. Adjustable rear sight, blade front sight. Military-type full stock. *Note:* The Ross was originally issued as a Canadian service rifle in 1907. There were a number of variations; it was the official weapon at the beginning of World War I, has been obsolete for many years. For Ross sporting rifle, see listing under Ross Rifle Co.

Colt's Firearms Division, Hartford, Connecticut

Colt Lightning Magazine Rifle $385

Slide action. Calibers: 32-20, 38-40, 44-40. 15-shot tubular magazine. 26-inch barrel, round or octagon. Weight, 6¾ pounds (round barrel model). Open rear sight, bead or blade front sight. Walnut stock and forearm. Made from 1885 to 1900.

Colt Lightning Carbine $400

Same as Lightning Magazine Rifle, except has 12-shot magazine, 20-inch barrel, weighs 6¼ pounds.

Colt Lightning Baby Carbine $425

Same as Lightning Carbine, except lighter weight (5½ pounds.)

Colt 22 Lightning Magazine Rifle $275

Slide Action. Caliber, 22 Rim Fire (Short or Long). Tubular magazine holding 15 long or 16 short. 24-inch barrel, round or octagon. Weight, 5¾ pounds (round barrel model). Open rear sight, bead front sight. Walnut stock and forearm. Made from 1885 to 1903.

Coltsman "Custom" Bolt Action Sporting Rifle . . $225

FN Mauser action, side safety, engraved floorplate. Calibers: 30-06, 300 H&H Mag. 5-shot box magazine. 24-inch barrel, ramp front sight. Fancy walnut stock, Monte Carlo comb, cheekpiece, pistol grip, checkered, Q.D. swivels. Weight, about 7¼ pounds. Made from 1957 to 1961. Value shown is for rifle, as furnished by manufacturer, without rear sight.

Coltsman "De Luxe" Rifle $200

FN Mauser action. Same as "Custom" model except plain floorplate, plainer wood and checkering. Made from 1957 to 1961. Value shown is for rifle, as furnished by manufacturer, without rear sight.

Coltsman "Standard" Rifle $175

FN Mauser action. Same as "DeLuxe" model except stock has no cheekpiece, barrel length is 22 inches. Made from 1957 to 1961. Value shown is for rifle, as furnished by manufacturer, without rear sight.

Coltsman Rifles, Models of 1957

Sako Medium action. Calibers: 243, 308. Weight, about 6¾ pounds. Other specifications similar to those of models with FN actions. Made from 1957 ot 1961.

"Custom" $225
"De Luxe" $200
"Standard" $175

Colteer 1-22 Single Shot Bolt Action Rifle $25

Caliber, 22 Long Rifle, Long, Short. 20 or 22-inch barrel. Open rear sight, ramp front sight. Pistol-grip stock with Monte Carlo comb. Weight, about 5 pounds. Made from 1957 to 1967.

Coltsman "Custom" Rifle, Model of 1961 . . . .$225

Sako action. Calibers: 222, 222 Mag., 223, 243, 264, 270, 308, 30-06, 300 H&H. 23, 24-inch barrel. Folding leaf rear sight, hooded ramp front sight. Fancy French walnut stock with Monte Carlo comb, rosewood fore-end tip and grip cap, skip checkering, recoil pad, sling swivels. Weight, 6½ to 7½ pounds depending upon caliber. Made from 1963 to 1965.

BSA Martini-International Mk. III

BSA Monarch DeLuxe

BSA Monarch DeLuxe Varmint

Colt Lightning Rifle

Coltsman DeLuxe

Coltsman 1957 Standard

Colteer 1-22

Coltsman 1961 Custom

Coltsman 1961 Standard

Colt AR-15 Sporter

Colteer Autoloader

Colt Stagecoach

Coltsman "Standard" Rifle, Model of 1961 .... $175

Same as "Custom" model except plainer, American walnut stock. Made from 1963 to 1965.

Colt AR-15 Sporter $200

Commercial semi-automatic version of U.S. M16 rifle. Gas-operated. Takedown. Caliber, 223 Rem. (5.56mm). 20-round magazine with spacer to reduce capacity to 5 rounds. 20-inch barrel with flash suppressor. Rear peep sight with windage adjustment in carrying handle. Front sight adjustable for windage. 3X scope and mount available as accessory equipment (adds $60 to value). Black molded butt stock of high-impact synthetic material, rubber butt plate. Barrel surrounded by handguards of black fiberglass with heat-reflecting inner shield. Swivels, black web sling strap. Weight, without accessories, 6.3 pounds. Made from 1964 to date.

Colteer 22 Autoloader $50

Caliber, 22 Long Rifle. 15-round tubular magazine. 19⅜" barrel. Open rear sight, hooded ramp front sight. Straight-grip stock, Western carbine style forearm with barrel band. Weight, about 4¾ pounds. Made from 1964 to 1975.

Colt Stagecoach 22 Autoloader $60

Same as Colteer 22 Autoloader, except has engraved receiver, saddle ring, 16½" barrel. Weight, 4 lbs. 10 oz. Made from 1965 to 1975.

Czechoslovakian Military Rifles manufactured by Ceska Zbrojovka, Brno, Czechoslovakia

Czech Model 1924 (VZ24) Mauser Military Rifle ... $125

Basically the same as the German Kar. 98k and F. N. (Belgian Model 1924. Caliber, 7.9mm. Mauser. 5-shot box magazine. 23¼-inch barrel. Weight, about 8½ pounds. Adjustable rear sight, blade front sight with guards. Military stock of Belgian-type, full handguard. Manufactured from 1924 through World War II. Many of these rifles were made for export. As produced during the German occupation, this model was known as Gewehr 24t.

Czech Model 1933 (VZ33) Mauser Military Carbine. $125

Modification of the German M/98 action with smaller receiver ring. Caliber, 7.9mm. Mauser. 19¼-inch barrel. Weight, about 7½ pounds. Adjustable rear sight, blade front sight with guards. Military-type full stock. Manufactured from 1933 through World War II; a similar model produced during the German occupation was designated Gew. 33/40.

Charles Daly Rifle made by Franz Jaeger & Co., Suhl, Germany, and distributed in the U.S. by Charles Daly, Inc. of New York City

Charles Daly Hornet Rifle $600

Same as Herold Rifle. See listing of that rifle for specifications. Imported during the 1930's.

Fabrique Nationale D'Armes de Guerre, Herstal, Belgium

F. N. Models 1924, 1934/30 and 1930 Mauser Military Rifles $125

Basically the same as the German Kar. 98k. Straight bolt handle. Calibers: 7mm, 7.65mm and 7.9mm Mauser. 5-shot box magazine. 23½-inch barrel. Weight, about 8½ pounds. Adjustable rear sight, blade front sight. Military stock of M/98 pattern with slight modification. Model differences are minor. Also produced in a short carbine model with 17¼-inch barrel. *Note:* These rifles were manufactured under contract for Abyssinia, Argentina, Belgium, Bolivia, Brazil, Chile, China, Colombia, Ecuador, Iran, Luxembourg, Mexico, Peru, Turkey, Uruguay and Yugoslavia. Such arms usually bear the coat of arms of the country for which they were made, together with the contractor's name and the date of manufacture. Also sold commercially and exported to all parts of the world.

F.N. Model 1950 Mauser Military Rifle $150

Same as previous F.N. models of Kar. 98K type, except chambered for 30-06.

F.N. Model 1949 Semi-Automatic Military Rifle $275

Gas-operated. Calibers: 7mm, 7.65mm, 7.92mm, 30M2 (30-06). 10-round box magazine, clip fed or loaded singly. 23.2-inch barrel. Weight, 9½ pounds. Tangent rear sight, shielded post front sight. Pistol-grip stock, handguard. *Note:* Adopted in cal. 30 by Belgium in 1949 and also by Belgian Congo, Brazil, Colombia, Luxembourg, and Netherlands East Indies; Venezuela bought this rifle in 7mm, Egypt in 7.92mm. Approximately 160,000 were made.

F. N. De Luxe Mauser Bolt Action Sporting Rifle .. $315

American calibers: 220 Swift, 243 Win., 244 Rem., 250/3000, 257 Roberts, 270 Win., 7mm, 300 Sav., 308 Win., 30-06; European calibers: 7X57, 8X57JS, 8X60S, 9.3X62, 9.5X57, 10.75X68mm. 5-shot box magazine. 24-inch barrel. Weight, about 7½ pounds; except in 270, 8¼ pounds. American model is standard with hooded ramp front sight and Tri-Range rear sight; Continental model has two-leaf rear sight. Checkered stock with cheekpiece, pistol grip, swivels. Made from 1947 to 1963.

F. N. De Luxe Mauser—Presentation Grade $500

Same as regular model except has select grade stock; engraving on receiver, trigger guard, floorplate and barrel breech. Discontinued 1963.

F.N. Supreme Mauser Bolt Action Sporting Rifle .. $350

Calibers: 243, 270, 7mm, 308, 30-06. 4-shot magazine in 243 and 308; 5-shot in other calibers. 22-inch barrel in 308; 24-inch in other calibers. Hooded ramp front sight, Tri-range peep rear sight. Checkered stock with Monte Carlo cheekpiece, pistol grip, swivels. Weight, about 7¾ pounds. Made from 1957 to date.

F.N. Supreme Magnum Mauser $365

Calibers: 264 Mag., 7mm Mag., 300 Win. Mag. Specifications same as for standard-caliber model except 3-shot magazine capacity.

Fabrique Nationale D'Armes de Guerre, Herstal, Belgium

FN Model 1950 Mauser

FN Model 1949 Semi-Auto

FN DeLuxe Mauser

FN DeLuxe Mauser, Presentation Grade

S.A. Luigi Franchi, Brescia, Italy

Franchi Deluxe Centennial

Franchi Centennial Automatic Rifle

Commemorates Franchi's 100th anniversary (1868-1968). Centennial seal engraved on receiver. Semi-automatic. Takedown. Caliber, .22 Long Rifle. 11-shot magazine in buttstock. 21-inch barrel. Weight, 5⅛ pounds. Open rear sight, gold bead front sight on ramp. Checkered walnut stock and fore-end. Deluxe model has fully engraved receiver, premium grade wood. Made in 1968.

Standard Model . . . . **$ 90**

Deluxe Model **$125**

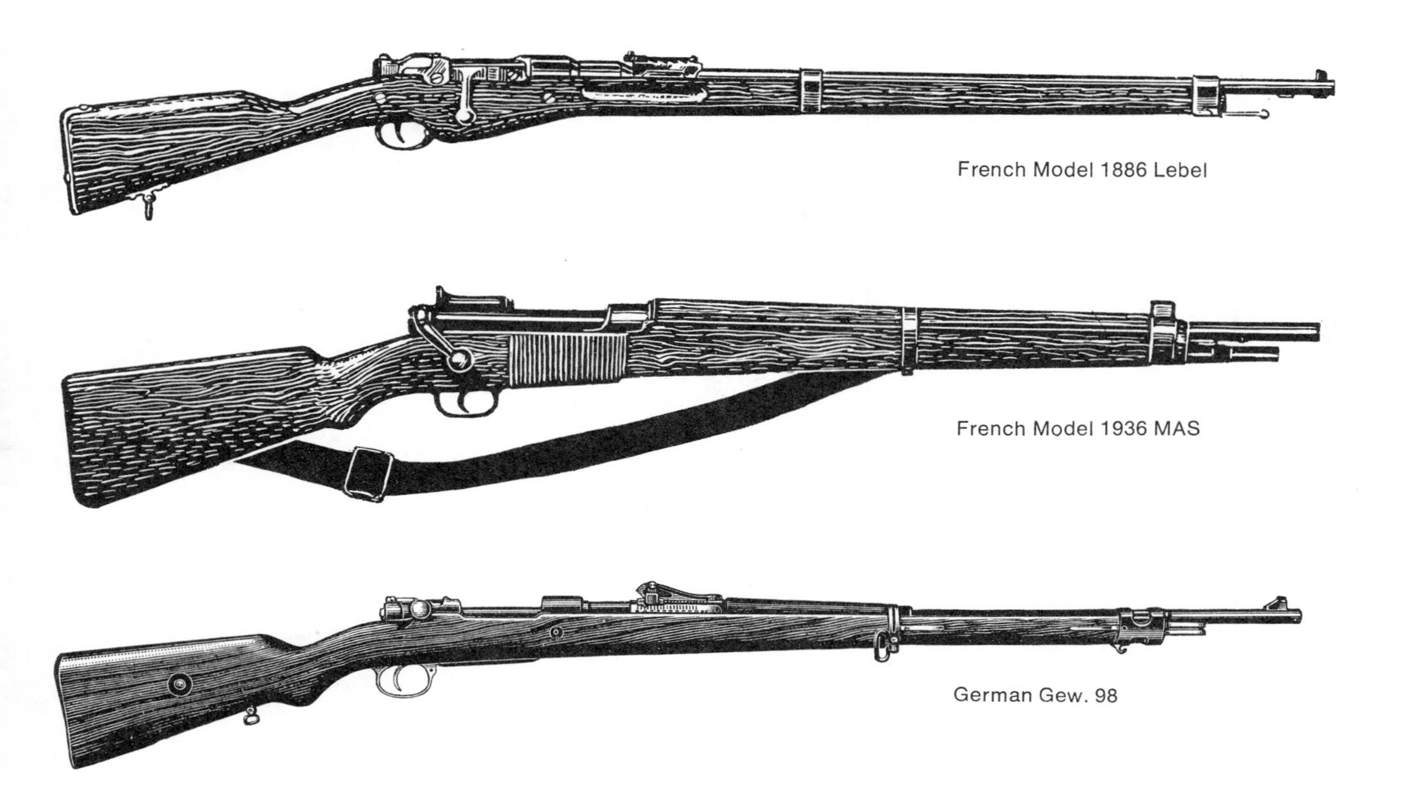

French Model 1886 Lebel

French Model 1936 MAS

German Gew. 98

French Government Plants, Chatellerault, St. Etienne

French Model 1886 Lebel Military Rifle $75

Bolt Action. Caliber, 8mm Lebel. 8-shot tubular magazine. 31½-inch barrel. Weight, about 9¼ pounds. Adjustable rear sight, blade front sight. Two-piece military stock. Made from 1886 through World War II with various modifications.

French Military Rifle manufactured by Manufacture Francaise d'Armes et de Cycles de St. Etienne (MAS), St. Etienne, Loire, France

French Model 1936 MAS Military Rifle $75

Bolt action. Caliber, 7.5mm MAS. 5-shot box magazine. 22½-inch barrel. Weight, about 8¼ pounds. Adjustable rear sight, blade front sight. Two-piece military-type stock. Bayonet carried in fore-end tube. Made from 1936 to 1940.

German Military Rifles manufactured by Ludwig Loewe & Co., Berlin; also by all German arsenals as well as other contractors such as Haenel and Schilling

German Model 1888 (Gew. 88) Mauser-Mannlicher Service Rifle $75

Bolt Action, straight handle. Caliber, 7.9mm Mauser (8X57mm). 5-shot Mannlicher box magazine. 29-inch barrel with jacket. Weight, about 8½ pounds. Fixed front sight, adjustable rear. Military-type full stock.

German Kar. 88

German Model 1888 (Kar. 88) Mauser-Mannlicher Carbine $75

Same general specifications as Gew. 88 except has 18-inch barrel without jacket, flat turned-down bolt handle, weighs about 6¾ pounds.

German Military Rifles manufactured by various plants under German Government control

German Model 1898 (Gew. 98) Mauser Military Rifle $125

Bolt action, straight handle. Caliber, 7.9mm Mauser (8X57mm). 5-shot box magazine. 29-inch stepped barrel. Weight, 9 pounds. Blade front sight, adjustable rear sight. Military-type full stock with rounded bottom pistol grip. Adopted in 1898.

German Model 1898A (Kar. 98A) Mauser Carbine . $125

Same general specifications as Model 1898 (Gew. 98) Rifle except has turned down bolt handle, smaller receiver ring, light 23½-inch straight taper barrel, front sight guards, sling is attached to left side of stock, weighs 8 pounds. *Note:* Some of these carbines are marked "Kar. 98"; the true Kar. 98 is the earlier original M/98 carbine with 17-inch barrel and is rarely encountered.

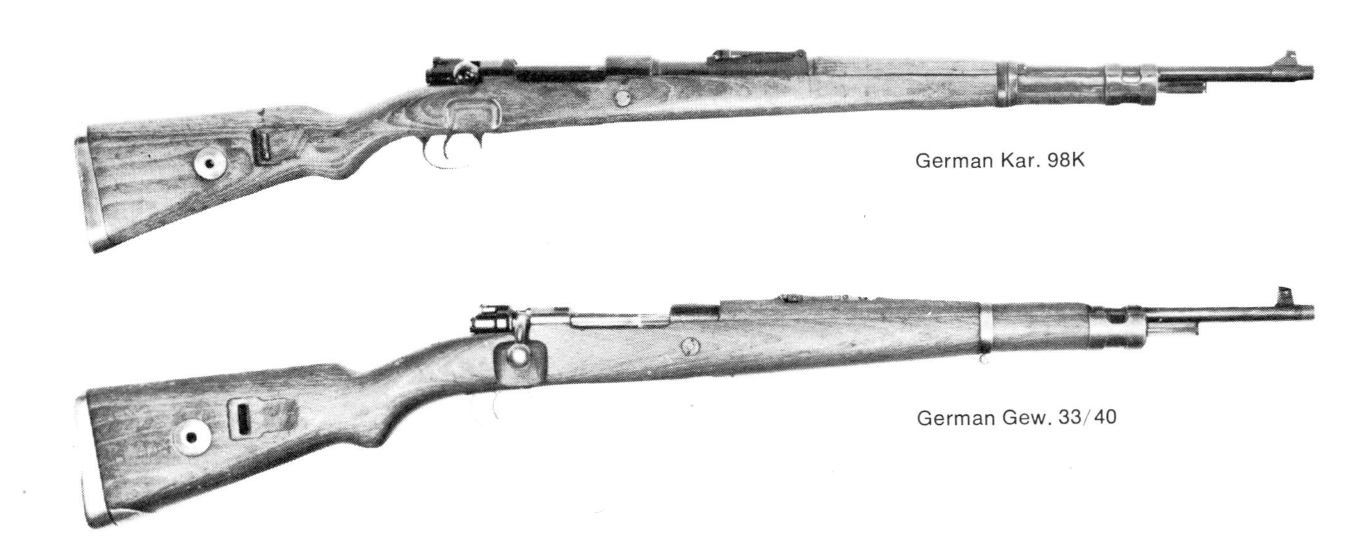

German Kar. 98K

German Gew. 33/40

German Model 1898B (Kar. 98B) Mauser Carbine . $125

Same general specifications as Model 1898 (Gew. 98) Rifle except has turned-down bolt handle and sling attached to left side of stock. This is the post World War I model.

German Model 1898K (Kar. 98K) Mauser Carbine . $125

Same general specifications as Model 1898 (Gew. 98) Rifle except has turned-down bolt handle, 23½-inch barrel, may have hooded front sight, sling is attached to left side of stock, weighs about 8½ pounds. Adopted in 1935, this was the standard German Service rifle during World War II. *Note:* Late war models had stamped sheet steel trigger guards and many of the Model 98k carbines made during World War II had laminated wood stocks, these weigh about ½ to ¾ pound more than the more than the previous model 98k. Value shown is for earlier type.

German Model 29/40 (Gew. 29/40) Mauser Rifle . $120

Same general specifications as Kar. 98k, differences are minor. Made in Poland during German occupation. Adopted in 1940.

German Model 33/40 (Gew 33/40) Mauser Rifle . . . $120

Same general specifications as the Czech Model 33 (VZ33) Mauser Carbine with minor modifications, has laminated wood stock as found in war-time Model 98k carbines. Made in Czechoslovakia during German occupation. Adopted in 1940.

German Model 24T (Gew. 24T) Mauser Rifle $120

Same general specifications as the Czech Model 24 (VZ24) Mauser Rifle with minor modifications, has laminated wood stock, weighs about 9¼ pounds. Made in Czechoslovakia during German occupation. Adopted in 1940.

Note: German Mauser Military Rifles (Gew. 98, Kar. 98) were made prior to and during World War I at the government arsenals at Amberg, Brunn, Danzig, Erfurt and Spandau; they were also manufactured by contractors such as Haenel, Loewe, Mauser, Schilling and Steyr. These rifles bear the Imperial Crown, maker's name and date of manufacture on the receiver ring. Post World War I Kar. 98b bears maker's name and date. During World War II as well as the years immediately preceding (probably from c.1935), a letter or number code was used to indicate maker. This code and date of manufacture will be found stamped on the receiver ring of rifles of this period. German Service Mausers also bear the model number **(Gew. 98, Kar. 98k, G. 33/40,** etc.) on the left side of the receiver. An exception is Model VK98, which usually bears no identifying marks.

German Model VK98 People's Rifle ("Volksgewehr") $85

Kar. 98K-type action. Caliber, 7.9mm. Single shot or repeater (latter with rough hole-in-the-stock 5-shot "magazine" or fitted with 10-shot clip of German Model 43 semiautomatic rifle). 20.9-inch barrel. Weight, 7 pounds. Fixed V-notch rear sight dovetailed into front receiver ring; front blade welded to barrel. Crude, unfinished, half-length stock without buttplate. Last ditch weapon made in 1945 for issue to German civilians. *Note:* Of value only as a military arms collector's item, this hastily-made rifle should be regarded as **unsafe** to shoot.

German Models 41 and 41-W (Gew. 41, Gew. 41-W) Semiautomatic Military Rifles $175

Gas-operated, muzzle cone system. Caliber, 7.9mm Mauser. 10-shot box magazine, 22½-inch barrel. Weight, about 10¾ pounds. Adjustable leaf rear sight, blade front sight. Military-type stock with semi-pistol grip, plastic handguard. *Note:* Model 41 lacks bolt release found on Model 41-W, otherwise the two models are the same. This is a Walther design and the early models were manufactured in that firm's Zella-Mehlis plant. Made from about 1941 to 1943.

German Gew. 43

German Models 43 and 44 (Gew. 43, Kar. 43, Kar. 44) Semiautomatic Military Rifles $175

Gas-operated, barrel vented as in Russian Tokarev. Caliber, 7.9mm Mauser. 10-shot detachable box magazine. 22-inch barrel. Weight, about 9 pounds. Adjustable rear sight, hooded front sight. Military-type stock with semi-pistolgrip, wooden handguard. *Note:* These rifles are alike except for minor details, have characteristic late World War II manufacturing short cuts: cast receiver and bolt cover, stamped steel parts, etc. Made 1943-44.

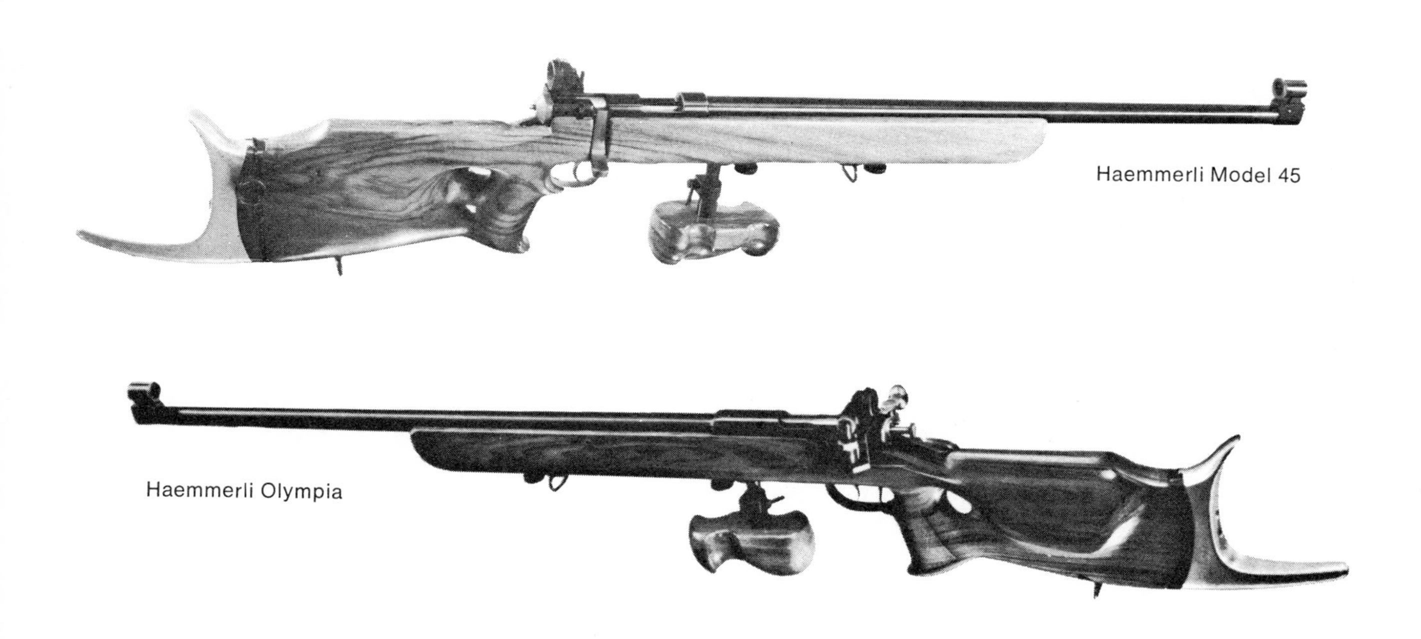

Haemmerli Model 45

Haemmerli Olympia

Haemmerli Jagd-und Sportwaffen-Fabrik AG, Lenzburg, Switzerland

Haemmerli Model Olympia 300 Meter Bolt Action Single Shot Free Rifle $500

Calibers: 30-06, 300 H&H Magnum for U.S.A.; ordinarily produced in 7.5mm, other calibers available on special order. 29½-inch heavy barrel. Double-pull trigger or double-set trigger. Micrometer peep rear sight, hooded front sight. Free rifle stock with cheekpiece, full pistol grip, thumb-hole, beavertail forearm, palm rest, Swiss-type buttplate, swivels. Made from 1949 to 1959.

Haemmerli Model 45 Smallbore Bolt Action Single Shot Match Rifle $400

Calibers: 22 Long Rifle, 22 Extra Long. 27½-inch heavy barrel. Weight, about 15½ pounds. Micrometer peep rear sight, hooded front sight. Free rifle stock with cheekpiece, full pistol-grip, thumb-hole, beavertail forearm, palm rest, Swiss-type buttplate, swivels. Made from 1947 to 1957.

C. G. Haenel, Suhl, Germany

Haenel Mauser-Mannlicher Bolt Action Sporting Rifle $250

Mauser M/88 type action. Calibers: 7X57, 8X57, 9X57mm. Mannlicher clip-loading box magazine, 5-shot. 22 or 24-inch half or full octagon barrel with raised matted rib. Double-set trigger. Weight, about 7½ pounds. Leaf-type open rear sight, ramp front sight. Sporting stock with cheekpiece, checkered pistol grip, raised side-panels, schnabel tip, swivels.

Haenel '88 Mauser Sporter $250

Same general specifications as Haenel Mauser-Mannlicher except has Mauser 5-shot box magazine.

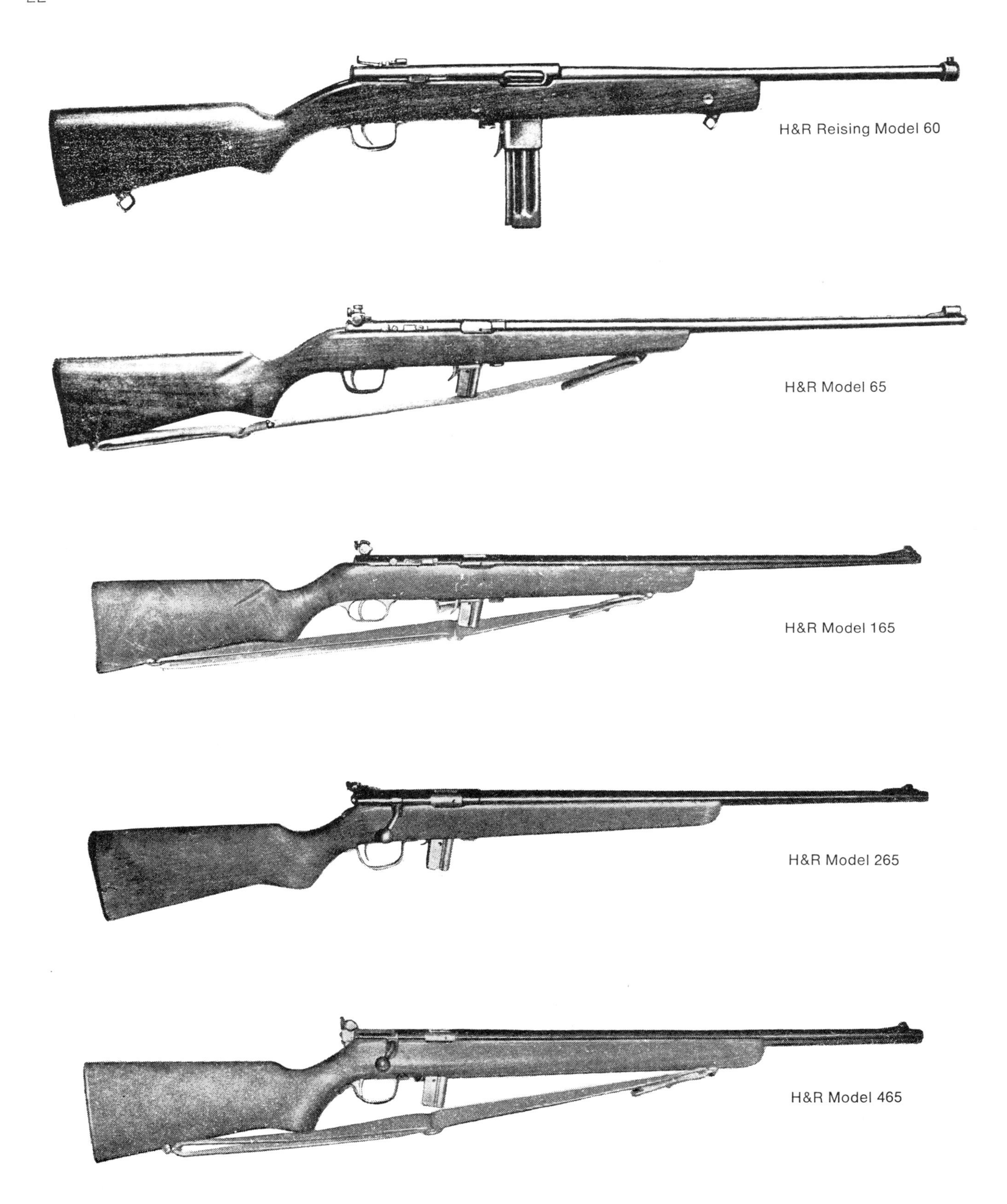

H&R Reising Model 60

H&R Model 65

H&R Model 165

H&R Model 265

H&R Model 465

Harrington & Richardson Arms Co., Worcester, Massachusetts

Harrington & Richardson Reising Model 60 Semiautomatic Rifle $250

Caliber, 45 Automatic. 12-shot and 20-shot detachable box magazines. 18¼-inch barrel. Weight, about 7½ pounds. Open rear sight, blade front sight. Plain pistol-grip stock. Made from 1944 to 1946.

Harrington & Richardson Model 65 Military Autoloading Rifle $150

Also called "General." Caliber, 22 Long Rifle. 10-shot detachable box magazine. 23-inch heavy barrel. Weight, about 9 pounds. Redfield 70 rear peep sight, blade front sight with protecting "ears." Plain pistol-grip stock, "Garand" dimensions. Made from 1944 to 1946. *Note:* This model was used as a training rifle by the U.S. Marine Corps.

Harrington & Richardson Model 165 "Leatherneck" Autoloading Rifle $85

Caliber, 22 Long Rifle. 10-shot detachable box magazine. 23-inch barrel. Weight, about 7½ pounds. Redfield 70 rear peep sight, blade front sight on ramp. Plain pistol-grip stock, swivels, web sling. Made from 1945 to 1961.

Harrington & Richardson Model 265 "Reg'lar" Bolt Action Repeating Rifle $35

Caliber, 22 Long Rifle. 10-shot detachable box magazine. 22-inch barrel. Weight, about 6½ pounds. Lyman 55 rear peep sight, blade front sight on ramp. Plain pistol-grip stock. Made from 1946 to 1949.

Harrington & Richardson Model 365 "Ace" Bolt Action Single Shot Rifle $25

Caliber, 22 Long Rifle. 22-inch barrel. Weight, about 6½ pounds. Lyman 55 rear peep sight, blade front sight on ramp. Plain pistol-grip stock. Made from 1946 to 1947.

Harrington & Richardson Model 465 "Targeteer Special" Bolt Action Repeating Rifle $60

Caliber, 22 Long Rifle. 10-shot detachable box magazine. 25-inch barrel. Weight, about 9 pounds. Lyman 57 rear peep sight, blade front sight on ramp. Plain pistol-grip stock, swivels, web sling strap. Made from 1946 to 1947.

Harrington & Richardson Model 451 "Medalist" Bolt Action Target Rifle $125

Caliber, 22 Long Rifle. 5-shot detachable box magazine. 26-inch barrel. Weight, about 10½ pounds. Lyman 524F extension rear sight, Lyman 77 front sight, scope bases. Target stock with full pistol grip and forearm, swivels and sling. Made from 1948 to 1961.

Harrington & Richardson Model 450 . . . . $110

Same as Model 451 except without front and rear sights.

Harrington & Richardson "Targeteer Jr." Bolt Action Rifle $60

Caliber, 22 Long Rifle. 5-shot detachable box magazine. 20-inch barrel. Weight, about 7 pounds. Redfield 70 rear peep sight, Lyman 17A front sight. Target stock, junior size, with pistol grip, swivels and sling. Made from 1948 to 1951.

Harrington & Richardson Model 250 "Sportster" Bolt Action Repeating Rifle $35

Caliber, 22 Long Rifle. 5-shot detachable box magazine. 23-inch barrel. Weight, about 6½ pounds. Open rear sight, blade front sight on ramp. Plain pistol-grip stock. Made from 1948 to 1961.

Harrington & Richardson Model 251 . . . . $40

Same as Model 250 except has Lyman 55H rear sight.

Harrington & Richardson Model 765 "Pioneer" Bolt Action Single Shot Rifle $20

Caliber, 22 Long Rifle, Long, Short. 24-inch barrel. Weight, about 5 pounds. Open rear sight, hooded bead front sight. Plain pistol-grip stock. Made from 1948 to 1954.

Harrington & Richardson Model 865 "Plainsman" Bolt Action Repeating Rifle $40

Caliber, 22 Long Rifle, Long, Short. 5-shot detachable box magazine. 24-inch barrel. Weight, about 5¼ pounds. Open rear sight and bead front sight. Plain pistol-grip stock. Made from 1949 to date.

Harrington & Richardson Model 866 Bolt Action Repeating Rifle $45

Same as Model 865, except has Mannlicher-style stock. Made in 1971.

Harrington & Richardson Model 150 "Leatherneck" Autoloading Rifle $50

Caliber, 22 Long Rifle only. 5-shot detachable box magazine. 22-inch barrel. Weight, about 7¼ pounds. Open rear sight, blade front sight on ramp. Plain pistol-grip stock. Made from 1949 to 1953.

Harrington & Richardson Model 151 . . . . $60

Same as Model 150 except with Redfield 70 rear peep sight.

Harrington & Richardson Model 852 "Fieldsman" Bolt Action Repeating Rifle $40

Caliber, 22 Long Rifle, Long, Short. Tubular magazine holds 21 Short, 17 Long, 15 Long Rifle. 24-inch barrel. Weight, about 5½ pounds. Open rear sight, bead front sight. Plain pistol-grip stock. Made from 1952 to 1953.

Harrington & Richardson Model 750 "Pioneer" Bolt Action Single Shot Rifle $30

Caliber, 22 Long Rifle, Long, Short. 24-inch barrel. Weight, about 5 pounds. Open rear sight, bead front sight. Plain pistol-grip stock. Made from 1954 to date.

Harrington & Richardson Model 751 Single Shot Rifle $35

Same as Model 750, except has Mannlicher-style stock. Made in 1971.

Harrington & Richardson Model 422 Slide Action Repeater $60

Caliber, 22 Long Rifle, Long, Short. Tubular magazine holds 21 Short, 17 Long, 15 Long Rifle. 24-inch barrel. Weight, about 6 pounds. Open rear sight, ramp front sight. Plain pistol-grip stock, grooved slide handle. Made from 1956 to 1958.

Harrington & Richardson Model 755 "Sahara" Single Shot Rifle $30

Blow-back action, automatic ejection. Caliber, 22 Long Rifle, Long, Short. 18-inch barrel. Weight, 4 pounds. Open rear sight, military type front-sight. Mannlicher-style stock. Made from 1963 to 1971.

Harrington & Richardson Model 760 Single Shot Rifle $30

Same as Model 755, except has conventional sporter stock. Made from 1965 to 1970.

Harrington & Richardson Model 800 "Lynx" Autoloading Rifle $45

Caliber, 22 Long Rifle. 5 or 10-shot clip magazine. 22-inch barrel. Open sights. Weight, 6 pounds. Plain pistol-grip stock. Made from 1958 to 1960.

Harrington & Richardson Model 158 "Topper Jet" Single Shot Combination Rifle

Shotgun-type action with visible hammer, side lever, automatic ejector. Caliber, 22 Rem. Jet. 22-inch barrel (interchanges with 30-30, 410 ga., 20 ga. barrels). Weight, 5 pounds. Lyman folding adjustable open rear sight, ramp front sight. Plain pistol-grip stock and forearm, recoil pad. Made from 1963 to 1967.
Rifle only **$40**
Interchangeable barrel—30-30, **$20,** shotgun **$15**

Harrington & Richardson Model 158 "Topper 30" . . $40

Same as Model 158 "Topper Jet," except calibers 22 Hornet and 30-30. Made from 1963 to date.

Harrington & Richardson Model 163 "Mustang" Single Shot Rifle $45

Same as Model 158 "Topper" except has gold-plated hammer and trigger, straight-grip stock and contoured forearm. Made from 1964 to 1967.

H&R Model 300

Harrington & Richardson Model 300 Ultra Bolt Action Rifle $185

FN Mauser action. Calibers: 22-250, 243 Win., 270 Win., 30-06, 308 Win., 7mm Rem. Mag., 300 Win. Mag. 3-round magazine in 7mm and 300 Mag. calibers, 5-round in others. 22-inch barrel. Open rear sight, ramp front sight. Checkered stock with roll-over cheekpiece and full pistol grip, contrasting wood forearm tip and pistol-grip cap, rubber buttplate, swivels. Weight, 7¾ pounds. Made from 1965 to date.

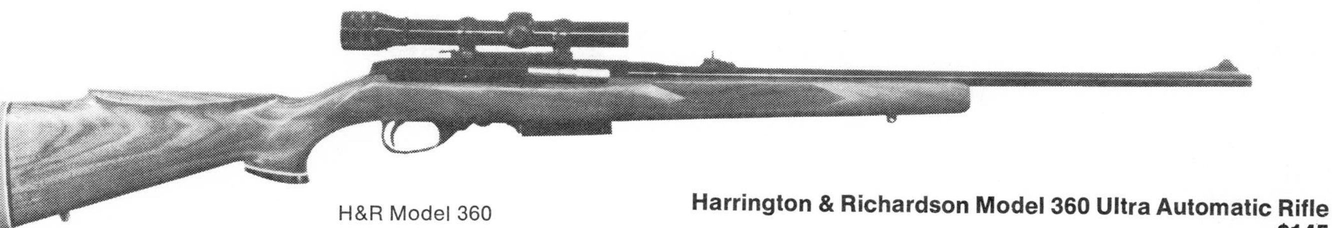

H&R Model 360

Harrington & Richardson Model 360 Ultra Automatic Rifle $145

Gas-operated semi-automatic. Calibers: 254 Win., 308 Win. 3-round detachable box magazine. 22-inch barrel. Open rear sight, ramp front sight. Checkered stock with roll-over cheekpiece, full pistol grip, contrasting wood forearm tip and pistol-grip cap, rubber buttplate, sling swivels. Weight, 7½ pounds. Made from 1965 to date. (*Note:* Originally designated Model 308, number changed to 360 in 1967.)

H&R Officer's Model 1873
Springfield Replica

Harrington & Richardson 100th Anniversary (1871-1971) Commemorative Officer's Model Springfield Replica, Model 1873 . . . . $250

Model 1873 "trap door" single-shot action. Engraved breech block, receiver, hammer, lock, band, and butt plate. Caliber, 45-70. 26-inch barrel. Peep rear sight, blade front sight. Checkered walnut stock with anniversary plaque. Ramrod. Weight, about 8 pounds. 10,000 made in 1971. Value is for rifle in new, unfired condition.

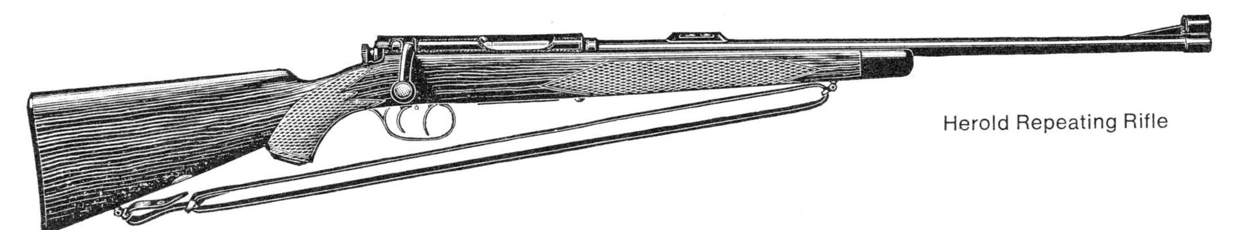
Herold Repeating Rifle

Herold Rifle made by Franz Jaeger & Co., Suhl, Germany

Herold Bolt Action Repeating Sporting Rifle $600

"Herold-Repetierbuchse." Miniature Mauser-type action with unique 5-shot box magazine on hinged floorplate. Double-set triggers. Caliber, 22 Hornet. 24-inch barrel. Leaf rear sight, ramp front sight. Weight, about 7¾ pounds. Fancy checkered stock. Made prior to World War II. *Note:* These rifles were imported by Charles Daly and A. F. Stoeger Inc. of New York City and sold under their own names.

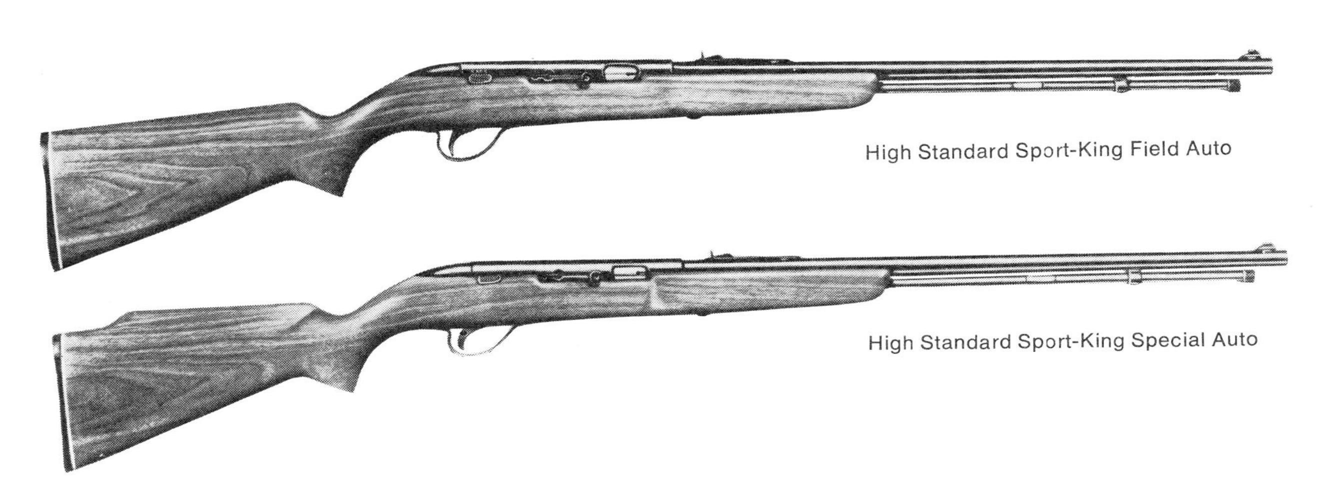
High Standard Sport-King Field Auto

High Standard Sport-King Special Auto

The High Standard Mfg. Corp., Hamden, Connecticut

High Standard Sport-King "Field" Autoloading Rifle $45

Caliber, 22 Long Rifle, 22 Long, 22 Short (high speed). Tubular magazine holds 15 L.R., 17 Long, or 21 Short. 22¼-inch barrel. Weight, 5½ pounds. Open rear sight, beaded post front sight. Plain pistol-grip stock. Made from 1960 to 1966.

High Standard Sport-King "Special" Autoloading Rifle $50

Same as Sport-King "Field" except stock has Monte Carlo comb and semi-beavertail forearm. Made from 1960 to 1966.

High Standard Sport-King Autoloading Carbine $60

Same as Sport-King "Field" Autoloader, except has 18¼ inch barrel, Western style straight-grip stock with barrel band, sling and swivels. Made from 1964 to 1973.

High Standard Sport-King De Luxe Autoloader $55

Same as Sport-King "Special" Autoloader, except has checkered stock. Made from 1966 to 1975.

High Standard Hi-Power Deluxe Bolt Action Rifle . . $175

Mauser-type action, sliding safety. Calibers: 270, 30-06. 4-Shot magazine. 22-inch barrel. Weight, 7 pounds. Folding open rear sight, ramp front sight. Walnut stock with checkered pistol grip and forearm, Monte Carlo comb, Q.D. swivels. Made from 1962 to 1966.

High Standard Hi-Power "Field" Bolt Action Rifle . $150

Same as Hi-Power Deluxe except has plain field style stock. Made from 1962 to 1966.

High Standard Flite-King Pump Rifle $55

Hammerless slide action. Caliber, 22 Long Rifle, 22 Long, 22 Short. Tubular magazine holds 17 Long Rifle, 19 Long, or 24 Short. 24-inch barrel. Weight 5½ pounds. Patridge rear sight, bead front sight. Monte Carlo stock with pistol grip, serrated semi-beavertail forearm. Made from 1962 to 1975.

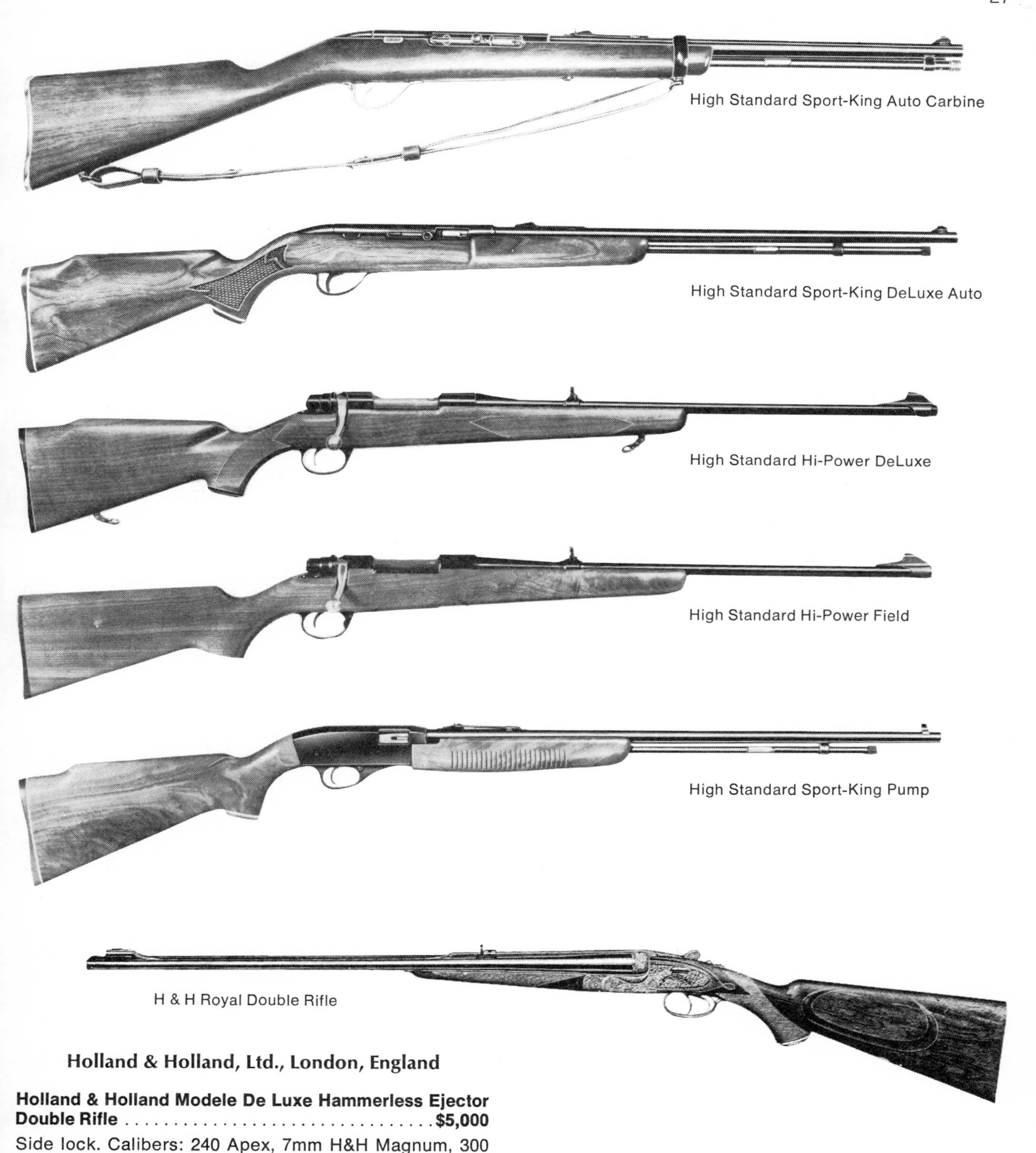

High Standard Sport-King Auto Carbine

High Standard Sport-King DeLuxe Auto

High Standard Hi-Power DeLuxe

High Standard Hi-Power Field

High Standard Sport-King Pump

H & H Royal Double Rifle

Holland & Holland, Ltd., London, England

Holland & Holland Modele De Luxe Hammerless Ejector Double Rifle $5,000

Side lock. Calibers: 240 Apex, 7mm H&H Magnum, 300 H&H Magnum, 375 H&H Magnum, 458 Win., 465 H&H. 24 to 28-inch barrels. Weights, from 7½ to 10½ pounds depending upon caliber and barrel length. Folding leaf rear sight, ramp front sight. Cheekpiece stock, checkered pistol grip and forearm, swivels. Currently manufactured. Same specifications apply to pre-war model.

Holland & Holland Royal Hammerless Ejector Double Rifle $4,000

Same general specifications as Modele de Luxe but not of as high quality. Currently manufactured.

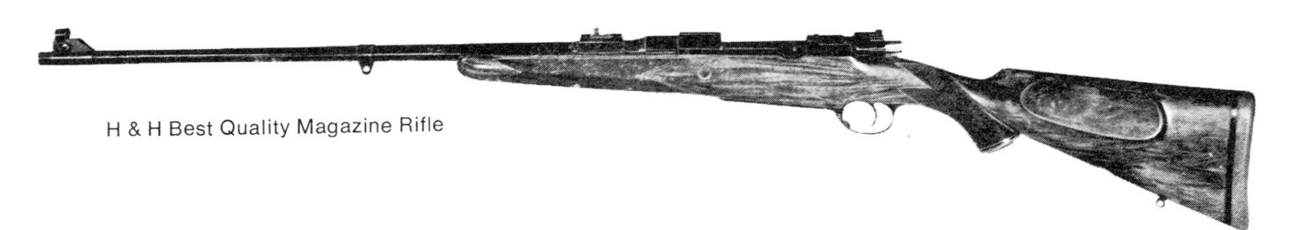

H & H Best Quality Magazine Rifle

Holland & Holland No. 2 Model Hammerless Ejector Double Rifle **$3,000**

Same general specifications as Modele de Luxe and Royal Model except plainer finish. Currently manufactured.

Holland & Holland Best Quality Magazine Rifle **$800**

Mauser or Enfield action. Calibers: 240 Apex, 300 H&H Magnum, 375 H&H Magnum. 4-shot box magazine. 24-inch barrel. Weight, about 7¼ pounds in 300 Magnum caliber; about 8¼ pounds in 300 Magnum caliber; about 8¼ pounds in 375 Magnum caliber. Folding leaf rear sight, hooded ramp front sight. Detachable French walnut stock with cheekpiece, checkered pistol grip and forearm, swivels. Currently manufactured. Specifications given are those of the present model; however, in general they apply also to pre-war models.

Hungarian Military Rifles manufactured at Government Arsenal, Budapest, Hungary

Hungarian Model 1935M Mannlicher Military Rifle . . **$75**

Caliber, 8X52mm Hungarian. Bolt action, straight handle. 5-shot projecting box magazine. 24-inch barrel. Weight, about 9 pounds. Adjustable leaf rear sight, hooded front blade. Two-piece military-type stock. Made from 1935 to c.1940.

Hungarian Model 1943M (German Gew. 98/40) Mannlicher Military Rifle **$75**

Modification, during German occupation, of the Model 1935M. Caliber, 7.9mm Mauser. Turned down bolt handle and Mauser M/98-type box magazine; other differences are minor. Made from 1940 to end of war in Europe.

Husqvarna Vapenfabrik A.B., Huskvarna, Sweden

Husqvarna Hi-Power Bolt Action Sporting Rifle . . . **$150**

Mauser-type action. Calibers: 220 Swift, 270 Win., 30-06 (see note below). 5-shot box magazine. 23¾-inch barrel. Weight, about 7¾ pounds. Open rear sight, hooded ramp front sight. Sporting stock of Arctic beech, checkered pistol-grip and forearm, swivels. *Note:* Husqvarna sporters were first introduced in the United States about 1948; earlier models were also available in calibers 6.5X55, 8X57 and 9.3X57. Specifications given above are those of the 1950 model. Made from 1946 to 1951.

Husqvarna 1951 Model **$160**

Same as 1950 Model except has high comb stock, low safety.

Husqvarna De Luxe Model Hi-Power Bolt Action Sporting Rifles, Series 1100 . . . . **$200**

Same as 1951 Model except has "jewelled" bolt, European walnut stock. Made from 1952 to 1956.

Husqvarna Super Grade, Series 1000 . . . . **$200**

Same as 1951 Model except has European walnut sporter stock with Monte Carlo comb and cheekpiece. Made from 1952 to 1956.

Husqvarna Crown Grade, Series 3100 . . . . **$210**

HVA improved Mauser action. Calibers: 243, 270, 7mm, 30-06, 308 Win. 5-shot box magazine, 23¾-inch barrel. Weight, 7¼ pounds. Open rear sight, hooded ramp front sight. European walnut stock, checkered, cheekpiece, pistol-grip cap, black foretip, swivels. Made from 1954 to date.

Husqvarna Crown Grade, Series 3000 . . . . **$210**

Same as Series 3100, except has Monte Carlo comb stock.

Husqvarna Lightweight Rifle, Series 4100 . . . . **$200**

HVA improved Mauser action. Calibers: 243, 270, 7mm, 30-06, 308 Win. 5-shot box magazine. 20½-inch barrel. Weight, about 6¼ pounds. Open rear sight, hooded ramp front sight. Lightweight walnut stock with cheekpiece, pistol grip, snobble foretip, checkered, swivels. Made from 1954 to date.

Husqvarna Lightweight Rifle, Series 4000 . . . . **$200**

Same as Series 4100, except has no rear sight and has Monte Carlo comb stock.

Husqvarna Model 456 Lightweight Full-Stock Sporter **$210**

Same as Series 4000/4100 except has sporting-style full stock with slope-away cheek rest. Weight, 6½ pounds. Made from 1959 to 1970.

Husqvarna Imperial Custom Grade, Series 6000 . . **$260**

Same as Series 3100, except fancy grade stock, 3-leaf folding rear sight, adjustable trigger. Calibers: 243, 270, 7mm Rem. Mag., 308, 30-06. Made from 1968 to 1970.

Husqvarna Imperial Monte Carlo Lightweight, Series 7000 . . . . **$250**

Same as Series 4000 Lightweight, except fancy grade stock, 3-leaf folding rear sight, adjustable trigger. Calibers: 243, 270, 308, 30-06. Made from 1968 to 1970.

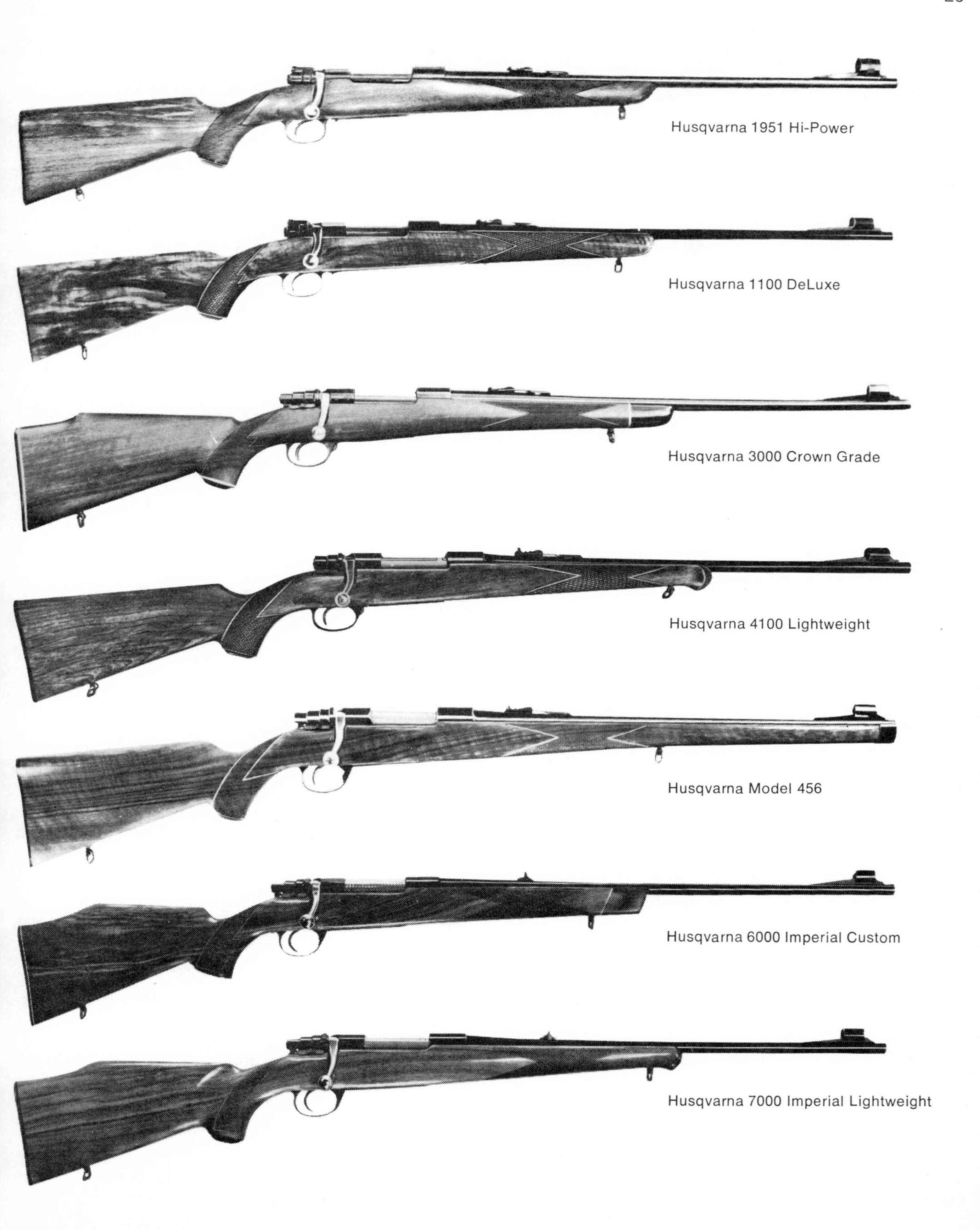

Husqvarna 1951 Hi-Power

Husqvarna 1100 DeLuxe

Husqvarna 3000 Crown Grade

Husqvarna 4100 Lightweight

Husqvarna Model 456

Husqvarna 6000 Imperial Custom

Husqvarna 7000 Imperial Lightweight

Husqvarna P-3000 Presentation Grade

Husqvarna 9000 Crown Grade

Husqvarna 8000 Imperial Grade

Italian Model 38

Husqvarna Presentation Rifle, Series P-3000 ...... $400

Same as Crown Grade Series 3000, except specially selected stock, engraved action, adjustable trigger. Calibers: 243, 270, 7mm Rem. Mag., 30-06. Made from 1968 to 1970.

Husqvarna Model 9000 Crown Grade Rifle $210

New design Husqvarna bolt action. Adjustable trigger. Calibers: 270, 7mm Rem. Mag., 30-06, 300 Win. Mag. 5-shot box magazine, hinged floorplate. 23¾-inch barrel. Folding leaf rear sight, hooded ramp front sight. Checkered walnut stock with Monte Carlo cheekpiece, rosewood forearm tip and pistol-grip cap. Weight, 7 lbs. 3 oz. Made from 1971 to 1972.

Husqvarna Model 8000 Imperial Grade Rifle $275

Same as Model 9000, except has jeweled bolt, engraved floor plate, deluxe French walnut stock, no sights. Made from 1971 to 1972.

Italian Military Rifles manufactured by Government plants at Brescia, Gardone, Terni and Turin, Italy

Italian Model 1891 Mannlicher-Carcano Military Rifle $65

Bolt action, straight handle. Caliber, 6.5mm. Italian Service. 6-shot modified Mannlicher-type box magazine. 30¾-inch barrel. Weight, about 9 pounds. Adjustable rear sight, blade front sight. Military-type straight-grip stock. Adopted 1891.

Italian Model 38 Military Rifle $65

Modification of Model 1891, has turned down bolt handle, detachable folding bayonet. Caliber 7.35mm Italian Service (many arms of this model were later converted to the old 6.5mm caliber). 6-shot box magazine. 21¼-inch barrel. Weight, about 7½ pounds. Adjustable rear sight, blade front sight. Military-type straight-grip stock. Adopted 1938.

Ithaca Model X5-T

Ithaca Model 49

Ithaca Gun Company, Inc.
Ithaca, New York

Ithaca Model X5-C Lightning Autoloader Clip Repeater $45

Takedown. Caliber, 22 Long Rifle. 7-shot clip magazine. 22-inch barrel. Weight, 6 pounds. Open rear sight, Ray-bar front sight. Pistol-grip stock, grooved forearm. Made from 1958 to 1964.

Ithaca Model X5-T Lightning Autoloader Tubular Repeater $45

Same as Model X5-C except has 16-shot tubular magazine, stock with plain forearm. Made from 1959 to 1963.

Ithaca Model 49 Saddlegun Lever Action Single Shot Rifle $35

Hand-operated rebounding hammer. Caliber, 22 Long Rifle, Long, Short. 18-inch barrel. Open sights. Western carbine-style stock. Weight, 5½ pounds. Made from 1961 to date.

Ithaca Model 49 Youth Saddlegun $35

Same as standard Model 49, except shorter stock for young shooters. Made from 1961 to date.

Ithaca Model 49 Magnum Saddlegun $40

Same as standard Model 49, except chambered for 22 Win. Mag. R.F. cartridge. Made from 1962 to date.

Ithaca Model 49 Deluxe Saddlegun $40

Same as standard Model 49, except has gold-plated hammer and trigger, figured walnut stock, sling swivels. Made from 1962 to 1975.

Ithaca St. Louis Bicentennial Model 49 Saddlegun. $125

Same as Model 49 Deluxe, except has commemorative inscription. 200 made in 1964.

Ithaca Model 49 Presentation Saddlegun $135

Same as standard Model 49 Saddlegun, except has gold-plated hammer and trigger, engraved receiver, full fancy figured walnut stock with gold nameplate. Available in 22 Long Rifle or 22 WMR. Made from 1962 to 1974.

Japanese Military Rifles manufactured by Government plant at Tokyo, Japan

Japanese Model 38 Arisaka Service Rifle $85

Mauser-type bolt action. Caliber, 6.5mm Japanese. 5-shot box magazine. Barrel lengths: 25⅜ inches, 31¼ inches. Weight about 9¼ pounds with long barrel. Fixed front sight, adjustable rear sight. Military-type full stock. Adopted in 1905, the 38th year of the Meiji reign, hence designation "Model 38."

Japanese Model 38 Arisaka Carbine $85

Same general specifications as Model 38 Rifle except has 19-inch barrel, heavy folding bayonet, weighs about 7¼ pounds.

Japanese Model 44 Cavalry Carbine $85

Same general specifications as Model 38 Rifle except has 19-inch barrel, heavy folding bayonet, weighs about 8½ pounds. Adopted in 1911, the 44th year of the Meiji reign, hence the designation "Model 44."

Japanese Model 99 Service Rifle $85

Modified Model 38. Caliber, 7.7mm Japanese. 5-shot box magazine. 25¾-inch barrel. Weight, about 8¾ pounds. Fixed front sight, adjustable aperture rear sight, anti-aircraft sighting bars on some early models; fixed rear sight on some late World War II rifles. Military-type full stock, may have bipod. Takedown paratroop model was also made during World War II. Adopted in 1939, Japanese year 2599 from which the designation "Model 99" is taken. *Note:* The last Model 99 rifles made were of very poor quality, some have cast steel receivers. Value shown is for earlier type.

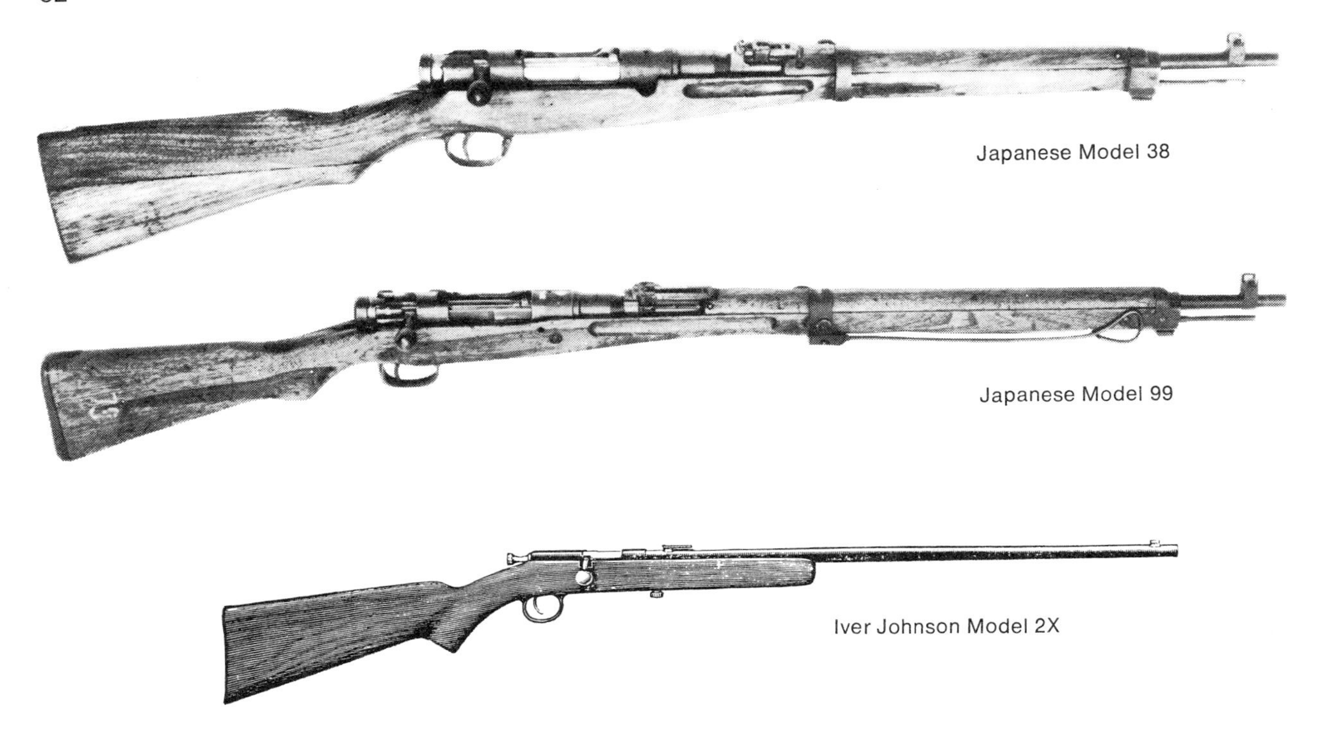

Japanese Model 38

Japanese Model 99

Iver Johnson Model 2X

Johnson Automatics, Inc., Providence, R. I.

Johnson Model 1941 Semiautomatic Military Rifle . . $500

Short-recoil-operated. Removable, air-cooled, 22-inch barrel. Calibers: 30-06, 7mm Mauser. 10-shot rotary magazine. Two-piece, wood stock, pistol-grip; perforated metal radiator sleeve over rear half of barrel. Receiver peep sight, protected post front sight. Weight, 9½ pounds. *Note:* The Johnson M/1941 was adopted by the Netherlands Government in 1940-41 and the major portion of the production of this rifle, 1941 to 1943, was on Dutch orders. A quantity was also purchased by the U.S. Government for use by Marine Corps parachute troops (1943) and for Lend Lease. All of these rifles were caliber 30-06; the 7mm Johnson rifles were made for a South American government.

Iver Johnson's Arms & Cycle Works, Fitchburg, Massachusetts

Iver Johnson Model X Bolt Action Single Shot Rifle . . $30

Takedown. Caliber, 22 Long Rifle, Long, Short. 22-inch barrel. Weight, about 4 pounds. Open rear sight, blade front sight. Pistol-grip stock with knob forend tip. Made from 1928 to 1932.

Iver Johnson Model 2X $40

Improved version of the Model X, has heavier 24-inch barrel, larger stock (without knob tip), weighs about 4½ pounds. Made from 1932 to 1955.

Mannlicher-Schoenauer Rifles manufactured by Steyr-Daimler-Puch, A.-G., Steyr, Austria

Mannlicher-Schoenauer Model 1903 Bolt Action Sporting Carbine $425

Caliber, 6.5X53mm (referred to in some European gun catalogues as 6.7X53mm, following the Austrian practice of designating calibers by bullet diameter). 5-shot rotary magazine. 450mm (17.7-inch) barrel. Weight, about 6½ pounds. Double-set trigger. Two-leaf rear sight, ramp front sight. Full-length sporting stock with cheekpiece, pistol grip, trap buttplate, swivels.

Mannlicher-Schoenauer Model 1905 Carbine $350

Same as Model 1903, except caliber 9X56mm and has 19.7-inch barrel, weighs about 6¾ pounds.

Mannlicher-Schoenauer Model 1908 Carbine $350

Same as Model 1905 except calibers 7X57mm and 8X56mm.

Mannlicher-Schoenauer Model 1910 Carbine $350

Same as Model 1905 except caliber 9.5X57mm.

Mannlicher-Schoenauer Model 1924 Carbine $450

Same as Model 1905 except caliber 30-06 (7.62X63mm).

Mannlicher-Schoenauer High Velocity Bolt Action Sporting Rifle $400

Calibers: 7X64 Brenneke, 30-06 (7.62X63), 8X60 Magnum, 9.3X62, 10.75X68mm. 23.6-inch barrel. Weight,

Mannlicher-Schoenauer Model 1903 Carbine

Mannlicher-Schoenauer Model 1905 Carbine

Mannlicher-Schoenauer High Velocity

Mannlicher-Schoenauer Model 1950 Rifle

Mannlicher-Schoenauer Model 1950 Carbine

about 7½ pounds. British-style 3-leaf open rear sight, ramp front sight. Half-length sporting stock with cheekpiece, pistol grip, checkered, trap buttplate, swivels. Also produced in takedown model.

Note: The preceding Mannlicher-Schoenauer models were produced prior to World War II. Manufacture of sporting rifles and carbines was resumed at the Steyr-Daimler-Puch plant in Austria during 1950 and the Model 1950 Rifles and Carbines were introduced at that time.

Mannlicher-Schoenauer Model 1950 Bolt Action Sporting Rifle $400

Calibers: 257 Roberts, 270 Win., 30-06. 5-shot rotary magazine. 24-inch barrel. Weight, about 7¼ pounds. Single trigger or double-set trigger. Redesigned low bolt handle, shotgun-type safety. Folding leaf open rear sight, hooded ramp front sight. Improved half-length stock with cheekpiece, pistol grip, checkered, ebony forend tip, swivels. Made from 1950 to 1952.

Mannlicher-Schoenauer Model 1950 Carbine $400

Same general specifications as Model 1950 Rifle except has 20-inch barrel, full-length stock, weighs about 7 pounds. Made from 1950 to 1952.

Mannlicher-Schoenauer Model 1950 6.5 Carbine . . . $400

Same as other Model 1950 Carbines except caliber 6.5X53mm, has 18¼-inch barrel, weighs 6¾ pounds. Made from 1950 to 1952.

Mannlicher-Schoenauer Model 1952 Rifle

Mannlicher-Schoenauer Model 1952 Carbine

Mannlicher-Schoenauer Model 1956 Rifle

Mannlicher-Schoenauer Model 1956 Carbine

Mannlicher-Schoenauer Model 1961-MCA Rifle

Mannlicher-Schoenauer Model 1961-MCA Carbine

Mannlicher-Schoenauer Improved Model 1952 Sporting Rifle $400

Same as Model 1950 except has swept-back bolt handle, redesigned stock. Calibers: 257, 270, 30-06, 9.3X62mm. Made from 1952 to 1956.

Mannlicher-Schoenauer Improved Model 1952 Carbine $400

Same as Model 1950 Carbine except has swept-back bolt handle, redesigned stock. Calibers: 257, 270, 7mm, 30-06. Made from 1952 to 1956.

Mannlicher-Schoenauer Improved Model 1952 6.5 Carbine $400

Same as Model 1952 Carbine except caliber 6.5X 53mm, has 18¼-inch barrel. Made from 1952 to 1956.

Mannlicher-Schoenauer Custom Model 1956 Sporting Rifle $400

Same general specifications as Models 1950 and 1952, except 22-inch barrel, redesigned stock with high comb. Calibers: 243 and 30-06. Made from 1956 to 1960.

Mannlicher-Schoenauer Custom Model 1956 Carbine $400

Same general specifications as Model 1950 and 1952 Carbines except has redesigned stock with high comb. Calibers: 243, 6.5mm, 257, 270, 7mm, 30-06, 308. Made from 1956 to 1960.

Mannlicher-Schoenauer Carbine, Model 1961-MCA $475

Same as Model 1956 Carbine except has universal Monte Carlo design stock. Calibers: 243 Win., 6.5mm, 270, 308, 30-06. Made from 1961 to 1971.

Mannlicher-Schoenauer Rifle, Model 1961-MCA . . . $475

Same as Model 1956 Rifle except has universal Monte Carlo design stock. Calibers: 243, 270, 30-06. Made from 1961 to 1971.

Marlin Firearms Company, New Haven, Connecticut

Marlin Model 92 Lever Action Repeating Rifle $275

Calibers: 22 Short, Long, Long Rifle; 32 Short, Long (rimfire or centerfire by changing firing pin). Tubular magazines: holding 25 Short, 20 Long, 18 Long Rifle (22); 17 Short, 14 Long (32); 16-inch barrel model has shorter magazine holding 15 Short, 12 Long, 10 Long Rifle. Barrel lengths: 16 (22 cal. only), 24, 26, 28-inch. Weight, with 24-inch barrel, about 5½ pounds. Open rear sight, blade front sight. Plain straight-grip stock and forearm. Made from 1892 to 1916. *Note:* Originally designated "Model 1892."

Marlin Model 93 Lever Action Repeating Rifle $250

Solid frame or takedown. Calibers: 25-36 Marlin, 30-30, 32 Special, 32-40, 38-55. Tubular magazine holds 10 cartridges. 26-inch round or octagon barrel standard; also made with 28, 30 and 32-inch barrels. Weight, about 7¼ pounds. Open rear sight, bead front sight. Plain straight-grip stock and forearm. Made from 1893 to 1936. *Note:* Prior to 1915, was designated "Model 1893."

Marlin Model 93 Carbine $400

Same as Standard Model 93 except calibers 30-30 and 32 Special only, 7-shot magazine, 20-inch round barrel, weighs about 6¾ pounds, carbine sights.

Marlin Model 93SC Sporting Carbine $400

Same as Model 93 Carbine except has 2/3 magazine holding 5 shots, weighs 6½ pounds.

Marlin Model 93 Musket $450

Same as Standard Model 93 except has 30-inch barrel, angular bayonet, ramrod under barrel, musket stock, full-length military-style forearm. Weight, 8 pounds. Made from 1893 to 1915.

Marlin Model 94 Lever Action Repeating Rifle $295

Solid frame or takedown. Calibers: 25-20, 32-20, 38-40, 44-40. 10-shot tubular magazine. 24-inch round or octagon barrel. Weight, about 7 pounds. Open rear sight, bead front sight. Plain straight-grip stock and forearm (also available with pistol-grip stock). Made from 1894 to 1934. *Note:* Prior to 1906, was designated "Model 1894."

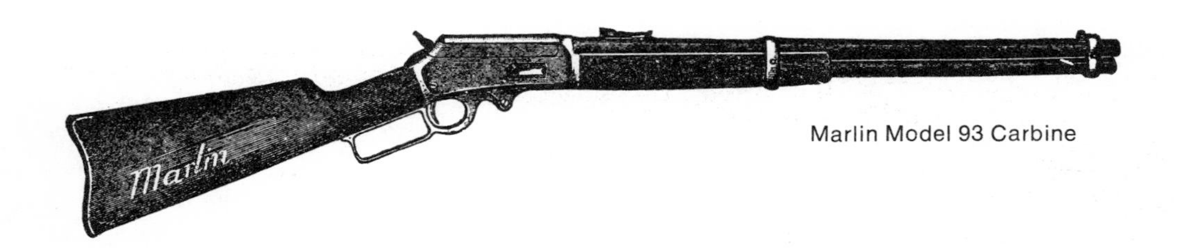

Marlin Model 93 Carbine

Marlin Model 1895

Marlin Model 1895 Lever Action Repeating Rifle . . . $350
Solid frame or takedown. Calibers: 33 WCF, 38-56, 40-65, 40-70, 40-82, 45-70. 9-shot tubular magazine. 24-inch round or octagon barrel standard (other lengths available). Weight, about 8 pounds. Open rear sight, bead front sight. Plain stock and forearm (also available with pistol-grip stock). Made from 1895 to 1915.

Marlin Model 1897 Lever Action Repeating Rifle . $200
Takedown. Caliber, 22 Long Rifle, Long, Short. Tubular magazine; full length holds 25 Short, 20 Long, 18 Long Rifle; half length holds 16 Short, 12 Long and 10 Long Rifle. Barrel lengths: 16, 24, 26, 28 inches. Weight, about 6 pounds. Open rear sight and bead front sight. Plain straight-grip stock and forearm (also available with pistol-grip stock). Made from 1897 to 1922. *Note:* Prior to 1905 was designated "Model 1897."

Marlin Model 18 Baby Slide Action Repeater $125
Exposed hammer. Solid frame. Caliber, 22 Long Rifle, Long, Short. Tubular magazine holds 14 Short. 20-inch barrel, round or octagon. Weight, 3¾ pounds. Open rear sight, bead front sight. Plain straight-grip stock and slide handle. Made from 1906 to 1909.

Marlin Model 20 Slide Action Repeating Rifle $125
Exposed hammer. Takedown. Caliber, 22 Long Rifle, Long, Short. Tubular magazine: half-length holds 15 Short, 12 Long, 10 Long Rifle; full-length holds 25 Short, 20 Long, 18 Long Rifle. 24-inch octagon barrel. Weight, about 5 pounds. Open rear sight, bead front sight. Plain straight-grip stock, grooved slide handle. Made from 1907 to 1922. *Note:* After 1920, was designated "Model 20-S."

Marlin Model 29 Slide Action Repeating Rifle $125
Similar to Model 20, has 23-inch round barrel, half magazine only, weighs about 5¾ pounds. Model 37 is same type except has 24-inch barrel and full magazine. Made from 1913 to 1916.

Marlin Model 25 Slide Action Repeating Rifle $125
Exposed hammer. Takedown. Caliber, 22 Short (also handles 22 CB Caps). Tubular magazine holds 15 Short. 23-inch barrel. Weight, about 4 pounds. Open rear sight, bead front sight. Plain straight-grip stock and slide handle. Made from 1909 to 1910.

Marlin Model 27 Slide Action Repeating Rifle $125
Exposed hammer. Takedown. Calibers: 25-20, 32-20. 2/3 magazine (tubular) holds 7 shots. 24-inch octagon barrel. Weight, about 5¾ pounds. Open rear sight, bead front sight. Plain straight-grip stock, grooved slide handle. Made from 1910 to 1916.

Marlin Model 32 Slide Action Repeating Rifle $125
Hammerless. Takedown. Caliber, 22 Long Rifle, Long, Short. 2/3 tubular magazine holds 15 Short, 12 Long, 10 L.R.; full magazine, 25 Short, 20 Long, 18 L.R. 24-inch octagon barrel. Weight, 5½ pounds. Open rear sight, bead front sight. Plain pistol-grip stock, grooved slide handle. Made from 1914 to 1915.

Marlin Model 27-S $125
Same as Model 27 except has round barrel, also chambered for 25 Stevens R.F. Made from 1920 to 1932.

Marlin Model 38 Slide Action Repeating Rifle $125
Hammerless. Takedown. Caliber, 22 Long Rifle, Long, Short. 2/3 magazine (tubular) holds 15 Short, 12 Long, 10 Long Rifle. 24-inch octagon barrel. Weight, about 5½ pounds. Open rear sight, bead front sight. Plain pistol-grip stock, grooved slide handle. Made from 1920 to 1930.

Marlin Model 39 Lever Action Repeating Rifle $200
Takedown. Caliber, 22 Long Rifle, Long, Short. Tubular magazine holds 25 Short, 20 Long, 18 Long Rifle. 24-inch octagon barrel. Weight, about 5¾ pounds. Open rear sight, bead front sight. Plain pistol-grip stock and forearm, weighs about 6½ pounds. Made from 1938 to date.

Marlin Model 39A $80
General specifications same as Model 39, except has round barrel, heavier stock with semi-beavertail forearm, weighs about 6½ pounds. Made from 1938 to 1957.

Marlin Model 39A "Mountie" Lever Action Repeating Rifle $80
Same as Model 39A, except has lighter, straight-grip stock, slimmer forearm. Weight, 6¼ pounds. Made from 1953 to 1960.

Marlin Model 39M "Mountie" Carbine $80
Same as Model 39A "Mountie" Rifle, except has 20-inch barrel and reduced magazine capacity: 21 Short, 16 Long, 15 Long Rifle. Weight, 6 pounds. Made from 1954 to date.

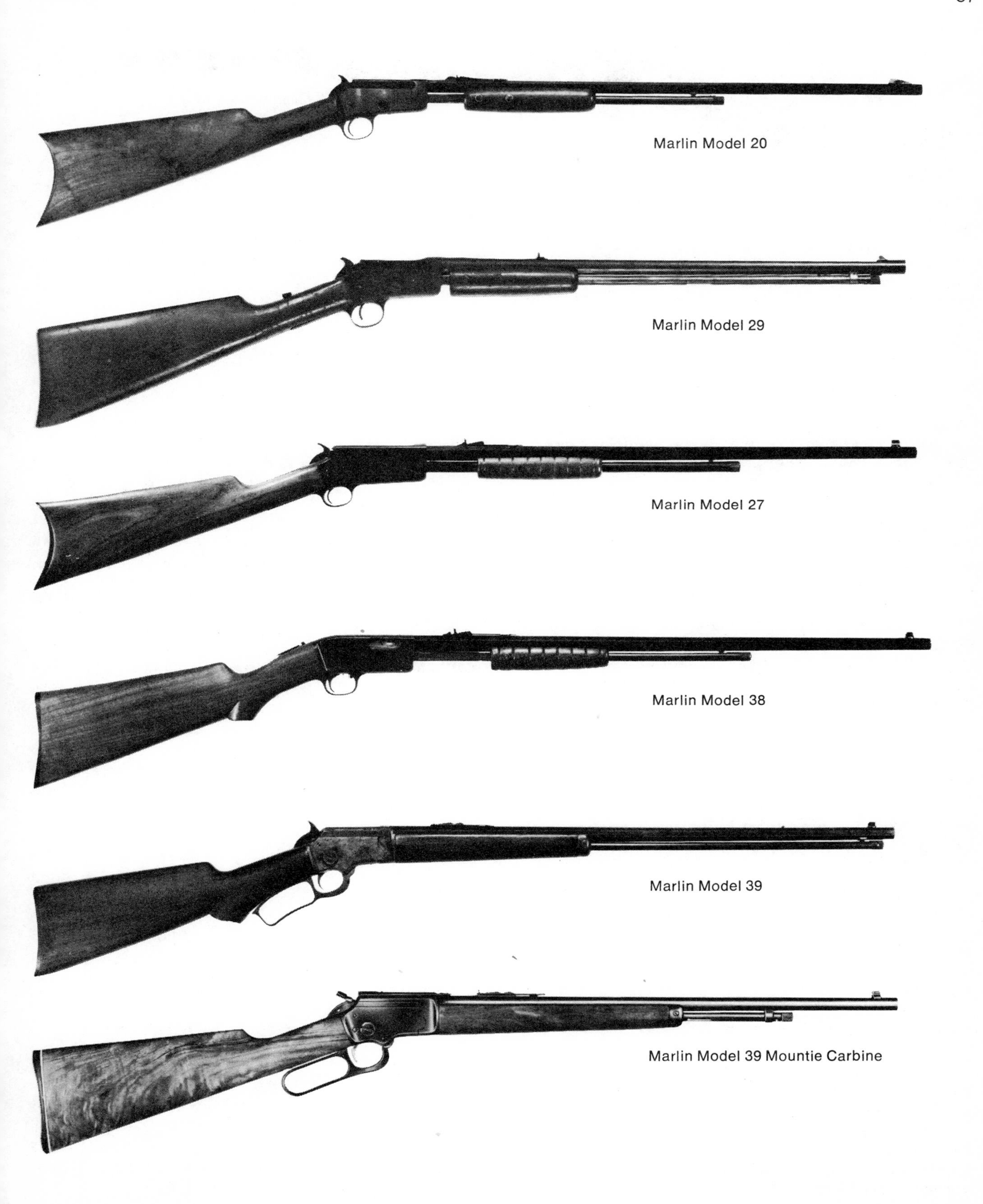

Marlin Model 20

Marlin Model 29

Marlin Model 27

Marlin Model 38

Marlin Model 39

Marlin Model 39 Mountie Carbine

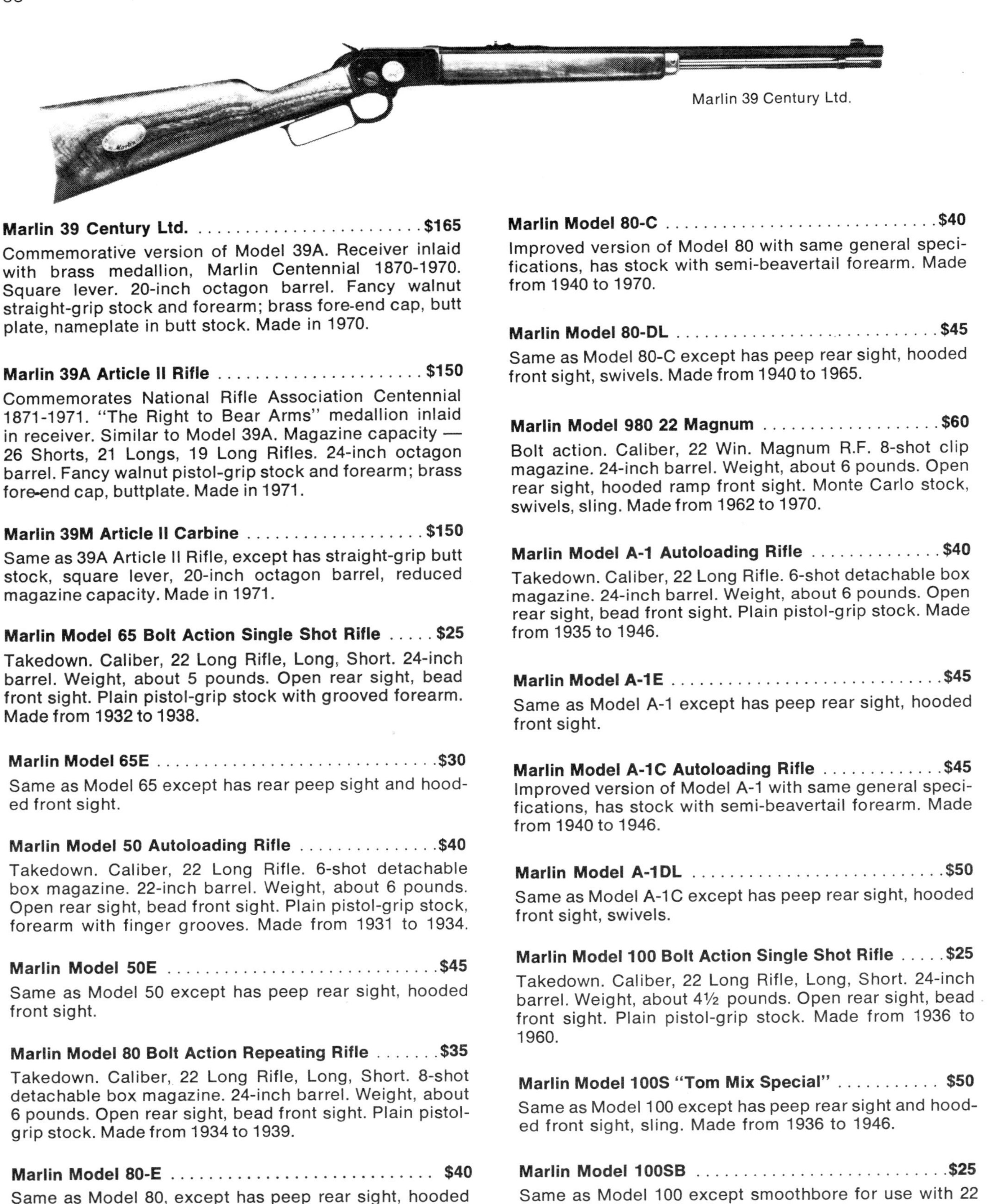

Marlin 39 Century Ltd.

Marlin 39 Century Ltd. **$165**

Commemorative version of Model 39A. Receiver inlaid with brass medallion, Marlin Centennial 1870-1970. Square lever. 20-inch octagon barrel. Fancy walnut straight-grip stock and forearm; brass fore-end cap, butt plate, nameplate in butt stock. Made in 1970.

Marlin 39A Article II Rifle **$150**

Commemorates National Rifle Association Centennial 1871-1971. "The Right to Bear Arms" medallion inlaid in receiver. Similar to Model 39A. Magazine capacity — 26 Shorts, 21 Longs, 19 Long Rifles. 24-inch octagon barrel. Fancy walnut pistol-grip stock and forearm; brass fore-end cap, buttplate. Made in 1971.

Marlin 39M Article II Carbine **$150**

Same as 39A Article II Rifle, except has straight-grip butt stock, square lever, 20-inch octagon barrel, reduced magazine capacity. Made in 1971.

Marlin Model 65 Bolt Action Single Shot Rifle **$25**

Takedown. Caliber, 22 Long Rifle, Long, Short. 24-inch barrel. Weight, about 5 pounds. Open rear sight, bead front sight. Plain pistol-grip stock with grooved forearm. Made from 1932 to 1938.

Marlin Model 65E **$30**

Same as Model 65 except has rear peep sight and hooded front sight.

Marlin Model 50 Autoloading Rifle **$40**

Takedown. Caliber, 22 Long Rifle. 6-shot detachable box magazine. 22-inch barrel. Weight, about 6 pounds. Open rear sight, bead front sight. Plain pistol-grip stock, forearm with finger grooves. Made from 1931 to 1934.

Marlin Model 50E **$45**

Same as Model 50 except has peep rear sight, hooded front sight.

Marlin Model 80 Bolt Action Repeating Rifle **$35**

Takedown. Caliber, 22 Long Rifle, Long, Short. 8-shot detachable box magazine. 24-inch barrel. Weight, about 6 pounds. Open rear sight, bead front sight. Plain pistol-grip stock. Made from 1934 to 1939.

Marlin Model 80-E **$40**

Same as Model 80, except has peep rear sight, hooded front sight. Made from 1934 to 1940.

Marlin Model 80-C **$40**

Improved version of Model 80 with same general specifications, has stock with semi-beavertail forearm. Made from 1940 to 1970.

Marlin Model 80-DL **$45**

Same as Model 80-C except has peep rear sight, hooded front sight, swivels. Made from 1940 to 1965.

Marlin Model 980 22 Magnum **$60**

Bolt action. Caliber, 22 Win. Magnum R.F. 8-shot clip magazine. 24-inch barrel. Weight, about 6 pounds. Open rear sight, hooded ramp front sight. Monte Carlo stock, swivels, sling. Made from 1962 to 1970.

Marlin Model A-1 Autoloading Rifle **$40**

Takedown. Caliber, 22 Long Rifle. 6-shot detachable box magazine. 24-inch barrel. Weight, about 6 pounds. Open rear sight, bead front sight. Plain pistol-grip stock. Made from 1935 to 1946.

Marlin Model A-1E **$45**

Same as Model A-1 except has peep rear sight, hooded front sight.

Marlin Model A-1C Autoloading Rifle **$45**

Improved version of Model A-1 with same general specifications, has stock with semi-beavertail forearm. Made from 1940 to 1946.

Marlin Model A-1DL **$50**

Same as Model A-1C except has peep rear sight, hooded front sight, swivels.

Marlin Model 100 Bolt Action Single Shot Rifle **$25**

Takedown. Caliber, 22 Long Rifle, Long, Short. 24-inch barrel. Weight, about 4½ pounds. Open rear sight, bead front sight. Plain pistol-grip stock. Made from 1936 to 1960.

Marlin Model 100S "Tom Mix Special" **$50**

Same as Model 100 except has peep rear sight and hooded front sight, sling. Made from 1936 to 1946.

Marlin Model 100SB **$25**

Same as Model 100 except smoothbore for use with 22 shot cartridges, shotgun sight. Made from 1936 to 1941.

Marlin Model 50

Marlin Model 80-C

Marlin Model 80-DL

Marlin Model 980

Marlin Model A-1

Marlin Model 100

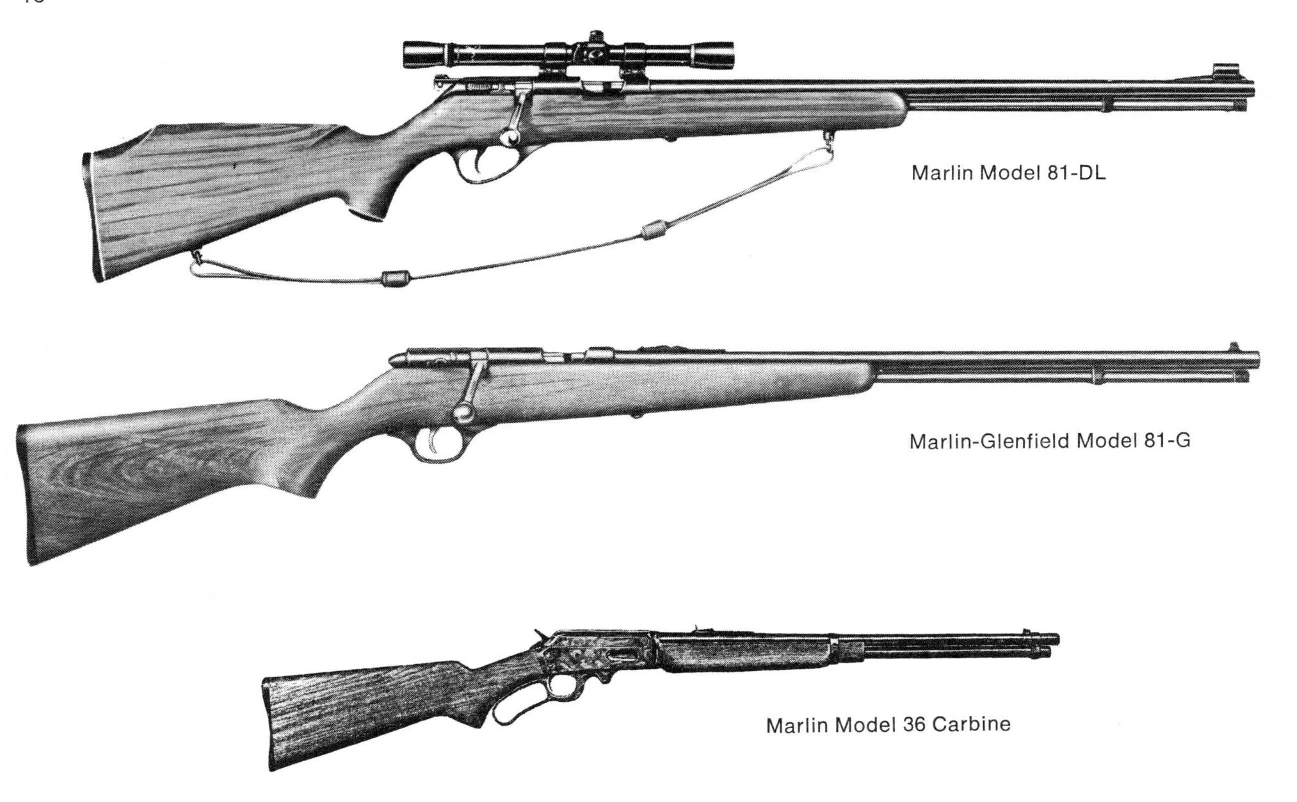

Marlin Model 81-DL

Marlin-Glenfield Model 81-G

Marlin Model 36 Carbine

Marlin Model 101 . . . . $25

Improved version of Model 100 with same general specifications except has stock with beavertail forearm, weighs about 5 pounds. Made from 1951 to date.

Marlin Model 101-DL $30

Same as Model 101 except has peep rear sight, hooded front sight, swivels. Discontinued.

Marlin Model 81 Bolt Action Repeating Rifle $35

Takedown. Caliber, 22 Long Rifle, Long, Short. Tubular magazine holds 24 Short, 20 Long, 18 Long Rifle. 24-inch barrel. Weight, about 6¼ pounds. Open rear sight, bead front sight. Plain pistol-grip stock. Made from 1937 to 1940.

Marlin Model 81E $40

Same as Model 81 except has peep rear sight, hooded front sight.

Marlin Model 81C $45

Improved version of Model 81 with same general specifications, has stock with semi-beavertail forearm. Made from 1940 to 1970.

Marlin Model 81-DL $50

Same as Model 81-C except has peep rear sight, hooded front sight, swivels. Discontinued 1965.

Marlin-Glenfield Model 81G $40

Same as Model 81C except has plainer stock, bead front sight. Made from 1960 to 1965.

Marlin Model 36 Lever Action Repeating Carbine . . $150

Calibers: 30-30, 32 Special. 6-shot tubular magazine. 20-inch barrel. Weight, about 6½ pounds. Open rear sight, bead front sight. Pistol-grip stock, semi-beavertail forearm with carbine barrel band. Made from 1936 to 1948.

Marlin Model 36A Lever Action Repeating Rifle . . . $150

Same as Model 36 Carbine, except has 2/3 magazine holding 5 cartridges, 24-inch barrel, weighs 6¾ pounds, has hooded front sight, semi-beavertail forearm.

Marlin Model 36A-DL $175

Same as Model 36A, except has de luxe checkered stock and forearm, swivels and sling.

Marlin Model 36 Sporting Carbine $150

Same as Model 36A rifle except has 20-inch barrel, weighs 6¼ pounds.

Marlin Model 336C Lever Action Carbine $90

Improved version of Model 36 Carbine with same general specifications, has improved action with round breech bolt. Made from 1948 to date. Cal. 35 Rem. introduced 1953. Cal. 32 Win. Spl. discontinued in 1963.

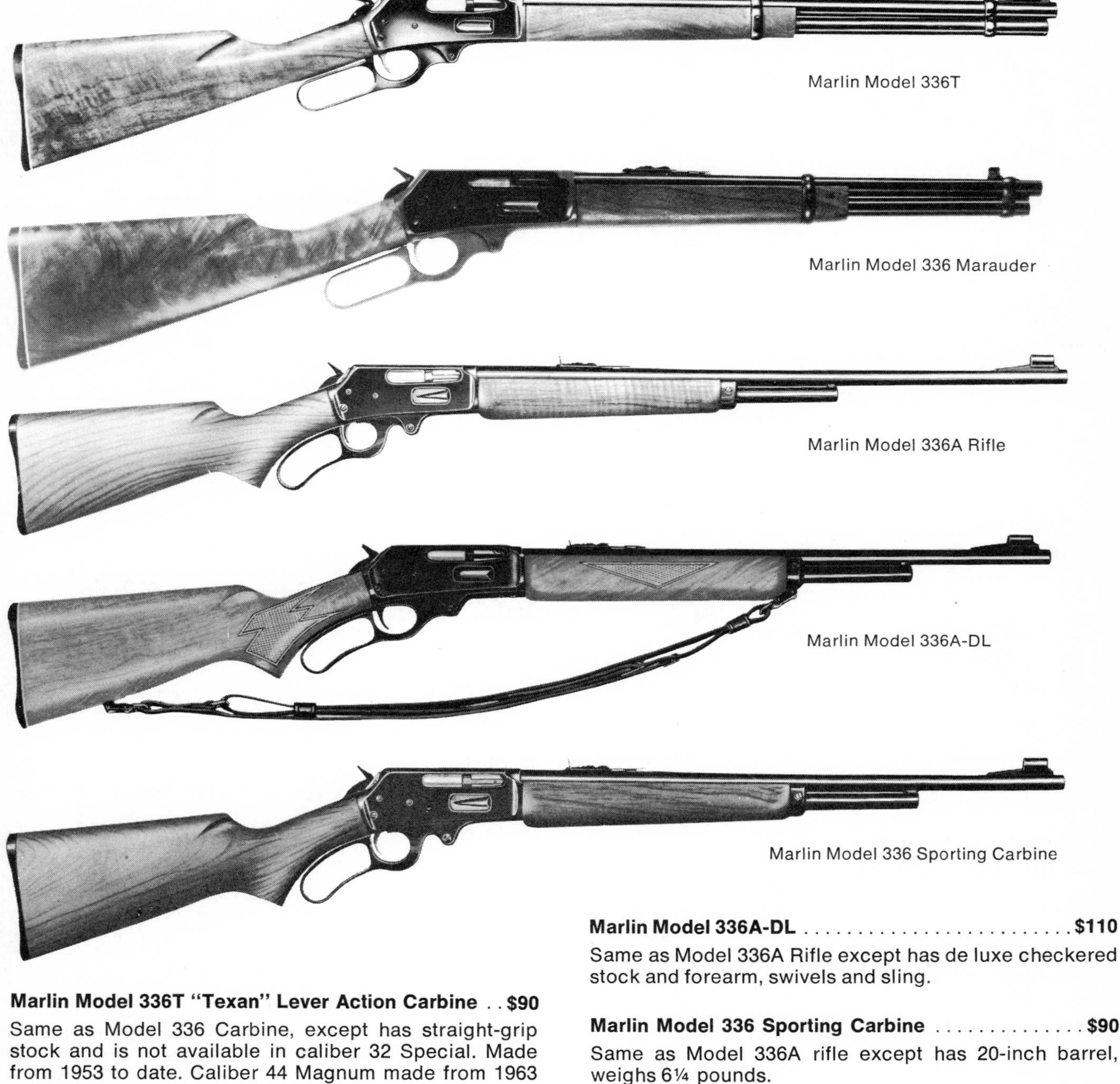

Marlin Model 336T

Marlin Model 336 Marauder

Marlin Model 336A Rifle

Marlin Model 336A-DL

Marlin Model 336 Sporting Carbine

Marlin Model 336T "Texan" Lever Action Carbine . . $90

Same as Model 336 Carbine, except has straight-grip stock and is not available in caliber 32 Special. Made from 1953 to date. Caliber 44 Magnum made from 1963 to 1967.

Marlin Model 336 "Marauder" $100

Same as Model 336 "Texan" Carbine except has 16¼-inch barrel, weighs about 6¼ pounds. Made from 1963 to 1964.

Model 336A Lever Action Repeating Rifle $90

Improved version of Model 36A Rifle with same general specifications, has improved action with round breech bolt. This model and sporting carbine in cal. 35 Rem. introduced 1950, discontinued 1963.

Marlin Model 336A-DL $110

Same as Model 336A Rifle except has de luxe checkered stock and forearm, swivels and sling.

Marlin Model 336 Sporting Carbine $90

Same as Model 336A rifle except has 20-inch barrel, weighs 6¼ pounds.

Marlin Model 336 "Micro Groove Zipper" $175

General specifications same as Model 336 Sporting Carbine, except caliber 219 Zipper. Made from 1955 to 1961.

Marlin Model 444 Lever Action Repeating Rifle $125

Action similar to Model 336. Caliber, 444 Marlin. 4-shot tubular magazine. 24-inch barrel. Weight, 7½ pounds. Open rear sight, hooded ramp front sight. Monte Carlo stock with straight grip, recoil pad. Carbine-style forearm with barrel band. Swivels, sling. Made from 1965 to 1971.

Marlin Model 88-C

Marlin Model 89-C

Marlin Model 98

Marlin Model 99-DL

Marlin Model 336 Zane Grey Century **$150**

Similar to Model 336A, except has 22-inch octagonal barrel, caliber 30-30; Zane Grey Centennial 1872-1972 medallion inlaid in receiver; selected walnut stock with classic pistol-grip and forearm; brass buttplate, fore end cap. Weight, 7 pounds. 10,000 produced (numbered ZG1 through ZG10,000). Made in 1972.

Marlin Model 88-C Autoloading Rifle **$45**

Takedown. Caliber, 22 Long Rifle. Tubular magazine in butt stock holds 14 cartridges. 24-inch barrel. Weight, about 6¾ pounds. Open rear sight, hooded front sight. Plain pistol-grip stock. Made from 1947 to 1956.

Marlin Model 88-DL **$50**

Same as Model 88-C except has receiver peep sight, checkered stock and sling swivels. Made from 1953 to 1956.

Marlin Model 89-C Autoloading Rifle **$45**

Clip magazine version of Model 88-C. 7-shot clip (12-shot in later models). Other specifications same. Made from 1950 to 1961.

Marlin Model 89-DL **$50**

Same as Model 89-C except has receiver peep sight and sling swivels.

Marlin Model 98 Autoloading Rifle **$45**

Solid frame. Caliber, 22 Long Rifle. Tubular magazine holds 15 cartridges. 22-inch barrel. Weight, about 6¾ pounds. Open rear sight, hooded ramp front sight. Monte Carlo stock with cheekpiece. Made from 1950 to 1961.

Marlin Model 99 Autoloading Rifle **$45**

Caliber, 22 Long Rifle. Tubular magazine holds 18 cartridges. 22-inch barrel. Weight, about 5½ pounds. Open rear sight, hooded ramp front sight. Plain pistol-grip stock. Made from 1959 to 1961.

Marlin Model 99C **$40**

Same as Model 99 except has gold-plated trigger, receiver grooved for tip-off scope mounts, Monte Carlo stock (checkered in current production). Made from 1962 to date.

Marlin Model 99DL **$40**

Same as Model 99 except has gold-plated trigger, jewelled breechbolt, Monte Carlo stock with pistol-grip, swivels and sling. Made from 1960 to 1965.

Marlin Model 989M2

Marlin Model 989

Marlin-Glenfield Model 989-G

Marlin Model 122

Marlin Model 455

Marlin Model 99M1 Carbine **$40**

Same as Model 99C except styled after U.S. 30M1 Carbine; 9-shot tubular magazine, 18-inch barrel, open rear sight, military-style ramp front sight, carbine stock with hand guard and barrel band, sling'swivels. Weight, 4½ pounds. Made from 1966 to date.

Marlin Model 989M2 Carbine **$40**

Same as Model 99M1 except clip-loading—7-shot magazine. Made from 1966 to date.

Marlin Model 989 Autoloading Rifle **$35**

Caliber, 22 Long Rifle, 7-shot clip magazine. 22-inch barrel. Weight, about 5½ pounds. Open rear sight, hooded ramp front sight. Monte Carlo walnut stock with pistol grip. Made from 1962 to 1966.

Marlin-Glenfield Model 989G Autoloading Rifle **$30**

Same as Model 989 except plain stock, bead front sight. Made from 1962 to 1964.

Marlin Model 122 Single Shot Junior Target Rifle **$35**

Bolt action. Caliber, 22 Long Rifle, 22 Long, 22 Short. 22-inch barrel. Weight, about 5 pounds. Open rear sight, hooded ramp front sight. Monte Carlo stock with pistol grip, swivels, sling. Made from 1691 to 1965.

Marlin Model 322 Bolt Action Varmint Rifle **$175**

Sako short Mauser action. Caliber, 222 Rem. 3-shot clip magazine. 24-inch medium weight barrel. Checkered stock. Two-position peep sight, hooded ramp front sight. Weight, about 7½ pounds. Made from 1954 to 1957.

Marlin Model 455 Bolt Action Sporter **$185**

FN Mauser action with Sako trigger. Calibers: 270, 30-06, 308. 5-shot box magazine. 24-inch medium weight stainless steel barrel. Monte Carlo stock with cheekpiece, checkered pistol grip and forearm. Lyman 48 receiver sight, hooded ramp front sight. Weight, about 8½ pounds. Made from 1957 to 1959.

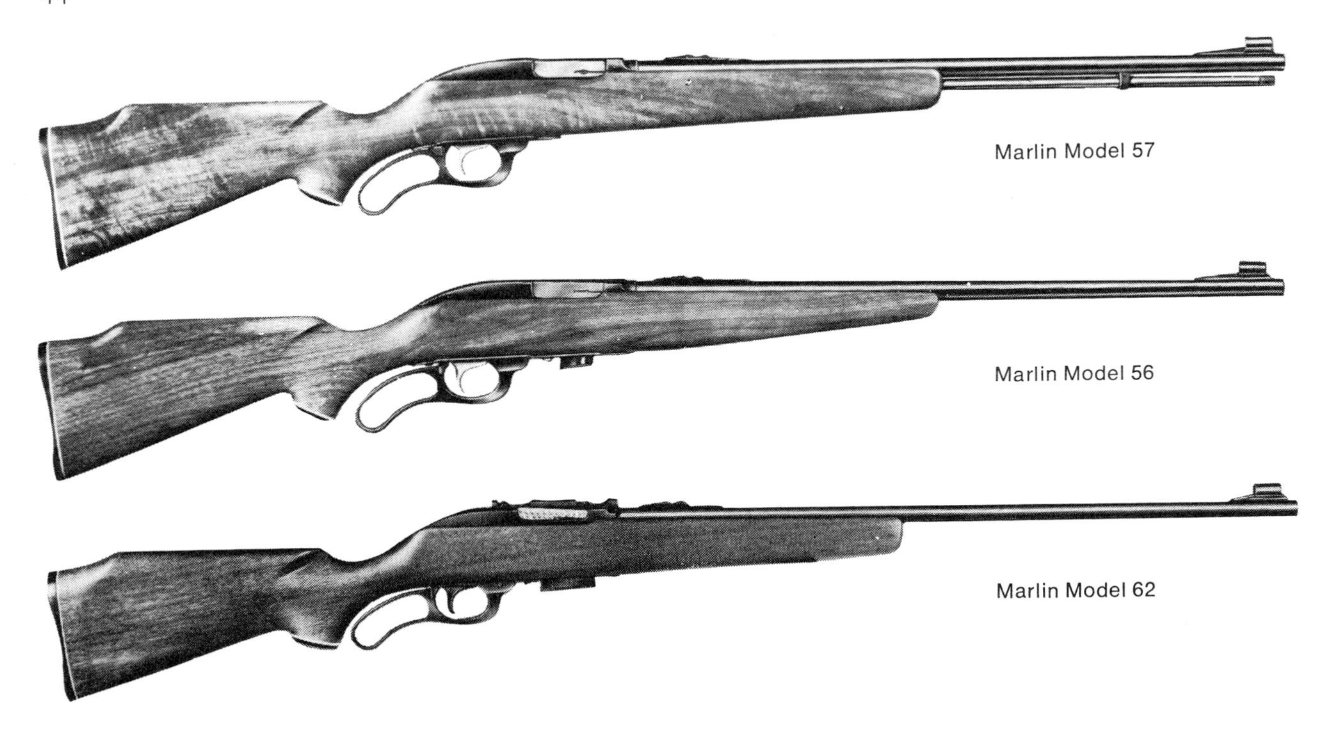

Marlin Model 57

Marlin Model 56

Marlin Model 62

Marlin Model 57 Levermatic Rifle **$60**

Lever action. Caliber, 22 Long Rifle, 22 Long, 22 Short. Tubular magazine holds 19 Long Rifle, 21 Long, 27 Short. 22-inch barrel. Weight, about 6¼ pounds. Open rear sight, hooded ramp front sight. Monte Carlo-style stock with pistol grip. Made from 1959 to 1965.

Marlin Model 57M Levermatic **$75**

Same as Model 57 except chambered for 22 Winchester Magnum Rim Fire cartridge, has 24-inch barrel, 15-shot magazine. Made from 1960 to 1969.

Marlin Model 56 Levermatic Rifle **$60**

Same as Model 57 except clip-loading. Magazine holds eight rounds. Weight, about 5¾ pounds. Made from 1955 to 1964.

Marlin Model 62 Levermatic Rifle **$85**

Lever action. Calibers: 256 Magnum, 30 Carbine. 4-shot clip magazine. 23-inch barrel. Weight, 7 pounds. Open rear sight, hooded ramp front sight. Monte Carlo-style stock with pistol grip, swivels and sling. Made in 256 Magnum from 1963 to 1966; in 30 Carbine from 1966 to 1969.

Marlin Centennial 1870-1970 Matched Pair, Models 336 and 39 . . . . **$1,000**

Presentation grade rifles in luggage-style case. Matching serial numbers. Fancy walnut straight-grip buttstock and forearm, brass buttplate and fore-end cap. Engraved receiver with inlaid medallion; square lever. 20-inch octagon barrel. Model 336: 30-30, 7-shot, 7 pounds. Model 39: 22 Short, Long, Long Rifle; tubular magazine holds 21 Short, 16 Long, 15 Long Rifle. 1,000 sets produced. Made in 1970.

Mauser Werke A.-G., Oberndorf am Neckar, Germany

Mauser Sporting Rifles were manufactured in the Mauser factory in Oberndorf am Neckar, Germany. The "Original-Mauser" is sometimes referred to as the "Oberndorf Mauser." Prior to the end of World War I, the firm was "Waffenfabrik Mauser A.-G."; shortly after World War I, it was changed to "Mauser Werke A.-G." This may be used as a general clue to the age of Mauser arms as all genuine Mausers bear either of these firm names.

Mauser Bolt Action Sporting Rifle **$400**

Calibers: 6.5X55, 6.5X58, 7X57, 8X57, 9X57, 9.3X62, 10.75X68. 5-shot box magazine, 23½-inch barrel. Weight, about 7 to 7½ pounds. Double-set trigger. Tangent curve rear sight, ramp front sight. Pistol-grip stock, forearm with "schnabel" tip, swivels.

Mauser Bolt Action Sporting Rifle, Short Model . . . **$400**

Calibers: 6.5X54, 8X51mm. 19¾-inch barrel. Weight, about 6¼ pounds. Other specifications same as for Standard Rifle.

Mauser Bolt Action Sporting Carbine **$400**

Calibers: 6.5X54, 6.5X58, 7X57, 8X57, 9X57mm. 19¾-inch barrel. Weight, about 7 pounds. Full-stocked to muzzle. Other specifications same as for standard rifle.

Mauser Bolt Action Sporting Rifle, Military Type . . . **$350**

So called because of "stepped" M/98-type barrel, military front sight and double-pull trigger. Calibers 7X57, 8X57, 9X57mm. Other specifications same as standard rifle.

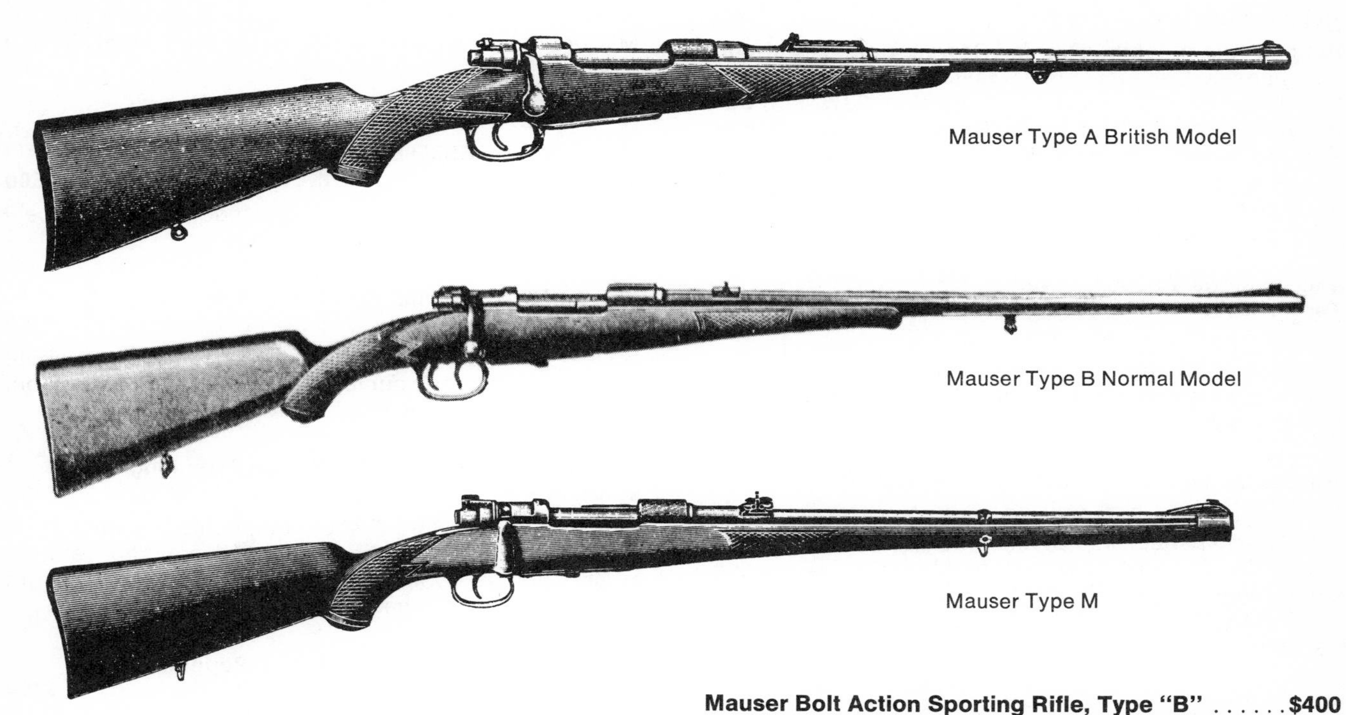

Mauser Type A British Model

Mauser Type B Normal Model

Mauser Type M

Note: The foregoing Mauser Sporting Rifles were manufactured prior to World War I. Those that follow were produced during the period between World Wars I and II. The early Mauser models can generally be identified by the pistol grip which is rounded instead of capped and the M/98 military-type magazine floorplate and catch; the later models have hinged magazine floorplate with lever or button release.

Mauser Bolt Action Sporting Rifle Type "A" $450

Special British Model. Calibers: 7X57, 30-06 (7.62X63), 8X60, 9X57, 9.3X62mm. 5-shot box magazine. 23½-inch round barrel. Weight, about 7¼ pounds. Military-type single trigger. Express rear sight, hooded ramp front sight. Circassian walnut sporting stock with checkered pistol grip and forearm, with or without cheekpiece, buffalo horn forend tip and grip cap, detachable swivels. Variations: octagon barrel, double-set trigger, shotgun-type safety, folding peep rear sight, tangent curve rear sight, three-leaf rear sight.

Mauser Bolt Action Sporting Rifle Type "A" $450

Short Model. Same as standard Type "A" except has short action, 21½-inch round barrel, weighs about 6 pounds, calibers: 250-3000, 6.5X54, 8X51mm.

Mauser Bolt Action Sporting Rifle, Type "A" $500

Magnum Model. Same general specifications as standard Type "A" except has Magnum action, weighs 7½ to 8½ pounds, calibers 280 Ross, 318 Westley Richards Express, 10.75X68mm. 404 Nitro Express.

Mauser Bolt Action Sporting Rifle, Type "B" $400

Normal Model. Calibers: 7X57, 30-06 (7.62X63), 8X57, 8X60, 9X57, 9.3X62, 10.75X68mm. 5-shot box magazine. 23½-inch round barrel. Weight, about 7¼ pounds. Double-set trigger. Three-leaf rear sight, ramp front sight. Fine walnut stock with checkered pistol grip, "schnabel" forend tip, cheekpiece, grip cap, swivels. Variations: octagon or half-octagon barrel, military-type single trigger, shotgun-type trigger, shotgun-type safety, folding peep rear sight, tangent curve rear sight, telescopic sight.

Mauser Bolt Action Sporting Rifle, Type "K" $400

Light Short Model. Same general specifications as Normal Type "B" model except has short action, 21½-inch round barrel, weighs about 6 pounds, calibers: 250-3000, 6.5X54, 8X51mm.

Mauser Bolt Action Sporting Carbine, Type "M" ... $450

Calibers: 6.5X54, 7X57, 30-06 (7.62X63), 8X51, 8X60, 9X57mm. 5-shot box magazine. 19¾-inch round barrel. Weight, about 6 to 6¾ pounds. Double-set trigger, flat bolt handle. Three-leaf rear sight, ramp front sight. Stocked to muzzle, cheekpiece, checkered pistol grip and forearm, grip cap, steel forend cap, swivels. Variations: military-type single trigger, shotgun-type trigger, shotgun-type safety, tangent curve rear sight, telescopic sight.

Mauser Bolt Action Sporting Carbine, Type "S" $400

Calibers: 6.5X54, 7X57, 8X51, 8X60, 9X57mm. 5-shot box magazine. 19¾-inch round barrel. Weight, about 6 to 6¾ pounds. Double-set trigger. Three-leaf rear sight, ramp front sight. Stocked to muzzle, "schnabel" forend tip, cheekpiece, checkered pistol grip with cap, swivels. Variations: same as listed for Normal Model Type "B."

Mauser Standard Model Rifle $400

Refined version of the German Service Kar.98k. Straight bolt handle. Calibers: 7mm Mauser (7X57mm), 7.9mm Mauser (8X57mm). 5-shot box magazine. 23½-inch barrel. Weight, about 8½ pounds. Blade front sight, adjustable rear sight. Walnut stock of M/98 military-type. *Note:* These rifles were made for commercial sale and are of the high quality found in the Oberndorf Mauser sporters. They bear the Mauser trademark on the receiver ring.

Mauser Model ES340 Bolt Action Single Shot Target Rifle $180

Caliber, 22 Long Rifle. 25½-inch barrel. Weight, about 6½ pounds. Tangent curve rear sight, ramp front sight. Sporting stock with checkered pistol grip and grooved forearm, swivels.

Mauser Model ES350 Bolt Action Single Shot Target Rifle $325

"Meistershaftsbuchse" (Championship Rifle). Caliber, 22 Long Rifle, 27½-inch barrel. Weight, about 7¾ pounds. Open micrometer rear sight, ramp front sight. Target stock with checkered pistol grip and forearm, grip cap, swivels.

Mauser Model MM410 Bolt Action Repeating Sporting Rifle $250

Caliber, 22 Long Rifle. 5-shot detachable box magazine. 23½-inch barrel. Weight, about 5 pounds. Tangent curve open rear sight, ramp front sight. Sporting stock with checkered pistol grip, swivels.

Mauser Model MS420 Bolt Action Repeating Sporting Rifle $250

Caliber, 22 Long Rifle. 5-shot detachable box magazine. 25½-inch barrel. Weight, about 6½ pounds. Tangent curve open rear sight, ramp front sight. Sporting stock with checkered pistol grip, grooved forearm swivels.

Mauser Model EN310 Bolt Action Single Shot Sporting Rifle $150

Caliber, 22 Long Rifle. ("22 Lang fur Buchsen.") 19¾-inch barrel. Weight, about 4 pounds. Fixed open rear sight, blade front sight. Plain pistol-grip stock.

Mauser Model EL320 Bolt Action Single Shot Sporting Rifle $175

Caliber, 22 Long Rifle. 23½-inch barrel. Weight, about 4¼ pounds. Adjustable open rear sight, bead front sight. Sporting stock with checkered pistol grip, swivels.

Note: The foregoing series of Mauser 22 Rifles was superseded about 1935 by the "B" series (Model MS-350B, ES350B, etc.) of improved models, as well as the Sportmodel DSM34. The Military Model KKW was introduced just prior to World War II.

Mauser Model MS350B Bolt Action Repeating Target Rifle $350

Caliber, 22 Long Rifle. 5-shot detachable box magazine. Receiver and barrel grooved for detachable rear sight or scope. 26¾-inch barrel. Weight, about 8½ pounds. Micrometer open rear sight, ramp front sight. Target stock with checkered pistol grip and forearm, grip cap, sling swivels.

Mauser Model ES350B Bolt Action Single Shot Target Rifle $300

Same general specifications as Model MS350B except single shot, weighs about 8¼ pounds.

Mauser Model ES340B Bolt Action Single Shot Target Rifle $250

Caliber, 22 Long Rifle. 26¾-inch barrel. Weight, about 8 pounds. Tangent curve open rear sight, ramp front sight. Plain pistol-grip stock, swivels.

Mauser Model MM410B Bolt Action Repeating Sporting Rifle $300

Caliber, 22 Long Rifle. 5-shot detachable box magazine. 23½-inch barrel. Weight, about 6¼ pounds. Tangent curve open rear sight, ramp front sight. Lightweight sporting stock with checkered pistol grip, swivels.

Mauser Model MS420B Bolt Action Repeating Target Rifle $300

Caliber, 22 Long Rifle. 5-shot detachable box magazine. 26¾-inch barrel. Weight, about 8 pounds. Tangent curve open rear sight, ramp front sight. Target stock with checkered pistol grip, grooved forearm, swivels.

Mauser Model DSM34 Bolt Action Single Shot Sporting Rifle $250

Also called "Sport-model." Caliber, 22 Long Rifle. 26-inch barrel. Weight, about 7¾ pounds. Tangent curve open rear sight, barley-corn front sight. M/98 military-type stock, swivels.

Mauser Model KKW Bolt Action Single Shot Target Rifle $275

Caliber, 22 Long Rifle. 26-inch barrel. Weight, about 8¾ pounds. Tangent curve open rear sight, barleycorn front sight. M/98 military-type stock, swivels. *Note:* This rifle has an improved design Mauser 22 action with separate non-rotating bolt head. In addition to being produced for commercial sale, this model was used as a training rifle by the German armed forces; it was also made by Walther and Gustloff.

Gebruder Merkel, Suhl, Germany

Merkel Over-And-Under Rifles ("Bockdoppelbuchsen")

See listing under Merkel Shotguns.

Mexican Military Rifle manufactured by Government Arsenal, Mexico, D.F.

Mexican Model 1936 Mauser Military Rifle $175

Same as the German Kar.98k with minor variations, has U.S. M/1903 Springfield-type knurled cocking piece.

Mauser Standard Model

Mauser Model MS350B

Mauser Model MM410B

Mauser Model M420B

Mossberg Model K

Mossberg Model L

O. F. Mossberg & Sons, Inc., New Haven, Connecticut

Mossberg Model K Slide Action Repeater **$50**

Hammerless. Takedown. Caliber, 22 Long Rifle, Long, Short. Tubular magazine holds 20 Short, 16 Long, 14 Long Rifle. 22-inch barrel. Weight, about 5 pounds. Open rear sight, bead front sight. Plain straight-grip stock, grooved slide handle. Made from 1922 to 1931.

Mossberg Model M Slide Action Repeater **$60**

Specifications same as for Model K except has 24-inch octagon barrel, pistol-grip stock, weighs about 5½ pounds. Made from 1928 to 1931.

Mossberg Model L Single Shot Rifle **$150**

Martini-type falling-block lever action. Takedown. Caliber, 22 Long Rifle, Long, Short. 24-inch barrel. Weight, about 5 pounds. Open rear sight and bead front sight. Plain pistol-grip stock and forearm. Made from 1929 to 1932.

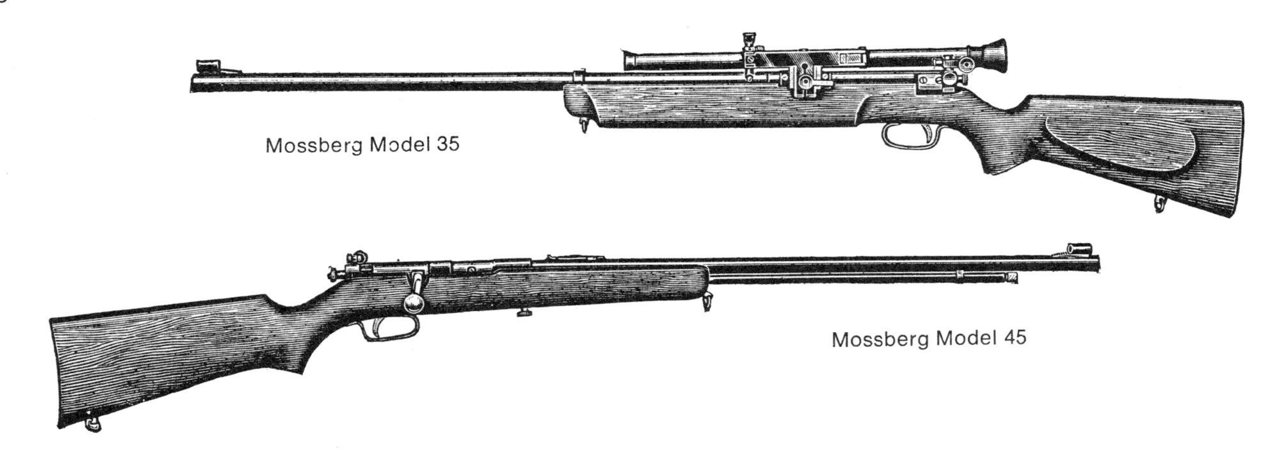

Mossberg Model 35

Mossberg Model 45

Mossberg Model B Single Shot Bolt Action Rifle . . . $25

Takedown. Caliber, 22 Long Rifle, Long, Short. 22-inch barrel. Open rear sight, bead front sight. Plain pistol-grip stock. Made from 1930 to 1932.

Mossberg Model R Bolt Action Repeating Rifle $30

Takedown. Caliber, 22 Long Rifle, Long, Short. Tubular magazine. 24-inch barrel. Open rear sight, bean front sight. Plain pistol-grip stock. Made from 1930 to 1932.

Mossberg Model 10 Bolt Action Single Shot Rifle . . . $25

Takedown. Caliber, 22 Long Rifle, Long, Short. 22-inch barrel. Weight, about 4 pounds. Open rear sight, bead front sight. Plain pistol-grip stock with swivels and sling. Made from 1933 to 1935.

Mossberg Model 20 Bolt Action Single Shot Rifle . . . $25

Takedown. Caliber, 22 Long Rifle, Long, Short. 24-inch barrel. Weight, about 4½ pounds. Open rear sight, bead front sight. Plain pistol-grip stock and forearm with finger grooves, sling and swivels. Made from 1933 to 1935.

Mossberg Model 30 Bolt Action Single Shot Rifle . . . $25

Takedown. Caliber, 22 Long Rifle, Long, Short. 24-inch barrel. Weight, about 4½ pounds. Peep rear sight, bead front sight on hooded ramp. Plain pistol-grip stock, forearm with finger grooves. Made from 1933 to 1935.

Mossberg Model 40 Bolt Action Repeating Rifle . . . $30

Same specifications as Model 30 except has a tubular magazine (holds 16 Long Rifle) and weighs about 5 pounds. Made from 1933 to 1935.

Mossberg Model 14 Bolt Action Single Shot Rifle . . . $25

Takedown. Caliber, 22 Long Rifle, Long, Short. 24-inch barrel. Weight, about 5¼ pounds. Peep rear sight, hooded ramp front sight. Plain pistol-grip stock with semi-beavertail forearm, 1¼-inch swivels. Made from 1934 to 1935.

Mossberg Model 34 Bolt Action Single Shot Rifle . . . $25

Takedown. Caliber, 22 Long Rifle, Long, Short. 24-inch barrel. Weight, 5½ pounds. Peep rear sight, hooded ramp front sight. Plain pistol-grip stock with semi-beavertail forearm, 1¼-inch swivels. Made from 1934 to 1935.

Mossberg Model 44 Bolt Action Repeating Rifle $35

Takedown. Caliber, 22 Long Rifle, Long, Short. Tubular magazine holds 16 Long Rifle. 24-inch barrel. Weight, 6 pounds. Peep rear sight, hooded ramp front sight. Plain pistol-grip stock with semi-beavertail forearm, 1¼-inch swivels. Made from 1934 to 1935. *Note:* Do not confuse this rifle with the later Models 44B and 44US which are clip repeaters.

Mossberg Model 25 Bolt Action Single Shot Rifle . . $25

Takedown. Caliber, 22 Long Rifle, Long, Short. 24-inch barrel. Weight, about 5 pounds. Peep rear sight, hooded ramp front sight. Plain pistol-grip stock with semi-beavertail forearm. 1¼-inch swivels. Made from 1935 to 1936.

Mossberg Model 25A $25

Same as Model 25 with minor improvements. Made from 1936 to 1938.

Mossberg Model 35 Target Grade Bolt Action Single Shot Rifle $60

Caliber, 22 Long Rifle. 26-inch heavy barrel. Weight, about 8¼ pounds. Micrometer click rear peep sight, hooded ramp front sight. Large target stock with full pistol-grip, cheekpiece, full beavertail forearm, 1¼-inch swivels. Made from 1935 to 1937.

Mossberg Model 42 Bolt Action Repeating Rifle $35

Takedown. Caliber, 22 Long Rifle, Long, Short. 7-shot detachable box magazine. 24-inch barrel. Weight, about 5 pounds. Receiver peep sight, open rear sight, hooded ramp front sight. Pistol-grip stock. 1¼-inch swivels. Made from 1935 to 1937.

Mossberg Model 45 Bolt Action Repeating Rifle $35

Takedown. Caliber, 22 Long Rifle, Long, Short. Tubular magazine holds 15 Long Rifle, 18 Long, 22 Short. 24-inch barrel. Weight, about 6¾ pounds. Rear peep sight, hooded ramp front sight. Plain pistol-grip stock, 1¼-inch swivels. Made from 1935 to 1937.

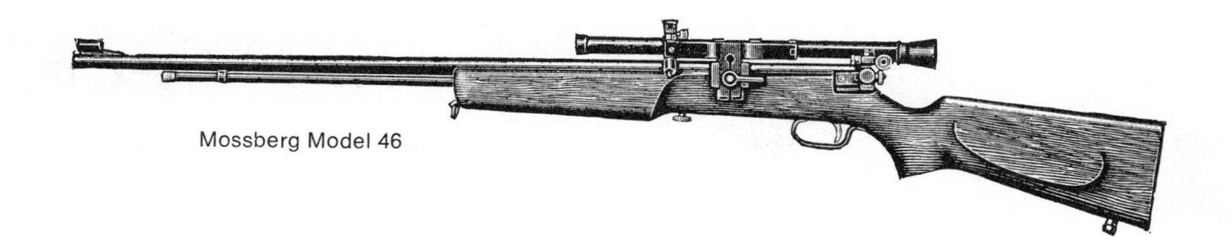
Mossberg Model 46

Mossberg Model 45C **$30**

Same as Model 45 but without rear peep sight and ramp front sight; intended for use with telescopic sight only. Made from 1935 to 1937.

Mossberg Model 46 Bolt Action Repeating Rifle **$35**

Takedown. Caliber, 22 Long Rifle, Long, Short. Tubular magazine holds 15 Long Rifle, 18 Long, 22 Short. 26-inch barrel. Weight, 7½ pounds. Micrometer click rear peep sight, hooded ramp front sight. Pistol-grip stock with cheekpiece, full beavertail forearm, 1¼-inch swivels. Made from 1935 to 1937.

Mossberg Model 46C **$40**

Same as Model 46 except has a heavier barrel and stock than that model, weighs 8½ pounds. Made from 1936 to 1937.

Mossberg Model 35A Bolt Action Single Shot Rifle . . **$40**

Caliber, 22 Long Rifle. 26-inch heavy barrel. Weight, about 8¼ pounds. Micrometer click peep rear sight and hooded front sight. Target stock with cheekpiece, full pistol grip and forearm, 1¼-inch sling swivels. Made from 1937 to 1938.

Mossberg Model 35A-LS **$50**

Same as Model 35A but with Lyman 57 rear sight and 17A front sight.

Mossberg Model 42A Bolt Action Repeating Rifle . . . **$35**

Takedown. Caliber, 22 Long Rifle, Long, Short. 7-shot detachable box magazine. 24-inch barrel. Weight, about 5 pounds. Receiver peep sight, open rear sight, ramp front sight. Plain pistol-grip stock. Made from 1937 to 1938.

Mossberg Model L42A **$35**

Same as Model 42A but with left-hand action. Made from 1937 to 1941.

Mossberg Model 43 Bolt Action Repeating Rifle **$50**

Speed lock, adjustable trigger pull. Caliber, 22 Long Rifle. 7-shot detachable box magazine. 26-inch heavy barrel. Weight, about 8¼ pounds. Lyman 57 rear sight, selective aperture front sight. Target stock with cheekpiece, full pistol grip, beavertail forearm, adjustable front swivel. Made from 1937 to 1938.

Mossberg Model L43 . . . . **$50**

Same as Model 43 except has left-hand action. Made from 1937 to 1938.

Mossberg Model 45A Bolt Action Repeating Rifle . . . **$35**

Takedown. Caliber, 22 Long Rifle, Long, Short. Tubular magazine holds 15 Long Rifle, 18 Long, 22 Short. 24-inch barrel. Weight, about 6¾ pounds. Receiver peep sight, open rear sight, hooded ramp front sight. Plain pistol-grip stock, 1¼-inch swivels. Made from 1937 to 1938.

Mossberg Model 45AC **$30**

Same as Model 45A except without receiver peep sight.

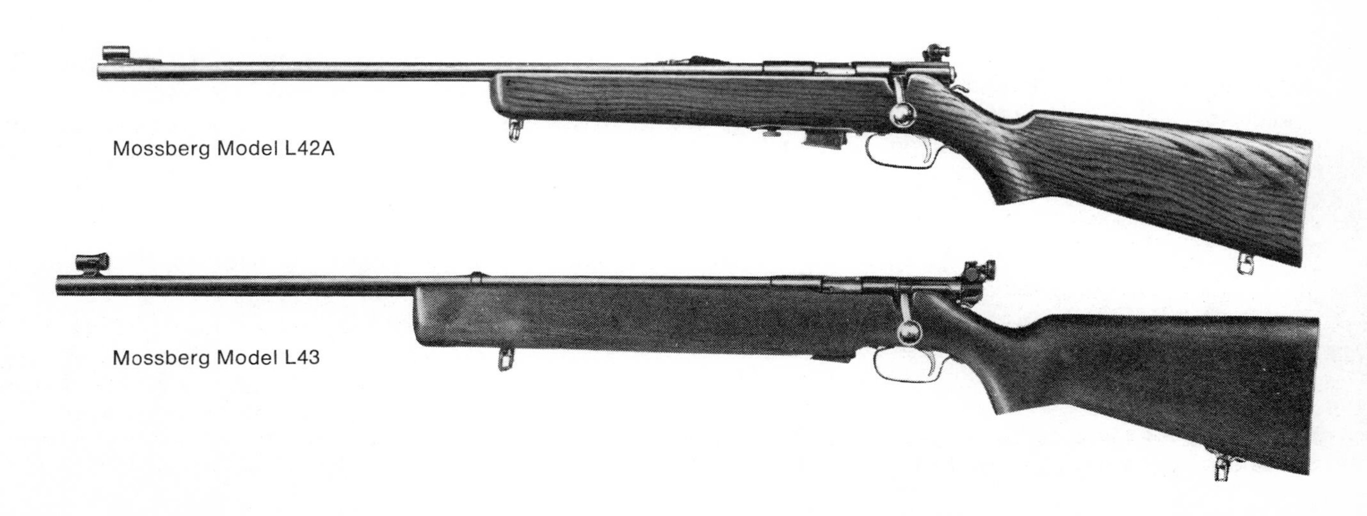
Mossberg Model L42A

Mossberg Model L43

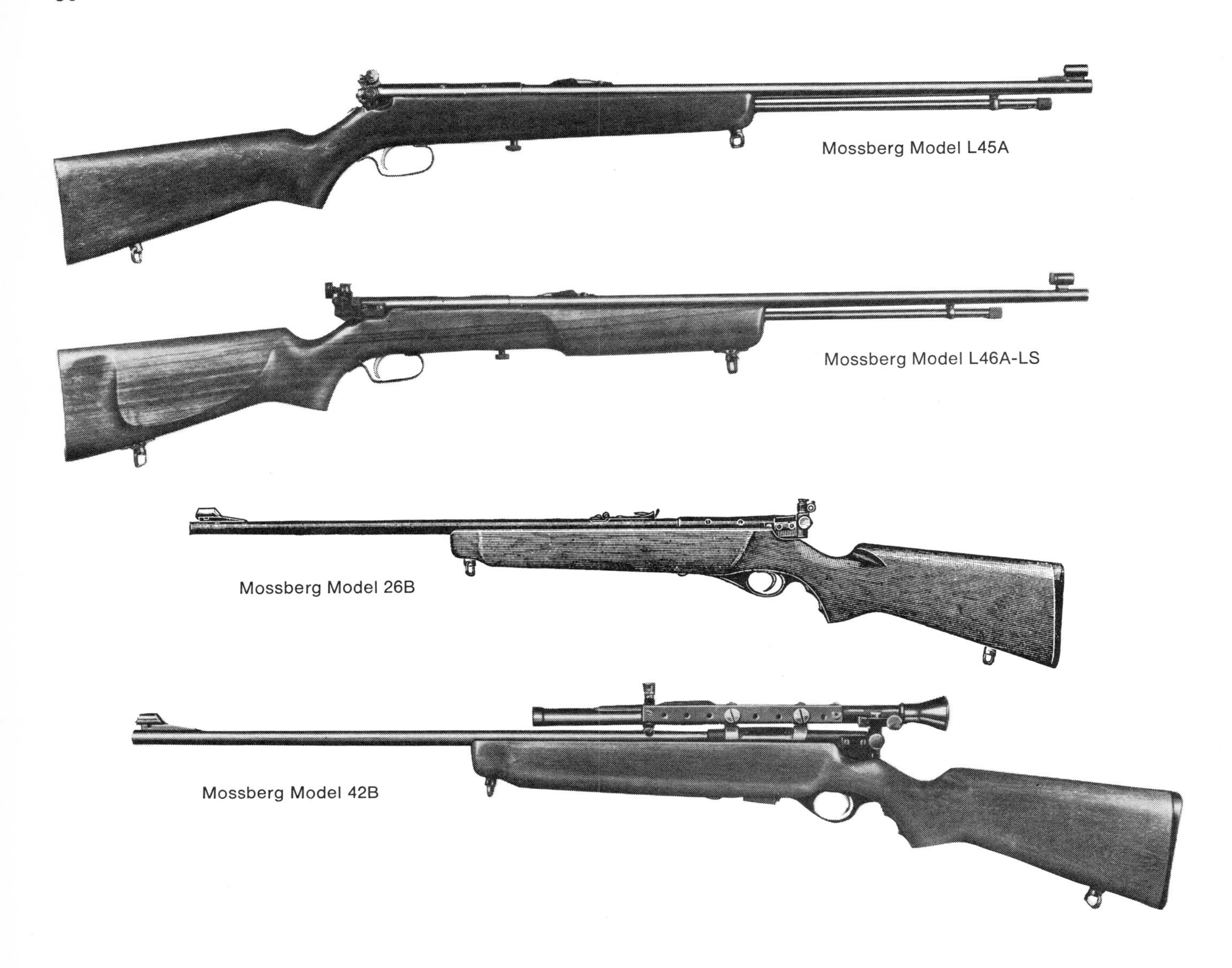

Mossberg Model L45A **$40**

Same as Model 45A except has left-hand action. Made from 1937 to 1938.

Mossberg Model 46A Bolt Action Repeating Rifle ... **$40**

Takedown. Caliber, 22 Long Rifle, Long, Short. Tubular magazine holds 15 Long Rifle, 18 Long, 22 Short. 26-inch barrel. Weight, about 7¼ pounds. Micrometer click receiver peep sight, open rear sight, hooded ramp front sight. Pistol-grip stock with cheekpiece and beavertail forearm, quick-detachable swivels. Made from 1937 to 1938.

Mossberg Model 46AC **$40**

Same as Model 46A except without open rear sight.

Mossberg Model 46A-LS **$50**

Same as Model 46A except with Lyman 57 receiver sight.

Mossberg Model L-46A-LS **$50**

Same as Model 46A-LS except has left-hand action. Made from 1937 to 1938.

Mossberg Model 26B Bolt Action Single Shot Rifle . **$30**

Takedown. Caliber, 22 Long Rifle, Long, Short. 26-inch barrel. Weight, about 5½ pounds. Micrometer click rear peep sight, open rear sight, hooded ramp front sight. Plain pistol-grip stock, swivels. Made from 1938 to 1941.

Mossberg Model 26C **$25**

Same as Model 26B except without rear peep sight and swivels.

Mossberg Model 42B Bolt Action Repeating Rifle ... **$35**

Takedown. Caliber, 22 Long Rifle, Long, Short. 5-shot detachable box magazine. 24-inch barrel. Weight, about 6 pounds. Micrometer click receiver peep sight, open rear sight, hooded ramp front sight. Plain pistol-grip stock, swivels. Made from 1938 to 1941.

Mossberg Model 42C **$35**

Same as Model 42B except without rear peep sight.

Mossberg Model 44B Bolt Action Target Rifle **$60**

Caliber, 22 Long Rifle. 7-shot detachable box magazine. 26-inch heavy barrel. Weight, about 8 pounds. Micrometer click receiver peep sight, hooded front sight. Target stock with full pistol grip, cheekpiece, beavertail forearm, adjustable swivel. Made from 1938 to 1941.

Mossberg Model 35B **$50**

Same specifications as Model 44B except single shot. Made from 1938 to 1940.

Mossberg Model 43B **$70**

Same as Model 44B except with Lyman 57 receiver sight and 17A front sight. Made from 1938 to 1939.

Mossberg Model 45B Bolt Action Repeating Rifle . . . **$40**

Takedown. Caliber, 22 Long Rifle, Long, Short. Tubular magazine holds 15 Long Rifle, 18 Long, 22 Short. 24-inch barrel. Weight, about 6¼ pounds. Open rear sight, hooded front sight. Plain pistol-grip stock, swivels. Made from 1938 to 1940.

Mossberg Model 46B Bolt Action Repeating Rifle . . . **$40**

Takedown. Caliber, 22 Long Rifle, Long, Short. Tubular magazine holds 15 Long Rifle, 18 Long, 22 Short. 26-inch barrel. Weight, about 7 pounds. Micrometer click receiver peep sight, open rear sight, hooded front sight. Plain pistol-grip stock with cheekpiece, swivels. *Note:* Post-war version of this model has full magazine holding 20 Long Rifle, 23 Long, 30 Short. Made from 1938 to 1950.

Mossberg Model 46BT **$50**

Same as Model 46B except has heavier barrel and stock, weighs 7¾ pounds. Made from 1938 to 1939.

Mossberg Model 51 Autoloading Rifle $50

Takedown. Caliber, 22 Long Rifle. 15-shot tubular magazine in buttstock. 24-inch barrel. Weight, about 7¼ pounds. Micrometer click receiver peep sight, open rear sight, hooded ramp front sight. Cheekpiece stock with full pistol grip and beavertail forearm, swivels. Made in 1939 only.

Mossberg Model 50 Autoloading Rifle $45

Same as Model 51 except has plain stock without beavertail, cheekpiece, swivels or receiver peep sight. Made from 1939 to 1942.

Mossberg Model 51M Autoloading Rifle $50

Caliber, 22 Long Rifle. 15-shot tubular magazine. 20-inch barrel. Weight, about 7 pounds. Microclick receiver peep sight, open rear sight, hooded ramp front sight. Two-piece Mannlicher-type stock with pistol grip and cheekpiece, swivels. Made from 1939 to 1946.

Mossberg Model 151M Autoloading Rifle $50

Improved version of Model 51M with same general specifications, complete action is instantly removable without use of tools. Made from 1946 to 1958.

Mossberg Model 151K $45

Same as Model 151M except has 24-inch barrel, weighs about 6 pounds, has no peep sight, plain stock with Monte Carlo comb and cheekpiece, pistol-grip knob forend tip, without swivels. Made from 1950 to 1951.

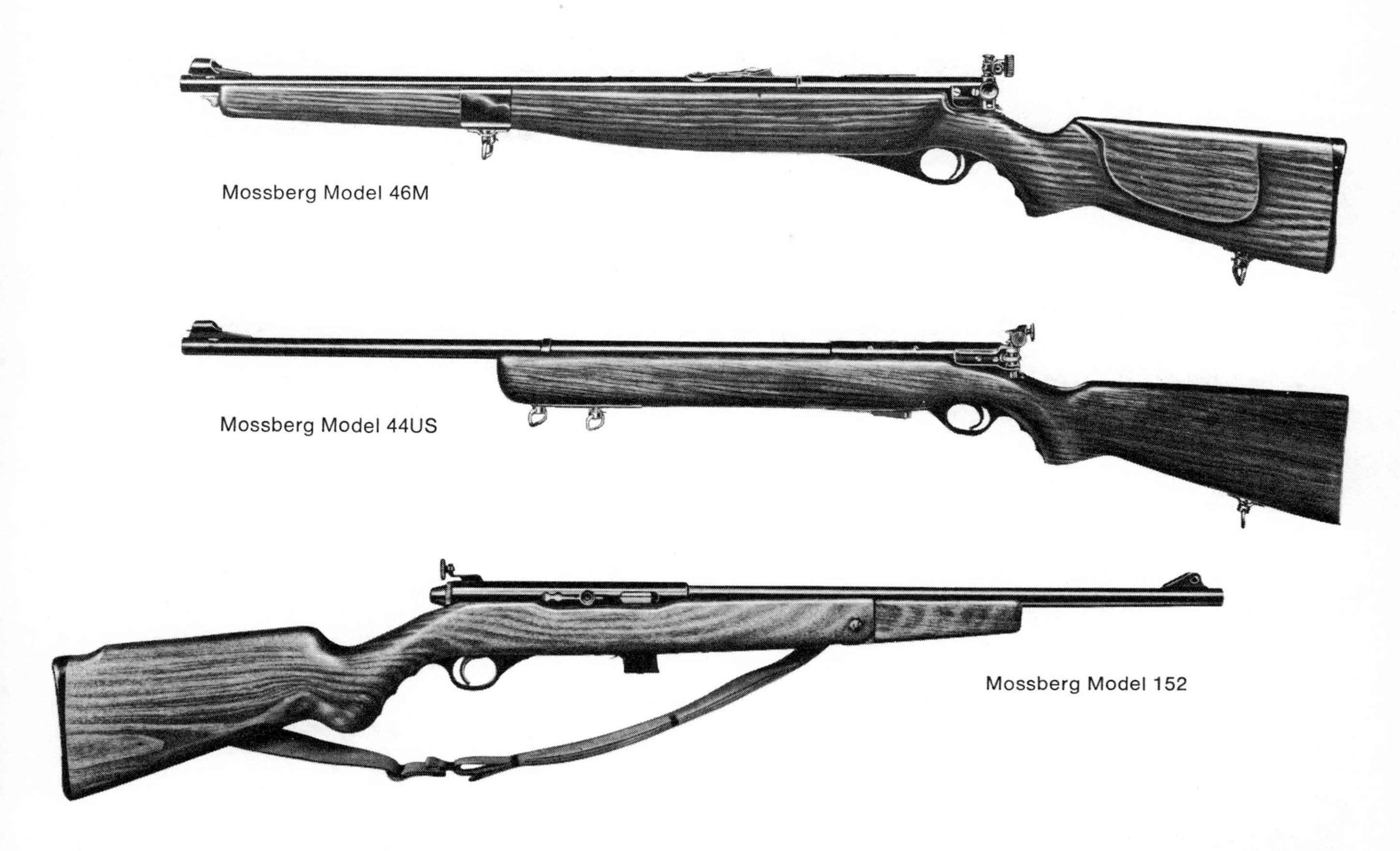
Mossberg Model 46M

Mossberg Model 44US

Mossberg Model 152

Mossberg Model 42M Bolt Action Repeating Rifle . . $40

Caliber, 22 Long Rifle, Long, Short. 7-shot detachable box magazine. 23-inch barrel. Weight, about 6¾ pounds. Micro-click receiver peep sight, open rear sight, hooded ramp front sight. Two-piece Mannlicher-type stock with cheekpiece and pistol-grip, swivels. Made from 1940 to 1950.

Mossberg Model 46M Bolt Action Repeating Rifle . . . $45

Caliber, 22 Long Rifle, Long, Short. Tubular magazine holds 22 Short, 18 Long, 15 Long Rifle. 23-inch barrel. Weight, about 7 pounds. Microclick receiver peep sight, open rear sight, hooded ramp front sight. Two-piece Mannlicher-type stock with cheekpiece and pistol grip, swivels. Made from 1940 to 1952.

Mossberg Model 44US Bolt Action Repeating Rifle $60

Caliber, 22 Long Rifle. 7-shot detachable box magazine. 26-inch heavy barrel. Weight, about 8½ pounds. Micrometer click receiver peep sight, hooded front sight. Target stock, swivels. Made from 1943 to 1948. *Note:* This model was used as a training rifle by the U.S. Armed Forces during World War II.

Mossberg Model 152 Autoloading Carbine $60

Caliber, 22 Long Rifle. 7-shot detachable box magazine. 18-inch barrel. Weight, about 5 pounds. Peep rear sight, military-type front sight. Monte Carlo stock with pistol grip, hinged forearm pulls down to form hand-grip, sling mounted on swivels on left side of stock. Made from 1948 to 1957.

Mossberg Model 152K $60

Same as Model 152 except with open instead of peep rear sight. Made from 1950 to 1957.

Mossberg Model 142-A Bolt Action Repeating Carbine $40

Caliber, 22 Short, Long, Long Rifle. 7-shot detachable box magazine. 18-inch barrel. Weight, about 6 pounds. Peep rear sight, military-type front sight. Monte Carlo stock with pistol grip, hinged forearm pulls down to form hand-grip, sling swivels mounted on left side of stock. Made from 1949 to 1957.

Mossberg Model 142K $40

Same as Model 142 except has open rear sight. Made from 1953 to 1957.

Mossberg Model 144 Bolt Action Target Rifle $60

Caliber, 22 Long Rifle. 7-shot detachable box magazine. 26-inch heavy barrel. Weight, about 8 pounds. Microclick receiver peep sight, hooded front sight. Pistol-grip target stock with beavertail forearm, adjustable hand stop, swivels. Made from 1949 to 1954.

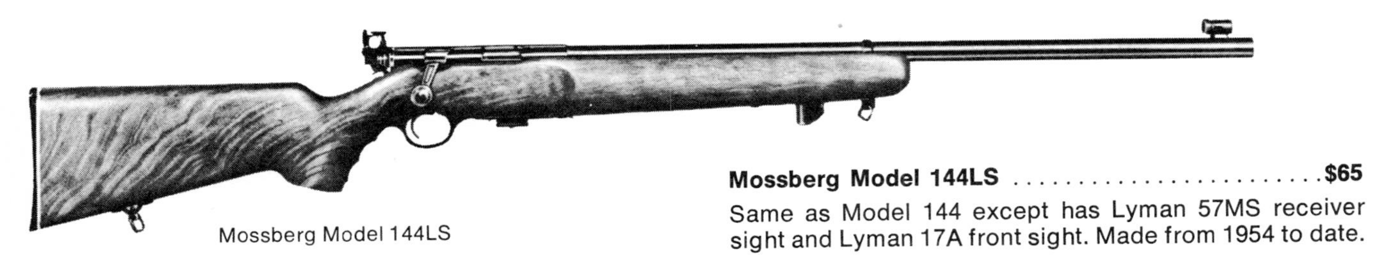

Mossberg Model 144LS

Mossberg Model 144LS **$65**

Same as Model 144 except has Lyman 57MS receiver sight and Lyman 17A front sight. Made from 1954 to date.

Mossberg Model 146B

Mossberg Model 146B Bolt Action Repeating Rifle . . **$45**

Takedown. Caliber, 22 Long Rifle, Long, Short. Tubular magazine holds 30 Shorts, 23 Long, 20 Long Rifle. 26-inch barrel. Weight, about 7 pounds. Micrometer click rear peep sight, open rear sight, hooded front sight. Plain stock with pistol grip, Monte Carlo comb and cheekpiece, knob forend tip, swivels. Made from 1949 to 1954.

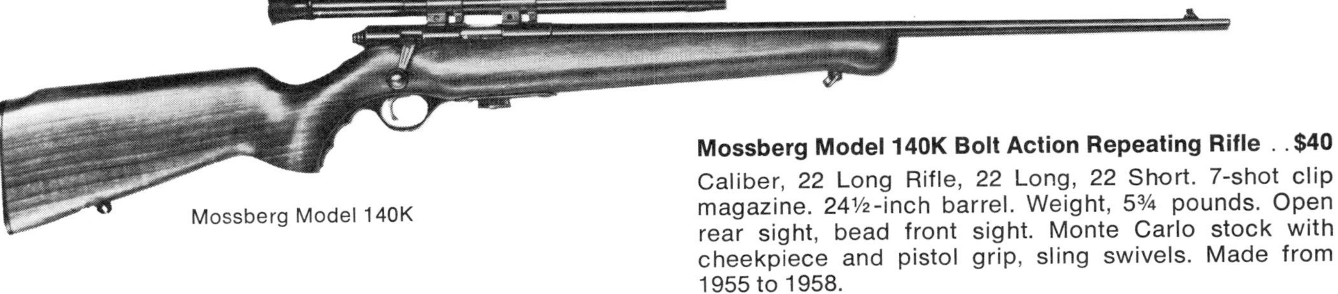

Mossberg Model 140K

Mossberg Model 140K Bolt Action Repeating Rifle . . **$40**

Caliber, 22 Long Rifle, 22 Long, 22 Short. 7-shot clip magazine. 24½-inch barrel. Weight, 5¾ pounds. Open rear sight, bead front sight. Monte Carlo stock with cheekpiece and pistol grip, sling swivels. Made from 1955 to 1958.

Mossberg Model 140B

Mossberg Model 140B Sporter-Target Rifle **$45**

Same as Model 140K except has peep rear sight, hooded ramp front sight. Made from 1957 to 1958.

Mossberg Model 346K

Mossberg Model 346K Hammerless Bolt Action Repeating Rifle **$45**

Caliber, 22 Short, Long, Long Rifle. Tubular magazine holds 25 Short, 20 Long, 18 Long Rifle. 24-inch barrel. Weight, about 6½ pounds. Open rear sight, bead front sight. Walnut stock with Monte Carlo comb, cheekpiece, pistol grip, sling swivels. Made from 1958 to 1971.

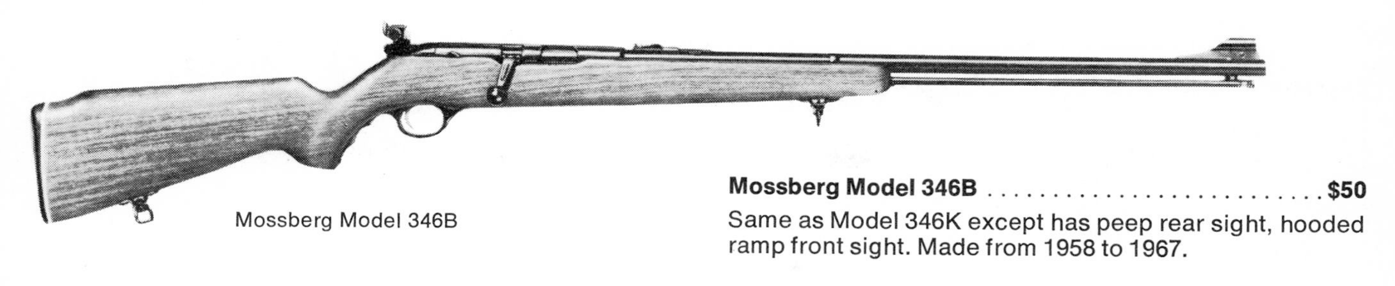
Mossberg Model 346B

Mossberg Model 346B $50

Same as Model 346K except has peep rear sight, hooded ramp front sight. Made from 1958 to 1967.

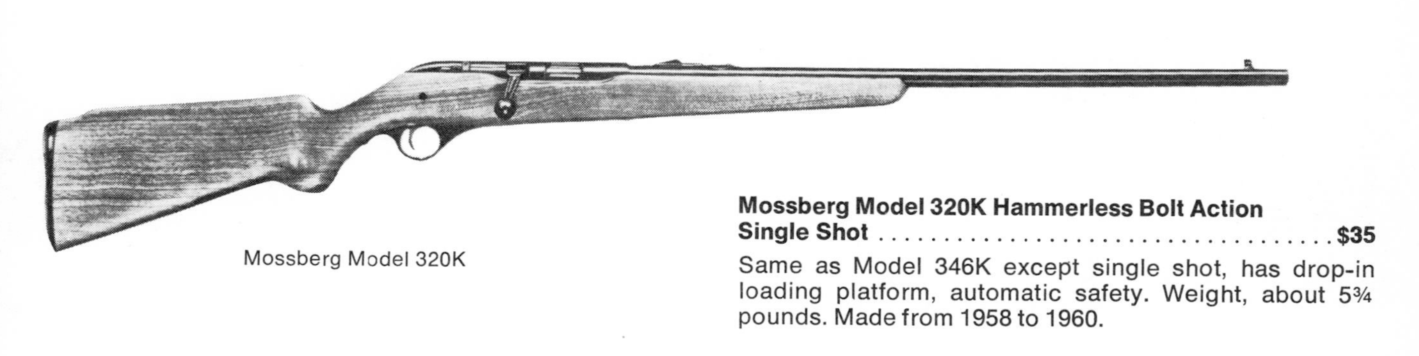
Mossberg Model 320K

Mossberg Model 320K Hammerless Bolt Action Single Shot $35

Same as Model 346K except single shot, has drop-in loading platform, automatic safety. Weight, about 5¾ pounds. Made from 1958 to 1960.

Mossberg Model 340K

Mossberg Model 340K Hammerless Bolt Action Repeating Rifle $40

Same as Model 346K except clip type, 7-shot magazine. Made from 1958 to 1971.

Mossberg Model 340B

Mossberg Model 340B Target Sporter $45

Same as Model 340K except has peep rear sight, hooded ramp front sight. Made from 1958 to date.

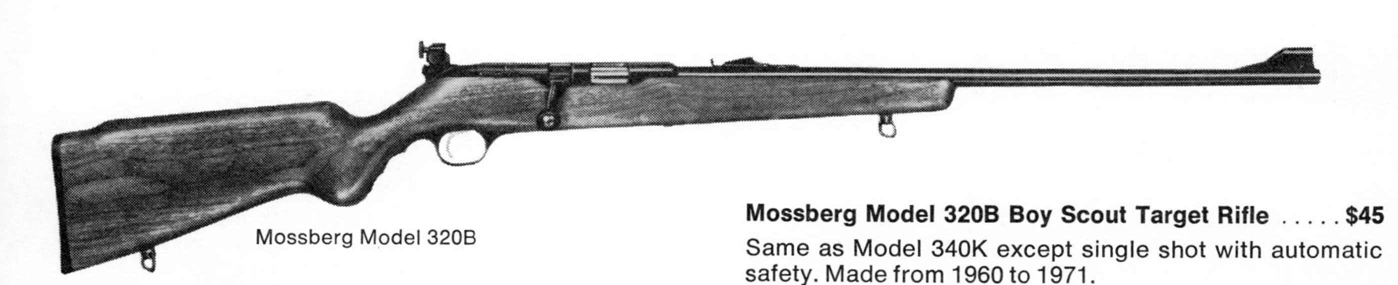
Mossberg Model 320B

Mossberg Model 320B Boy Scout Target Rifle $45

Same as Model 340K except single shot with automatic safety. Made from 1960 to 1971.

Mossberg Model 342K

Mossberg Model 350K

Mossberg Model 352K

Mossberg Model 351K

Mossberg Model 340M **$50**

Same as Model 340K except has 18½ inch barrel, Mannlicher-style stock with swivels and sling. Weight, 5¼ pounds. Made from 1970 to 1971.

Mossberg Model 342K Hammerless Bolt Action Carbine $40

Same as Model 340K except has 18-inch barrel, stock has no cheekpiece, extension fore-end is hinged, pulls down to form hand-grip; sling swivels and web strap on left side of stock; weight, about 5 pounds. Made from 1958 to date.

Mossberg Model 350K Autoloading Rifle—Clip Type $45

Caliber, 22 Short (high speed), Long, Long Rifle. 7-shot clip magazine. 23½-inch barrel. Weight, about 6 pounds. Open rear sight, bead front sight. Monte Carlo stock with pistol grip. Made from 1958 to 1971.

Mossberg Model 352K Autoloading Carbine **$45**

Caliber, 22 Short, Long, Long Rifle. 7-shot clip magazine. 18-inch barrel. Weight, about 5 pounds. Open rear sight, bead front sight. Monte Carlo stock with pistol grip; extension fore-end of Tenite is hinged, pulls down to form hand-grip; sling swivels, web strap. Made from 1958 to 1971.

Mossberg Model 351K Automatic Sporter **$40**

Caliber, 22 Long Rifle. 15-shot tubular magazine in buttstock. 24-inch barrel. Weight, about 6 pounds. Open rear sight, bead front sight. Monte Carlo stock with pistol grip. Made from 1960 to 1971.

Mossberg Model 351C Automatic Carbine **$45**

Same as Model 351K except has 18½-inch barrel, Western carbine-style stock with barrel band and sling swivels. Weight, 5½ pounds. Made from 1965 to 1971.

Mossberg Model 640K

Mossberg Model 402

Musketeer Mauser

Navy Arms Model 66

Mossberg Model 640K "Chuckster" Hammerless Bolt Action Rifle $50

Caliber, 22 R.F. Magnum. 5-shot detachable clip magazine. 24-inch barrel. Weight, about 6 pounds. Open rear sight, bead front sight. Monte Carlo stock with cheekpiece, pistol grip, sling swivels. Made from 1959 to date.

Mossberg Model 402 "Palomino" Lever Action Rifle $60

Hammerless. Caliber, 22 Short, Long, Long Rifle. Tubular magazine holds 18 Short, 15 Long, 13 Long Rifle. 20-inch barrel. Weight, about 4¾ pounds. Open rear sight, bead front sight. Monte Carlo stock with checkered pistol grip; checkered beavertail forearm; barrel band, sling swivels. Made from 1961 to 1971.

Mossberg Model 430 Automatic Rifle $50

Caliber, 22 Long Rifle. 18-shot tubular magazine. 24-inch barrel. Weight, about 6¼ pounds. Open rear sight, bead front sight. Monte Carlo stock with checkered pistol grip; checkered forearm. Made from 1970 to 1971.

Mossberg Model 432 Western Style Auto Carbine . . $45

Same as Model 430 except has plain straight-grip carbine-type stock and forearm, barrel band, sling swivels. Magazine capacity, 15 cartridges. Weight, about 6 pounds. Made from 1970 to 1971.

Musketeer Rifles manufactured by Firearms International Corp., Washington, D.C.

Musketeer Mauser Sporter $175

FN Mauser bolt action. Calibers: 243, 25-06, 270, 264 Mag., 308, 30-06, 7mm Mag., 300 Win. Mag. Magazine holds 5 standard, 3 magnum cartridges. 24-inch barrel. Weight, about 7¼ pounds. No sights. Monte Carlo stock with checkered pistol grip and forearm, swivels. Made from 1963 to 1972.

Navy Arms Rifles manufactured in Italy for Navy Arms Co., Ridgefield, New Jersey

Navy Arms Model 66 Lever Action Repeating Rifle $135

Styled after Winchester Model 1866. Caliber, 22 Short, Long, Long Rifle. Full-length tubular magazine holds 14 22 LR. 19-inch barrel. Polished brass frame, other metal parts blued. Open leaf rear sight, blade front sight. Weight, 7 pounds. Carbine-type straight-grip stock, forearm with barrel band. Made from 1966 to date.

Newton Sporting Rifles manufactured by Newton Arms Co., Charles Newton Rifle Corp., and Buffalo Newton Rifle Co., all of Buffalo, N.Y.

Newton-Mauser Sporting Rifle $250

Mauser (Oberndorf) action. Caliber, 256 Newton. 5-shot box magazine, hinged floorplate. Double-set triggers. 24-inch barrel. Open rear sight, ramp front sight. Sporting stock with checkered pistol grip. Weight, about 7 pounds. Made c. 1914 by Newton Arms Co.

Newton Standard Model Sporting Rifle—First Type $300

Newton bolt action, interrupted screw-type breech-locking mechanism, double-set triggers. Calibers: 22, 256, 280, 30, 33, 35 Newton; 30-06. 24-inch barrel. Open rear sight or cocking-piece peep sight, ramp front sight. Checkered pistol-grip stock. Weight, 7 to 8 pounds, depending upon caliber. Made c. 1916-18 by Newton Arms Co.

Newton Standard Model Sporting Rifle—Second Type $300

Newton bolt action, improved design; distinguished by reversed-set trigger and 1917-Enfield-type bolt handle. Calibers: 256, 30, 35 Newton; 30-06. 5-shot box magazine. 24-inch barrel. Open rear sight, ramp front sight. Checkered pistol-grip stock. Weight, 7¾ to 8¼ pounds, depending upon caliber. Made c. 1921 by Charles Newton Rifle Corp.

Buffalo Newton Sporting Rifle $300

Same general specifications as Standard Model — 2nd Type. Made c. 1922-32 by Buffalo Newton Rifle Co.

Noble Mfg. Co., Haydenville, Massachusetts

Noble Model 33 Slide Action Repeater $35

Hammerless. Caliber, 22 Long Rifle, Long, Short. Tubular magazine holds 21 Short, 17 Long, 15 Long Rifle. 24-inch barrel. Weight, 6 pounds. Open rear sight, bead front sight. Tenite stock and slide handle. Made from 1949 to 1953.

Noble Model 33A $40

Same general specifications as Model 33 except has wood stock and slide handle. Made from 1953 to 1955.

Noble Model 236 Slide Action Repeating Rifle $40

Hammerless. Caliber, 22 Short, Long, Long Rifle. Tubular magazine holds 21 Short, 17 Long, 15 Long Rifle. 24-inch barrel. Weight, about 5½ pounds. Open rear sight, ramp front sight. Pistol-grip stock, grooved slide handle. Made from 1951 to date.

Noble Model 10 Bolt Action Single Shot Rifle $20

Caliber, 22 Long Rifle, Long, Short. 24-inch barrel. Plain pistol-grip stock. Open rear sight, bead front sight. Weight, about 4 pounds. Made from 1955 to 1958.

Noble Model 20 Bolt Action Single Shot Rifle $20

Manually cocked. Caliber, 22 Long Rifle, Long, Short. 22-inch barrel. Weight, about 5 pounds. Open rear sight, bead front sight. Walnut stock with pistol grip. Made from 1958 to 1963.

Noble Model 222 Bolt Action Single Shot Rifle $25

Manually cocked. Caliber, 22 Long Rifle, Long, Short Barrel integral with receiver. Overall length, 38 inches. Weight, about 5 pounds. Interchangeable V-notch and peep rear sight, ramp front sight. Scope mounting base. Pistol-grip stock. Made from 1958 to 1971.

Noble Model 236

Noble Model 10

Noble Model 222

Noble Model 275

Noble Model 275 Lever Action Rifle **$50**

Hammerless. Caliber, 22 Short, Long, Long Rifle. Tubular magazine holds 21 Short, 17 Long, 15 Long Rifle. 24-inch barrel. Weight, about 5½ pounds. Open rear sight, ramp front sight. Stock with semi-pistol-grip. Made from 1958 to 1971.

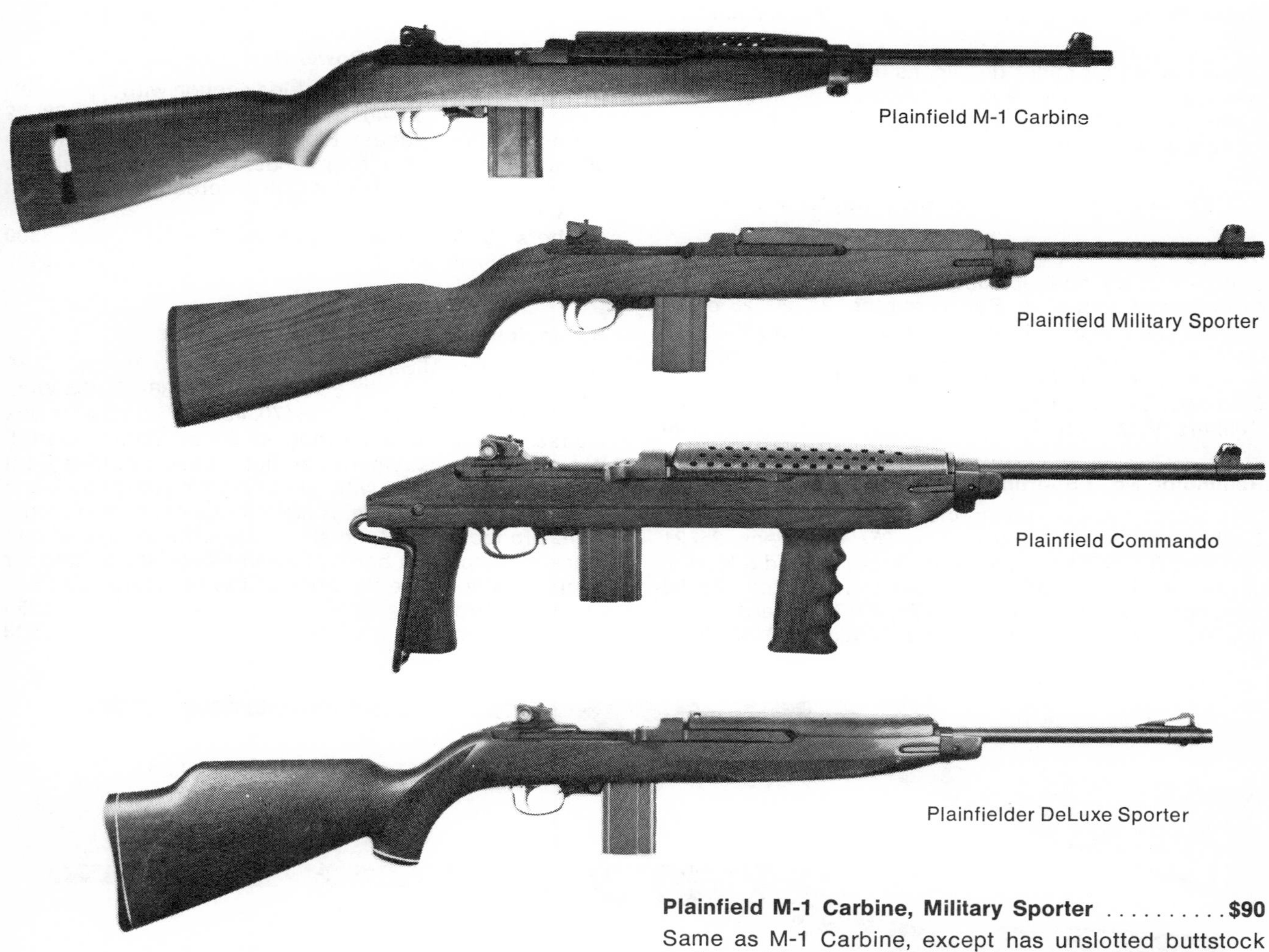

Plainfield M-1 Carbine

Plainfield Military Sporter

Plainfield Commando

Plainfielder DeLuxe Sporter

Plainfield Machine Company, Dunellen, New Jersey

Plainfield M-1 Carbine **$90**

Same as U.S. Carbine, Cal. 30, M1, except also available in caliber 5.7mm (22 with necked-down 30 Carbine cartridge case). Current production has ventilated metal hand guard and barrel band without bayonet lug; earlier models have standard military-type fittings. Made from 1960 to date.

Plainfield M-1 Carbine, Military Sporter **$90**

Same as M-1 Carbine, except has unslotted buttstock and wood handguard. Made from 1960 to date.

Plainfield M-1 Carbine, Commando Model **$100**

Same as M-1 Carbine, except has paratrooper-type stock with telescoping wire shoulder piece. Made from 1960 to date.

Plainfielder De Luxe Sporter **$115**

Same as M-1 Carbine, except has Monte Carlo sporting stock. Made from 1960 to 1973.

Polish Military Rifles manufactured by Government Arsenals at Radom and Warsaw

Polish Model 1898 (Karabin 98, WZ98A) Mauser Military Rifle $125

Same, except for minor details, as the German Gew. 98 used in World War I. Manufacture begun c. 1921.

Polish Model 1898 (Karabinek 98, K98) Mauser Military Carbine $125

Same, except for minor details, as the German Kar. 98a. First manufactured during early 1920's.

Polish Model 1929 (Karabin 29, WZ29) Mauser Military Rifle $125

Same, except for minor details, as the Czech Model 24. Manufactured from 1929 through World War II; a similar model produced during the German occupation was designated Gew. 29/40.

Remington Arms Company, Ilion, New York

Remington No. 2 Sporting Rifle

Single-shot, rolling-block action. Calibers: 22, 25, 32, 38, 44 rimfire or centerfire. Barrel lengths: 24, 26, 28 or 30 inches. Weight, 5 to 6 pounds. Open rear sight, bead front sight. Straight-grip sporting stock and knobtip forearm of walnut. Made from 1873 to 1910.
Calibers 22 through 32 . . . . **$100**
Calibers 38 through 44 . . . . **$200**

Remington No. 3 Sporting Rifle $300

Single-shot. Hepburn falling-block action with side-lever. Calibers: 22 WCF, 22 Extra Long, 25/20 Stevens, 25/21 Stevens, 25/25 Stevens, 32 WCF, 32/40 Ballard & Marlin, 32/40 Remington, 38 WCF, 38/40 Remington, 38/50 Remington, 38/55 Ballard & Marlin, 40/60 Ballard & Marlin, 40/60 WCF, 40/65 Remington Straight, 40/82 WCF, 45/70 Government, 45/90 WCF; also was supplied on special order in bottle-necked 40/50, 40/70, 40/90, 44/77, 44/90, 44/105, 50/70 Government, 50/90 Sharps Straight. Barrel lengths: 26-inch (22, 25, 32 cal. only), 28-inch, 30-inch; half octagon or full octagon. Weight, from 8 to 10 pounds depending upon barrel length and caliber. Open rear sight, blade front sight. Checkered pistol-grip stock and forearm. Made from 1880 to about 1911.

Remington No. 3 Creedmore and Scheutzen Rifles were produced in a variety of styles and calibers. These are collector's items and bring far higher prices than the sporting types. The Scheutzen Special, which has an under-lever action, is especially rare—perhaps less than 100 having been made.

Remington No. 3 High Power Rifle

Single-shot. Hepburn falling-block action with side-lever. Calibers: 30/30, 30/40, 32 Special, 32/40, 38/55, 38/72 (high-power cartridges). Barrel lengths: 26-inch, 28-inch 30-inch. Weight, about 8 pounds. Open sporting sights. Checkered pistol-grip stock and forearm. Made from 1893 to 1907.
Calibers 30/30, 30/40, 32 Special, 32/40 . . . . **$300**
Calibers 38/55, 38/72 . . . . **$400**

Remington-Lee Bolt Action Sporting Rifle

Calibers: 6mm U.S.N., 30-30, 30-40, 7mm Mauser, 7.65 Mauser, 32 Rem., 32-40, 35 Rem., 38-55, 38-72, 405 Win., 43 Spanish, 44/77 Sharps, 45/70, 45/90. Detachable box magazine holding 5 cartridges. 24 or 26-inch barrel. Weight, 7 pounds. Open rear sight, bead or blade front sight. Walnut stock with checkered pistol grip. Made from 1886 to 1906. *Note:* A limited number of this model were produced in "Special" Grade with de luxe walnut stock, half-octagon barrel, Lyman sights; these sold for approximately twice the price of the Standard Grade.
Standard Model **$250**
De luxe Model **$500**

Remington No. 2

Remington No. 3

Remington-Lee Sporter

Remington Light Baby Carbine **$250**

Single shot. Rolling block action. Caliber, 44 Winchester. 20-inch barrel. Weight, 5¾ pounds. Open rear sight, blade front sight. Plain straight-grip carbine-style stock and forearm, barrel band. Made from 1883 to 1910.

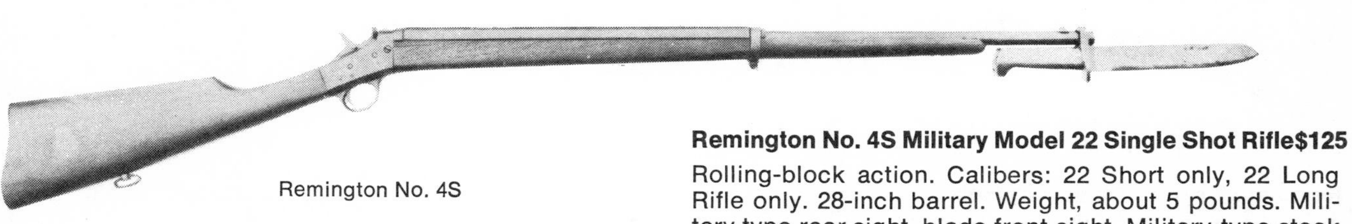

Remington No. 4

Remington No. 4 Single Shot Rifle **$85**

Rolling-block action. Solid frame or takedown. Calibers: 22 Short and Long, 22 Long Rifle, 25 Stevens R.F., 32 Short and Long R.F. 22½-inch octagon barrel, 24-inch available in 32 caliber only. Weight, about 4½ pounds. Open rear sight, blade front sight. Plain walnut stock and forearm. Made from 1890 to 1933.

Remington No. 4S

Remington No. 4S Military Model 22 Single Shot Rifle$125

Rolling-block action. Calibers: 22 Short only, 22 Long Rifle only. 28-inch barrel. Weight, about 5 pounds. Military-type rear sight, blade front sight. Military-type stock with handguard, stacking swivel, sling. Has a bayonet stud on the barrel; bayonet and scabbard were regularly supplied. *Note:* At one time the "Military Model" was the official rifle of the Boy Scouts of America and was called the "Boy Scout Rifle." Made from 1913 to 1933.

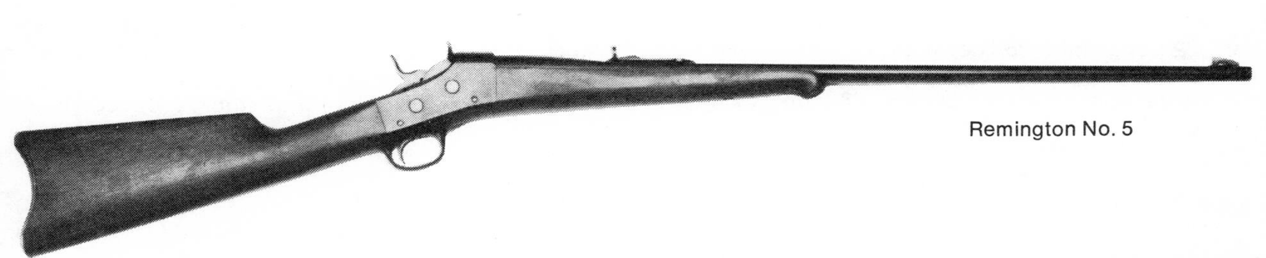

Remington No. 5

Remington No. 5 Special Rifle

Single shot. Rolling-block action. Calibers: 7mm Mauser, 30-30, 30-40 Krag, 303 British, 32-40, 32 Special, 38-55 (high power cartridges). Barrel lengths: 24, 26 and 28 inches. Weight, about 7 pounds. Open sporting sights. Plain straight-grip stock and forearm. Made from 1902 to 1918. *Note:* Models 1897 and 1902 Military Rifles, intended for the export market, are almost identical with the No. 5 except for 30-inch barrel, full military stock and weight (about 8½ pounds); a carbine was also supplied. The military rifles were produced in caliber 8mm Lebel for France, 7.62mm Russian for Russia and 7mm Mauser for the Central and South American government trade. At one time, Remington also offered these military models to retail purchasers.

Sporting Model **$230**
Military Model **$150**

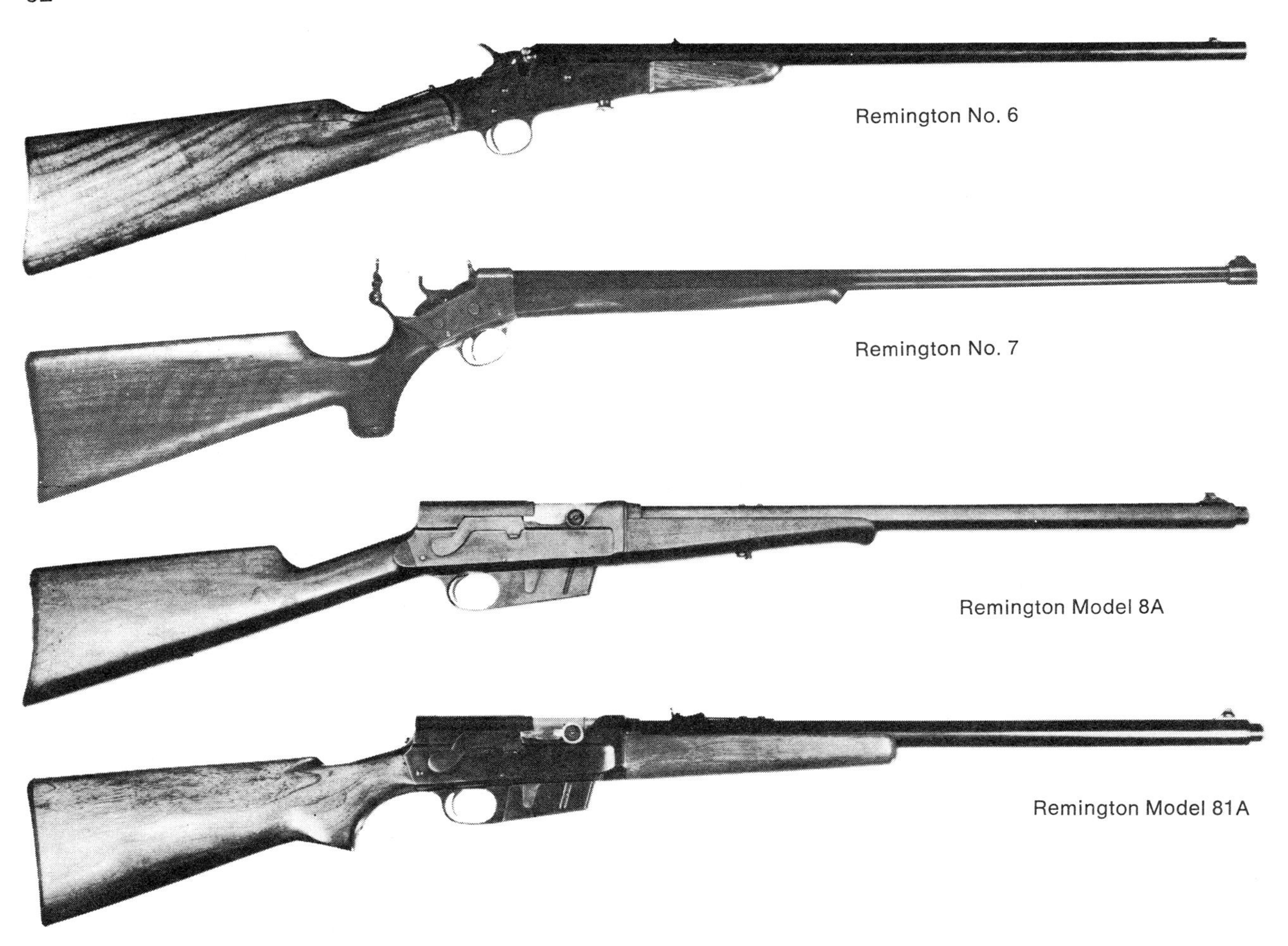

Remington No. 6

Remington No. 7

Remington Model 8A

Remington Model 81A

Remington No. 6 Takedown Rifle **$75**

Single-shot. Rolling-block action. Calibers: 22 Short, 22 Long, 22 Long Rifle, 32 Short and Long R.F. 20-inch barrel. Weight, about 4 pounds. Open front and rear sights, tang peep sight. Plain straight-grip stock and forearm. Made from 1901 to 1933.

Remington No. 7 Target and Sporting Rifle **$325**

Single-shot. Rolling-block Army Pistol frame. Calibers: 22 Short, 22 Long Rifle, 25 Stevens R.F. (other calibers as available in No. 2 Rifle were supplied on special order). Half-octagon barrels: 24, 26, 28-inch. Weight, about 6 pounds. Lyman combination rear sight, Beach combination front sight. Fancy walnut stock and forearm; Swiss butt plate available as an extra. Made from 1903 to 1911.

Remington Model 8A Autoloading Rifle **$170**

Standard Grade. Takedown. Calibers: 25, 30, 32 and 35 Rem. Detachable box magazine holds five cartridges. 22-inch barrel. Weight, 7¾ pounds. Open rear sight, bead front sight. Plain straight-grip stock and forearm of walnut. Made from 1906 to 1936.

Remington Model 81A "Woods-Master" Autoloading Rifle **$175**

Standard Grade. Takedown. Calibers: 30, 32 and 35 Rem. 300 Sav. 5-shot box magazine (not detachable). 22-inch barrel. Weight, 8¼ pounds. Open rear sight, bead front sight. Plain, pistol-grip stock and forearm of walnut. Made from 1936 to 1950.

Remington Model 12A Slide Action Repeating Rifle $95

Standard Grade. Hammerless. Takedown. Caliber, 22 Short, Long or Long Rifle. Tubular magazine holds 15 Short, 12 Long or 10 Long Rifle cartridges. 22-inch round barrel. Weight, 4½ pounds. Open rear sight, bead front sight. Plain, straight-grip stock, grooved slide handle. Made from 1909 to 1936.

Remington Model 12B **$90**

Same as Model 12A except chambered for 22 Short only.

Remington Model 12C **$120**

Target Grade. Same as Model 12A except has 24-inch octagon barrel, pistol-grip stock.

Remington Model 12CS **$100**

Same as Model 12C except chambered for 22 Remington Special (22 W.R.F.). Magazine holds 12 rounds.

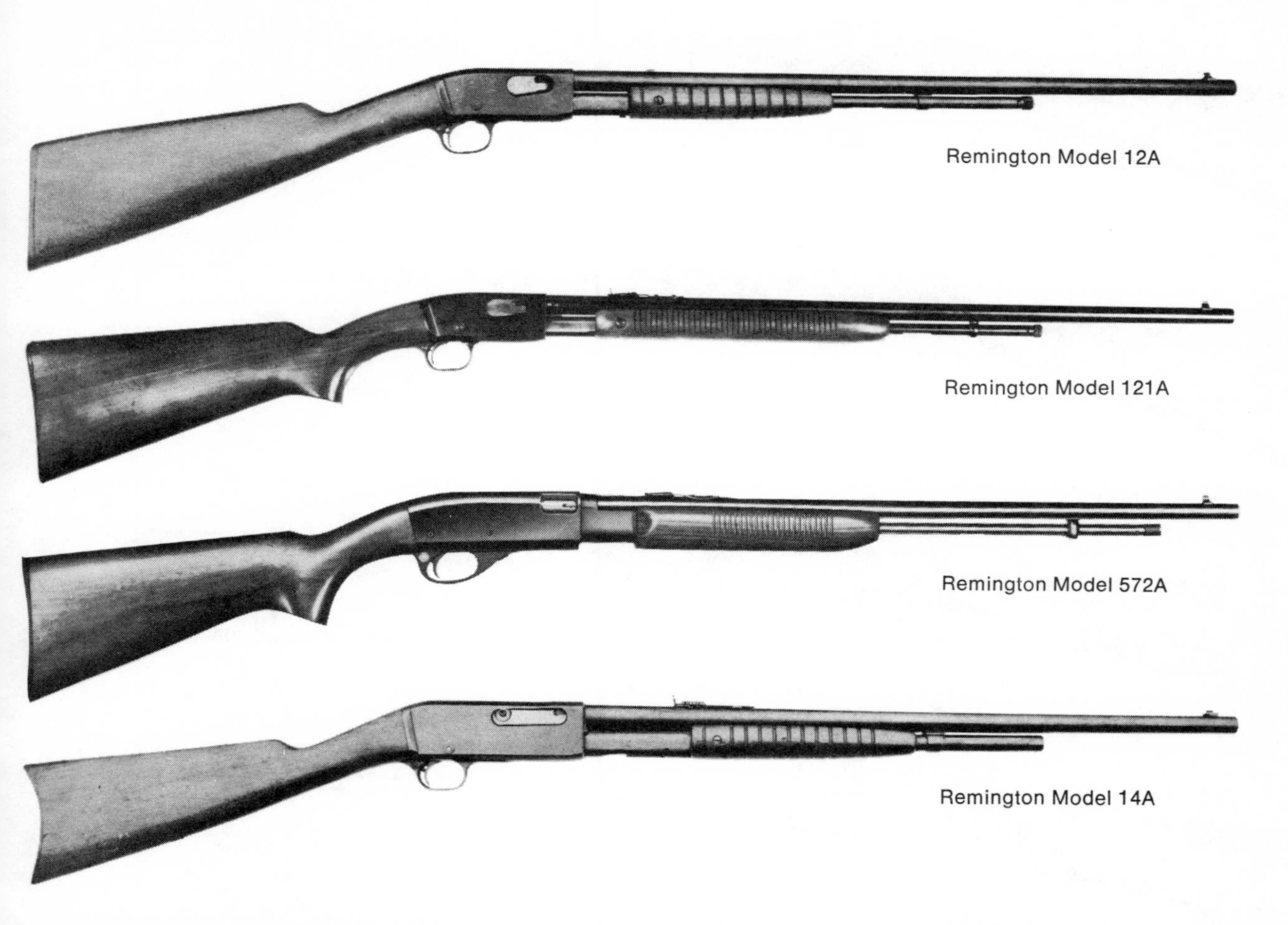

Remington Model 12A

Remington Model 121A

Remington Model 572A

Remington Model 14A

Remington Model 121A "Fieldmaster" Slide Action Repeating Rifle $150

Standard Grade. Hammerless. Takedown. Caliber, 22 Short, Long, Long Rifle. Tubular magazine holds 20 Short, 15 Long or 14 Long Rifle cartridges. 24-inch round barrel. Weight, 6 pounds. Plain, pistol-grip stock and grooved semi-beavertail slide handle. Made from 1936 to 1954.

Remington Model 121S $100

Same as Model 121A, except chambered for 22 Remington Special (22 W.R.F.). Magazine holds 12 rounds. Discontinued.

Remington Model 121SB $100

Same as Model 121A, except smoothbore. Discontinued.

Remington Model 572A "Field-Master" Slide Action Repeater $60

Hammerless. Caliber, 22 Short, Long, Long Rifle. Tubular magazine holds 20 Short, 17 Long, 15 Long Rifle. 25-inch barrel. Weight, about 5½ pounds. Open rear sight, ramp front sight. Pistol-grip stock, grooved forearm. Made from 1955 to date.

Remington Model 14A High Power Slide Action Repeating Rifle $155

Standard Grade. Hammerless. Takedown. Calibers: 25, 30, 32 and 35 Rem. 5-shot tubular magazine. 22-inch barrel. Weight, about 6¾ pounds. Open rear sight, head front sight. Plain, pistol-grip stock and grooved slide handle of walnut. Made from 1912 to 1935.

Remington Model 14R Carbine $200

Same as Model 14A except has 18½-inch barrel, straight-grip stock, weighs about 6 pounds.

Remington Model 14½ Rifle $165

Similar to Model 14A, except calibers 38/40 and 44/40, 11-shot full magazine, 22½-inch barrel. Made from 1912 to early 1920's.

Remington Model 14½ Carbine $200

Same as Model 14½ Rifle, except has 9-shot magazine, 18½-inch barrel.

Remington Model 141A Gamemaster Slide Action Repeating Rifle $150

Standard Grade. Hammerless. Takedown. Calibers: 30, 32 and 35 Rem. 5-shot tubular magazine. 24-inch barrel.

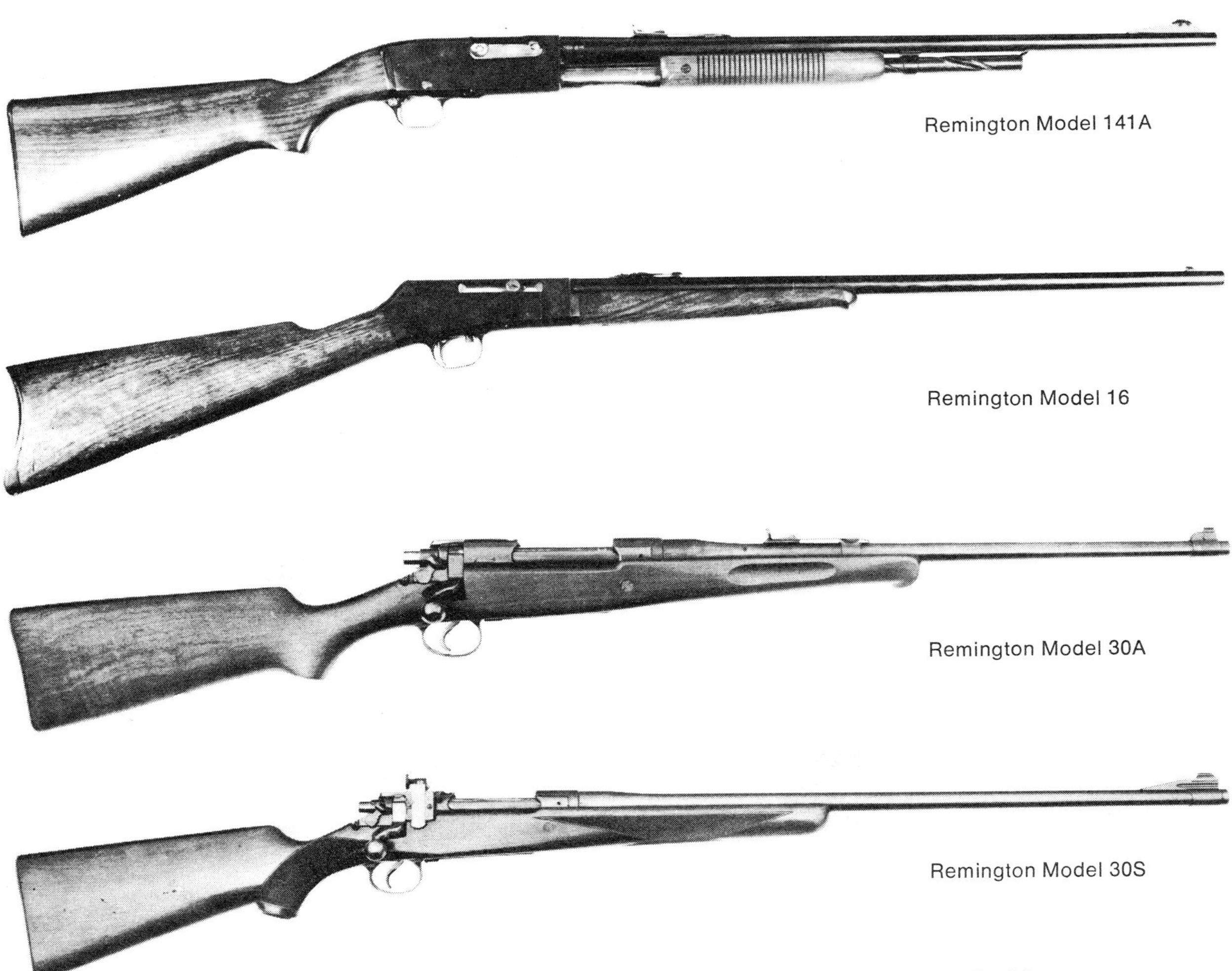

Remington Model 141A

Remington Model 16

Remington Model 30A

Remington Model 30S

Weight, about 7¾ pounds. Open rear sight, bead front sight on ramp. Plain, pistol-grip stock, semi-beavertail fore-end (slide-handle). Made from 1936 to 1950.

Remington Model 16 Autoloading Rifle $125

Takedown. Closely resembles the Winchester Model 03. Calibers: 22 Short, 22 Long Rifle, 22 W.R.F., 22 Remington Auto. 15-shot tubular magazine in butt-stock. 22-inch barrel. Weight, 5¾ pounds. Open rear sight, bead front sight. Plain straight-grip stock and forearm. Made from 1914 to 1928. *Note:* This model was discontinued in all calibers except 22 Rem. Auto in 1918 and specifications given are for the 22 Rem. Auto model.

Remington Model 30A Bolt Action Express Rifle . . $150

Standard Grade. Modified M/1917 Enfield Action. Calibers: 25, 30, 32 and 35 Rem., 7mm Mauser, 30-06. 5-shot box magazine. 22-inch barrel. Weight, about 7¼ pounds. Open rear sight, bead front sight. Walnut stock with checkered pistol grip and forearm. Made from 1921 to 1940. *Note:* Early Model 30's had a slender forend with "schnabel" tip, military-type double-pull trigger, 24-inch barrel.

Remington Model 30R Carbine $150

Same as Model 30A, except has 20-inch barrel, plain stock, weighs about 7 pounds.

Remington Model 30S Sporting Rifle $200

Special Grade. Same action as Model 30A. Calibers: 257 Roberts, 7mm Mauser, 30-06. 5-shot box magazine. 24-inch barrel. Weight, about 8 pounds. Lyman #48 Receiver sight, bead front sight. Special high comb stock with long, full forearm, checkered. Made from 1930 to 1940.

Remington Model 24A Autoloading Rifle $100

Standard Grade. Takedown. Calibers: 22 Short only, 22 Long Rifle only. Tubular magazine in butt-stock, holds 15 Short or 10 Long Rifle. 21-inch barrel. Weight, about 5 pounds. Open rear sight, bead front sight. Plain walnut stock and forearm. Made from 1922 to 1935.

Remington Model 241A "Speedmaster" Autoloading Rifle $165

Standard Grade. Takedown. Calibers: 22 Short only, 22 Long Rifle only. Tubular magazine in butt stock, holds 15 Short or 10 Long Rifle. 24-inch barrel. Weight, about 6 pounds. Open rear sight, bead front sight. Plain walnut stock and forearm. Made from 1935 to 1951.

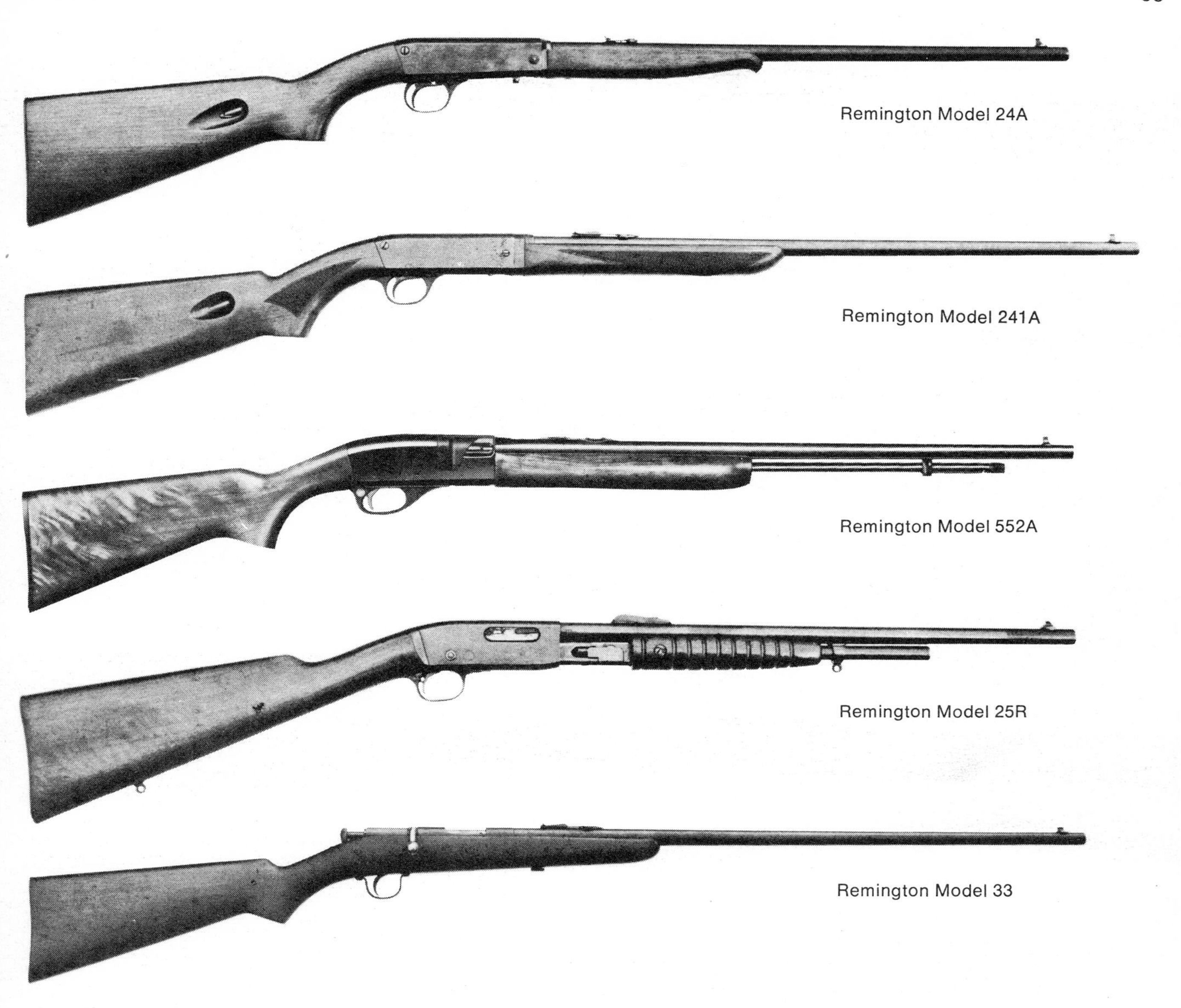

Remington Model 24A

Remington Model 241A

Remington Model 552A

Remington Model 25R

Remington Model 33

Remington Model 552A "Speedmaster" Autoloading Rifle $60

Caliber, 22 Short, Long, Long Rifle. Tubular magazine holds 20 Short, 17 Long, 15 Long Rifle. 25-inch barrel. Weight, about 5½ pounds. Open rear sight, bead front sight. Pistol-grip stock, semi-beavertail forearm. Made from 1958 to date.

Remington Model 552C Carbine $60

Same as Model 552A except has 21-inch barrel.

Remington Model 552GS Gallery Special $60

Same as Model 552A except chambered for 22 Short only.

Remington Model 25A Slide Action Repeating Rifle $80

Standard Grade. Hammerless. Takedown. Calibers: 25/20, 32/20. 10-shot tubular magazine. 24-inch barrel. Weight, about 5½ pounds. Open rear sight, bead front sight. Plain, pistol-grip stock, grooved slide handle. Made from 1923 to 1936.

Remington Model 25R Carbine $100

Same as Model 25A, except has 18-inch barrel, 6-shot magazine, straight-grip stock, weighs about 4½ pounds.

Remington Model 33 Bolt Action Single Shot Rifle . . $40

Takedown, Caliber: 22 Short, Long, Long Rifle. 24-inch barrel. Weight, about 4½ pounds. Open rear sight, bead front sight. Plain, pistol-grip stock, forearm with grasping grooves. Made from 1931 to 1936.

Remington Model 33 NRA Junior Target Rifle $50

Same as Model 33 Standard, except has Lyman peep rear sight, Patridge-type front sight, ⅞-inch sling and swivels, weighs about 5 pounds.

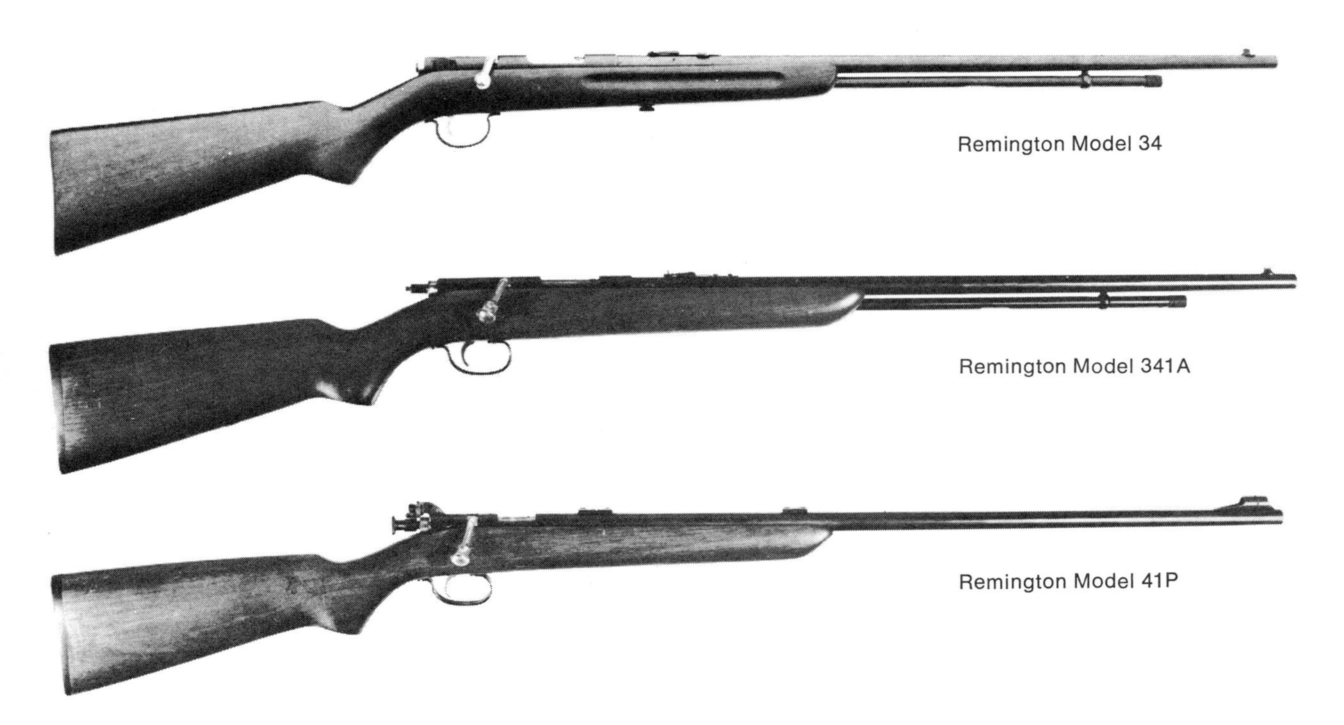

Remington Model 34

Remington Model 341A

Remington Model 41P

Remington Model 34 Bolt Action Repeating Rifle . . $45

Takedown. Caliber, 22 Short, Long, Long Rifle, Tubular magazine holds 22 Short, 17 Long or 15 Long Rifle. 24-inch barrel. Weight, about 5¼ pounds. Open rear sight, bead front sight. Plain, pistol-grip stock, forearm with grasping grooves. Made from 1932 to 1936.

Remington Model 34 NRA Target Rifle $50

Same as Model 34 Standard, except has Lyman peep rear sight, Patridge-type front sight, ⅞-inch sling and swivels, weighs about 5¾ pounds.

Remington Model 341A Sportmaster Bolt Action Repeating Rifle $45

Takedown. Caliber, 22 Short, Long, Long Rifle. Tubular magazine holds 22 Short, 17 Long, 15 Long Rifle. 27-inch barrel. Weight, about 6 pounds. Open rear sight, bead front sight. Plain pistol-grip stock. Made from 1936 to 1940.

Remington Model 341P $50

Same as Model 341A except has peep rear sight, hooded front sight.

Remington Model 341SB $40

Same as Model 341A except smoothbore for use with shot cartridges.

Remington Model 41A Targetmaster Bolt Action Single Shot Rifle $40

Takedown. Caliber, 22 Short, Long, Long Rifle. 27-inch barrel. Weight, about 5½ pounds. Open rear sight, bead front sight. Plain pistol-grip stock. Made from 1936 to 1940.

Remington Model 41AS $35

Same as Model 41A except chambered for 22 Remington Special (22 W.R.F.).

Remington Model 41P $45

Same as Model 41A except has peep rear sight, hooded front sight.

Remington Model 41SB $35

Same as Model 41A except smoothbore for use with shot cartridges.

Remington Model 37 Rangemaster Bolt Action Target Rifle

Model of 1937. Caliber, 22 Long Rifle. 5-shot box magazine, single shot adapter also supplied as standard equipment. 28-inch heavy barrel. Weight, about 12 pounds. Remington front and rear sights, scope bases. Target stock, swivels, sling. *Note:* original 1937 model had a stock with outside barrel band similar in appearance to that of the old style Winchester Model 52; forearm design was modified and barrel band eliminated in 1938. Made from 1937 to 1940.
With factory sights $200
Without sights $175

Remington Model 37 Rangemaster Bolt Action Target Rifle

Model of 1940. Same as Model of 1937, except has "Miracle" trigger mechanism and Randle design stock with high comb, full pistol grip and wide beavertail fore-end. Made from 1940 to 1954.
With factory sights $235
Without sights $210

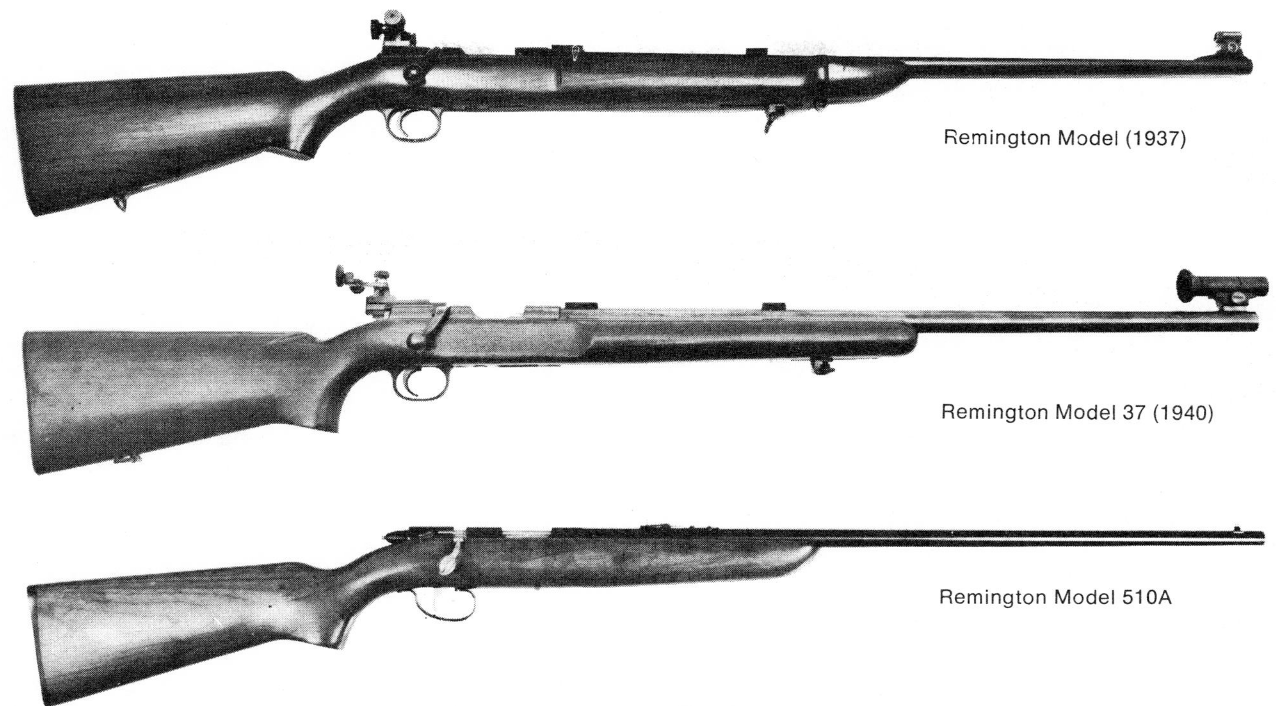

Remington Model (1937)

Remington Model 37 (1940)

Remington Model 510A

Remington Model 510A Targetmaster Bolt Action Single Shot Rifle $40

Takedown. Caliber, 22 Short, Long, Long Rifle. 25-inch barrel. Weight, about 5½ pounds. Open rear sight, bead front sight. Plain pistol-grip stock. Made from 1939 to 1962.

Remington Model 510P $45

Same as Model 510A except has peep rear sight, Patridge front sight on ramp.

Remington Model 510SB $40

Same as Model 510A except smoothbore for use with shot cartridges, shotgun bead front sight, no rear sight.

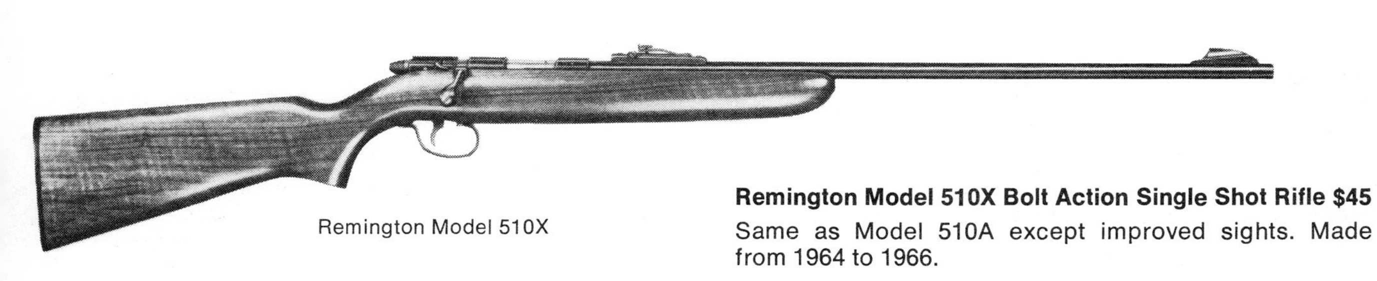

Remington Model 510X

Remington Model 510X Bolt Action Single Shot Rifle $45

Same as Model 510A except improved sights. Made from 1964 to 1966.

Remington Model 511A

Remington Model 511A Scoremaster Bolt Action Box Magazine Repeating Rifle $50

Takedown. Caliber, 22 Short, Long, Long rifle. 6-shot detachable box magazine. 25-inch barrel. Weight, about 5½ pounds. Open rear sight, bead front sight. Plain pistol-grip stock. Made from 1939 to 1962.

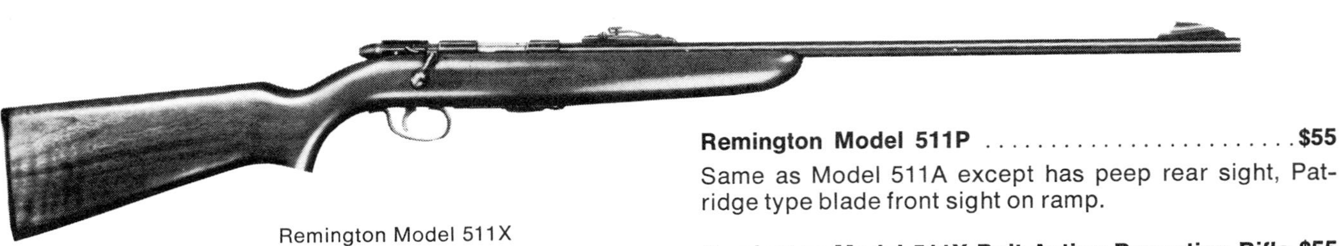

Remington Model 511X

Remington Model 511P **$55**

Same as Model 511A except has peep rear sight, Patridge type blade front sight on ramp.

Remington Model 511X Bolt Action Repeating Rifle $55

Clip type. Same as Model 511A except improved sights. Made from 1964 to 1966.

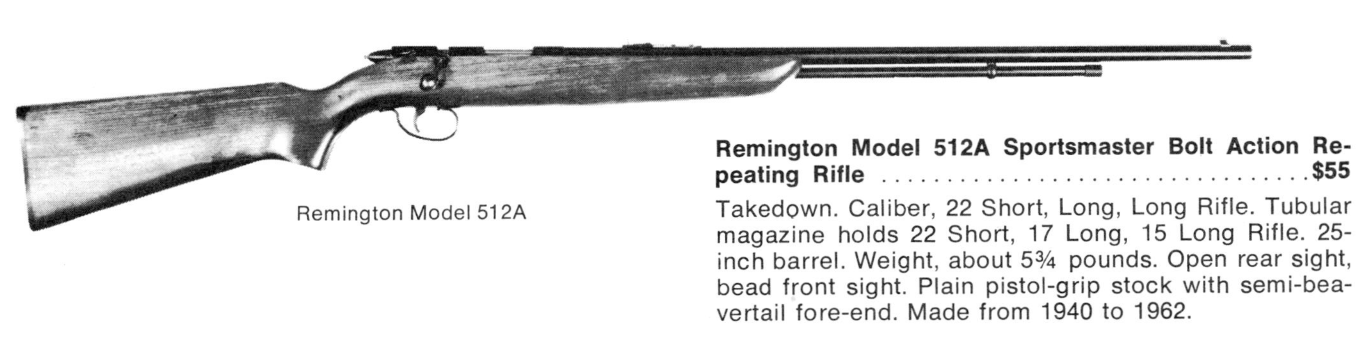

Remington Model 512A

Remington Model 512A Sportsmaster Bolt Action Repeating Rifle **$55**

Takedown. Caliber, 22 Short, Long, Long Rifle. Tubular magazine holds 22 Short, 17 Long, 15 Long Rifle. 25-inch barrel. Weight, about 5¾ pounds. Open rear sight, bead front sight. Plain pistol-grip stock with semi-beavertail fore-end. Made from 1940 to 1962.

Remington Model 512P **$60**

Same as Model 512A except has peep rear sight, blade front sight on ramp.

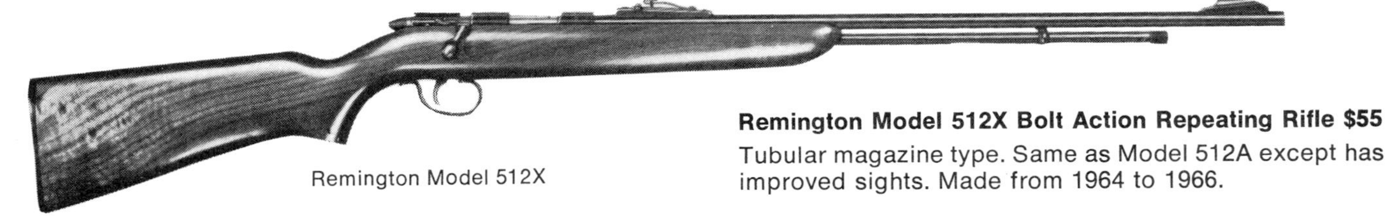

Remington Model 512X

Remington Model 512X Bolt Action Repeating Rifle $55

Tubular magazine type. Same as Model 512A except has improved sights. Made from 1964 to 1966.

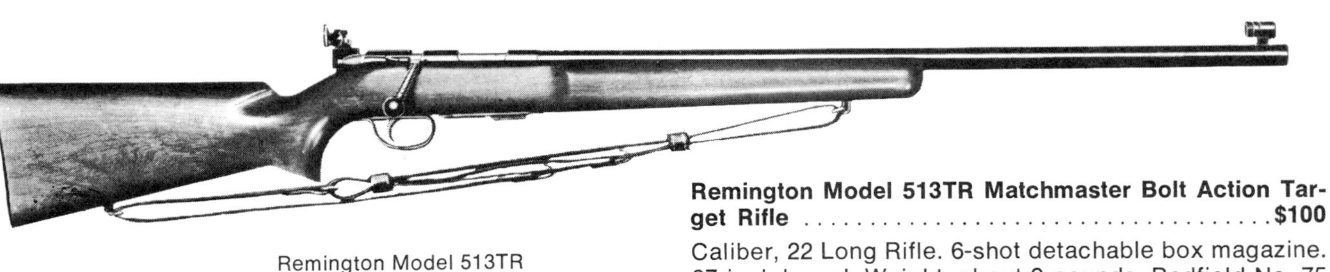

Remington Model 513TR

Remington Model 513TR Matchmaster Bolt Action Target Rifle **$100**

Caliber, 22 Long Rifle. 6-shot detachable box magazine. 27-inch barrel. Weight, about 9 pounds. Redfield No. 75 rear sight and globe front sight. Target stock. Sling and swivels. Made from 1941 to 1969.

Remington Model 513S

Remington Model 513S Bolt Action Sporting Rifle . . **$90**

Caliber, 22 Long Rifle. 6-shot detachable box magazine. 27-inch barrel. Weight, about 6¾ pounds. Marble open rear sight, Patridge type front sight. Checkered sporter stock. Made from 1941 to 1956.

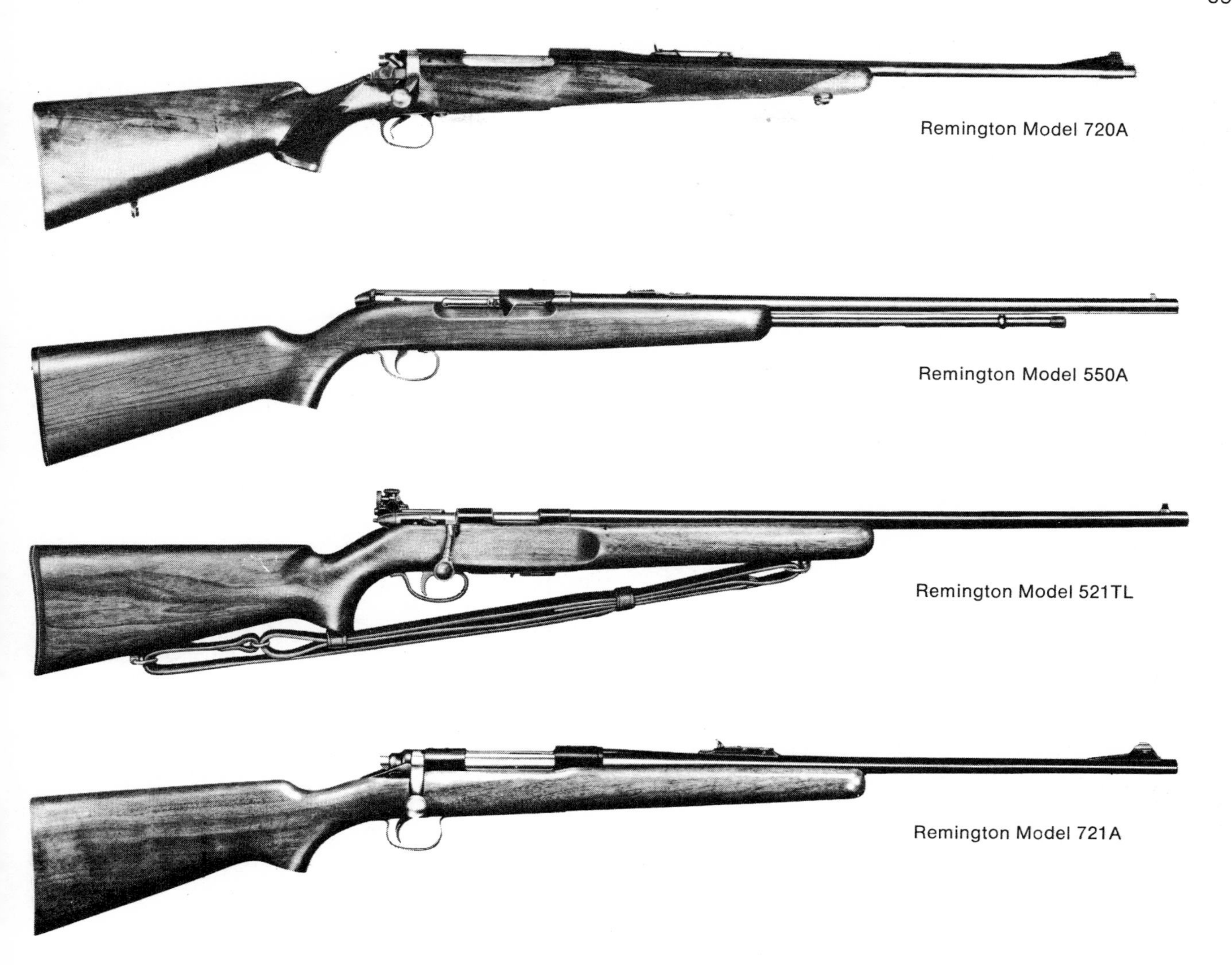

Remington Model 720A

Remington Model 550A

Remington Model 521TL

Remington Model 721A

Remington Model 720A Bolt Action High Power Rifle $150

Modified M/1917 Enfield action. Calibers: 257 Roberts, 270 Winchester, 30-06. 5-shot box magazine. 22-inch barrel. Weight, about 8 pounds. Open rear sight, bead front sight on ramp. Pistol-grip stock, checkered. Made in 1941.

Remington Model 720R $150

Same as Model 720A except has 20-inch barrel.

Remington Model 720S $150

Same as Model 720A except has 24-inch barrel.

Remington Model 550A Autoloading Rifle $60

Has "Power Piston" or floating chamber which permits interchangeable use of 22 Short, Long or Long Rifle cartridges. Tubular magazine holds 22 Short, 17 Long, 15 Long Rifle. 24-inch barrel. Weight, about 6¼ pounds. Open rear sight, bead front sight. Plain, one-piece pistol-grip stock. Made from 1941 to 1971.

Remington Model 550P $65

Same as Model 550A except has peep rear sight, blade front sight on ramp.

Remington Model 550-2G $60

"Gallery Special." Same as Model 550A except has 22-inch barrel, screweye for counter chain and fired shell deflector.

Remington Model 521TL Junior Target Bolt Action Repeating Rifle $75

Takedown. Caliber, 22 Long Rifle. 6-shot detachable box magazine. 25-inch barrel. Weight, about 7 pounds. Lyman No. 57RS rear sight, blade front sight. Target stock. Sling and swivels. Made from 1947 to 1969.

Remington Model 721A Standard Grade Bolt Action High Power Rifle $125

Calibers: 270 Winchester, 30-06. 4-shot box magazine. 24-inch barrel. Weight, about 7¼ pounds. Open rear sight, bead front sight on ramp. Plain sporting stock. Made from 1948 to 1962.

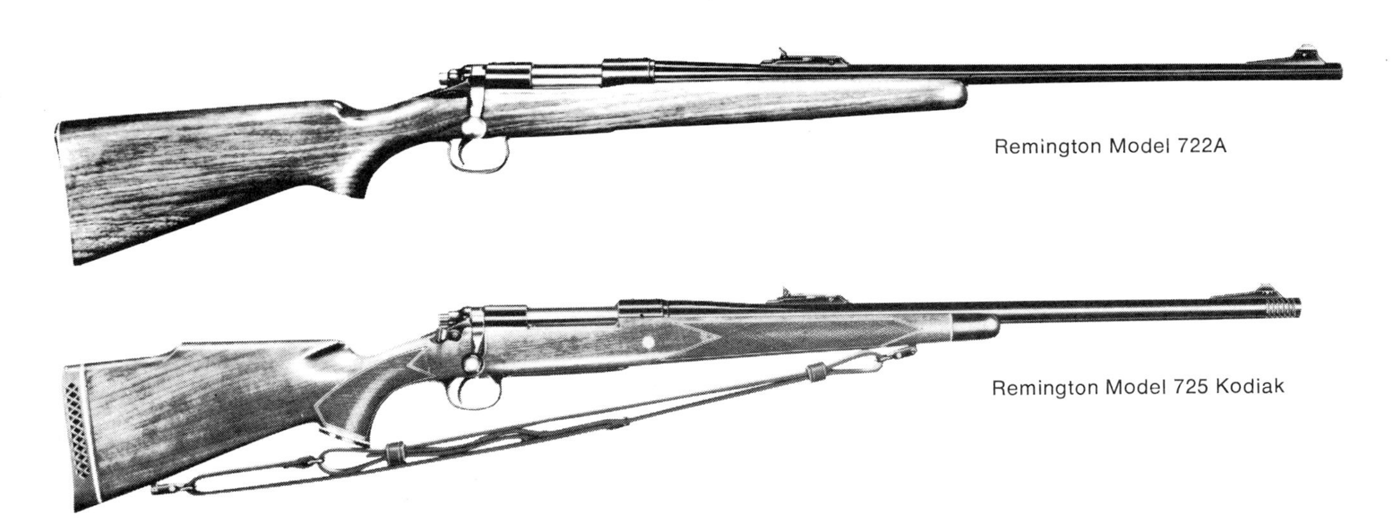

Remington Model 722A

Remington Model 725 Kodiak

Remington Model 721ADL De Luxe Grade $140

Same as model 721A except has deluxe checkered stock.

Remington Model 721BDL De Luxe Special Grade $150

Same as Model 721ADL except selected wood.

Remington Model 721A 300 Magnum Standard Grade $140

Caliber, 300 H&H Magnum. Same as standard model except has 26-inch heavy barrel, 3-shot magazine, recoil pad, weighs 8¼ pounds.

Remington Model 721ADL 300 Magnum De Luxe Grade $155

Same as Model 721A 300 Magnum except has de luxe checkered stock.

Remington Model 721BDL 300 Magnum De Luxe Special Grade $165

Same as Model 721ADL 300 Magnum except selected wood.

Remington Model 722A Standard Grade Bolt Action Sporting Rifle $125

Same as Model 721A, except shorter action, calibers 257 Roberts, 308 Win., 300 Savage, weighs 7 pounds. Made from 1948 to 1962.

Remington Model 722ADL De Luxe Grade $140

Same as Model 722A except has de luxe checkered stock.

Remington Model 722BDL De Luxe Special Grade . $150

Same as Model 722ADL except selected wood.

Remington Model 722A 222 Standard Grade $150

Caliber, 222 Rem. Same as standard model except has 26-inch barrel, 5-shot magazine, weighs about 8 pounds. Made from 1950 to 1962.

Remington Model 722ADL 222 De Luxe Grade $165

Same as Model 722A 222 except has de luxe checkered stock.

Remington Model 722BDL 222 De Luxe Special Grade $175

Same as Model 722ADL 222 except selected wood.

Remington Model 722A 244 Standard Grade $150

Caliber, 244 Rem. Specifications same as Model 722A 222 except magazine capacity is four rounds. Made from 1955 to 1962.

Remington Model 722ADL 244 De Luxe Grade . . . $165

Same as Model 722A 244 except has de luxe checkered stock.

Remington Model 722BDL 244 De Luxe Special Grade $175

Same as Model 722ADL except selected wood.

Remington Model 725ADL Bolt Action Repeating Rifle $185

Calibers: 222, 243, 244, 270, 280, 30-06. 4-shot box magazine (5-shot in 222). 22-inch barrel (24-inch in 222). Weight, about 7 pounds. Open rear sight, hooded ramp front sight. Monte Carlo comb stock with pistol grip, checkered, swivels. Made from 1958 to 1961.

Remington Model 725 "Kodiak" Magnum Rifle $385

Similar to Model 725ADL. Calibers: 375 H&H Mag., 458 Win. Mag. 3-shot magazine. 26-inch barrel with recoil reducer built into muzzle. Weight, about 9 pounds. Deluxe, reinforced Monte Carlo stock with recoil pad, black fore-end tip, swivels, sling. Made in 1961.

Remington Model 514

Remington Model 760 Standard

Remington Model 760ADL

Remington Model 760BDL

Remington Model 514 Bolt Action Single Shot Rifle $30

Caliber, 22 Short, Long, Long Rifle. 24-inch barrel. Weight, about 4¾ pounds. Open rear sight, bead front sight. Plain pistol-grip stock. Made from 1948 to 1971.

Remington Model 514P $35

Same as Model 514 except has a rear peep sight, ramp front sight.

Remington Model 760 Gamemaster Standard Grade Slide Action Repeating Rifle $125

Hammerless. Calibers: 223 Rem., 6mm Rem., 243 Win., 257 Roberts, 270 Win., 30-06, 300 Sav., 308 Win., 35 Rem. 22-inch barrel. Weight, about 7½ pounds. Open rear sight, bead front sight on ramp. Plain pistol-grip stock, grooved slide handle on early models; current production has checkered stock and slide handle. Made from 1952 to date.

Remington Model 760 Carbine $125

Same as Model 760 Rifle, except made in calibers 30-06 and 308 only, has 18½ inch barrel, weighs 7¼ pounds.

Remington Model 760ADL De Luxe Grade $135

Same as Model 760 except has de luxe checkered stock, standard or high comb, grip cap, sling swivels.

Remington Model 760BDL Custom De Luxe $140

Same as Model 760 Rifle, except made in calibers 270, 30-06 and 308 only, has Monte Carlo cheekpiece stock, forearm with black tip, basket-weave checkering. Available in right or left hand models.

Remington Model 740A

Remington Model 742 Carbine

Remington Model 742 BDL

Remington Model 740A Woodsmaster Autoloading Rifle **$150**

Standard Grade. Gas-operated. Calibers, 30-06 or 308. 4-shot detachable box magazine. 22-inch barrel. Weight, about 7½ pounds. Plain pistol-grip stock, semi-beavertail fore-end with finger grooves. Open rear sight, ramp front sight. Made from 1955 to 1960.

Remington Model 740ADL De Luxe Grade **$165**

Same as Model 740A except has de luxe checkered stock, standard or high comb, grip cap, sling swivels.

Remington Model 740BDL De Luxe Special Grade $175

Same as Model 740ADL except selected wood.

Remington Model 742 Woodsmaster Automatic Big Game Rifle **$145**

Gas-operated semi-automatic. Calibers: 6mm Rem., 243 Win., 280 Rem., 30-06, 308 Win. 4-shot clip magazine. 22-inch barrel. Weight, 7½ pounds. Open rear sight, bead front sight on ramp. Checkered pistol-grip stock and forearm. Made from 1960 to date.

Remington Model 742 Carbine **$145**

Same as Model 742 Rifle, except made in calibers 30-06 and 308 only, has 18½ inch barrel, weighs 6¾ pounds.

Remington Model 742BDL Custom De Luxe **$160**

Same as Model 742 Rifle, except made in calibers 30-06 and 308 only, has Monte Carlo cheekpiece stock, forearm with black tip, basket weave checkering. Available in right and left hand models.

Remington Model 40X Heavyweight Bolt Action Target Rifle

Caliber, 22 Long Rifle. Single Shot. Action similar to Model 722. Click adjustable trigger. 28-inch heavy barrel. Redfield Olympic sights. Scope bases. High comb target stock, bedding device, adjustable swivel, rubber butt plate. Weight, 12¾ pounds. Made from 1955 to 1964.
With sights **$160**
Without sights **$135**

Remington Model 40X Standard Barrel

Same as Model 40X Heavyweight except has lighter barrel. Weight, 10¾ pounds.
With sights **$155**
Without sights **$130**

Remington Model 40X Center Fire **$185**

Specifications same as for Model 40X Rim Fire. Calibers: 222 Rem., 222 Rem. Mag., 7.62mm NATO, 30-06 (others were available on special order). Made from 1961 to 1964. Value shown is for rifle without sights.

Remington International Match Free Rifle **$275**

Calibers: 22 Long Rifle, 222 Rem., 222 Rem. Mag., 7.62mm NATO, 30-06 (others were available on special order). Model 40X type bolt action, single shot. 2-oz. adjustable trigger. 28-inch heavy barrel. Weight, about 15½ pounds. "Free rifle"-style stock with thumbhole (furnished semi-finished by manufacturer); interchangeable and adjustable rubber buttplate and hook buttplate, adjustable palm rest, adjustable sling swivel. Made from 1961 to 1964. Value shown is for rifle with professionally-finished stock, no sights.

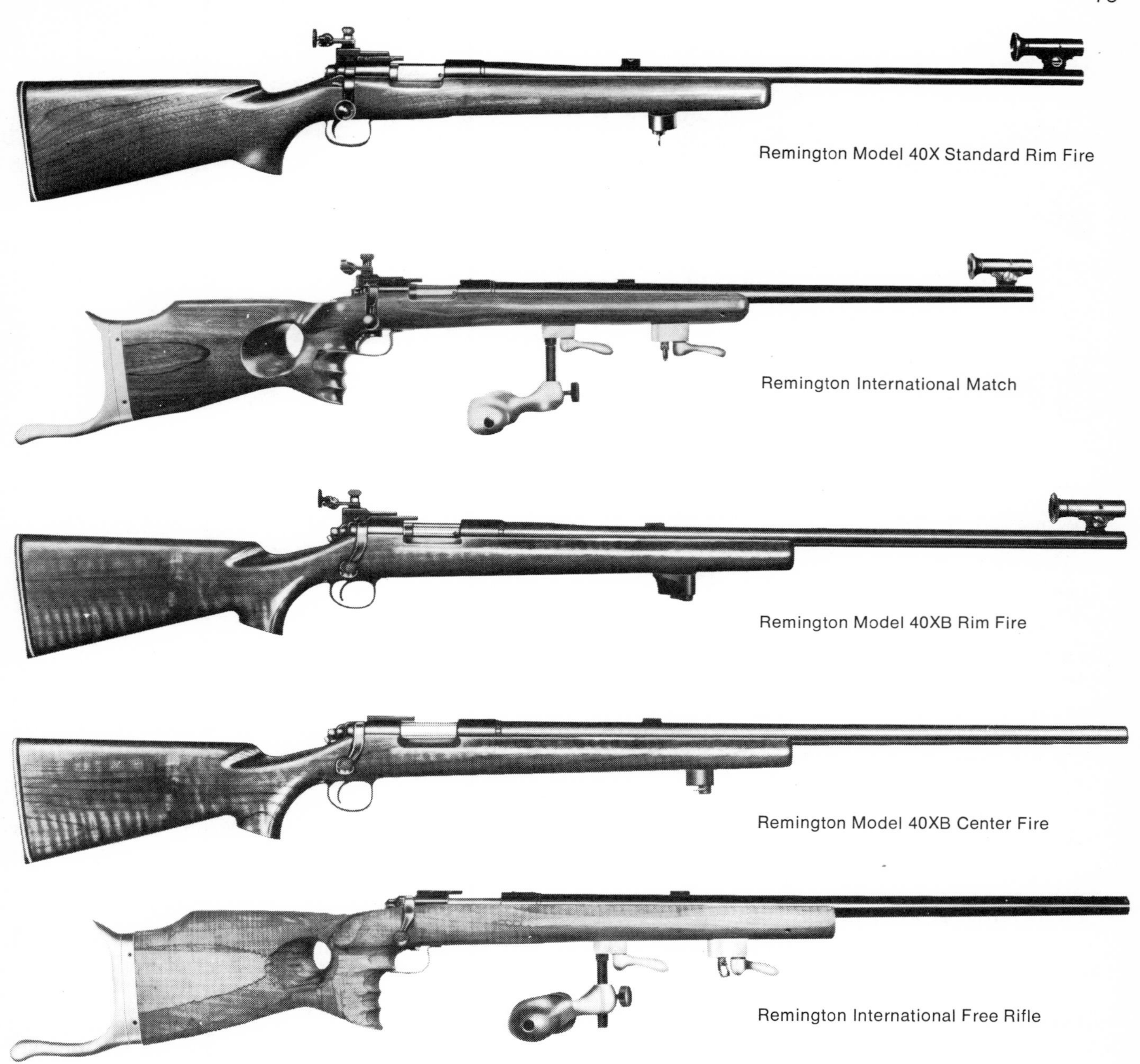

Remington Model 40X Standard Rim Fire

Remington International Match

Remington Model 40XB Rim Fire

Remington Model 40XB Center Fire

Remington International Free Rifle

Remington Model 40-XB Rangemaster Rim Fire Match Rifle $185

Bolt action single shot. Caliber, 22 Long Rifle. 28-inch standard or heavy barrel. Target stock with adjustable front swivel block on guide rail, rubber buttplate. Weight, without sights: standard barrel, 10 pounds; heavy barrel, 11¼ pounds. Value shown is for rifle without sights. Made from 1964 to 1974.

Remington Model 40-XB Center Fire Match Rifle . . $215

Bolt action single shot. Calibers: 222 Rem., 222 Rem. Mag., 223 Rem., 30-06, 308 Win. (7.65 NATO). 27¼-inch standard or heavy barrel. Target stock with adjustable front swivel block on guide rail, rubber butt plate. Weight, without sights: standard barrel, 9¼ pounds; heavy barrel, 11¼ pounds. Value shown is for rifle without sights. Made from 1964 to date.

Remington International Free Rifle $300

Same as Model 40-XB rim fire and center fire, except has "free rifle"-type stock with adjustable butt plate and hook, adjustable palm rest, movable front sling swivel, 2-ounce trigger; weight, about 15 pounds. Made from 1964 to 1974. Value shown is for rifle with professionally finished stock, no sights.

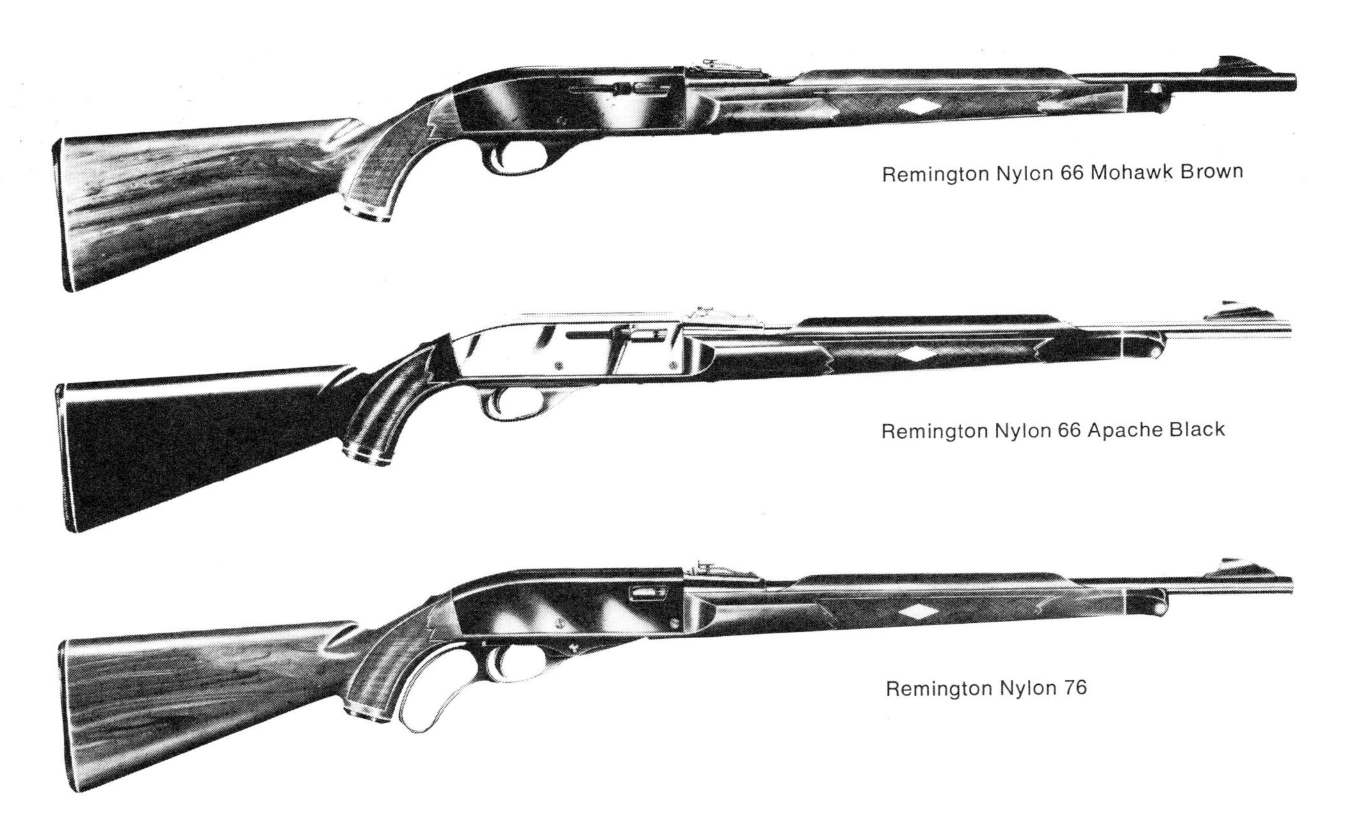

Remington Nylon 66 Mohawk Brown

Remington Nylon 66 Apache Black

Remington Nylon 76

Remington Nylon 66 "Mohawk Brown" Autoloading Rifle **$50**

Caliber, 22 Long Rifle. Tubular magazine in buttstock holds 14 rounds. 19½-inch barrel. Weight, about 4 pounds. Open rear sight, blade front sight. Brown nylon stock and forearm. Made from 1959 to date.

Remington Nylon 66 "Apache Black" **$50**

Same as Nylon 66 "Mohawk Brown" except barrel and receiver cover chrome-plated, black stock.

Remington Nylon 76 Lever Action Repeating Rifle . . **$50**

Short-throw lever action. Other specifications same as for Nylon 66. Made from 1962 to 1964.

Remington Nylon 11 Bolt Action Repeating Rifle . . **$40**

Clip type. Caliber 22 Short, Long, Long Rifle, 6 or 10-shot clip magazine. 19⅝-inch barrel. Weight, about 4¼ pounds. Open rear sight, blade front sight. Nylon stock. Made from 1962 to 1964.

Remington Nylon 12 Bolt Action Repeating Rifle . . **$40**

Same as Nylon 11 except has tubular magazine holding 22 Short, 17 Long, 15 Long Rifle. Made from 1962 to 1964.

Remington Nylon 10 Bolt Action Single Shot Rifle . . **$25**

Same as Nylon 11 except single shot. Made from 1962 to 1964.

Remington Model 600 Bolt Action Carbine **$135**

Calibers: 222 Rem., 6mm Rem., 243 Win., 308 Win., 35 Rem. 5-shot box magazine (6-shot in 222 Rem.). 18½-inch barrel with ventilated rib. Weight, 6 pounds. Open rear sight, blade ramp front sight. Monte Carlo stock with pistol grip. Made from 1964 to 1967.

Remington Model 600 Magnum **$180**

Same as Model 600 except calibers 6.5mm Rem. Mag. and 350 Rem. Mag., 4-shot magazine, special magnum type barrel with bracket for scope back-up, laminated walnut-and-beech stock with recoil pad, QD swivels and sling; weight, about 6½ pounds. Made from 1965 to 1967.

Remington Model 660 Bolt Action Carbine **$150**

Calibers: 222 Rem., 6mm Rem., 243 Win., 308 Win. 5-shot box magazine (6-shot in 222). 20-inch barrel. Weight, 6½ pounds. Open rear sight, bead front sight on ramp. Monte Carlo stock, checkered, black pistol-grip cap and fore-end tip. Made from 1968 to 1971.

Remington Model 660 Magnum **$185**

Same as Model 660 except calibers 6.5mm Rem. Mag. and 350 Rem. Mag., 4-shot magazine, laminated walnut-and-beech stock with recoil pad, QD swivels and sling. Made from 1968 to 1971.

Remington Nylon 11

Remington Nylon 12

Remington Nylon 10

Remington Model 600

Remington Model 600 Magnum

Remington Model 660

Remington Model 660 Magnum

John Rigby & Co., London, England

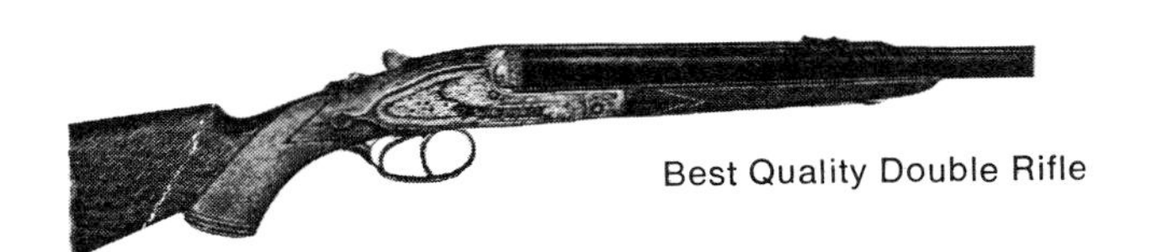
Best Quality Double Rifle

Rigby "Best Quality" Hammerless Ejector Double Rifle $3,000

Side Lock. Calibers: 275 Magnum, 350 Magnum, 470 Nitro Express. 24 to 28-inch barrels. Weights, from 7½ to 10½ pounds depending upon caliber. Folding leaf rear sight, bead front sight. Checkered pistol-grip stock and forearm.

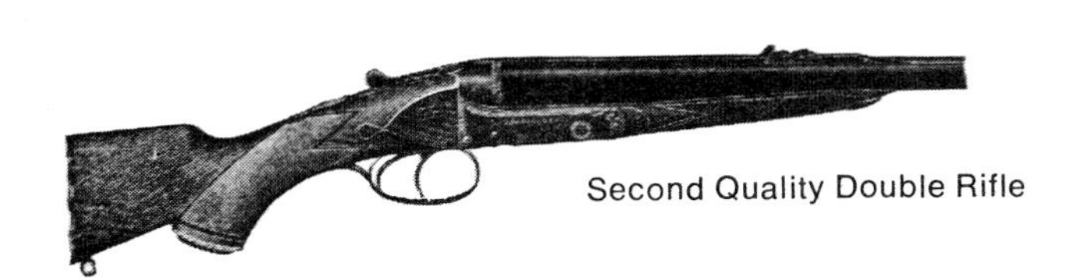
Second Quality Double Rifle

Rigby Second Quality Hammerless Ejector Double Rifle $2,300

Same general specifications as "Best Quality" double rifle except box lock.

Rigby Third Quality Hammerless Ejector Double Rifle $1,500

Same as "Second Quality" double rifle except plainer finish and not of as high quality.

Rigby 350 Magnum

Rigby 350 Magnum Magazine Sporting Rifle $750

Mauser action. Caliber, 350 Magnum. 5-shot box magazine. 24-inch barrel. Weight, about 7¾ pounds. Folding leaf rear sight, bead front sight. Sporting stock with full pistol grip, checkered. Currently manufactured.

Rigby 416 Big Game Magazine Sporting Rifle $785

Mauser action. Caliber, 416 Big Game. 4-shot box magazine. 24-inch barrel. Weight, about 9 to 9¼ pounds. Folding leaf rear sight, bead front sight. Sporting stock with full pistol grip, checkered. Currently manufactured.

Rigby 275 Magazine

Rigby 275 Magazine Sporting Rifle $750

Mauser action. Caliber, 275 High Velocity or 7X57mm. 5-shot box magazine. 25-inch barrel. Weight, about 7½ pounds. Folding leaf rear sight, bead front sight. Sporting stock with half-pistol grip, checkered. Specifications given are those of current model; however, in general, they apply also to pre-war model.

Rigby 275 Light-Weight Model Magazine Rifle $750

Same as standard 275 rifle except has 21-inch barrel and weighs only 6¾ pounds.

Ross Rifle Co., Quebec, Canada

Ross Model 1910 Bolt Action Sporting Rifle $200

Straight pull bolt action with interrupted-screw-type lugs. Calibers: 280 Ross, 303 British. 4-shot or 5-shot magazine. Barrel lengths: 22, 24, 26-inch. Two-leaf open rear sight, bead front sight. Checkered sporting stock. Weight, about 7 pounds. Made from c. 1910 to end of World War I. *Note:* Most firearms authorities are of the opinion that this and other Ross models with interrupted-screw-type lugs are unsafe to fire.

Ruger Rifles manufactured by Sturm, Ruger & Co., Southport, Connecticut

Ruger Model 44 Standard Autoloading Carbine . . . $100

Gas-operated. Caliber, 44 Magnum. 4-shot tubular magazine (with magazine release button since 1967). 18½ inch barrel. Weight, 5¾ pounds. Folding leaf rear sight, gold bead front sight. Carbine-style stock with barrel band and curved buttplate. Made from 1961 to date.

Ruger Model 44RS Carbine $105

Same as Standard Model 44, except has built-in peep sight, sling swivels.

Ruger Model 44 Sporter $120

Same as Standard Model 44, except has Monte Carlo sporter stock with finger-grooved forearm, grip cap, flat buttplate, sling swivels. Discontinued 1971.

Ruger Model 44 International $130

Same as Standard Model 44, except has Mannlicher-style full stock, swivels. Discontinued 1971.

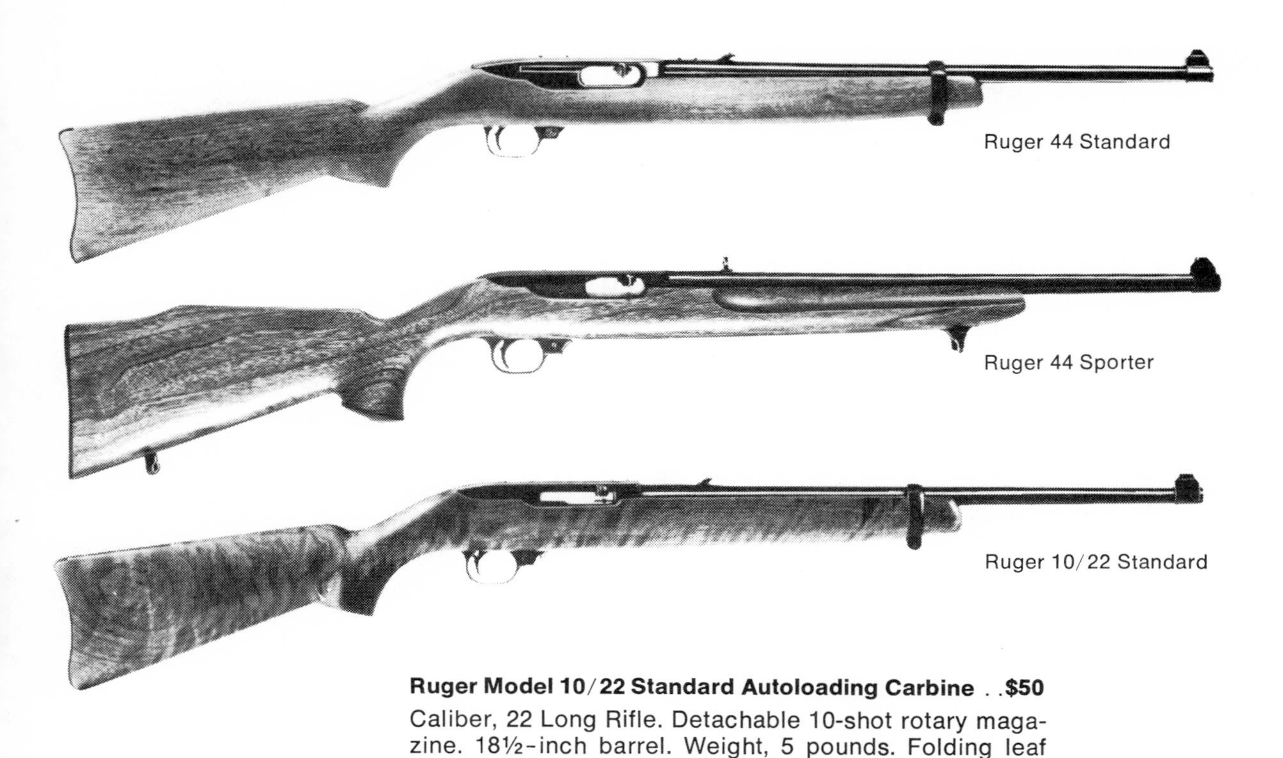

Ruger 44 Standard

Ruger 44 Sporter

Ruger 10/22 Standard

Ruger Model 10/22 Standard Autoloading Carbine . . $50

Caliber, 22 Long Rifle. Detachable 10-shot rotary magazine. 18½-inch barrel. Weight, 5 pounds. Folding leaf rear sight, bead front sight. Carbine-style stock with barrel band and curved buttplate. Made from 1964 to date.

Ruger Model 10/22 Sporter $55

Same as Standard Model 10/22, except has Monte Carlo sporter stock with finger-grooved forearm, grip cap, flat buttplate, sling swivels. Discontinued 1971.

Ruger Model 10/22 International $75

Same as Standard Model 10/22, except has Mannlicher style full stock, swivels. Discontinued 1971.

Ruger 10/22 Sporter

Ruger 10/22 International

Russian Model 1891 Moisin

Russian Military Rifles. Principal U.S.S.R. Arms Plant is located at Tula

Russian Model 1891 Moisin Military Rifle **$65**

Nagant system bolt action. Caliber, 7.62mm Russian. 5-shot box magazine. 31½-inch barrel. Weight, about 9 pounds. Open rear sight, blade front sight. Full stock with straight grip. Specifications given are for World War II version, earlier types differ slightly. *Note:* In 1916, Remington Arms Co. and New England Westinghouse Co. produced 250,000 of these rifles on a contract from the Imperial Russian Government. Few were delivered to Russia and the balance were purchased by the U.S. Government for training purposes in 1918. Eventually, many of these rifles were sold to N.R.A. members for about $3 each by the Director of Civilian Marksmanship.

Russian Tokarev Model 40 Semi-Automatic Military Rifle **$175**

Gas-operated. Caliber, 7.62mm Russian. 10-shot detachable box magazine. 24½-inch barrel. Muzzle brake. Weight, about 9 pounds. Leaf rear sight, hooded post front sight. Full stock with pistol grip. Differences between Models 1938, 1940 and 1941 are minor.

Sako Rifles manufactured by Oy Sako Ab Finland

Sako Vixen Sporter **$195**

L-461 short Mauser-type bolt action. Calibers: 218 Bee, 22 Hornet, 222 Rem., 222 Rem. Mag., 223 Rem. 5-shot magazine. 23½-inch barrel. Weight, 6½ pounds. Hooded ramp front sight. Sporter stock with Monte Carlo cheekpiece, checkered pistol grip and forearm, swivels. Made from 1946 to date.

Sako Vixen Carbine **$215**

Same as Vixen Sporter, except has 20-inch barrel, Mannlicher-type full stock.

Sako Vixen Heavy Barrel **$200**

Same as Vixen Sporter, except calibers (222 Rem., 222 Rem. Mag., 223 Rem.), heavy barrel, target-style stock with beavertail forearm; weight, 7½ pounds.

Sako High-Power Mauser Sporting Rifle **$250**

FN Mauser action. Calibers: 270, 30-06. 5-shot magazine. 24-inch barrel. Open rear leaf sight, patridge front sight, hooded ramp. Checkered stock with Monte Carlo comb and cheekpiece. Weight, about 7½ pounds. Discontinued 1961.

Sako Magnum Mauser **$275**

Same general specifications as standard model, except has recoil pad. Calibers: 300 H&H Magnum, 375 H&H Magnum. Discontinued 1961.

Sako Forester Sporter **$280**

L-579 medium-length Mauser-type bolt action. Calibers: 22-250, 243 Win., 308 Win. 5-shot magazine. 23-inch barrel. Weight, 6½ pounds. Hooded ramp front sight. Sporter stock with Monte Carlo cheekpiece, checkered pistol grip and forearm, swivels. Made from 1957 to 1971.

Sako Forester Carbine **$300**

Same as Forester Sporter, except has 20-inch barrel, Mannlicher-type full stock.

Sako Forester Heavy Barrel **$290**

Same as Forester Sporter, except has 24-inch heavy barrel, weighs 7½ pounds.

Sako Finnbear Carbine **$300**

Same as Finnbear Sporter, except has 20-inch barrel, Mannlicher-type full stock.

Sako Finnbear Sporter **$280**

L-61 long Mauser-type bolt action. Calibers: 25-06, 264 Mag., 270, 30-06, 300 Win. Mag., 338 Mag., 7mm Mag., 375 H&H Mag. Magazine holds 5 standard or 4 magnum cartridges. 24-inch barrel. Weight, about 7 pounds. Hooded ramp front sight. Sporter stock with Monte Carlo cheekpiece, checkered pistol grip and forearm, recoil pad, swivels. Made from 1961 to 1971.

Sako Finnwolf Lever Action Rifle **$225**

Hammerless. Calibers: 243 Win., 308 Win. 4-shot clip magazine. 23-inch barrel. Weight, 6¾ pounds. Hooded ramp front sight. Sporter stock with Monte Carlo cheekpiece, checkered pistol grip and forearm, swivels (available with right or left hand stock). Made from 1964 to 1972.

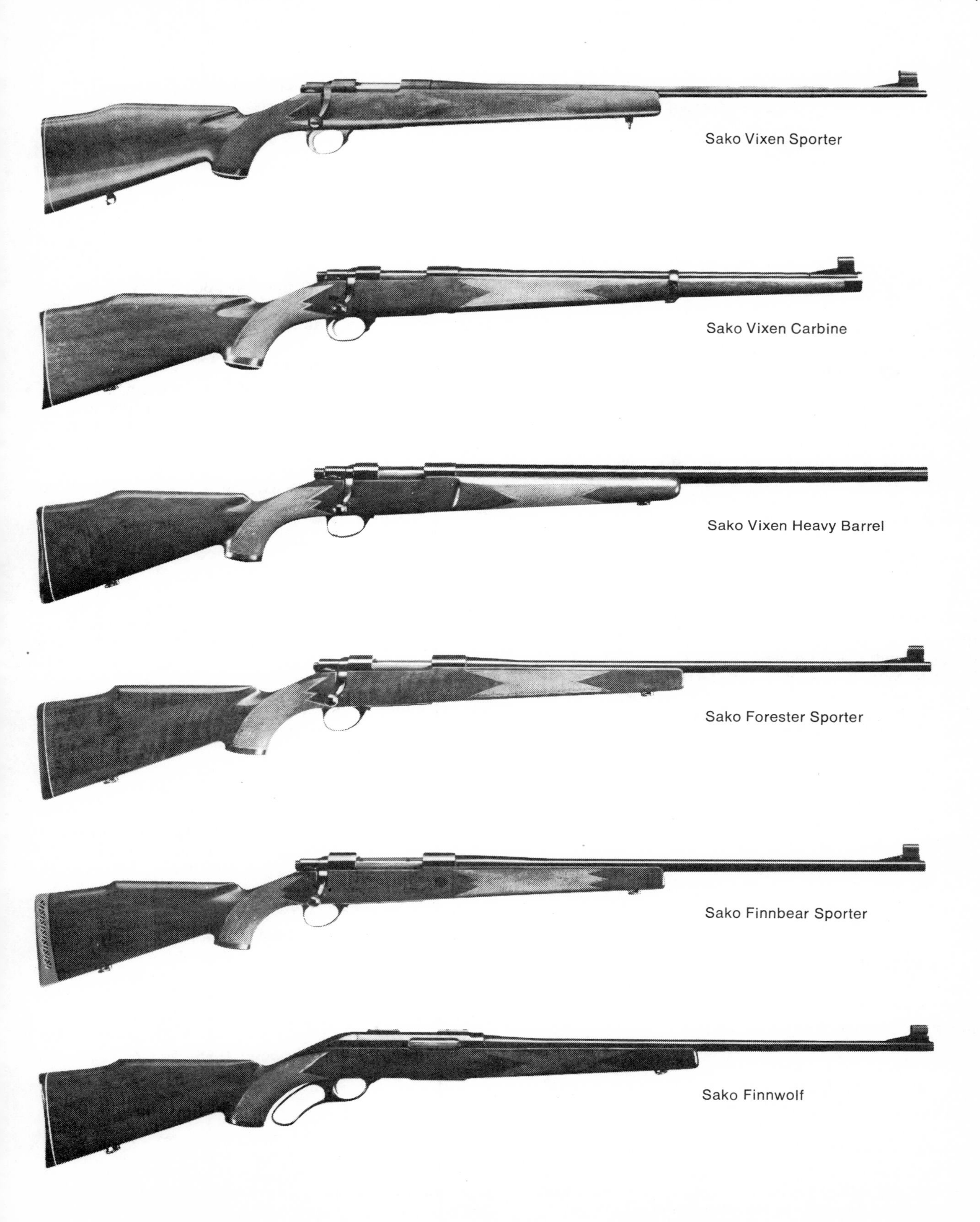

Sako Vixen Sporter

Sako Vixen Carbine

Sako Vixen Heavy Barrel

Sako Forester Sporter

Sako Finnbear Sporter

Sako Finnwolf

Sauer Mauser

J. P. Sauer & Sohn, Suhl, Germany

Sauer Mauser Bolt Action Sporting Rifle $300

Calibers: 7X57 and 8X57mm are the most common, but these rifles were produced in a variety of calibers including most of the popular Continental numbers as well as our 30-06. 5-shot box magazine. 22 or 24-inch Krupp steel barrel, half octagon with raised matted rib. Double set trigger. Weight, about 7½ pounds. Three-leaf open rear sight, ramp front sight. Sporting stock with cheekpiece, checkered pistol grip, raised side-panels, "schnabel" tip, swivels. Also made with 20-inch barrel and full-length stock.

Savage Arms, formerly of Utica, N.Y. now located at Westfield, Massachusetts

Savage Model 99 Lever Action Repeating Rifle

Introduced in 1899, this model has been produced in a number of styles and calibers. Early rifles and carbines (similar to Models 99A, 99B and 99H) were supplied in calibers 25-35, 30-30, 303 Sav., 32-40 and 38-55. Models 99F, 99G, 99H, 99K and 99T were discontinued in 1940, Models 99A, 99B and 99E a few years earlier. Models 99EG, 99R and 99RS were discontinued in 1961. Current production consists of Model 99F (1955) and Model 99DL (1960), which have safety on top tang, Model 99E (1961) with conventional M/99 safety on right side of trigger guard, Model 99C (1965) with detachable clip magazine.

Savage Model 99A $125

Hammerless. Solid frame. Calibers: 30/30. 300 Sav., 303 Sav., Five-shot rotary magazine. 24-inch barrel. Weight, about 7¼ pounds. Open rear sight, bead front sight on ramp. Plain straight-grip stock, tapered forearm. This model designation first used about 1922.

Savage Model 99B $160

Takedown. Otherwise same as Model 99A except weight about 7½ pounds.

Savage Model 99H Carbine $150

Solid frame. Calibers: 250/3000, 30/30, 303 Sav. Carbine stock and forearm. Weight, about 6½ pounds. Other specifications same as Model 99A.

Savage Model 99E $150

Pre-World-War-II type. Solid frame. Calibers: 22 Hi-Power, 250/3000, 30/30, 300 Sav., 303 Sav. with 22-inch barrel; 300 Sav. 24-inch. Weight, about 7 pounds. Other specifications same as Model 99A.

Savage Model 99E Carbine $110

Current model. Solid frame. Calibers: 243 Win., 300 Sav., 308 Win. 20-inch barrel. Checkered pistol-grip stock and forearm. Weight, about 7 pounds. Made from 1961 to date.

Savage Model 99F Featherweight $180

Pre-World-War-II type. Takedown. Specifications same as Model 99E except weight about 6½ pounds.

Savage Model 99F Featherweight $150

Postwar model. Solid frame. Calibers: 243 Win., 300 Sav., 308 Win. 22-inch barrel. Checkered pistol-grip stock and forearm. Weight, about 6½ pounds. Made from 1955 to 1973.

Savage Model 99G $125

Takedown. Checkered pistol-grip stock and forearm. Weight, about 7¼ pounds. Other specifications same as Model 99E.

Savage Model 99K $500

De Luxe version of Model G with same specifications except has fancy stock and engraving on receiver and barrel, Lyman peep rear sight and folding middle sight.

Savage Model 99EG $105

Post-World-War-II type. Same as pre-war model except stock and forearm. Otherwise same as Model G.

Savage Model 99EG $105

Post-World-War-II .ype. Same as pre-war model except has checkered stock and forearm. Calibers: 250 Sav., 300 Sav., 308 Win. (introduced 1955), 243 Win. and 358 Win. Made from 1955 to 1961.

Savage Model 99T $185

Feather-weight. Solid frame. Calibers: 22 Hi-Power, 30/30, 303 Sav. with 20-inch barrel; 300 Sav. with 22-inch barrel. Checkered pistol-grip stock and beavertail forearm. Weight, about 7 pounds. General specifications same as other Model 99 rifles.

Savage Model 99A

Savage Model 99H

Savage Model 99E (pre-WWII)

Savage Model 99F (pre-WWII)

Savage Model 99K

Savage Model 99EG (post-WWII)

Savage Model 99T

Savage Model 99R (pre-WWII)

Savage Model 99R (post-WII)

Savage Model 99RS (pre-WWII)

Savage Model 99PE

Savage Model 99DE

Savage Model 99R **$190**

Pre-World-War-II type. Solid frame. Caliber 250/3000 with 22-inch barrel; 300 Sav. with 24-inch barrel. Weight, about 7½ pounds. Special large pistol-grip stock and forearm, checkered. General specifications same as other Model 99 rifles.

Savage Model 99R **$150**

Post-World-War-II type. Same as pre-war model except made with 24-inch barrel only, has screw eyes for sling swivels. Calibers: 250 Sav., 300 Sav., 308 Win., 243 Win. and 358 Win. Made from 1955 to 1961.

Savage Model 99RS **$200**

Pre-World-War-II type. Same as pre-war Model 99R except equipped with Lyman rear peep sight and folding middle sight, quick detachable swivels and sling.

Savage Model 99RS **$160**

Post-World-War-II type. Same as post-war Model 99R except equipped with Redfield 70LH receiver sight, blank in middle sight slot. Made from 1955 to 1961.

Savage Model 99DL Deluxe **$135**

Postwar model. Calibers: 243 Win., 308 Win. Same as Model 99F, except has high comb Monte Carlo stock, sling swivels; weight, about 6¾ pounds. Made from 1960 to 1973.

Savage Model 99C **$130**

Current model. Same as Model 99F except has clip magazine instead of rotary. Calibers: 243 Win., 284 Win., 308 Win. 4-shot detachable magazine holds one round less in 284). Weight, about 6¾ pounds. Made from 1965 to date.

Savage Model 99PE Presentation Grade **$300**

Same as Model 99DL, except has engraved receiver (game scenes on sides), tang and lever; fancy walnut Monte Carlo stock and forearm with hand checkering, QD swivels. Calibers: 243, 284, 308. Made from 1968 to 1970.

Savage Model 99DE Citation Grade **$230**

Same as Model 99PE, except less elaborate engraving. Made from 1968 to 1970.

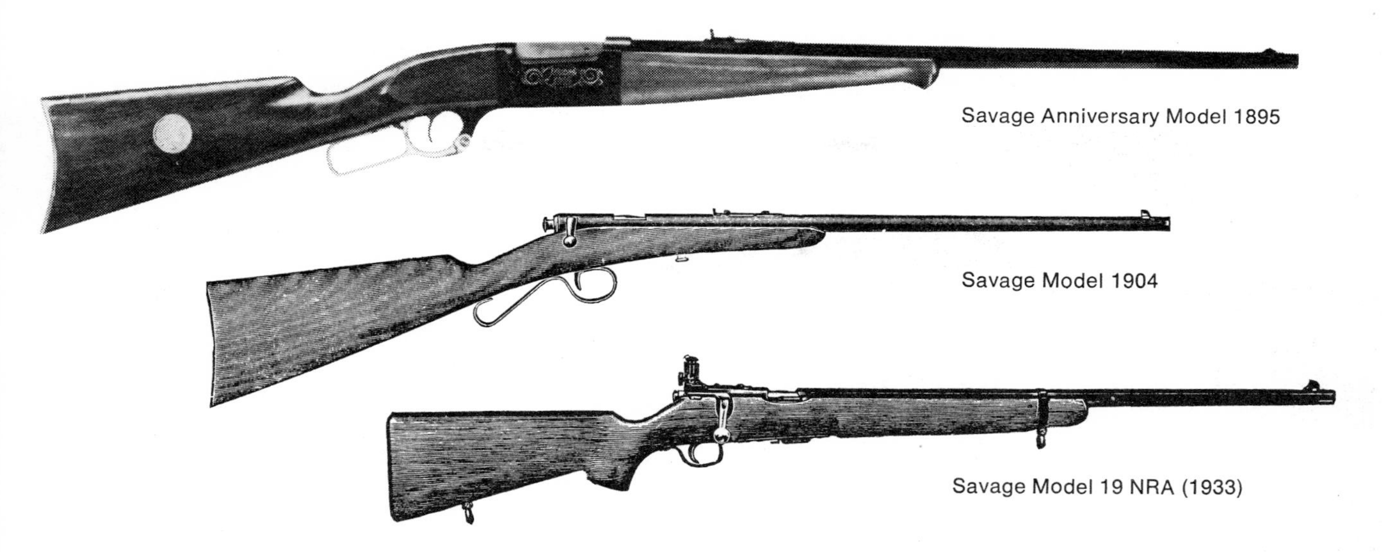
Savage Anniversary Model 1895

Savage Model 1904

Savage Model 19 NRA (1933)

Savage Anniversary Model 1895 Lever Action Rifle $195

Replica of Savage Model 1895 Hammerless Lever Action Rifle issued to commemorate the 75th anniversary (1895-1970) of Savage Arms. Caliber, 308 Win. 5-shot rotary magazine. 24-inch full-octagon barrel. Engraved receiver. Brass-plated lever. Open rear sight, brass blade front sight. Plain straight-grip butt stock, schnabel-type fore-end; brass medallion inlaid in butt stock, brass crescent-shaped butt plate. 9,999 produced. Made in 1970 only. Value is for new, unfired specimen.

Savage Model 1903 Slide Action Repeating Rifle . . $75

Hammerless. Takedown. Caliber, 22 Short, Long, Long Rifle. Detachable box magazine. 24-inch octagon barrel. Weight, about 5 pounds. Open rear sight, bead front sight. Pistol-grip stock, grooved slide handle.

Savage Model 1904 Bolt Action Single Shot Rifle . . $40

Takedown. Caliber, 22 Short, Long, Long Rifle. 18-inch barrel. Weight, about 3 pounds. Open rear sight, bead front sight. Plain, straight-grip, one-piece stock.

Savage Model 1905 Bolt Action Single Shot Rifle . . $40

Takedown. Caliber, 22 Short, Long, Long Rifle. 22-inch barrel. Weight, about 5 pounds. Open rear sight, bead front sight. Plain, straight-grip, one-piece stock.

Savage Model 1909 Slide Action Repeater $75

Hammerless. Takedown. Similar to Model 1903 except has 20-inch round barrel, plain stock and forearm, weighs about 4¾ pounds.

Savage Model 1912 Autoloading Rifle $75

Takedown. Caliber, 22 Long Rifle only. 7-shot detachable box magazine. 20-inch barrel. Weight, about 4½ pounds. Open rear sight, bead front sight. Plain straight-grip stock and forearm.

Savage Model 1914 Slide Action Repeating Rifle . . $75

Hammerless. Takedown. Caliber, 22 Short, Long, Long Rifle. Tubular magazine holds 20 short, 17 long, 15 long rifle. 24-inch octagon barrel. Weight, about 5¾ pounds. Open rear sight, bead front sight. Plain pistol-grip stock, grooved slide handle. Made from 1914 to 1924.

Savage Model 19 NRA (1919)

Savage Model 19 N.R.A. Bolt Action Match Rifle . . . $95

Model of 1919. Caliber, 22 Long Rifle. 5-shot detachable box magazine. 25-inch barrel. Weight, about 7 pounds. Adjustable rear peep sight, blade front sight. Full military stock with pistol grip. Made from 1919 to 1933.

Savage Model 19 Bolt Action Target Rifle $100

Model of 1933. Speed lock. Caliber, 22 Long Rifle. 5-shot detachable box magazine. 25-inch barrel. Weight, about 8 pounds. Adjustable rear peep sight and blade front sight on early models, later production equipped with extension rear sight and hooded front sight. Target stock with full pistol grip and beavertail forearm. Made from 1933 to 1946.

Savage Model 19L $110

Same as standard Model 19 (1933) except equipped with Lyman 48Y receiver sight and 17A front sight.

Savage Model 19M $110

Same as standard Model 19 (1933) except has heavy 28-inch barrel with scope bases, weighs about 9¼ pounds.

Savage Model 19H $150

Same as standard Model 19 (1933) except chambered for 22 Hornet, has Model 23D-type bolt mechanism, loading port and magazine.

Savage Model 1920 Hi-Power Bolt Action Rifle $150

Short Mauser-type action. Calibers: 250/3000, 300 Sav. 5-shot box magazine. 22-inch barrel in 250 cal.; 24-inch in 300 cal. Weight, about 6 pounds. Open rear sight, bead front sight. Checkered pistol-grip stock with slender forearm and "schnabel" tip. Made from 1920 to 1926.

Savage Model 20 (1926)

Savage Model 23A

Savage Model 23AA

Savage Model 23B

Savage Model 23D

Savage Model 20-1926 Hi-Power Bolt Action Rifle .$165

Same as Model 1920 except has 24-inch medium weight barrel, improved stock, Lyman 54 rear peep sight, weighs about 7 pounds. Made from 1926 to 1929.

Savage Model 23A Bolt Action Sporting Rifle $90

Caliber, 22 Long Rifle. 5-shot detachable box magazine. 23-inch barrel. Weight, about 6 pounds. Open rear sight, blade or bead front sight. Plain pistol-grip stock with slender forearm and "schnabel" tip. Made from 1923 to 1933.

Savage Model 23AA $100

Model of 1933. Improved version of the Model 23A with same general specifications except has speed lock, improved stock, weighs about 6½ pounds. Made from 1933 to 1942.

Savage Model 23B $90

Same as Model 23A except caliber 25/20, has 25-inch barrel. Model of 1933 has improved stock with full forearm instead of the slender forearm with "schnabel" found on earlier production, weighs about 6½ pounds. Discontinued 1942.

Savage Model 23C $90

Same as Model 23B except caliber 32/20.

Savage Model 23D $150

Same as Model 23B except caliber 22 Hornet. Made from 1933 to 1947.

Savage Model 25 Slide Action Repeating Rifle $75

Takedown. Hammerless. Caliber, 22 Short, Long, Long Rifle. Tubular magazine holds 20 Short, 17 Long, 15 Long Rifle. 24-inch octagon barrel. Weight, about 5¾ pounds. Open rear sight, blade front sight. Plain pistol-grip stock, grooved slide handle. Made from 1925 to 1929.

Savage Model 40

Savage Model 45

Savage Model 29

Savage Model 3

Savage Model 4

Savage Model 40 Bolt Action Sporting Rifle $150

Standard Grade. Calibers: 250/3000, 300 Sav., 30/30, 30/06. 4-shot detachable box magazine. 22-inch barrel in calibers 250/3000 and 30/30; 24-inch in 300 Sav. and 30/06. Weight, about 7½ pounds. Open rear sight, bead front sight on ramp. Plain pistol-grip stock with tapered forearm and "schnabel" tip. Made from 1928 to 1940.

Savage Model 45 Super Sporter $175

Special Grade. Same as Model 40 except has checkered pistol-grip and forearm, Lyman No. 40 receiver sight. Made from 1928 to 1940.

Savage Model 29 Slide Action Repeating Rifle $95

Takedown. Hammerless. Caliber, 22 Short, Long, Long Rifle. Tubular magazine holds 20 Short, 17 Long, 15 Long Rifle. 24-inch barrel, octagon on pre-war, round on post-war production. Weight, about 5½ pounds. Open rear sight, bead front sight. Stock with checkered pistol-grip and slide handle on pre-war, plain stock and grooved forearm on post-war production. Made from 1929 to 1967.

Savage Model 3 Bolt Action Single Shot Rifle $25

Takedown. Caliber, 22 Short, Long, Long Rifle. 26-inch barrel on pre-war rifles, current production has 24-inch barrel. Weight, about 5 pounds. Open rear sight, bead front sight. Plain pistol-grip stock. Made from 1933 to 1952.

Savage Model 3S $25

Same as Model 3 except has peep rear sight and hooded front sight.

Savage Model 3ST $30

Same as Model 3S except fitted with swivels and sling. Discontinued about 1941.

Savage Model 4 Bolt Action Repeating Rifle $35

Takedown. Caliber, 22 Short, Long, Long Rifle. 5-shot detachable box magazine. 24-inch barrel. Weight, about 5½ pounds. Open rear sight, bead front sight. Checkered pistol-grip stock on pre-war models, early production had grooved forearm; post-war rifles have plain stocks. Made from 1933 to 1965.

Savage Model 4S $40

Same as Model 4 except has peep rear sight and hooded front sight.

Savage Model 4M $45

Same as Model 4 except chambered for 22 Rimfire Magnum. Made from 1961 to 1965.

Savage Model 5 Bolt Action Repeating Rifle $45

Same as Model 4 except has tubular magazine (holds 21 Short, 17 Long, 15 Long Rifle), weighs about 6 pounds. Made from 1936 to 1961.

Savage Model 5S $45

Same as Model 5 except has peep rear sight and hooded front sight.

Savage Model 219 Single Shot Rifle $45

Hammerless. Takedown. Shotgun-type action with top lever. Calibers: 22 Hornet, 25/20, 32/20, 30/30. 26-inch barrel. Weight, about 6 pounds. Open rear sight, bead front sight. Plain pistol-grip stock and forearm. Made from 1938 to 1965.

Savage Model 219L $45

Same as Model 219, except has side lever. Made from 1965 to 1967.

Savage Model 221 Utility Gun $60

Same as Model 219 except caliber 30/30 only, supplied in combination with an interchangeable 30-inch 12 gauge shotgun barrel.

Savage Model 222 . . . . $60

Same as Model 221 except shotgun barrel is 28-inch, 16 gauge.

Savage Model 223 . . . . $60

Same as Model 221 except shotgun barrel is 28-inch, 20 gauge.

Savage Model 227 . . . . $60

Same as Model 221 except caliber 22 Hornet and 30-inch, 12 gauge barrel.

Savage Model 228 . . . . $60

Same as Model 227 except shotgun barrel is 28-inch, 16 gauge.

Savage Model 229 . . . . $60

Same as Model 227 except shotgun barrel is 28-inch, 20 gauge. *Note:* Model 219 in 25/20 and 32/20, as well as all models of Utility Gun, discontinued.

Savage Model 6 Autoloading Rifle $50

Takedown. Caliber, 22 Short, Long, Long Rifle. Tubular magazine holds 21 Short, 17 Long, 15 Long Rifle. 24-inch barrel. Weight, about 6 pounds. Open rear sight, bead front sight. Checkered pistol-grip stock on pre-war models, post-war rifles have plain stocks. Made from 1938 to 1968.

Savage Model 6S $55

Same as Model 6 except has peep rear sight, bead front sight.

Savage Model 7 Autoloading Rifle $40

Same general specifications as Model 6 except has 5-shot detachable box magazine. Made from 1939 to 1951.

Savage Model 7S $45

Same as Model 7 except has peep rear sight and hooded front sight.

Savage Model 340 Bolt Action Repeating Rifle $75

Calibers: 22 Hornet, 222 Rem., 30-30. Clip magazine, 4-shot capacity in 22 Hornet and 222 Rem., 3-shot in 30-30. Barrel lengths: 20″ in 30-30, 22″ in 22 Hornet and 30-30, 24″ in 22 Hornet and 222 Rem. Weight, 6½ pounds (average). Open rear sight, ramp front sight. Plain pistol-grip stock. Made from 1950 to date. (*Note:* From 1947 to 1950, this was Stevens Model 322/325. 222 Rem. introduced 1953. 22 Hornet discontinued 1964. Current model, introduced 1965, has checkered stock).

Savage Model 340C Carbine $75

Same as Model 340 except caliber 30-30, 18½-inch barrel, weight about 6 pounds. Made from 1962 to 1964.

Savage Model 340S De Luxe $85

Same as Model 340 except has checkered stock, screw eyes for sling, peep rear sight and hooded front sight. Discontinued.

Savage Model 342 . . . . $75

Designation, prior to 1953, of Model 340 22 Hornet.

Savage Model 342S De Luxe $85

Designation, prior to 1953, of Model 340S 22 Hornet.

Savage Model 110 Sporter Bolt Action Repeating Rifle $90

Calibers: 243, 270, 308, 30-06. 4-shot box magazine. 22-inch barrel. Weight, about 6¾ pounds. Open rear sight, ramp front sight. Standard sporter stock with pistol grip, checkered. Made from 1958 to 1963.

Savage Model 110MC $100

Same as Model 110, except has Monte Carlo-style stock. Calibers: 22-250, 243, 270, 308, 30-06. 24-inch barrel in 22-250. Made from 1959 to 1969.

Savage Model 110MCL $105

Same as Model 110MC, except has left-hand action. Made from 1959 to 1969.

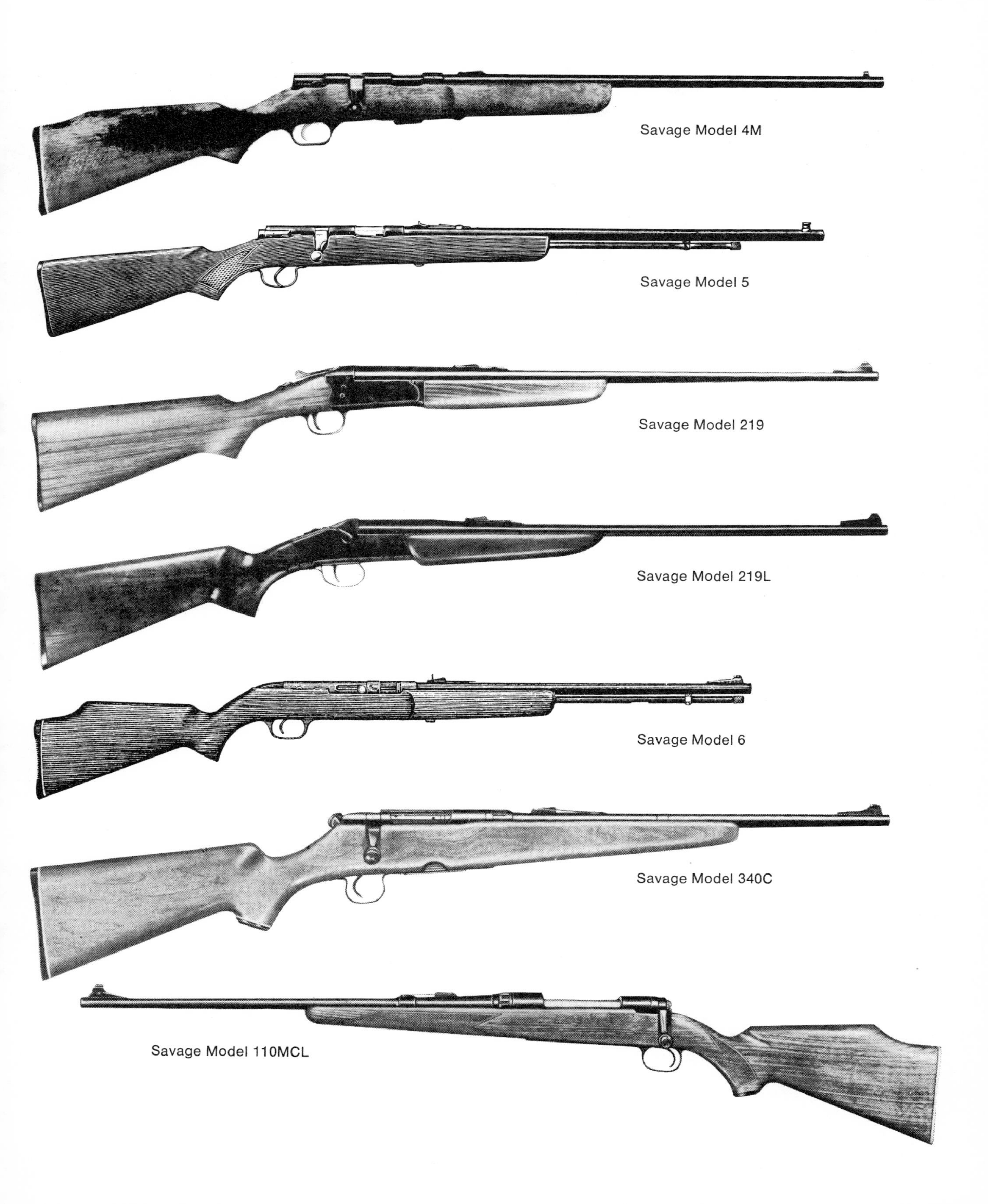

Savage Model 4M

Savage Model 5

Savage Model 219

Savage Model 219L

Savage Model 6

Savage Model 340C

Savage Model 110MCL

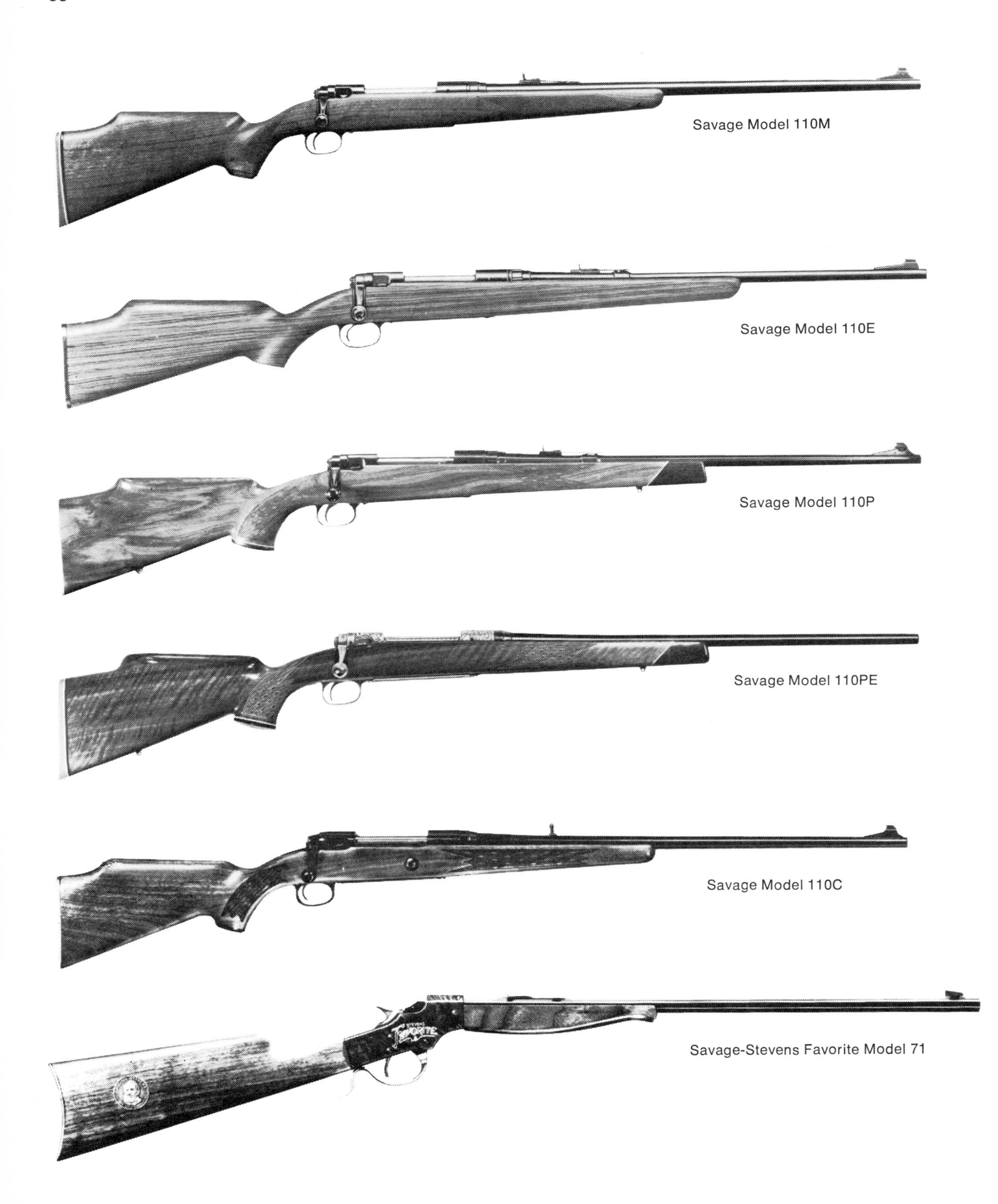

Savage Model 110M

Savage Model 110E

Savage Model 110P

Savage Model 110PE

Savage Model 110C

Savage-Stevens Favorite Model 71

Savage Model 110M Magnum $100

Same as Model 110MC, except calibers: 7mm Rem. Mag., 264, 300 and 338 Win. 24-inch barrel. Stock with recoil pad. Weight, 7¾ to 8 pounds. Made from 1963 to 1969.

Savage Model 110ML Magnum $105

Same as Model 110M Magnum, except has left-hand action.

Savage Model 110E

Calibers: 243 Win., 7mm Rem. Mag., 30-06. 4-shot box magazine (3-shot in Magnum). 20-inch barrel (24-inch stainless steel in Magnum). Weight, 6¾ pounds (Magnum 7¾ pounds). Open rear sight, ramp front sight. Plain Monte Carlo stock on early production; current models have checkered stocks (Magnum has recoil pad). Made from 1963 to date.
Caliber 243 Win. or 30-06 . . . . **$ 95**
Caliber 7mm Rem. Mag. **$105**

Savage Model 110EL

Same as Model 110E, except has left-hand action, made in calibers 30-06 and 7mm Rem. Mag. only.
Caliber 30-06 . . . . **$100**
Caliber 7mm Rem. Mag. **$110**

Savage Model 110P Premier Grade

Calibers: 243 Win., 7mm Rem. Mag., 30-06. 4-shot box magazine (3-shot in Magnum). 22-inch barrel (24-inch stainless steel in Magnum). Weight, 7 pounds (Magnum 7¾ pounds). Open rear folding leaf sight, ramp front sight. French walnut stock with Monte Carlo comb and cheekpiece, rosewood fore-end tip and pistol-grip cap, skip checkering, sling swivels (Magnum has recoil pad). Made from 1964 to 1970.
Caliber 243 Win. or 30-06 . . . . **$240**
Caliber 7mm Rem. Mag. **$250**

Savage Model 110PL Premier Grade

Same as Model 110P, except has left-hand action.
Calibers 243 Win. and 30-06 . . . . **$240**
Caliber 7mm Rem. Mag. **$250**

Savage Model 110PE Presentation Grade

Same as Model 110P, except has engraved receiver, floorplate and trigger guard, stock of choice grade French walnut. Made from 1968 to 1970.
Calibers 243 and 30-06 . . . . **$400**
Caliber 7mm Rem. Mag. **$410**

Savage Model 110PEL Presentation Grade

Same as Model 110PE, except has left-hand action.
Calibers 243 and 30-06 . . . . **$400**
Caliber 7mm Rem. Mag. **$410**

Savage Model 110C

Calibers: 22-250, 243, 25-06, 270, 308, 30-06, 7mm Rem. Mag., 300 Win. Mag. 4-shot detachable clip magazine (3-shot in Magnum calibers). 22-inch barrel (24-inch in 22-250 Magnum calibers). Weight, 6¾ pounds (Magnum 7¾ to 8 pounds). Open rear sight, ramp front sight. Checkered Monte Carlo–style walnut stock (Magnum has recoil pad). Made from 1966 to date.
Standard calibers **$115**
Magnum calibers **$125**

Savage/Anschutz Model 153 Bolt Action Sporting Rifle $225

Caliber, 222 Rem. 3-shot clip magazine. 24-inch barrel. Folding leaf open rear sight, hooded ramp front sight. Weight, 6¾ pounds. French walnut stock with cheekpiece, skip checkering, rosewood fore-end tip and grip cap, swivels. Made from 1964 to 1967. (Manufactured for Savage by J. G. Anschutz GmbH, Ulm, West Germany.)

Savage Model 71 "Stevens Favorite" Single Shot Lever Action Rifle $95

Replica of the original Stevens Favorite issued as a tribute to Joshua Stevens, "Father of 22 Hunting." Caliber, 22 Long Rifle. 22-inch full-octagon barrel. Brass-plated hammer and lever. Open rear sight, brass blade front sight. Weight, 4½ pounds. Plain straight-grip butt stock and schnabel fore-end; brass commemorative medallion inlaid in butt stock, brass crescent-shaped buttplate. 15,000 produced. Made in 1971 only. Value is for new, unfired specimen.

V. C. Schilling, Suhl, Germany

Schilling Mauser-Mannlicher Bolt Action Sporting Rifle $250

Same general specifications as given for the Haenel Mauser-Mannlicher Sporter.

Schilling '88 Mauser Sporter $250

Same general specifications as Haenel '88 Mauser Sporter.

R. F. Sedgley, Inc., Philadelphia, Pennsylvania

Sedgley Springfield Sporter $250

Springfield '03 bolt action. Calibers: 220 Swift, 218 Bee, 22-3000, R2, 22-4000, 22 Hornet, 25-35, 250-3000, 257 Roberts, 270 Win., 7mm, 30-06. 24-inch barrel. Weight, 7½ pounds. Lyman No. 48 receiver sight, bead front sight on matted ramp. Checkered walnut stock, grip cap, sling swivels. Discontinued 1941.

Sedgley Springfield Left-Hand Sporter $275

Bolt action reversed for left-handed shooter. Otherwise the same as the standard Sedgley Springfield Sporter.

Sedgley Springfield Mannlicher-Type Sporter $275

Same as the standard Sedgley Springfield Sporter except has 20-inch barrel, Mannlicher-type full stock with cheekpiece, weighs 7¾ pounds.

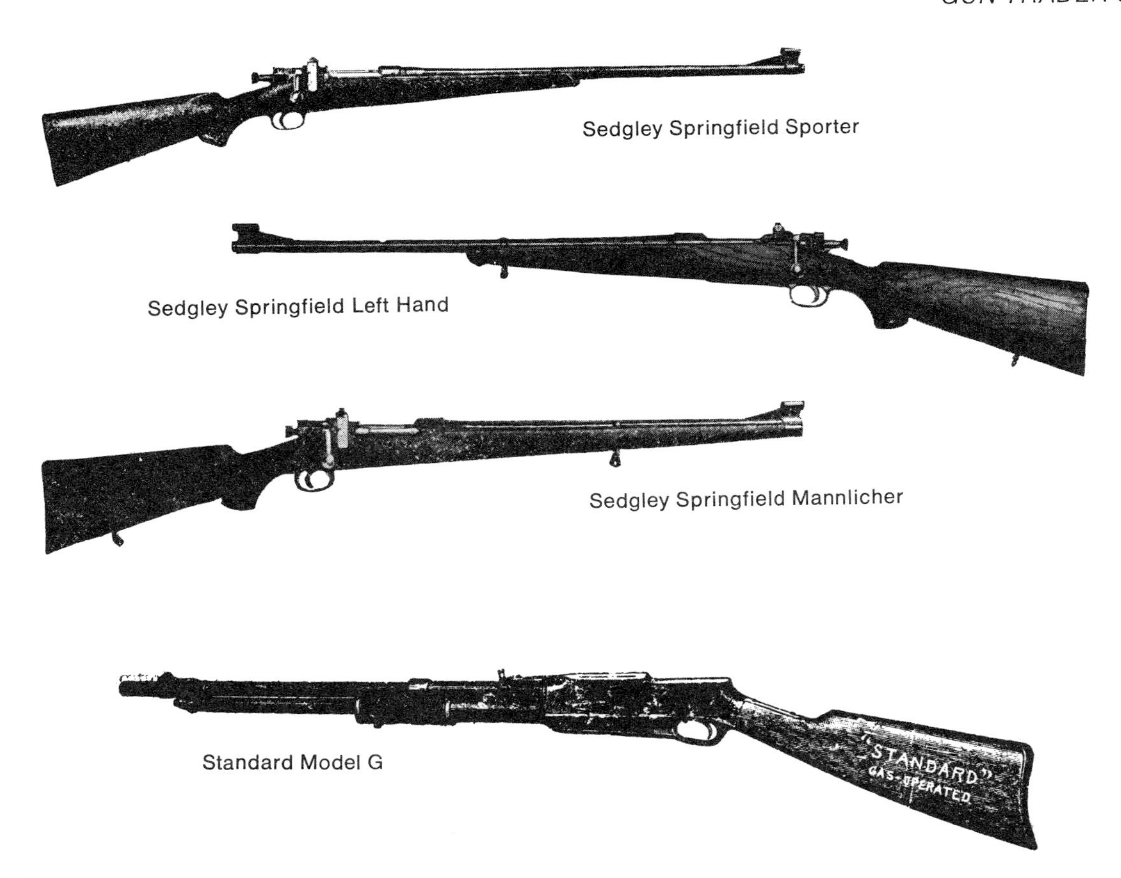

Sedgley Springfield Sporter

Sedgley Springfield Left Hand

Sedgley Springfield Mannlicher

Standard Model G

Standard Arms Company, Wilmington, Del.

Standard Model G Automatic Rifle $250

Gas-operated. Autoloading. Hammerless. Takedown. Calibers: 25-35, 30-30, 25 Rem., 30 Rem., 35 Rem. Magazine capacity: 4 rounds in 35 Rem., 5 rounds in other calibers. 22⅜-inch barrel. Weight, about 7¾ pounds. Open sporting rear sight, ivory bead front sight. Shotgun-type stock. Made c. 1910. *Note:* This was the first gas-operated rifle manufactured in the U.S. While essentially an autoloader, the gas port can be closed and the rifle operated as a slide action repeater.

Standard Model M Hand-Operated Rifle $185

Slide action repeater with same general specifications as Model G except lacks autoloading feature; weight, about 7 pounds.

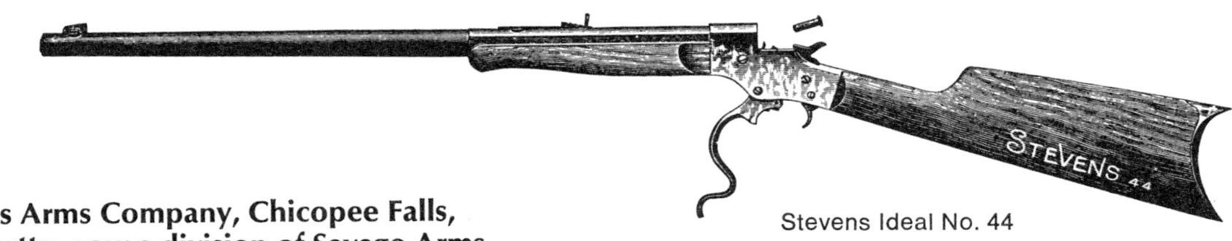

Stevens Ideal No. 44

J. Stevens Arms Company, Chicopee Falls, Massachusetts; now a division of Savage Arms Corporation

Stevens "Ideal" No. 44 Single Shot Rifle $195

Rolling block. Lever Action. Takedown. Calibers: 22 Long Rifle, 25 R.F., 32 R.F., 25-20 S.S., 32-20, 32-40, 38-40, 38-55, 44-40. Barrel lengths: 24-inch, 26-inch (round, half-octagon, full octagon). Weight, about 7 pounds with 26-inch round barrel. Open rear sight, Rocky Mountain front sight. Plain straight-grip stock and forearm. Made from 1894 to 1932.

Stevens "Ideal" No. 44½ Single Shot Rifle $275

Falling-block lever action. Aside from the new design action introduced in 1903, the specifications of this model are the same as those of Model 44. The Model 44½ was discontinued about 1916.

Stevens Ideal Scheutzen

Stevens Favorite No. 17

Stevens Visible Loading No. 70

Stevens Armory Model 414

Stevens "Ideal" Single Shot Rifles No. 45 to 54. These are the higher grade models, differing from the standard No. 44 and No. 44½ chiefly in finish, engraving, set triggers, levers, barrels, stocks, etc. The Schuetzen types (including the "Stevens-Pope" models) are in this series. Model Nos. 45 to 54 were introduced about 1896 and originally had the No. 44-type rolling-block action which was superseded in 1903 by the No. 44½ type falling block action. These models were all discontinued about 1916. Generally speaking the 45-54 series rifles particularly the "Stevens-Pope" and higher grade Schuetzen models, are collector's items bringing very much higher prices than the ordinary No. 44 and 44½.

Stevens "Favorite" No. 17 Single Shot Rifle $75

Lever action. Takedown. Calibers: 22 Long Rifle, 25 R.F., 32 R.F. 24-inch round barrel, other lengths were available. Weight, about 4½ pounds. Open rear sight, Rocky Mountain front sight. Plain straight-grip stock, small tapered forearm. Made from 1894 to 1935.

Stevens "Favorite" No. 18 . . . . $80

Same as No. 17 except has Vernier peep rear sight, leaf middle sight, Beach combination front sight.

Stevens "Favorite" No. 19 . . . . $80

Same as No. 17 except has Lyman combination rear sight, leaf sight, Lyman front sight.

Stevens "Favorite" No. 20 . . . . $70

Same as No. 17 except has smoothbore barrel for 22 R.F. and 32 R.F. shot cartridges.

Stevens "Favorite" No. 27 . . . . $80

Same as No. 17 except has octagon barrel.

Stevens "Favorite" No. 28 . . . . $85

Same as No. 18 except has octagon barrel.

Stevens "Favorite" No. 29 . . . . $85

Same as No. 19 except has octagon barrel.

Stevens "Visible Loading" No. 70 Slide Action Repeating Rifle $80

Exposed hammer. Caliber, 22 Long Rifle, Long, Short. Tubular magazine holds 11 Long Rifle, 13 Long, 15 Short. 22-inch barrel. Weight, about 4½ pounds. Open rear sight, bead front sight. Plain straight-grip stock, grooved slide handle. Made from 1907 to 1934. *Note:* Nos. 70½ 71, 71½, 72, 72½ are essentially the same as No. 70, differing chiefly in barrel length or sight equipment.

Stevens "Armory Model" No. 414 Single Shot Rifle $185

No. 44-type lever action. Calibers: 22 Long Rifle only. 22 Short only. 26-inch barrel. Weight, about 8 pounds. Lyman receiver peep sight, blade front sight. Plain straight-grip stock, military-type forearm, swivels. Made from 1912 to 1932.

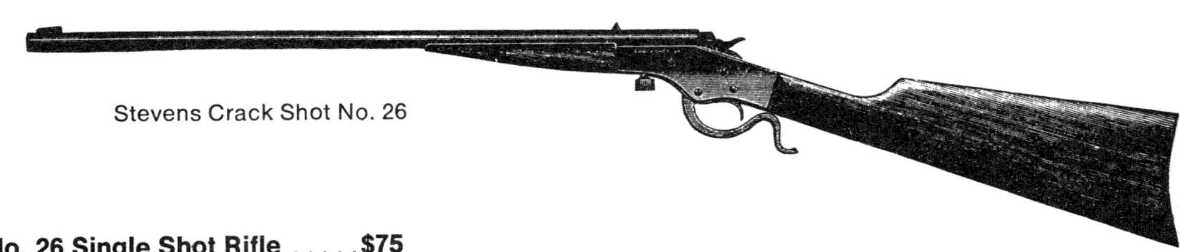

Stevens Crack Shot No. 26

Stevens "Crack Shot" No. 26 Single Shot Rifle $75

Lever action. Takedown. Calibers: 22 Long Rifle, 32 R.F. 18-inch or 22-inch barrel. Weight, about 3¼ pounds. Open rear sight, blade front sight. Plain straight-grip stock, small tapered forearm. Made from 1913 to 1939.

Stevens "Crack Shot" No. 26½ $70

Same as No. 26 except has smoothbore barrel for shot cartridges.

Stevens "Marksman" No. 12 Single Shot Rifle $60

Lever Action, tip-up. Takedown. Calibers: 22 Long Rifle, 25 R.F., 32 R.F. 22-inch barrel. Plain straight-grip stock, small tapered forearm.

Stevens Marksman No. 12

Stevens "Little Scout" No. 14½ Single Shot Rifle ..$50

Rolling block. Takedown. Caliber, 22 Long Rifle. 18 or 20-inch barrel. Weight, about 2¾ pounds. Open rear sight, blade front sight. Plain straight-grip stock, small tapered forearm.

Stevens Little Scout No. 14½

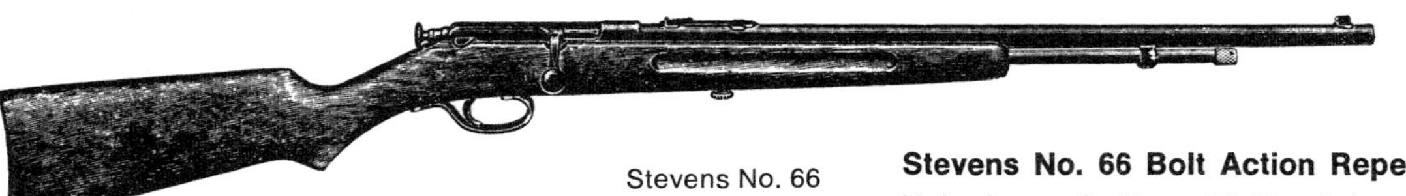

Stevens No. 66

Stevens No. 66 Bolt Action Repeating Rifle $35

Takedown. Caliber, 22 Short, Long, Long Rifle. Tubular magazine holds 13 Long Rifle, 15 Long, 19 Short. 24-inch barrel. Weight, about 5 pounds. Open rear sight, bead front sight. Plain pistol-grip stock with grooved forearm. Made from 1931 to 1935.

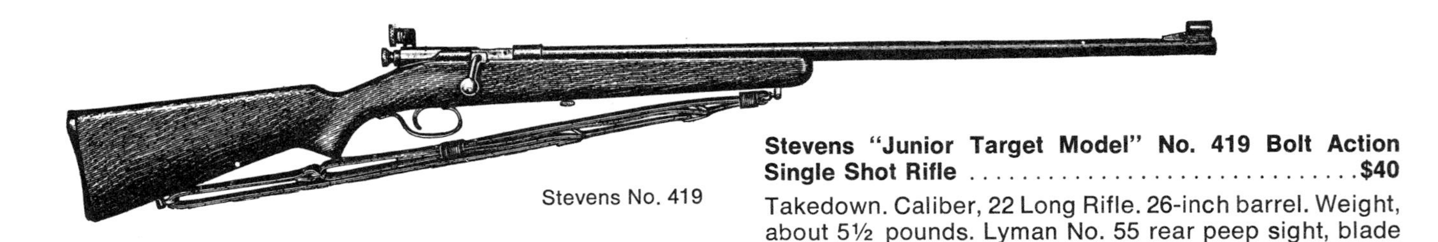

Stevens No. 419

Stevens "Junior Target Model" No. 419 Bolt Action Single Shot Rifle $40

Takedown. Caliber, 22 Long Rifle. 26-inch barrel. Weight, about 5½ pounds. Lyman No. 55 rear peep sight, blade front sight. Plain junior target stock with pistol grip and grooved forearm, swivels, sling. Made from 1932 to 1936.

Stevens "Walnut Hill" No. 417-0 Single Shot Target Rifle $300

Lever action. Calibers: 22 Long Rifle only, 22 Short only, 22 Hornet. 28-inch heavy barrel (extra heavy 29-inch barrel also available). Weight, about 10½ pounds. Lyman 52L extension rear sight, 17A front sight, scope bases. Target stock with full pistol grip, beavertail forearm, barrel band, swivels, sling. Made from 1932 to 1947.

Stevens "Walnut Hill" No. 417-1 . . . . $300

Same as No. 417-0 except has Lyman 48L receiver sight.

Stevens "Walnut Hill" No. 417-2 . . . . $300

Same as No. 417-0 except has Lyman No. 144 tang sight.

Stevens "Walnut Hill" No. 417-3 . . . . $285

Same as No. 417-0 except without sights.

Stevens "Walnut Hill" No. 417½ Single Shot Rifle $300

Lever action. Calibers: 22 Long Rifle, 22 W.R.F., 25 R.F., 22 Hornet. 28-inch barrel. Weight, about 8½ pounds. Lyman No. 144 tang peep sight, folding middle sight, bead front sight. Sporting stock with pistol grip, semi-beavertail forearm, swivels, sling. Made from 1932 to 1940.

Stevens "Walnut Hill" No. 418 Single Shot Rifle . $175

Lever action. Takedown. Calibers: 22 Long Rifle only, 22 Short only. 26-inch barrel. Weight, about 6½ pounds. Lyman No. 144 tang peep sight, blade front sight. Pistol-grip stock, semi-beavertail forearm, swivels, sling. Made from 1932 to 1940.

Stevens "Walnut Hill" No. 418½ $160

Same as No. 418 except also available in calibers 22 W.R.F. and 25 Stevens R.F., has Lyman No. 2A tank peep sight, bead front sight.

Stevens Model 053

Stevens Model 056

Stevens Model 066

Stevens-Springfield Model 82

Stevens-Springfield Model 83

Stevens "Buckhorn" Model 053 Bolt Action Single Shot Rifle $30

Takedown. Calibers: 22 Short, Long, Long Rifle, 22 W.R.F., 25 Stevens R.F. 24-inch barrel. Weight, about 5½ pounds. Receiver peep sight, open middle sight, hooded front sight. Sporting stock with pistol grip and black forend tip. Made from 1935 to 1948.

Stevens "Buckhorn" Model 53 .... $25

Same as "Buckhorn" Model 053 except has open rear sight and plain bead front sight.

Stevens "Buckhorn" Model 056 Bolt Action Repeating Rifle $35

Takedown. Caliber, 22 Long Rifle, Long, Short. 5-shot detachable box magazine. 24-inch barrel. Weight, about 6 pounds. Receiver peep sight, open middle sight, hooded front sight. Sporting stock with pistol grip and black forend tip. Made from 1935 to 1948.

Stevens "Buckhorn" Model 56 .... $30

Same as "Buckhorn" Model 056 except has open rear sight and plain bead front sight.

Stevens "Buckhorn" Model 066 Bolt Action Repeating Rifle $35

Takedown. Caliber, 22 Long Rifle, Long, Short. Tubular magazine holds 21 Short, 17 Long, 15 Long Rifle. 24-inch barrel. Weight, about 6 pounds. Receiver peep sight, open middle sight, hooded front sight. Sporting stock with pistol grip and black forend tip. Made from 1935 to 1948.

Stevens "Buckhorn" Model 66 .... $30

Same as "Buckhorn" Model 066 except has open rear sight, plain bead front sight.

Stevens-Springfield Model 82 Bolt Action Single Shot Rifle $25

Takedown. Caliber, 22 Long Rifle, Long, Short. 22-inch barrel. Weight, about 4 pounds. Open rear sight, gold bead front sight. Plain pistol-grip stock with grooved forearm. Made from 1935 to 1939.

Stevens-Springfield Model 83 Bolt Action Single Shot Rifle $25

Takedown. Calibers: 22 Long Rifle, Long, Short; 22

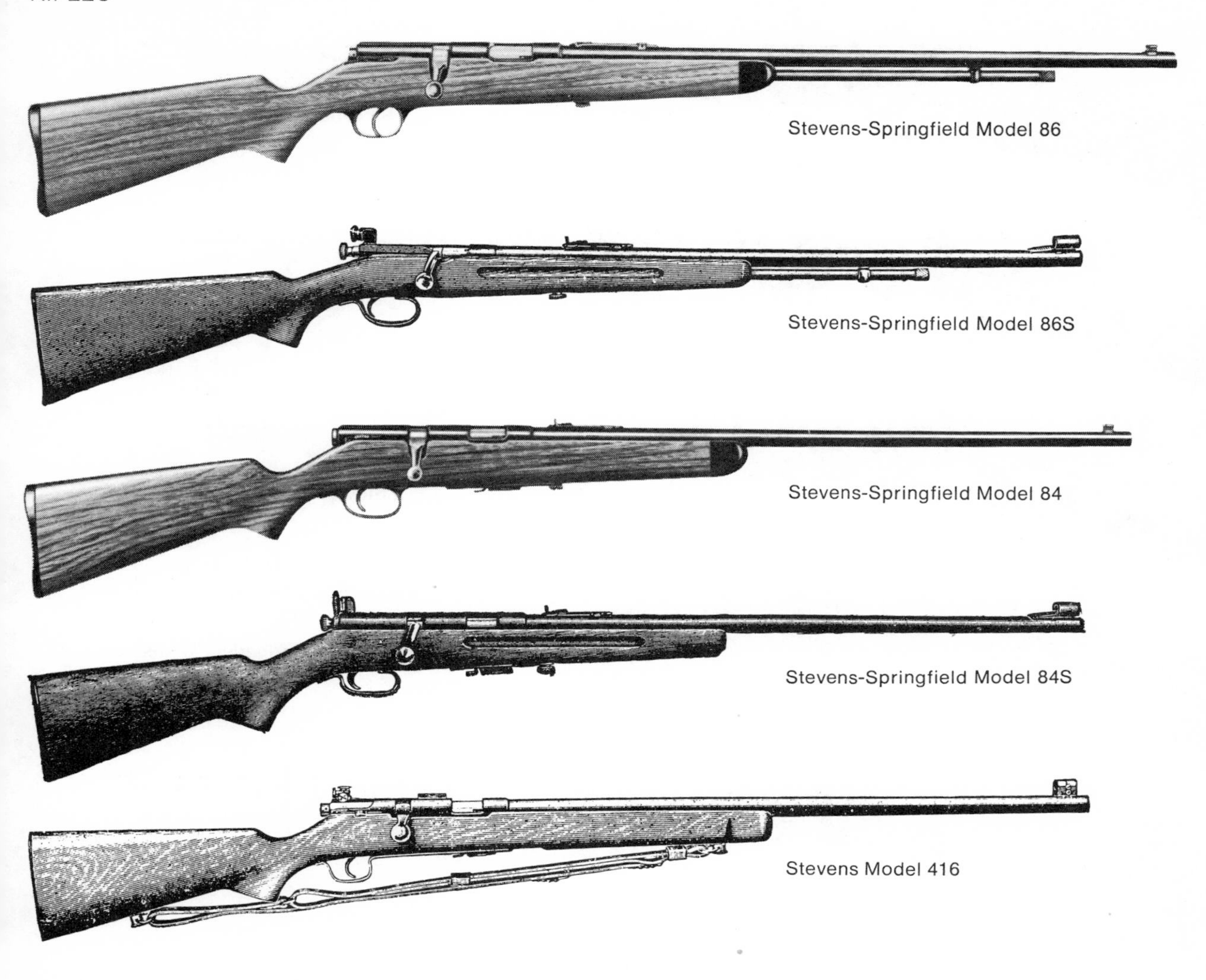

Stevens-Springfield Model 86

Stevens-Springfield Model 86S

Stevens-Springfield Model 84

Stevens-Springfield Model 84S

Stevens Model 416

W.R.F., 25 Stevens R.F. 24-inch barrel. Weight, about 4½ pounds. Peep rear sight, open middle sight, hooded front sight. Plain pistol-grip stock with grooved fore-arm. Made from 1935 to 1939.

Stevens-Springfield Model 86 Bolt Action Repeating Rifle $35

Takedown. Caliber, 22 Long Rifle, Long, Short. Tubular magazine holds 15 Long Rifle, 17 Long, 21 Short. 24-inch barrel. Weight, about 6 pounds. Open rear sight, gold bead front sight. Pistol-grip stock, black forend tip on current production. Made from 1935 to 1965. *Note:* This model originally bore the "Springfield" brand name which was discontinued in 1948.

Stevens-Springfield Model 86-S (086) $35

Same as Model 86 except has peep rear sight and hooded front sight. Pre-1948 rifles of this model were designated as Springfield Model 086, later known as Stevens Model 86-S. Discontinued.

Stevens-Springfield Model 84 . . . . $35

Same as Model 86 except has 5-shot detachable box magazine. Pre-1948 rifles of this model were designated as Springfield Model 84, later known as Stevens Model 84. Made from 1940 to 1965.

Stevens-Springfield Model 84-S (084) $35

Same as Model 84 except has peep rear sight and hooded front sight. Pre-1948 rifles of this model were designated as Springfield Model 084, later known as Stevens Model 84-S. Discontinued.

Stevens Model 416 Bolt Action Target Rifle $100

Caliber, 22 Long Rifle. 5-shot detachable box magazine. 26-inch heavy barrel. Weight, about 9½ pounds. Receiver peep sight, hooded front sight. Target stock, swivels, sling. Made from 1937 to 1949.

Stevens Model 87 Autoloading Rifle $35

Takedown. Caliber, 22 Long Rifle. 15-shot tubular magazine. 24-inch barrel (20-inch on current model). Weight, about 6 pounds. Open rear sight, bead front sight. Pistol-grip stock. Made from 1938 to date. *Note:* This model originally bore the "Springfield" brand name which was discontinued in 1948.

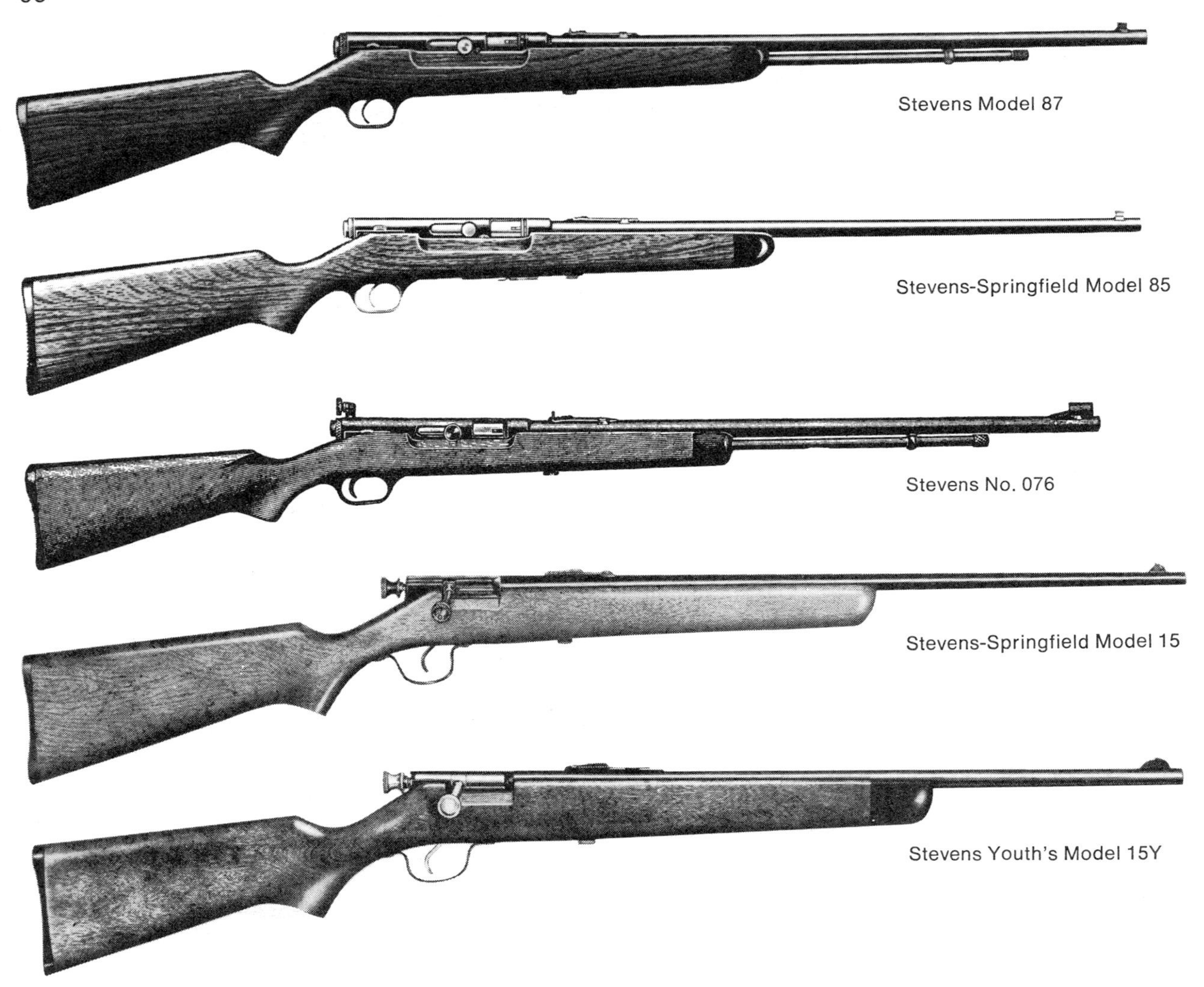

Stevens Model 87

Stevens-Springfield Model 85

Stevens No. 076

Stevens-Springfield Model 15

Stevens Youth's Model 15Y

Stevens-Springfield Model 87-S (087) $35

Same as Model 87 except has peep rear sight and hooded front sight. Pre-1948 rifles of this model were designated as Springfield Model 087, later known as Stevens Model 87-S. Discontinued.

Stevens-Springfield Model 85 . . . . $35

Same as Model 87 except has 5-shot detachable box magazine. Made from 1939 to date. Pre-1948 rifles of this model were designated as Springfield Model 85, currently known as Stevens Model 85.

Stevens-Springfield Model 85-S (085) $35

Same as Model 85 except has peep rear sight and hooded front sight. Pre-1948 rifles of this model were designated as Springfield Model 085, currently known as Stevens Model 85-S.

Stevens "Buckhorn" No. 076 Autoloading Rifle $30

Takedown. Caliber, 22 Long Rifle. 15-shot tubular magazine. 24-inch barrel. Weight, about 6 pounds. Receiver peep sight, open middle sight, hooded front sight. Sporting stock with pistol grip, black forend tip. Made from 1938 to 1948.

Stevens "Buckhorn" No. 76 . . . . $30

Same as "Buckhorn" No. 076 except has open rear sight, plain bead front sight.

Stevens "Buckhorn" No. 57 . . . . $30

Same as Model 76 except has 5-shot detachable box magazine. Made from 1939 to 1948.

Stevens "Buckhorn" No. 057 . . . . $30

Same as Model 076 except has 5-shot detachable box magazine. Made from 1939 to 1948.

Stevens-Springfield Model 15 Single Shot Bolt Action Rifle $20

Takedown. Caliber, 22 Long Rifle, Long, Short. 22-inch barrel. Weight, about 4 pounds. Open rear sight, bead front sight. Plain pistol-grip stock. Made from 1937 to 1948.

Stevens Model 15 . . . . **$25**

Same as Stevens-Springfield Model 15, except has 24-inch barrel, weighs about 5 pounds, has redesigned stock. Made from 1948 to 1965.

Stevens Youth's Model 15Y **$25**

Same as Model 15, except has 21-inch barrel, short butt-stock, weighs about 4¾ pounds. Made from 1958 to 1965.

Stevens Model 322 Hi-Power Bolt Action Carbine . . **$70**

Caliber, 22 Hornet. 4-shot detachable box magazine. 21-inch barrel. Weight, about 6¾ pounds. Open rear sight, ramp front sight. Pistol-grip stock. Made from 1947 to 1950. (See Savage Models 340, 342)

Stevens Model 322-S **$70**

Same as Model 325 except has peep rear sight. (See Savage Models 340S, 342S)

Stevens Model 325 Hi-Power Bolt Action Carbine . . . **$70**

Caliber, 30-30. 3-shot detachable box magazine. 21-inch barrel. Weight, about 6¾ pounds. Open rear sight, bead front sight. Plain pistol-grip stock. Made from 1947 to 1950. (See Savage Model 340)

Stevens Model 325-S **$70**

Same as Model 325 except has peep rear sight. (See Savage Model 340S)

Steyr-Daimler-Puch A.-G., Steyr, Austria (see listings under "Mannlicher-Schoenauer")

Steyr Small Bore Carbine **$200**

Bolt action repeater. Caliber, 22 Long Rifle. 5-shot detachable box magazine. 19½-inch barrel. Leaf rear sight, hooded bead front sight. Mannlicher-type stock, checkered, swivels. Made from 1953 to date.

U.S. Military Rifles manufactured at Springfield Armory, Springfield, Massachusetts

U.S. Model 1898 Krag-Jorgensen Military Rifle . . . **$150**

Bolt action. Caliber, 30-40 Krag. 5-shot hinged box magazine. 30-inch barrel. Weight, about 9 pounds. Adjustable rear sight, blade front sight. Military-type stock, straight grip. *Note:* The foregoing specifications apply, in general, to Rifle Models 1892 and 1896 which differed from Model 1898 only in minor details. Made from 1894 to 1904.

U.S. Model 1898 Krag-Jorgensen Carbine **$250**

Same general specifications as Model 1898 Rifle except has 22-inch barrel, weighs about 8 pounds, carbine-type stock. *Note:* The foregoing specifications apply, in general, to Carbine Models 1896 and 1899 which differed from Model 1898 only in minor details.

U.S. Model 1903 Springfield Military Rifle

Modified Mauser-type bolt action. Caliber, 30-06. 5-shot box magazine. 23.79-inch barrel. Weight, about 8¾ pounds. Adjustable rear sight, blade front sight. Military-type stock, straight grip. *Note:* M/1903 rifles of Springfield manufacture with serial numbers under 800,000. (1903-1918) have case-hardened receivers, those between 800,000 and 1,275,767 (1918-1927) were double-heat-treated, rifles numbered over 1,275,767 have nickel-steel bolts and receivers; Rock Island production from No. 1 to 285,507 have case hardened receivers, improved heat treatment was adopted in May 1918 with No. 285,-207, about three months later with No. 319,921 the use of nickel steel was begun, but the production of some double-heat-treated carbon steel receivers and bolts continued. Made from 1903 to 1930 at Springfield Armory; during World War I, M/1903 rifles were also made at Rock Island Arsenal, Rock Island, Ill.

With case hardened receiver **$100**
With double-heat-treated receiver **$115**
With nickel steel receiver **$150**

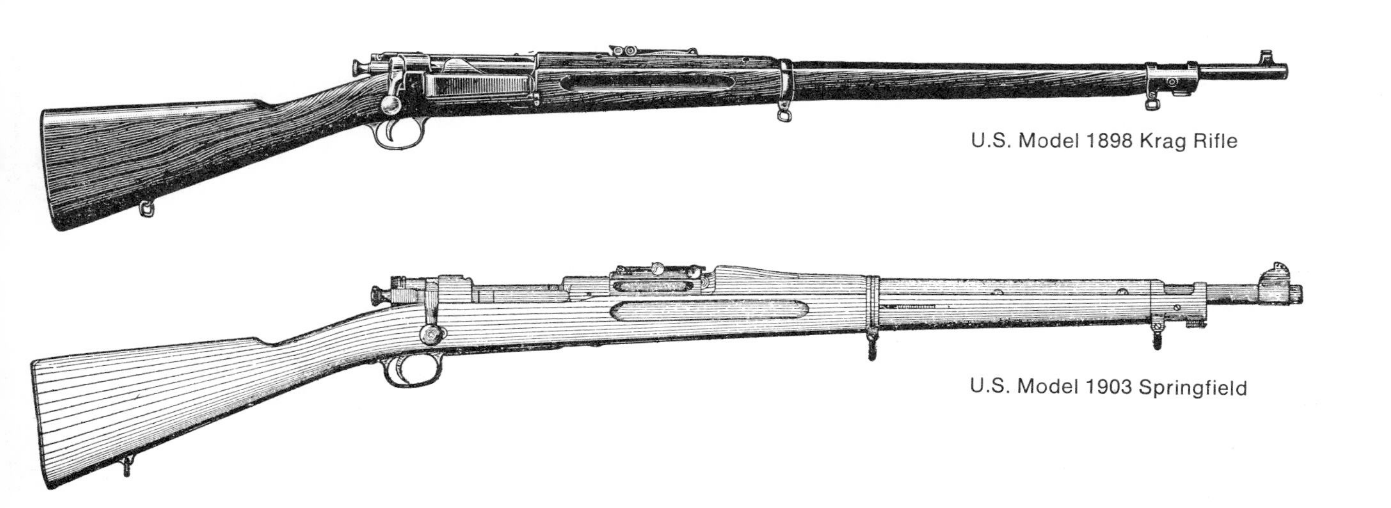

U.S. Model 1898 Krag Rifle

U.S. Model 1903 Springfield

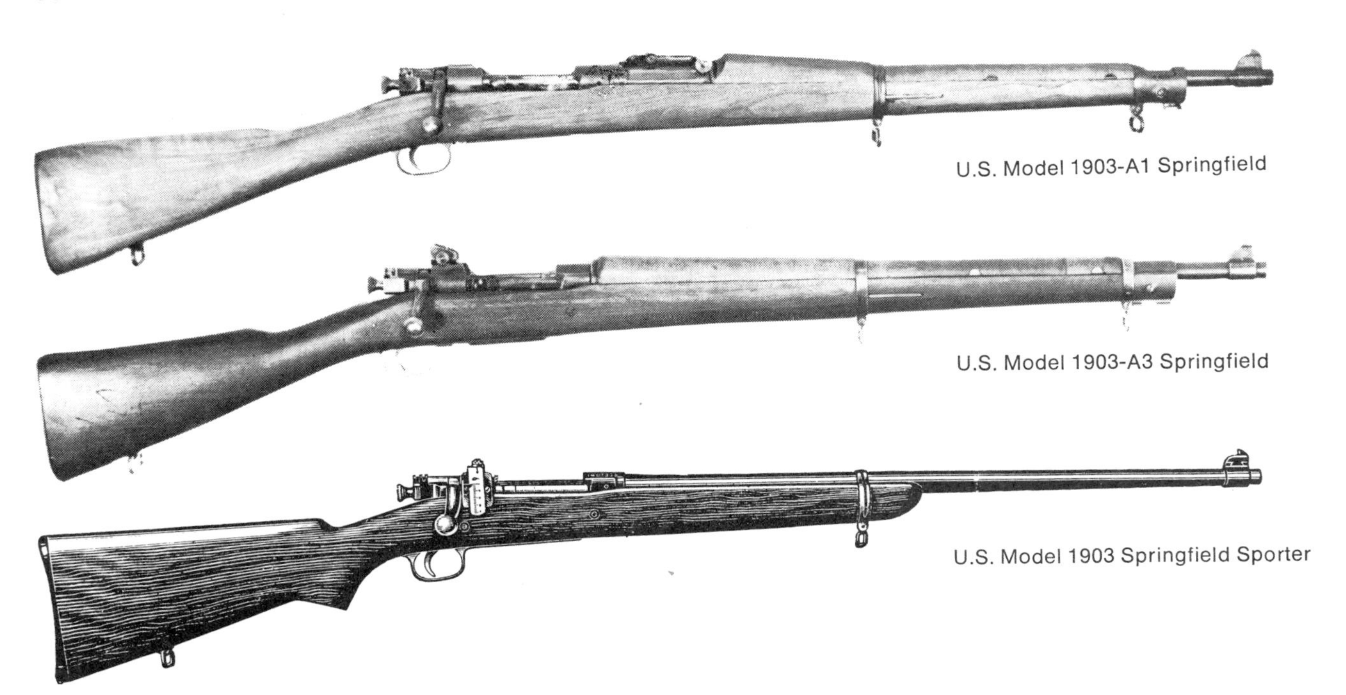

U.S. Model 1903-A1 Springfield

U.S. Model 1903-A3 Springfield

U.S. Model 1903 Springfield Sporter

U.S. Model 1903 Mark I Springfield $150

Same as Model 1903 except altered to permit use of the Pedersen Device. This device, officially designated as "U.S. Automatic Pistol Model 1918", converted the M/1903 to a semi-automatic weapon firing a 30 caliber cartridge similar to the 32 automatic pistol ammunition. The Mark I rifles have a slot milled in the left side of the receiver to serve as an ejection port when the Pedersen Device was in use, these rifles were also fitted with a special sear and cut-off. Some 65,000 of these devices were manufactured and presumably a like number of M/1903 rifles converted to handle them. During the early 1920's the Pedersen Devices were all destroyed and the Mark I rifles were reconverted by replacement of the special sear and cut-off with standard parts. Value shown is for the Mark I rifle without the Pedersen Device — as far as the author is able to determine none of these devices were ever sold and the few remaining examples are in government museums; however many of the altered rifles were purchased by members of the National Rifle Association through the Director of Civilian Marksmanship.

U.S. Model 1903-A1 Springfield

Same general specifications as Model 1903 except has Type C pistol-grip stock adopted in 1930. The last Springfields produced at the Springfield Armory were of this type, final serial number was 1,532,878 made in 1939. *Note:* Late in 1941, the Remington Arms Company, Ilion, N.Y. began production under government contract of Springfield rifles of this type with a few minor modifications. These rifles are numbered from 3,000,001 to 3,348,085 and were manufactured prior to the adoption of Model 1903-A3.
Springfield manufacture **$175**
Remington manufacture **$150**

U.S. Model 1903-A3 Springfield $135

Same general specifications as Model 1903-A1 except modified to permit increased production and lower cost, may have either straight-grip or pistol-grip stock, bolt is not interchangeable with earlier types, has receiver peep sight, many parts are stamped sheet steel including the trigger guard and magazine assembly. Quality of these rifles, lower than that of other M/1903 Springfields, reflects the emergency conditions under which they were produced. Manufactured during World War II by Remington Arms Co. and L. C. Smith Corona Typewriters, Inc.

U.S. Model 1903 National Match Springfield $300

Same general specifications as the standard Model 1903 except specially selected with star-gauged barrel, Type C pistol-grip stock, polished bolt assembly, early types have headless firing pin assembly and reversed safety lock. These rifles were produced especially for target shooting.

U.S. Model 1903 Springfield Sporter $300

Same general specifications as the National Match except has sporting design stock, Lyman No. 48 receiver sight.

U.S. Model 1903 Style T Springfield Match Rifle .. $400

Same general specifications as the Springfield Sporter except has heavy barrel (26, 28 or 30-inch), scope bases, globe front sight, weighs about 12½ pounds with 26-inch barrel.

U.S. Model 1903 Type A Springfield Free Rifle $400

Same as Style T except made with 28-inch barrel only, has Swiss butt-plate, weighs about 13¼ pounds.

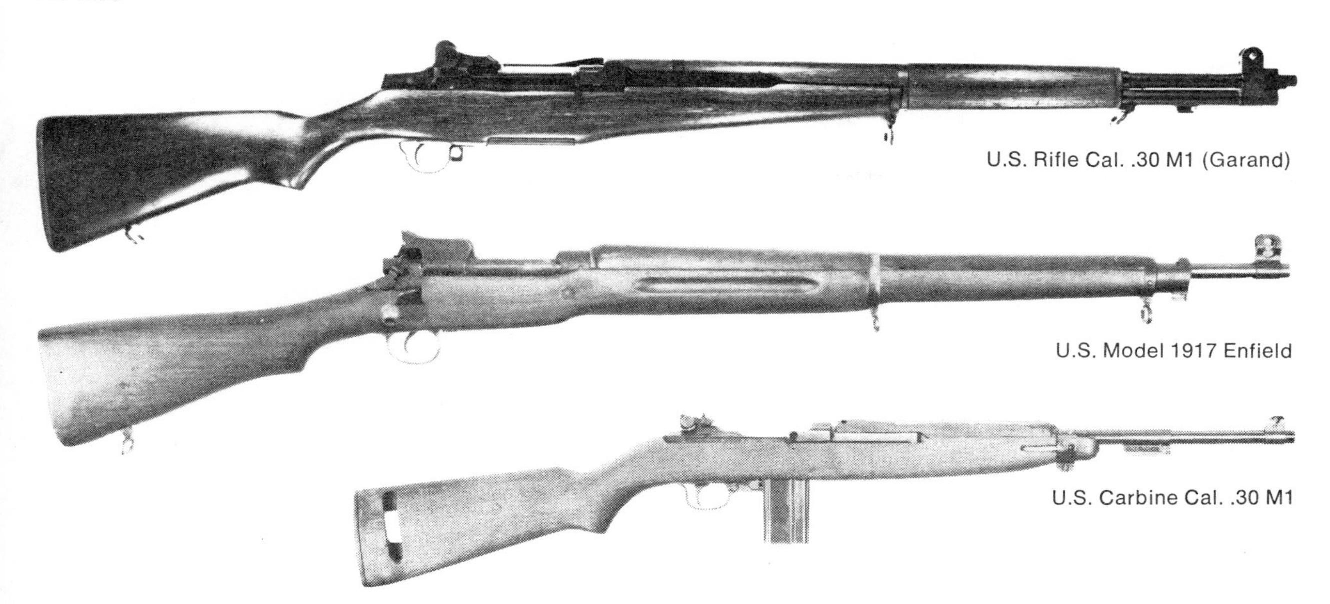

U.S. Rifle Cal. .30 M1 (Garand)

U.S. Model 1917 Enfield

U.S. Carbine Cal. .30 M1

U.S. Model 1903 Type B Springfield Free Rifle . . . $500

Same as Type A except has cheekpiece stock, palm rest, Woodie double-set triggers, Garand fast firing pin, weighs about 14¾ pounds.

U.S. Model 1922-MI 22 Springfield Target Rifle . . . $250

Modified Model 1903. Caliber, 22 Long Rifle. 5-shot detachable box magazine. 24½-inch barrel. Weight, about 9 pounds. Lyman No. 48C receiver sight, blade front sight. Sporting-type stock similar to that of the Model 1903 Springfield Sporter. Issued 1927. *Note:* The earlier Model 1922 which is seldom encountered, differs from the foregoing chiefly in the bolt mechanism and magazine.

U.S. M2 22 Springfield Target Rifle $325

Same general specifications as Model 1922-MI except has speedlock, improved bolt assembly adjustable for headspace. *Note:* These improvements were later incorporated in many rifles of the preceding models (M1922, M1922MI) and arms so converted were marked "M1922 M2" or "M1922MII".

U.S. Rifle, Caliber 30, M1 (Garand) Military Rifle . . $285

Clip-fed, gas-operated, air-cooled, semiautomatic. Uses a clip containing eight rounds. 24-inch barrel. Weight (without bayonet), 9½ pounds. Adjustable peep rear sight, blade front sight with guards. Pistol-grip stock, hand guards. Made from 1937 to 1957. *Note:* In addition to manufacture at Springfield Armory, Garand rifles have been produced by Winchester Repeating Arms Co., Harrington & Richardson Arms Co., and International Harvester Co.

U.S. Rifle, Caliber 30, M1, National Match $375

Accurized target version of the Garand. Glass-bedded stock; match grade barrel, sights, gas cylinder. "NM" stamped on barrel forward of handguard.

U.S. Military Rifle manufactured by Remington Arms Company of Delaware (later Midvale Steel & Ordnance Co.), Eddystone, Pa.; Remington Arms Company, Ilion, New York; Winchester Repeating Arms Company, New Haven, Connecticut

U.S. Model 1917 Enfield Military Rifle $125

Modified Mauser-type bolt action. Caliber, 30-06. 5-shot box magazine. 26-inch barrel. Weight, about 9¼ pounds. Adjustable rear sight, blade front sight with guards. Military-type stock with semi-pistol grip. This design originated in Great Britain as their "Pattern '14" and were manufactured in caliber 303 for the British Government in three U.S. plants. In 1917, the U.S. Government contracted with these firms to produce the same rifle in caliber 30-06. Made only from 1917 to 1918, over two million of these Model 1917 Enfields were manufactured. While no more were produced after World War I, the U.S. supplied over a million of them to Great Britain during World War II.

U.S. Carbine manufactured by Inland Mfg. Div. of G.M.C., Dayton, Ohio; Winchester Repeating Arms Co., New Haven, Conn.; other contractors.*

U.S. Carbine, Caliber 30, M1 . . . . $150

Gas-operated (short-stroke piston), semiautomatic. 15 or 30-round detachable box magazine. 18-inch barrel. Weight, about 5½ pounds. Adjustable rear sight, blade front sight with guards. Pistol-grip stock with handguard, side-mounted web sling. Made from 1942 to 1945. *Note:* In 1963, 150,000 surplus M1 Carbines were sold at $20 each to members of the National Rifle Assn. by the Dept. of the Army.

*International Business Machines Corp., Poughkeepsie, N.Y.; National Postal Meter Co., Rochester, N.Y.; Quality Hardware & Machine Co., Chicago, Ill.; Rock-Ola Co., Chicago, Ill.; Saginaw Steering Gear Div. of G.M.C., Saginaw, Mich.; Standard Products Co., Port Clinton, Ohio; Underwood-Elliott-Fisher Co., Hartford, Conn.

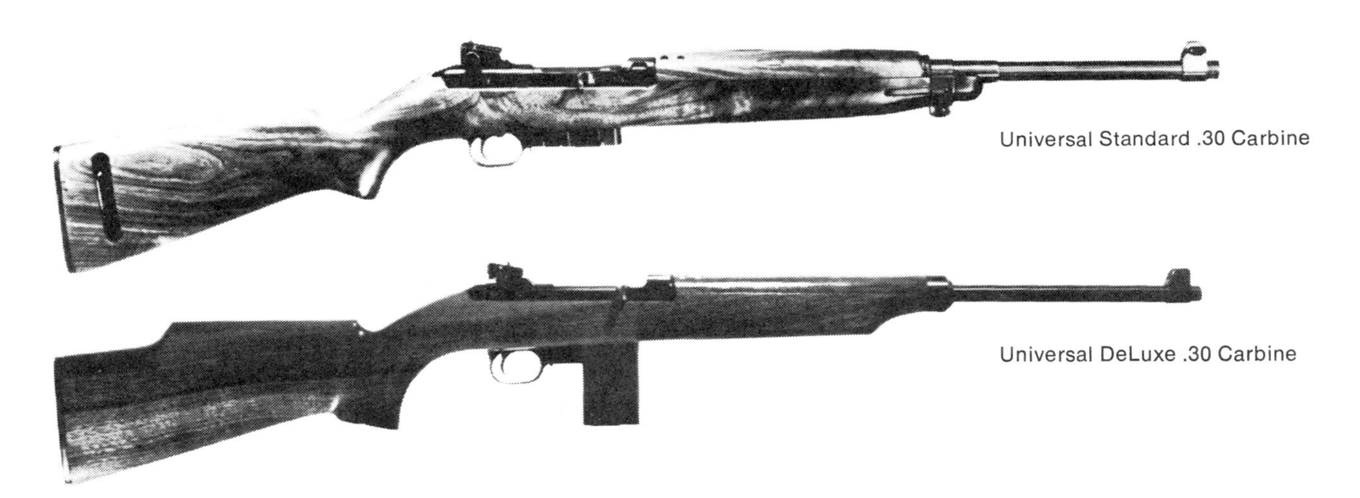

Universal Standard .30 Carbine

Universal DeLuxe .30 Carbine

Universal Firearms Corporation Hialeah, Florida

Universal Standard 30 Caliber Carbine **$90**

Same as U.S. Carbine, Cal. 30, M1, except current production lacks bayonet lug on barrel band, 5-shot clip magazine standard. Made from 1964 to date.

Universal De Luxe 30 Caliber Carbine

Same as Standard Model, except has Monte Carlo sporting stock; blued, nickel-plated, or gold-finished metal parts. Made from 1965 to 1973.

Blued finish **$100**
Nickel-plated **$115**
Gold-plated **$150**

Universal Ferret Semi-Automatic Rifle **$135**

Same as DeLuxe Carbine, except caliber 256; blued finish; no iron sights, has Universal 4X scope. Made from 1965 to 1973.

Waffenfabric Walther, Zeller-Mehlis (Thur.), Germany (Pre-World War II Manufacture)

Walther Olympic Bolt Action Single Shot Match Rifle **$375**

Caliber, 22 Long Rifle. 26-inch heavy barrel. Weight, about 13 pounds. Micrometer extension rear sight, interchangeable front sights. Target stock with checkered pistol grip, thumb-hole, full beavertail forearm covered with corrugated rubber, palm-rest, adjustable Swiss-type buttplate, swivels.

Walther Model 2 Autoloading Rifle **$200**

Bolt action, may be used as autoloader, manually-operated repeater or single shot. Caliber, 22 Long Rifle. 5 or 9-shot detachable box magazine. 24½-inch barrel. Weight, about 7 pounds. Tangent curve rear sight, ramp front sight. Sporting stock with checkered pistol grip, grooved forearm, swivels.

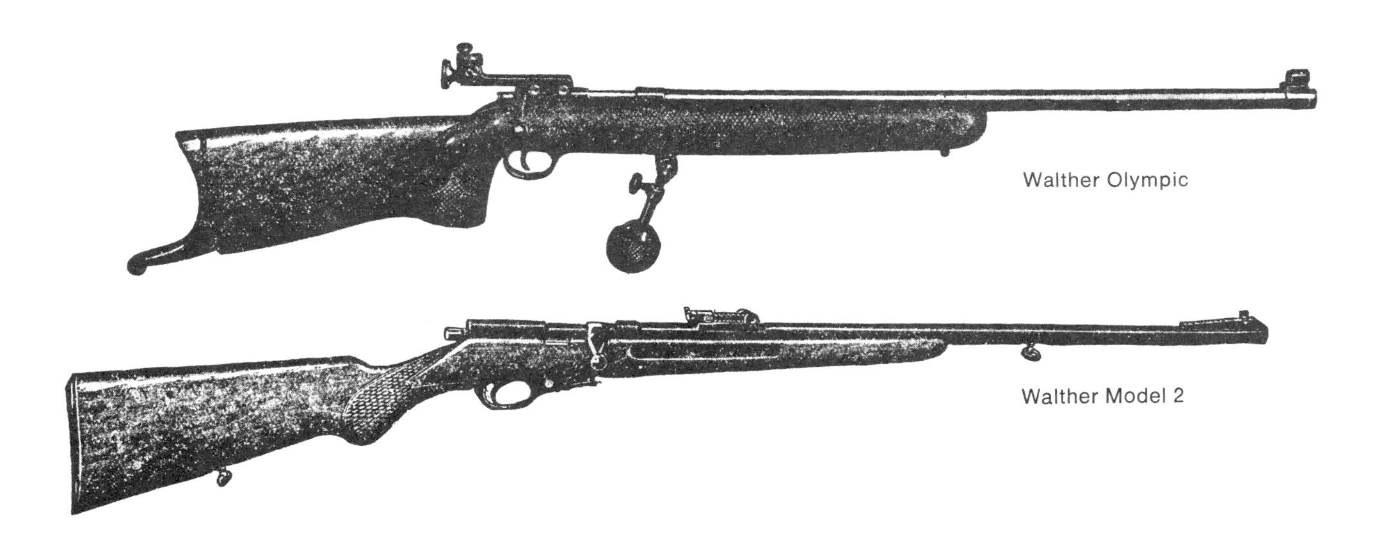

Walther Olympic

Walther Model 2

Weatherby DeLuxe Magnum

Weatherby DeLuxe 378 Magnum

Weatherby Mark V

Weatherby Mark XXII

Walther Model 1 Autoloading Rifle, Light Model . . $200

Similar to Standard Model but with 20-inch barrel, lighter stock, weighs about 4½ pounds.

Walther Model V Bolt Action Single Shot Sporting Rifle $175

Caliber, 22 Long Rifle. 26-inch barrel. Weight, about 7 pounds. Open rear sight, ramp front sight. Plain pistol-grip stock with grooved forearm.

Walther Model V "Meisterbuchse" (Champion Rifle) $200

Same as standard Model V except has micrometer open rear sight and checkered pistol grip.

Weatherby, Inc., South Gate, Calif.

Weatherby De Luxe Magnum Rifle $195

Calibers: 220 Rocket, 257 Weatherby Magnum, 270 W.M., 7mm W.M., 300 W.M., 375 W.M. Specially processed FN Mauser action. 24-inch barrel (26-inch in 375 cal.). Monte Carlo-style stock with cheekpiece, black forend tip, grip cap, checkered pistol grip and forearm, quick-detachable sling swivels. Value shown is for rifle without sights. Discontinued 1958.

Weatherby De Luxe 378 Magnum Rifle $210

Same general specifications as De Luxe Magnum in other calibers, except: caliber, 378 W.M.; Schultz & Larsen action; 26-inch barrel. Discontinued 1958.

Weatherby De Luxe Rifle $170

Same general specifications as De Luxe Magnum, except chambered for standard calibers such as 270, 30-06, etc. Discontinued 1958.

Weatherby Mark V De Luxe Bolt Action Sporting Rifle

Mark V action, right or left hand. Calibers: 22/250, 30-06; 224 Weatherby Varmintmaster; 240, 257, 270, 7mm, 300, 340, 378, 460 Weatherby Magnums. Box magazine holds 2 to 5 cartridges depending upon caliber. 24 or 26-inch barrel. Weight, 6½ to 10½ pounds depending upon caliber. Monte Carlo-style stock with cheekpiece, skip checkering, fore-end tip, pistol-grip cap, recoil pad, QD swivels. Values shown are for rifle without sights. Made from 1958 to date.

Calibers 22/250, 224 . . . . **$260**
Caliber 378 Weatherby Magnum **$350**
Caliber 460 Weatherby Magnum **$400**
Other calibers **$275**
Add for left-hand action . . . . **$ 10**

Weatherby Mark XXII De Luxe 22 Automatic Sporter $105

Semi-automatic with single shot selector. Caliber, 22 Long Rifle. 5 and 10-shot clip magazines. 24-inch barrel. Weight, 6 pounds. Folding leaf open rear sight, ramp front sight. Monte Carlo-type stock with cheekpiece, pistol grip, fore-end tip, grip cap, skip checkering, QD swivels. Made from 1964 to date.

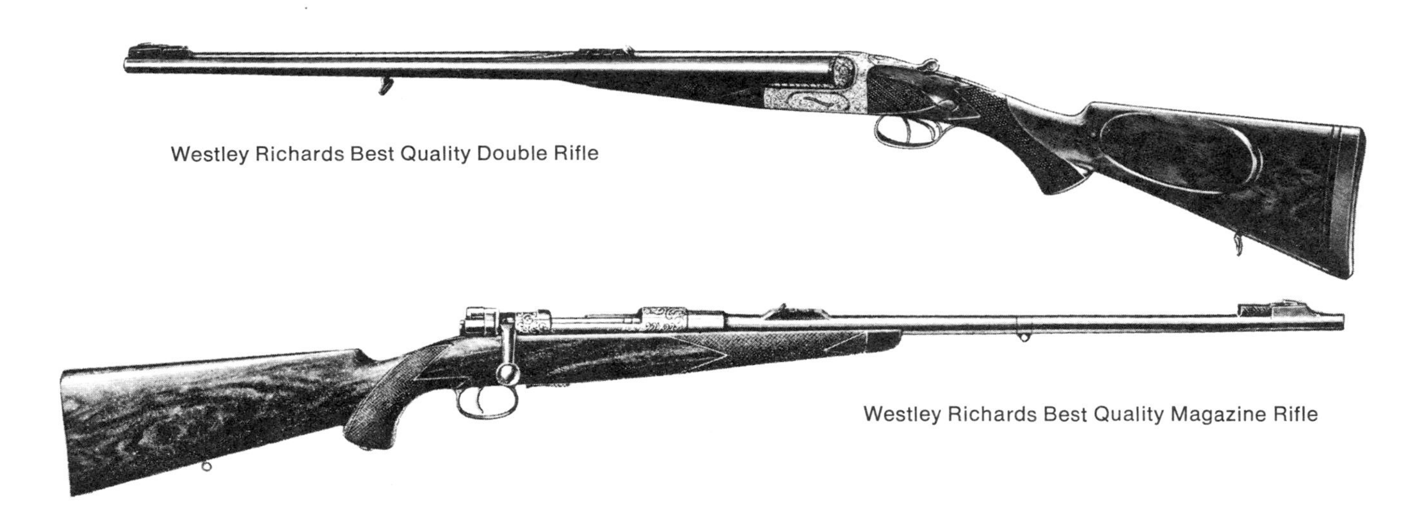

Westley Richards Best Quality Double Rifle

Westley Richards Best Quality Magazine Rifle

Westley Richards & Co., Ltd., London, England

Westley Richards Best Quality Double Rifle $2,500

Box Lock, hammerless, ejector. Hand detachable locks. Calibers: 30-06, 318 Accelerated Express, 375 Magnum, 425 Magnum Express, 465 Nitro Express, 470 Nitro Express. 25-inch barrels. Weights, 8½ to 11 pounds depending upon caliber. Leaf rear sight, hooded front sight. French walnut stock with cheekpiece, checkered pistol grip and forend.

Westley Richards Best Quality Magazine Rifle $750

Mauser or Magnum Mauser Action. Calibers: 7mm High Velocity, 30-06, 318 Accelerated Express, 375 Magnum, 404 Nitro Express, 425 Magnum. Barrel lengths: 24-inch, except 7mm 22-inch and 425 caliber 25-inch. Weights, 7¼ to 9¼ pounds depending upon caliber. Leaf rear sight, hooded front sight. French walnut sporting stock with cheekpiece, checkered pistol grip and forearm, horn forend tip, swivels.

Winchester-Western Div., Olin Corp. (formerly Winchester Repeating Arms Company), New Haven, Connecticut

Winchester Model 73 Lever Action Repeating Rifle $600

Calibers: 32-20, 38-40, 44-40; a few were chambered for 22 rimfire. 15-shot magazine, also made with 6-shot half magazine. 24-inch barrel (round, half octagon, octagon). Weight, about 8½ pounds. Open rear sight, bead or blade front sight. Plain straight-grip stock and forearm. Made from 1873 to 1924. 720,610 rifles of this model were manufactured.

Winchester Model 73 Special Sporting Rifle $900

Same as Standard Model 73 Rifle, except this type has receiver case-hardened in colors, pistol-grip stock of selected walnut, octagon barrel only.

Winchester Model 73 Lever Action Carbine $750

Same as Standard Model 73 Rifle, except has 20-inch barrel, 12-shot magazine, weighs 7¼ pounds.

Winchester Model 73 Rifle — One of One Thousand $10,000+

During the late 1870's, Winchester offered Model 73 rifles of superior accuracy and extra finish, designated "One of One Thousand" grade, at a price of $100. These rifles are marked "1 of 1000" or "One of One Thousand". Only 136 of this model are known to have been manufactured. This is one of the rarest of shoulder arms and, because so very few have been sold in recent years, it is extremely difficult to assign a value; however, in the author's opinion, an "excellent" specimen would probably bring a price upward of $10,000.

Winchester Single Shot Rifle

Design by John M. Browning, this falling-block lever action arm was manufactured from 1885 to 1920 in a variety of models and chambered for most of the popular cartridges of the period, rimfire and centerfire, from 22 to 50 caliber. There are two basic styles of frame, low-wall and high-wall. The former style was used only for low-powered calibers; the latter was supplied in all calibers and was made in three types: the standard model for #3 and heavier barrels is the type commonly encountered, the thin-walled version was supplied with #1 and #2 light barrels and the thick-walled action in the heavier calibers. Made in solid frame and takedown models. The latter are generally considered less desirable. Barrels were available in five weights ranging from the lightweight #1 to the extra heavy #5 in round, half-octagon and full-octagon styles. Plain, single-set, double-set and double-Schuetzen triggers were offered. A complete listing of Winchester Single Shots is beyond the proper scope of this volume; included herein are the three standard types: Sporting Rifle, Musket and Schuetzen Rifle.

Winchester Single Shot Sporting Rifle $200

Low-wall. Plain model. Solid frame. Plain trigger. Standard lever. No. 1 28-inch round or octagon barrel. Weight, 7 pounds. Open rear sight, blade front sight. Plain stock and forearm.

Winchester Single Shot Sporting Rifle $300

High-wall. Plain model. Solid frame or takedown. Plain trigger. Standard lever. No. 3 30-inch octagon barrel. Weight, 9½ pounds. Open rear sight, blade front sight. Plain stock and forearm.

Winchester Single Shot Sporting Rifle $450

Special Grade. Same as Plain Model High-wall, but with fancy walnut stock and forearm, checkered.

Winchester Single Shot Scheutzen Rifle $1,000

Solid frame or takedown. High-wall action. Scheutzen double-set trigger. Spur finger level. No. 3 30-inch octagon barrel. Weight, 12 pounds. Vernier rear peep sight, wind-gauge front sight. Fancy walnut Scheutzen stock with checkered pistol grip and forearm, Scheutzen butt plate. Adjustable palm-rest.

Winchester Single Shot "Winder" Musket $250

Solid frame or takedown. High-wall. Plain trigger. Standard finger lever. Calibers: 22 Short, 22 Long Rifle. 28-inch round barrel. Weight, 8½ pounds. Musket rear sight, blade front sight. Military-type stock and forearm.

Winchester Single Shot Musket $200

Solid frame. Low-wall. Plain trigger. Standard finger lever. Calibers: 22 Short, 22 Long Rifle. 28-inch round barrel. Weight, 8½ pounds. Lyman rear peep sight, blade front sight. Military-type stock and forearm. *Note:* The U.S. Government purchased a large quantity of these Single Shot Muskets during World War I for training purposes. Many of these rifles were later sold through the Director of Civilian Marksmanship, to National Rifle Association members. The price was $1.50.

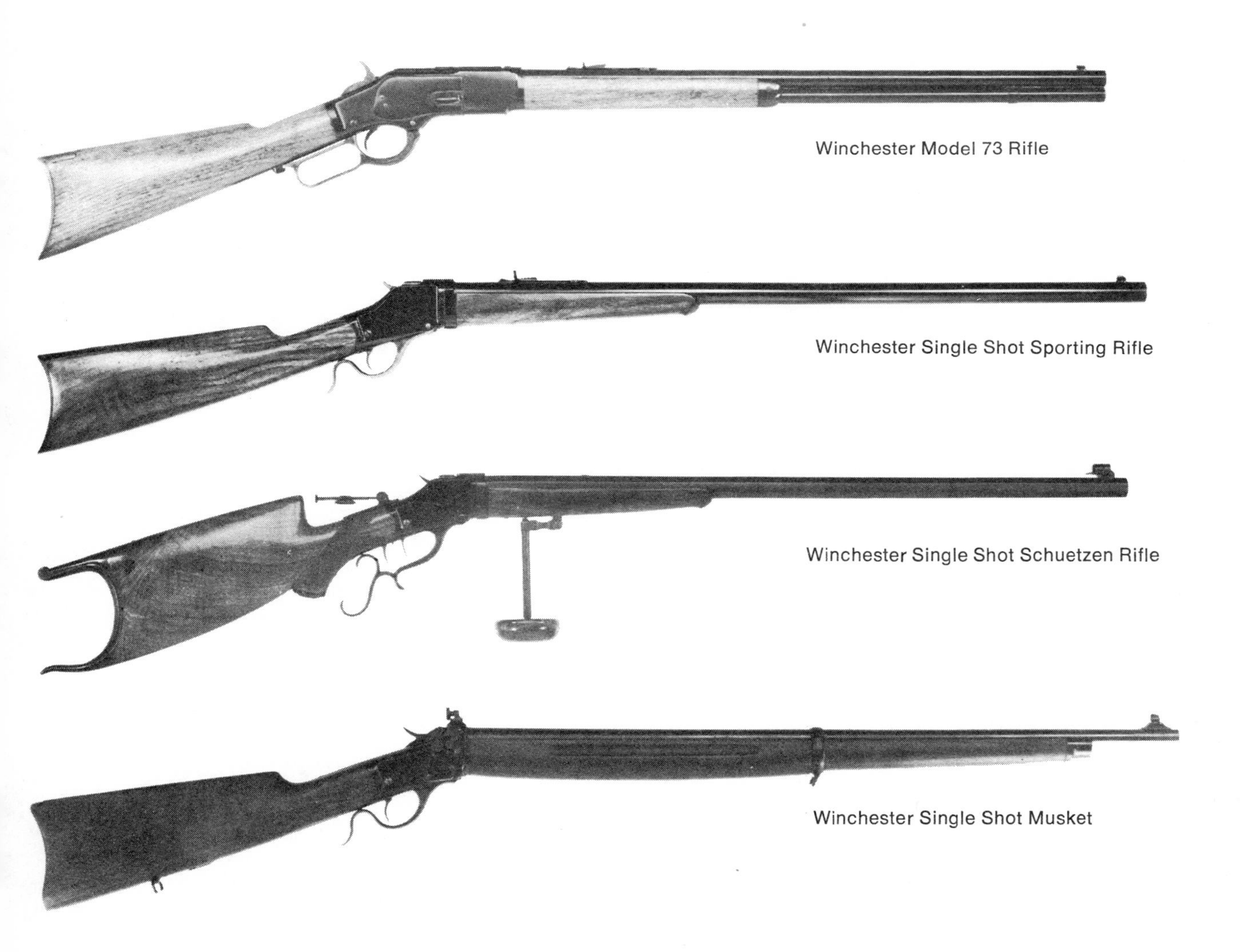

Winchester Model 73 Rifle

Winchester Single Shot Sporting Rifle

Winchester Single Shot Schuetzen Rifle

Winchester Single Shot Musket

Winchester Model 86 Rifle

Winchester Model 90

Winchester Model 86 Lever Action Repeater $450

Solid frame or takedown style. Calibers: 45/70, 38/56, 45/90/300, 40/82/260, 40/65/260, 38/56/255, 38/70/255, 40/70/330, 50/110/300, 50/100/450, 33 Win. All but the first cartridge listed are now obsolete. 33 Win. and 45/70 were the last calibers in which this model was supplied. 8-shot tubular magazine, also 4-shot half-magazine. 22 or 26-inch barrel (round, half-octagon, octagon). Weight, from 7½ pounds up. Open rear sight, bead or blade front sight. Plain straight-grip stock and forearm. Made from 1886 to 1935.

Winchester Model 86 Lever Action Carbine $600

Same as standard Model 86 rifle, except with 22-inch barrel and weighs about 7¾ pounds.

Winchester Model 90 Slide Action Repeater $145

Visible hammer. Calibers: 22 Short, Long, Long Rifle; 22 W.R.F. (not interchangeable). Tubular magazine holds 15 Short, 12 Long, 11 Long Rifle; 12 W.R.F. 24-inch octagon barrel. Weight, 5¾ pounds. Open rear sight, bead front sight. Plain straight-grip stock, grooved slide handle. Originally solid frame, after No. 15,499 all rifles of this model were take-down type. Fancy checkered pistol-grip stock, stainless steel barrel supplied at extra cost. Made from 1890 to 1932.

Winchester Model 92 Lever Action Repeating Rifle $300

Solid frame or takedown. Calibers: 25/20, 32/20, 38/40, 44/40. 13-shot tubular magazine, also 7-shot half magazine. 24-inch barrel (round, octagon, half octagon). Weight, from 6¾ pounds up. Open rear sight, bead front sight. Plain straight-grip stock and forearm. (stock illustrated was extra cost option). Made from 1892 to 1941.

Winchester Model 92 Lever Action Carbine $375

Same as Model 1892 rifle, except has 20-inch barrel, 5-shot or 11-shot magazine, weighs about 5¾ pounds.

Winchester Model 53 Lever Action Repeating Rifle $300

Modification of Model 92. Solid frame or takedown. Calibers: 25/20, 32/20, 44/40. 6-shot tubular half-magazine in solid frame model. 7-shot in takedown. 22-inch nickel steel barrel. Weight, 5½ to 6½ pounds. Open rear sight, bead front sight. Redesigned straight-grip stock and forearm. Made from 1924 to 1932.

Winchester Model 65 Lever Action Repeating Rifle $300

Improved version of Model 53. Solid frame. Calibers: 25-20 and 32-20. Six-shot tubular half-magazine. 22-inch barrel. Weight, 6½ pounds. Open rear sight, bead front sight on ramp base. Plain pistol-grip stock and forearm. Made from 1933 to 1947.

Winchester Model 65—218 Bee $600

Same as Standard Model 65, except has 24-inch barrel, peep rear sight. Made from 1938 to 1947.

Winchester Model 94 Lever Action Repeating Rifle $275

Solid frame or takedown. Calibers: 25/35, 30/30, 32/40, 32 Special, 38/55. 7-shot tubular magazine or 4-shot half-magazine. 26-inch barrel (octagon, half-octagon round). Weight, about 7¾ pounds. Open rear sight, bead front sight. Plain straight-grip stock and forearm. Made from 1894 to 1937.

Winchester Model 94 Carbine

Same as Model 94 Rifle, except 20-inch round barrel, 6-shot full-length magazine, weight about 6½ pounds. Currently manufactured in calibers 30-30 and 32 Special, solid frame only.

Pre-World-War-II
(under No. 1,300,000) **$275**
Postwar, pre-1964 . . . . **$175**
Current model . . . . **$ 80**

Winchester Model 94 Antique Carbine . . . . $ 90

Same as standard Model 94 Carbine, except has receiver with decorative scrollwork and case-hardened in colors, brass-plated loading gate, saddle ring; caliber 30-30 only. Made from 1964 to date.

Winchester "Wyoming Diamond Jubilee" Commemorative Model 94 Carbine $450

Same as standard Model 94 Carbine, except caliber 30-30 only, receiver engraved and case-hardened in colors, brass saddle ring and loading gate, souvenir medallion embedded in buttstock, commemorative inscription on barrel. 1,500 made in 1964.

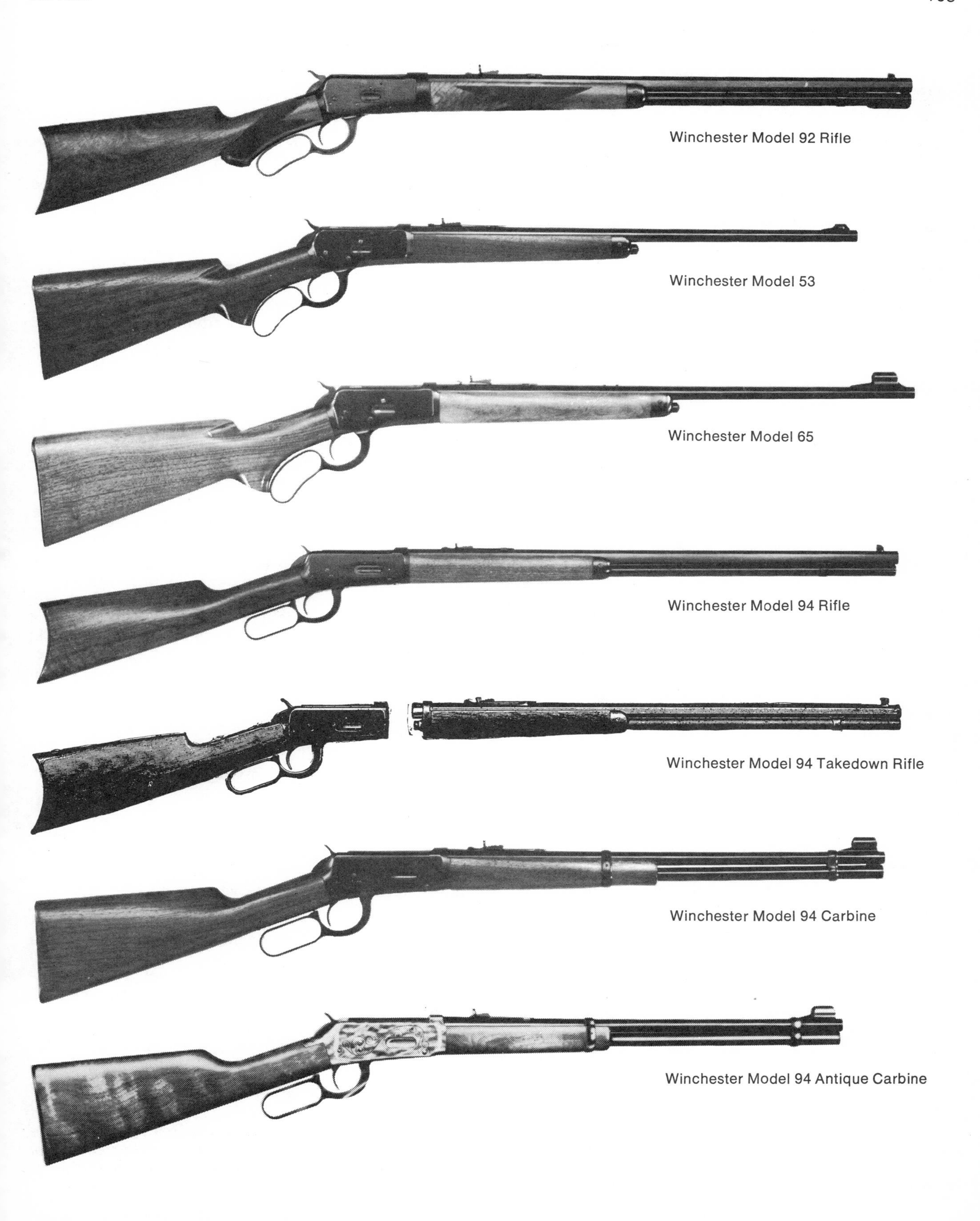

Winchester Model 92 Rifle

Winchester Model 53

Winchester Model 65

Winchester Model 94 Rifle

Winchester Model 94 Takedown Rifle

Winchester Model 94 Carbine

Winchester Model 94 Antique Carbine

Winchester Nebraska Centennial M/94 Carbine

Winchester "Nebraska Centennial" Commemorative Model 94 Carbine $350

Same as standard Model 94 Carbine, except: caliber 30-30 only; gold-plated hammer, loading gate, barrel band, and buttplate; souvenir medallion embedded in stock, commemorative inscription on barrel. 2,500 made in 1966.

Winchester "Centennial '66" Commemorative Rifle $200

Commemorates Winchester's 100th anniversary. Standard Model 94 action. Caliber, 30-30. Full-length magazine holds 8 rounds. 26-inch octagon barrel. Weight, 8 pounds. Gold-plated receiver and forearm cap. Open rear sight, post front sight. Saddle ring. Walnut buttstock and forearm with high-gloss finish, solid brass buttplate. Commemorative inscription on barrel and top tang of receiver. Made in 1966.

Winchester "Centennial '66" Carbine $200

Same as '66 Rifle, except has 20-inch barrel, magazine holds 6 rounds, weight is 7 pounds, forearm is shorter. Made in 1966.

Winchester "Centennial '66" Matched Set $500

Rifle and carbine were offered in sets with consecutive serial numbers.
Note: 100,478 Centennial '66's were made.

Winchester "Canadian Centennial" Model 67 Commemorative Rifle $150

Same as Centennial '66 Rifle except receiver—engraved with maple leaves—and forearm cap are black-chromed, butt plate is blued, commemorative inscription in gold on barrel and top tang: "Canadian Centennial 1867-1967." Made in 1967.

Winchester "Canadian Centennial" Model 67 Carbine $150

Same as Model 67 Rifle, except has 20-inch barrel, magazine holds 6 rounds, weight is 7 pounds, forearm is shorter. Made in 1967.

Winchester "Canadian Centennial" Model 67 Matched Set $350

Rifle and carbine were offered in sets with consecutive serial numbers.
Note: 90,398 Model 67's were made.

Winchester Model 94 Classic Rifle $125

Same as Model 67 Rifle, except without commemorative details; has scroll-engraved receiver, gold-plated loading gate. Made from 1968 to 1970.

Winchester Model 94 Classic Carbine $125

Same as Model 67 Carbine, except without commemorative details; has scroll-engraved receiver, gold-plated loading gate. Made from 1968 to 1970.

Winchester "Alaskan Purchase Centennial" Commemorative Model 94 Carbine $450

Same as "Wyoming" issue, except different medallion and inscription. 1,501 made in 1967.

Winchester "Buffalo Bill" Commemorative Model 94 Rifle $150

Same as Centennial '66 Rifle except receiver is black chromed scroll engraved and bears name "Buffalo Bill"; hammer, trigger, loading gate, saddle ring, forearm cap, and buttplate are nickel-plated; Buffalo Bill Memorial Assn. commemorative medallion embedded in buttstock; "Buffalo Bill Commemorative" inscribed on barrel, facsimile signature "W. F. Cody, Chief of Scouts" on tang. Made in 1968.

Winchester "Buffalo Bill" Model 94 Carbine $150

Same as Buffalo Bill Rifle, except has 20-inch barrel, magazine holds 6 rounds, weight is 7 pounds, forearm is shorter. Made in 1968.

Winchester "Buffalo Bill" Model 94 Matched Set . . $350

Rifle and carbine were offered in sets with consecutive serial numbers.
Note: 120,751 Buffalo Bill 94's were made.

Winchester "Illinois Sesquicentennial" Commemorative Model 94 Carbine $150

Same as standard Model 94 Carbine, except: caliber 30-30 only; gold-plated buttplate, trigger, loading gate, and saddle ring; receiver engraved with profile of Lincoln, commemorative inscriptions on receiver, barrel; souvenir medallion embedded in stock. 31,124 made in 1968.

Winchester "Golden Spike" Commemorative Model 94 Carbine $150

Same as standard Model 94 Carbine, except: caliber 30-30 only; gold-plated receiver, tangs and barrel bands; engraved receiver, commemorative medallion embedded in stock. 64,758 made in 1969.

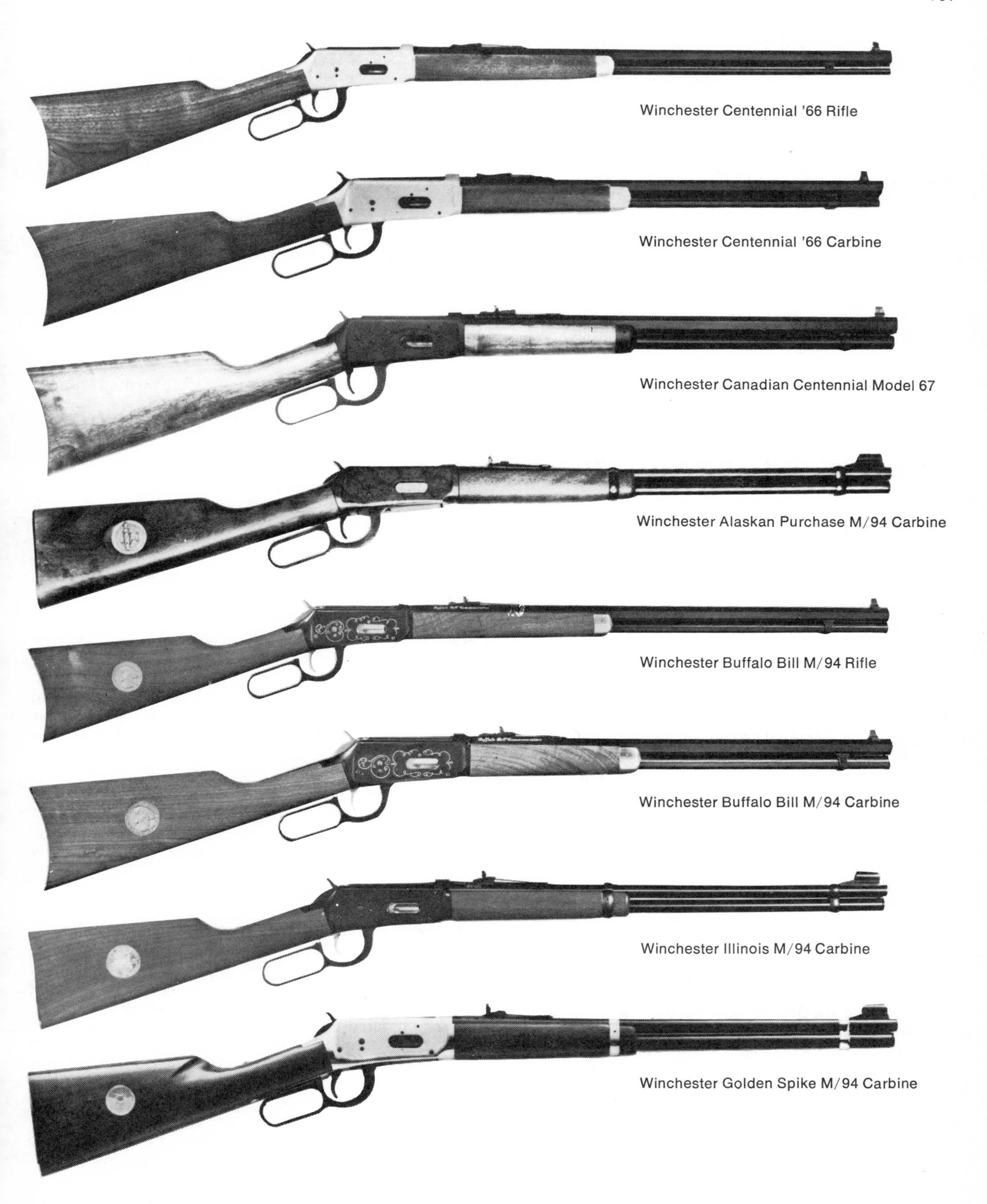

Winchester Centennial '66 Rifle

Winchester Centennial '66 Carbine

Winchester Canadian Centennial Model 67

Winchester Alaskan Purchase M/94 Carbine

Winchester Buffalo Bill M/94 Rifle

Winchester Buffalo Bill M/94 Carbine

Winchester Illinois M/94 Carbine

Winchester Golden Spike M/94 Carbine

Winchester Theodore Roosevelt M/94 Rifle

Winchester "Theodore Roosevelt" Commemorative Model 94 Rifle $150

Standard Model 94 action. Caliber, 30-30. Half magazine holds 6 rounds. 26-inch octagon barrel. Weight, 7½ pounds. White gold-plated receiver, upper tang, and fore-end cap; receiver engraved with American Eagle, "26th President 1901-1909," and Roosevelt's signature. Commemorative medallion embedded in buttstock. Saddle ring. Half pistol grip, contoured lever. Made in 1969.

Winchester "Theodore Roosevelt" Model 94 Carbine $150

Same as "Theodore Roosevelt" Rifle, except has 20-inch barrel, 6-shot full-length magazine, shorter forearm, weighs 7 pounds. Made in 1969.

Winchester "Theodore Roosevelt" Matched Set .. $350

Rifle and carbine were offered in sets with consecutive serial numbers.
Note: 49,505 "T.R." 94's were made.

Winchester "Cowboy" Commemorative Model 94 Carbine $150

Same as standard Model 94 Carbine, except: caliber 30-30 only; nickel-plated receiver, tangs, lever, barrel bands; engraved receiver, "Cowboy Commemorative" on barrel, commemorative medallion embedded in buttstock; curved buttplate. 20,915 made in 1970.

Winchester "Lone Star" Commemorative Model 94 Rifle $150

Same as "Theodore Roosevelt" Rifle, except: yellow-gold plating; "Lone Star" engraving on receiver and barrel, commemorative medallion embedded in buttstock. Made in 1970.

Winchester "Lone Star" Model 94 Carbine $150

Same as "Lone Star" Rifle, except has 20-inch barrel, 6-shot full-length magazine, shorter forearm, weighs 7 pounds. Made in 1970.

Winchester "Lone Star" Matched Set $350

Rifle and carbine were offered in sets with consecutive serial numbers.
Note: 30,669 Lone Star 94's were made.

Winchester "NRA Centennial" Model 94 Musket .. $150

Commemorates 100th anniversary of National Rifle Association of America. Stándard Model 94 action. Caliber, 30-30. 7-shot magazine. 26-inch barrel. Military folding rear sight and blade front sight. Black chrome-finished receiver engraved "NRA 1871-1971" plus scrollwork. Barrel inscribed "NRA Centennial Musket." Musket-style butt stock and full-length forearm; commemorative medallion embedded in butt stock. Weight, 7⅛ pounds. Made in 1971.

Winchester "NRA Centennial" Model 94 Rifle $150

Same as Model 64 Rifle, except has commemorative details as in "NRA Centennial" Musket (barrel inscribed "NRA Centennial Rifle"); caliber 30-30, 24-inch barrel, QD sling swivels. Made in 1971.

Winchester "NRA Centennial" Matched Set $325

Rifle and carbine were offered in sets with consecutive serial numbers.
Note: Production figure not available. These rifles were again offered in Winchester's 1972 catalog

Note on Commemorative Winchesters: Values indicated are for rifles in new condition. Data on these models supplied by Mr. Robert E. P. Cherry, Cherry's Sporting Goods, Geneseo, Illinois.

Winchester Model 55 Lever Action Repeating Rifle $350

Modification of Model 94. Solid frame or takedown. Calibers: 25/35, 30/30, 32 Win. Special. 3-shot tubular half magazine. 24-inch nickel steel barrel. Weight, about 7 pounds. Open rear sight, bead front sight. Plain straight-grip stock and forearm. Made from 1924 to 1932.

Winchester Model 64 Lever Action Repeating Rifle

Standard Grade. Improved version of Models 94 and 55. Solid frame. Calibers: 25/35, 30-30, 32 Win. Special. 5-shot tubular 2/3 magazine. 20 or 24-inch barrel. Weight about 7 pounds. Open rear sight, bead front sight on ramp with sight cover. Plain pistol-grip stock and forearm. Made from 1933 to 1956. Production resumed in 1972—caliber 30-30, 24-inch barrel—discontinued 1974.
Original model **$250**
1972-74 model **$125**

Winchester Model 64—219 Zipper $375

Same as Standard Grade Model 64, except has 26-inch barrel, peep rear sight. Made from 1937 to 1947.

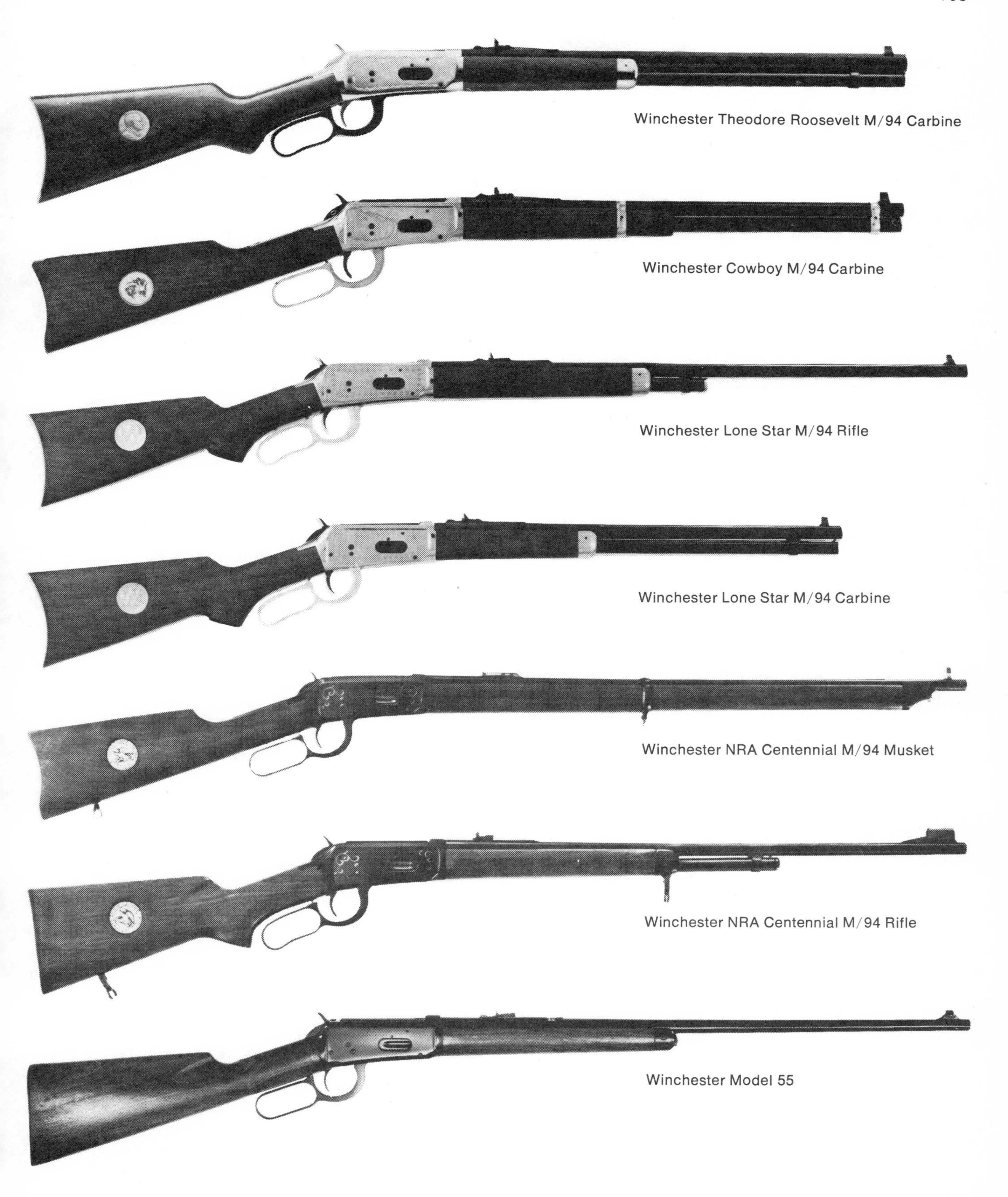

Winchester Theodore Roosevelt M/94 Carbine

Winchester Cowboy M/94 Carbine

Winchester Lone Star M/94 Rifle

Winchester Lone Star M/94 Carbine

Winchester NRA Centennial M/94 Musket

Winchester NRA Centennial M/94 Rifle

Winchester Model 55

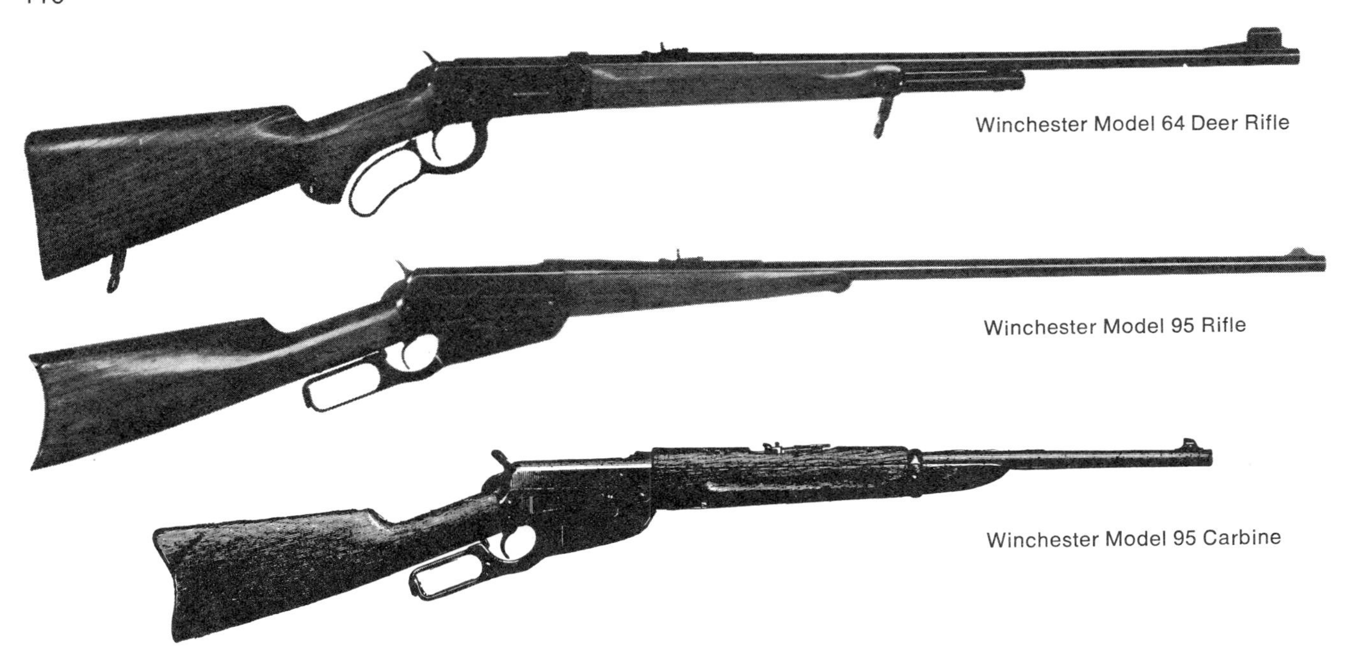

Winchester Model 64 Deer Rifle

Winchester Model 95 Rifle

Winchester Model 95 Carbine

Winchester Model 64 Deer Rifle $350

Same as Standard Model 64, calibers 30-30 and 32 Win. Special, except has checkered pistol grip and semi-beavertail forearm, swivels and sling, weighs 7¾ pounds. Made from 1933 to 1956.

Winchester Model 95 Lever Action Repeating Rifle $350

Calibers: 30-40 Krag, 30-30, 30-06, 303 British, 35 Win., 405 Win.; original model supplied in the new obsolete 38/72 and 40/72 calibers. 4-shot box magazine, except 30-40 and 303 which have 5-shot magazine. Barrel lengths: 24, 26, 28-inch (round, half-octagon, octagon). Weight, about 8½ pounds. Open rear sight, bead or blade front sight. Plain straight-grip stock and forearm (standard). Both solid frame and take-down models were available. Made from 1895 to 1931.

Winchester Model 95 Lever Action Carbine $500

Same as Model 95 Standard Rifle, except has 22-inch barrel, carbine style stock, weighs about 8 pounds, calibers 30-40, 30-30, 30-06 and 303, solid frame only.

Winchester Lee Straight-Pull Bolt Action Repeating Rifle — Musket Model $400

Commercial version of U.S. Navy Model 1895 Rifle, Caliber 6mm (1895-1897). Caliber, 236 U.S.N. 5-shot box magazine, clip-loaded. 28-inch barrel. Weight, 8½ pounds. Folding leaf rear sight, post front sight. Military type full stock with semi-pistol grip. Made from 1897 to 1902.

Winchester Lee Straight-Pull Sporting Rifle $450

Same as Musket Model except has 24-inch barrel, sporter-style stock, open sporting rear sight, bead front sight, weighs about 7½ pounds. Made from 1897 to 1902.

Winchester Model 1900 Bolt Action Single Shot Rifle $50

Takedown. Caliber, 22 Short and Long. 18-inch barrel. Weight, 2¾ pounds. Open rear sight, blade front sight. One-piece, straight-grip stock. Made from 1899 to 1902.

Winchester Model 02 Bolt Action Single Shot Rifle .. $60

Takedown. Basically the same as Model 1900 with minor improvements. Calibers: 22 Short and Long, 22 Extra Long, 22 Long Rifle. Weight, 3 pounds. Made from 1902 to 1931.

Winchester Thumb Trigger Model Bolt Action Single Shot Rifle $175

Takedown. Same as Model 02 except fired by pressing a button behind the cocking piece. Made from 1904 to 1923.

Winchester Model 04 Bolt Action Single Shot Rifle $60

Similar to Model 02. Takedown. Calibers: 22 Short, Long, Extra Long, Long Rifle. 21-inch barrel. Weight, 4 pounds. Made from 1904 to 1931.

Winchester Model 03 Self-Loading Rifle $100

Takedown. Caliber, 22 Win. Auto Rimfire. 10-shot tubular magazine in butt stock. 20-inch barrel. Weight, 5¾ pounds. Open rear sight, bead front sight. Plain straight-grip stock and forearm (stock illustrated was extra-cost option). Made from 1903 to 1936.

Winchester Model 05 Self-Loading Rifle $200

Takedown. Calibers: 32 Win., S.L., 35 Win. S.L. 5 or 10-shot detachable box magazine. 22-inch barrel. Weight, 7½ pounds. Open rear sight, bead front sight. Plain pistol-grip stock and forearm. Made from 1905 to 1920.

Winchester Model 06 Slide Action Repeater $185

Takedown. Visible hammer. Caliber, 22 Short, Long, Long Rifle. Tubular magazine holds 20 Short, 16 Long or 14 Long Rifle. 20-inch barrel. Weight, 5 pounds. Open rear sight, bead front sight. Straight-grip stock and grooved forearm. Made from 1906 to 1932.

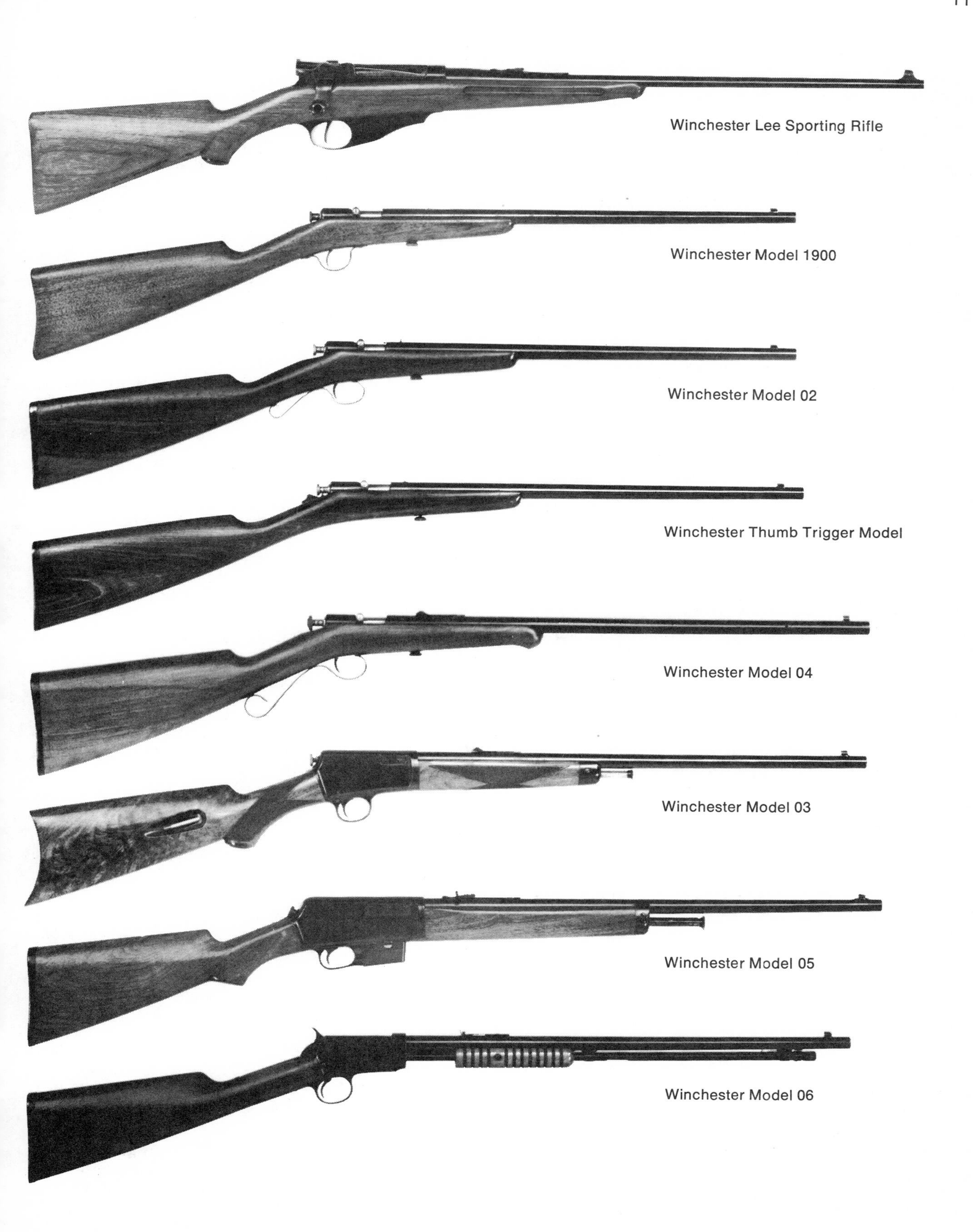

Winchester Lee Sporting Rifle

Winchester Model 1900

Winchester Model 02

Winchester Thumb Trigger Model

Winchester Model 04

Winchester Model 03

Winchester Model 05

Winchester Model 06

Winchester Model 07 Self-Loading Rifle $250

Takedown. Caliber, 351 Win. S.L. 5-shot or 10-shot detachable box magazine. 20-inch barrel. Weight, 7¾ pounds. Open rear sight, bead front sight. Plain pistol-grip stock and forearm. Made from 1907 to 1957.

Winchester Model 10 Self-Loading Rifle $200

Takedown. Caliber, 401 Win. S.L. 4-shot detachable box magazine. 20-inch barrel. Weight, 8½ pounds. Open rear sight, bead front sight. Plain pistol-grip stock and forearm. Made from 1910 to 1936.

Winchester Model 52 Bolt Action Target Rifle

Standard barrel. First type. Caliber, 22 Long Rifle. 5-shot box magazine. 28-inch barrel. Weight, 8¾ pounds. Folding leaf peep rear sight, blade front sight—standard sights, various other combinations available. Scope bases. Semi-military type target stock with pistol-grip; original model has grasping grooves in forearm; higher comb and semi-beavertail forearm on later models. Numerous changes were made in this model, the most important being the adoption of the speed lock in 1929; Model 52 rifles produced prior to this change are generally referred to as "slow lock" models. Last arms of this type bore serial numbers followed by the letter "A." Made from 1919 to 1937.

Slow lock model $150
Speed lock model $175

Winchester Model 52 Heavy Barrel $185

First type. Speed lock. Same general specifications as Standard Model 52 of this type, except has heavier barrel, Lyman 17G front sight, weighs 10 pounds.

Winchester Model 52 Sporting Rifle $500

First type. Same as Standard Model 52 of this type, except has lightweight 24-inch barrel, Lyman No. 48 receiver sight and gold bead front sight on hooded ramp, de luxe checkered sporting stock with cheekpiece, black forend tip, etc., weighs 7¾ pounds.

Winchester Model 52-B Bolt Action Target Rifle ... $175

Standard Barrel. Extensively redesigned action. Supplied with choice of "Target" stock, an improved version of the previous Model 52 stock, or "Marksman" stock with high comb, full pistol grip and beavertail forearm. Weight, 9 pounds. Offered with a wide choice of target sight combinations (Lyman, Marble-Goss, Redfield, Vaver, Winchester); value shown is for rifle less sight equipment. Other specifications as shown for first type. Made from 1935 to 1947.

Winchester Model 52-B Heavy Barrel $185

Same general specifications as Standard Model 52-B, except has heavier barrel, weighs 11 pounds.

Winchester Model 52-B Bull Gun $200

Same general specifications as Standard Model 52-B, except has extra heavy barrel, Marksman stock only, weighs 12 pounds.

Winchester Model 52-B Sporting Rifle $500

Model 52-B action, otherwise same as Model 52 Sporting Rifle.

Winchester Model 52-C Bolt Action Target Rifle .. $185

Heavy Barrel. Improved action with "Micro-Motion" trigger mechanism and new type "Marksman" stock. General specifications, same as shown for previous models. Made from 1947 to 1961. Value shown is for rifle less sights.

Winchester Model 52-C Standard Barrel $170

Same general specifications as Heavy Barrel Model, except has standard weight barrel, weighs 9¾ pounds. Made from 1947 to 1961.

Winchester Model 52-C Bull Gun $200

Same general specifications as Heavy Barrel Model, except has extra heavy "bull" barrel, weighs 12 pounds. Made from 1952 to 1961.

Winchester Model 52-D Bolt Action Target Rifle .. $200

Redesigned Model 52 action, single shot. Caliber, 22 Long Rifle. 28-inch standard or heavy barrel, free-floating, with blocks for standard target scopes. Weight: with standard barrel, 9¾ pounds; with heavy barrel, 11 pounds. Restyled Marksman stock with accessory channel and fore-end stop, rubber buttplate. Made from 1961 to date. Value shown is for rifle without sights.

Winchester Model 54 Bolt Action High Power Sporting Rifle $225

First type. Calibers: 270 Win., 7x57mm, 30-30, 30-06, 7.65x53mm, 9x57mm. 5-shot box magazine. 24-inch barrel. Weight, 7¾ pounds. Open rear sight, bead front sight. Checkered stock with pistol grip, tapered forearm with "schnabel" tip. This type has two-piece firing pin. Made from 1925 to 1930.

Winchester Model 54 Carbine $275

First type. Same as Model 54 rifle, except has 20-inch barrel, plain lightweight stock with grasping grooves in forearm. Weight, 7¼ pounds.

Winchester Model 54 Bolt Action High Power Sporting Rifle $250

Standard grade. Improved type with speed lock and one-piece firing pin. Calibers: 22 Hornet, 220 Swift, 250/3000, 257 Roberts, 270 Win., 7x57mm, 30-06. 5-shot box magazine. 24-inch barrel, 26-inch in cal. 220 Swift. Weight, about 8 pounds. Open rear sight, bead front sight on ramp. NRA type stock with checkered pistol grip and forearm. Made from 1930 to 1936.

Winchester Model 54 Carbine $300

Improved type. Same as Model 54 Standard Grade Sporting Rifle of this type, except has 20-inch barrel. Weight, about 7½ pounds. This model may have either NRA type stock or the lightweight stock found on the first type Model 54 Carbine.

Winchester Model 07

Winchester Model 10

Winchester Model 52 Standard Barrel

Winchester Model 52B Standard Barrel

Winchester Model 52B Sporter

Winchester Model 52C Heavy Barrel

Winchester Model 52D Heavy Barrel

Winchester Model 54 Standard Grade, Improved Type

Winchester Model 54 Super Grade

Winchester Model 54 National Match

Winchester Model 56

Winchester Model 57

Winchester Model 58

Winchester Model 54 Super Grade **$300**

Same as standard Model 54 Sporter, except has de luxe stock with cheekpiece, black forend tip, pistol-grip cap, quick detachable swivels, 1-inch sling strap.

Winchester Model 54 Sniper's Rifle **$300**

Same as standard Model 54, except has heavy 26-inch barrel, Lyman #48 rear peep sight and blade front sight, semi-military stock, weighs 11¾ pounds, caliber 30-06 only.

Winchester Model 54 Sniper's Match Rifle **$350**

Similar to the earlier Model 54 Sniper's Rifle, except has Marksman type target stock, scope bases, weighs 12½ pounds. Available in same calibers as Model 54 Standard Grade.

Winchester Model 54 National Match Rifle **$300**

Same as standard Model 54, except has Lyman sights, scope bases, Marksman type target stock, weighs 9½ pounds. Same calibers as standard model.

Winchester Model 54 Target Rifle **$325**

Same as standard Model 54, except has 24-inch medium-weight barrel (26-inch in cal. 220 Swift), Lyman sights, scope bases, Marksman type target stock, weighs 10½ pounds, same calibers as standard model.

Winchester Model 56 Bolt Action Sporting Rifle **$70**

Solid frame. Caliber, 22 Long Rifle, 22 Short. 5 or 10-shot detachable box magazine. 22-inch barrel. Weight, 4¾ pounds. Open rear sight, bead front sight. Plain pistol-grip stock with "schnabel" forend. Made from 1926 to 1929.

Winchester Model 57 Bolt Action Target Rifle **$100**

Solid frame. Same as Model 56, except available (until 1929) in 22 Short as well as Long Rifle, has semi-military style target stock, swivels and web sling, Lyman peep rear sight, blade front sight, weighs 5 pounds. Made from 1926 to 1936.

Winchester Model 58 Bolt Action Single Shot Rifle . . **$40**

Similar to Model 02. Takedown. Caliber, 22 Short, Long, Long Rifle. 18-inch barrel. Weight, 3 pounds. Open rear sight, blade front sight. Plain, flat, straight grip stock. Made from 1928 to 1931.

Winchester Model 60A

Winchester Model 61

Winchester Model 62

Winchester Model 63

Winchester Model 59 Bolt Action Single Shot Rifle $60

Improved version of Model 58, has 23-inch barrel, redesigned stock with pistol-grip, weighs 4½ pounds. Made in 1930.

Winchester Model 60 Bolt Action Single Shot Rifle . . $45

Redesign of Model 59. Caliber, 22 Short, Long, Long Rifle. 23-inch barrel (27-inch after 1933). Weight, 4¼ pounds. Open rear sight, blade front sight. Plain stock with pistol grip. Made from 1930 to 1934.

Winchester Model 60A Target Rifle $60

Essentially the same as Model 60, except has Lyman peep rear sight and square top front sight, semi-military target stock and web sling, weighs 5½ pounds. Made from 1932 to 1939.

Winchester Model 61 Hammerless Slide Action Repeater $175

Takedown. Caliber, 22 Short, Long, Long Rifle. Tubular magazine holds 20 Short, 16 Long, 14 Long Rifle. 24-inch round barrel. Weight, 5½ pounds. Open rear sight, bead front sight. Plain pistol-grip stock, grooved semi-beavertail slide handle. Also available with 24-inch full octagon barrel and chambered for 22 L.R. only, 22 Short only or 22 W.R.F. only. Made from 1932 to 1963.

Winchester Model 61 Magnum $225

Same as standard Model 61, except chambered for 22 R.F. Magnum cartridge; magazine holds 12 rounds. Made from 1960 to 1963.

Winchester Model 62 Visible Hammer Slide Action Repeater $175

Modernized version of Model 1890. Caliber, 22 Short, Long, Long Rifle. Tubular magazine holds 20 Short, 16 Long or 14 Long Rifle. 23-inch barrel. Weight, 5½ pounds. Plain straight grip stock, grooved semi-beavertail slide handle. Also available in Gallery Model chambered for 22 Short only. Made from 1932 to 1959.

Winchester Model 63 Self-Loading Rifle $225

Takedown. Caliber, 22 Long Rifle High Speed only. 10-shot tubular magazine in butt stock. 23-inch barrel. Weight, 5½ pounds. Open rear sight, bead front sight. Plain pistol-grip stock and forearm. Originally available with 20-inch barrel as well as 23-inch. Made from 1933 to 1959.

Winchester Model 67 Bolt Action Single Shot Rifle . . $45

Takedown. Calibers: 22 Short, Long, Long Rifle, 22 L.R. shot (smoothbore), 22 W.R.F. 27-inch barrel. Weight, 5 pounds. Open rear sight, bead front sight. Plain pistol-grip stock (original model had grasping grooves in fore-arm). Made from 1934 to 1963.

Winchester Model 67 Boy's Rifle $40

Same as Standard Model 67, except has shorter stock, 20-inch barrel, weighs 4¼ pounds.

Winchester Model 68 Bolt Action Single Shot Rifle . . $65

Same as Model 67, except has rear peep sight. Made from 1934 to 1946.

Winchester Model 69 Bolt Action Repeating Rifle . . $70

Takedown. Caliber, 22 Short, Long, Long Rifle. 5 or 10-shot box magazine. 25-inch barrel. Weight, 5½ pounds. Peep or open rear sight. Plain pistol-grip stock. Made from 1935 to 1963.

Winchester Model 69 Target Rifle $75

Same as Standard Model 69, except has Winchester peep rear sight, blade front sight, swivels and sling.

Winchester Model 69 Match Rifle $75

Same as Model 69 Target except has Lyman #57EW receiver sight.

Winchester Model 70 Bolt Action Repeating Rifle

Introduced in 1937, this model was offered in a number of styles and calibers; only minor design changes were made over a period of 27 years. More than one-half million of these rifles were sold. In 1964, the original Model 70 was superseded by a revised version with re-designed action, improved bolt, swaged barrel, restyled stock (barrel free-floating). This model again underwent major changes in 1972—most visible: new stock with contrasting fore-end tip and grip cap, cut checkering (instead of impressed as in predecessor), knurled bolt handle. Action (machined from a solid block of steel) and barrel are chrome molybdenum steel.

Winchester Model 70 Standard Grade $275

Calibers: 22 Hornet, 220 Swift, 243 Win., 250-3000, 257 Roberts, 270 Win., 7x57mm, 30-06, 308 Win., 300 H&H Mag., 375 H&H Mag. 5-shot box magazine (4-shot in Magnum calibers). 24-inch barrel standard; 26-inch in 220 Swift and 300 Mag.; 25-inch in 375 Mag.; at one time, a 20-inch barrel was available. Open rear sight, hooded ramp front sight. Checkered walnut stock; Monte Carlo comb standard on later production. Weight, from 7¾ pounds, depending upon caliber and barrel length. Made from 1937 to 1963.

Winchester Model 70 Super Grade $450

Same as Standard Grade Model 70, except has de luxe stock with cheekpiece, black forend tip, pistol-grip cap, quick detachable swivels, sling. Discontinued 1960.

Winchester Model 70 Featherweight Sporter $250

Same as Standard Model 70, except has redesigned stock and 22-inch barrel, aluminum trigger guard, floor-plate and buttplate. Calibers: 243 Win., 264 Win. Mag., 270 Win., 308 Win., 30-06, 358 Win. Weight, about 6½ pounds. Made from 1952 to 1963.

Winchester Model 70 Super Grade Featherweight . . $425

Same as Standard Grade Featherweight except has de luxe stock with cheekpiece, black fore-end tip, pistol grip cap, quick detachable swivels, sling. Discontinued 1960.

Winchester Model 70 National Match Rifle $350

Same as Standard Model 70, except has scope bases, Marksman type target stock, weighs 9½ pounds, caliber 30-06 only. Discontinued 1960.

Winchester Model 70 Target Rifle $375

Same as Standard Model 70, except has 24-inch medium weight barrel, scope bases, Marksman stock, weight about 10½ pounds. Originally offered in all of the Model 70 calibers, this rifle later was available in calibers 243 Win. and 30-06. Discontinued 1963.

Winchester Model 70 Bull Gun $400

Same as Standard Model 70, except has heavy 28-inch barrel, scope bases, Marksman stock, weighs 13¼ pounds, caliber 300 H&H Magnum and 30-06 only. Discontinued 1963.

Winchester Model 70 Varmint Rifle $350

Same general specifications as Standard Model 70, except has 26-inch heavy barrel, scope bases, special varminter stock. Calibers, 220 Swift, 243 Win. Made from 1956 to 1963.

Winchester Model 70 African Rifle $500

Same general specifications as Super Grade Model 70, except has 25-inch barrel, 3-shot magazine, Monte Carlo stock with recoil pad. Weight, about 9½ pounds. Caliber, 458 Winchester Magnum. Made from 1956 to 1963.

Winchester Model 70 Westerner $300

Same as Standard Model 70, except calibers 264 Win. Mag., 300 Win. Mag.; 3-shot magazine; 26-inch barrel in former caliber, 24-inch in latter; weight, about 8¼ pounds. Made from 1960 to 1963.

Winchester Model 70 Alaskan $300

Same as Standard Model 70, except calibers 338 Win. Mag., 375 H&H Mag.; 3-shot magazine in 338, 4-shot in 375 caliber; 25-inch barrel; stock with recoil pad; weight, 8 pounds in 338, 8¾ pounds in 375 caliber. Made from 1960 to 1963.

Winchester Model 70 Standard $140

Calibers: 22-250, 222 Rem., 225, 243, 270, 308 Win., 30-06. 5-shot box magazine. 22-inch barrel. Weight, 7½ pounds. Open rear sight, hooded ramp front sight. Monte Carlo stock with cheekpiece, checkering, swivels. Made from 1964 to 1971.

Winchester Model 67

Winchester Model 68

Winchester Model 69

Winchester Model 69 Match

Winchester Model 70 Standard (pre-1964)

Winchester Model 70 Standard (1964)

Winchester Model 70 Magnum (1964)

Winchester Model 70 African (1964)

Winchester Model 70 Target (1964)

Winchester Model 70 DeLuxe (1964)

Winchester Model 70 Mannlicher (1964)

Winchester Model 70 Magnum

Calibers: 7mm Rem. Mag.; 264, 300, 338 Win. Mag.; 375 H&H Mag. 3-shot magazine. 24-inch barrel. Weight, 7¾ to 8½ pounds. Open rear sight, hooded ramp front sight. Monte Carlo stock with cheekpiece, checkering, twin stock-reinforcing bolts, recoil pad, swivels. Made from 1964 to 1971.

Caliber 375 H&H Mag. **$175**
Other calibers **$150**

Winchester Model 70 African **$275**

Caliber, 458 Win. Mag. 3-shot magazine. 22-inch barrel. Weight, 8½ pounds. Special "African" sights. Monte Carlo stock with ebony fore-end tip, hand checkering, twin stock-reinforcing bolts, recoil pad, QD swivels. Made from 1964 to 1971.

Winchester Model 70 Varmint **$165**

Same as Model 70 Standard, except has 24-inch target weight barrel, blocks for target scope, no sights, available in calibers 22-250, 222 Rem., and 243 Win. only. Weight, 9¾ pounds. Made from 1964 to 1971.

Winchester Model 70 Target **$200**

Calibers, 308 Win. (7.62 NATO) and 30-06. 5-shot box magazine. 24-inch heavy barrel. Blocks for target scope, no sights. Weight, 10¼ pounds. High comb Marksman style stock, aluminum hand stop, swivels. Made from 1964 to 1971.

Winchester Model 70 De Luxe **$260**

Calibers: 243, 270 Win., 30-06, 300 Win. Mag. 5-shot box magazine (3-shot in Magnum). 22-inch barrel (24-inch in Magnum). Weight, 7½ pounds. Open rear sight, hooded ramp front sight. Monte Carlo stock with ebony fore-end tip, hand checkering, QD swivels, recoil pad on Magnum. Made from 1964 to 1971.

Winchester Model 70 Mannlicher **$300**

Calibers: 243, 270, 308 Win., 30-06. 5-shot box magazine. 19-inch barrel. Open rear sight, hooded ramp front sight. Weight, 7½ pounds. Mannlicher-style stock with Monte Carlo comb and cheekpiece, checkering, steel fore-end cap, QD swivels. Made from 1969 to 1971.

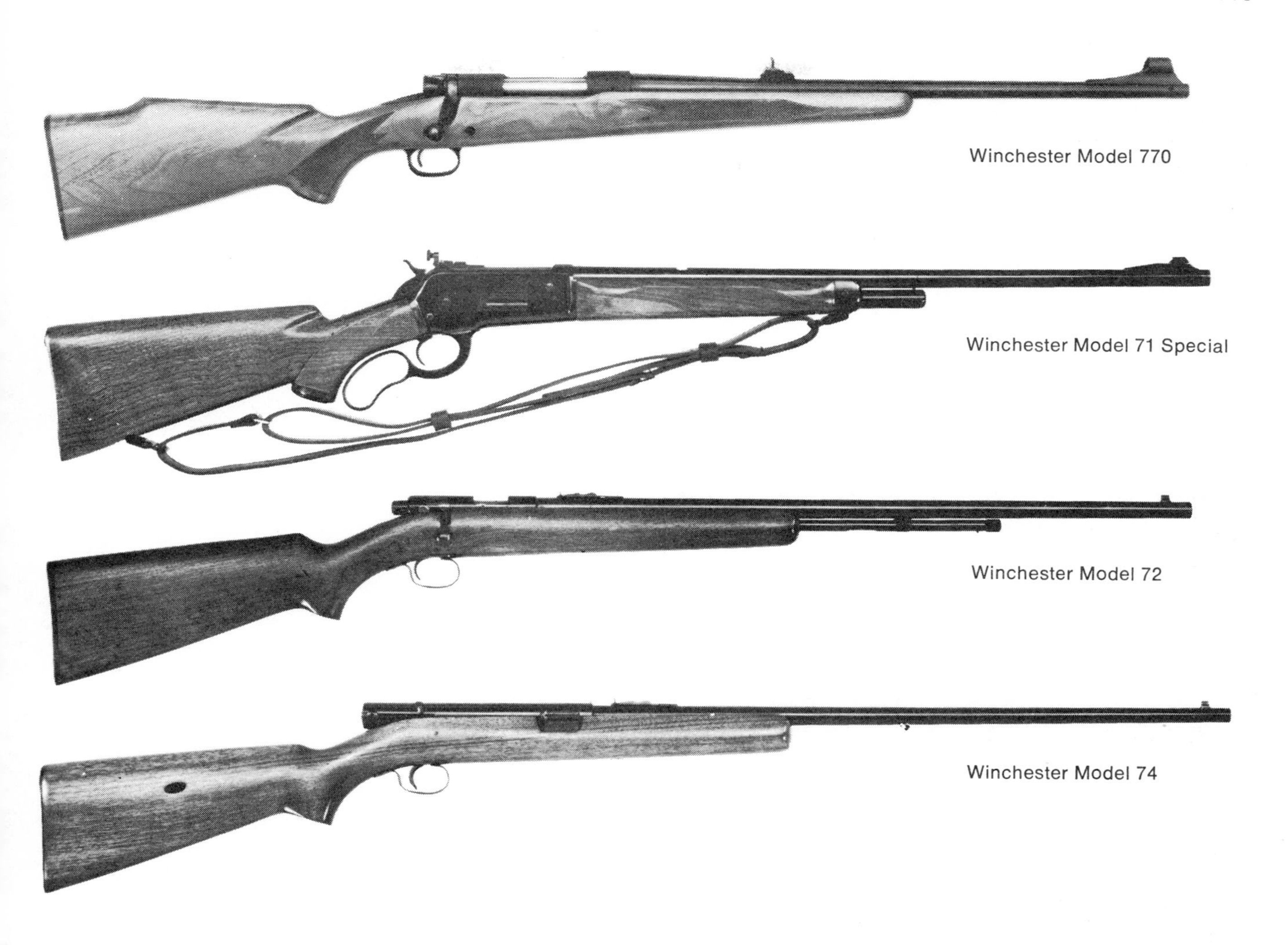

Winchester Model 770

Winchester Model 71 Special

Winchester Model 72

Winchester Model 74

Winchester Model 70 International Army Match Rifle $300

Caliber, 308 Win. (7.62 NATO). 5-shot box magazine. 24-inch heavy barrel. Externally adjustable trigger. Weight, 11 pounds. ISU stock with military oil finish, forearm rail for standard accessories, vertically adjustable butt-plate. Made in 1971. Value shown is for rifle without sights.

Winchester Model 770 Bolt Action Sporting Rifle . $105

Model 70 type action. Calibers: 22-250, 222 Rem., 243, 270 Win., 30-06. 4-shot box magazine. 22-inch barrel. Open rear sight, hooded ramp front sight. Weight, 7⅛ pounds. Monte Carlo stock, checkered, swivels. Made from 1969 to 1971.

Winchester Model 770 Magnum $125

Same as standard Model 770, except 24-inch barrel, weight 7¼ pounds, recoil pad. Calibers: 7mm Rem. Mag., 264 and 300 Win. Mag. Made from 1969 to 1971.

Winchester Model 71 Special Lever Action Repeating Rifle $450

Solid frame. Caliber, 348 Win. 4-shot tubular magazine, 20 or 24-inch barrel. Weight, 8 pounds. Open rear sight, bead front sight on ramp with hood. Walnut stock, checkered pistol grip and forearm, grip cap, quick-detachable swivels and sling. Made from 1935 to 1957.

Winchester Model 71 Standard Grade $350

Plain Model. Same as Model 71 Special, except lacks checkering, grip cap, sling and swivels.

Winchester Model 72 Bolt Action Repeating Rifle . . $50

Tubular magazine. Takedown. Caliber, 22 Short, Long, Long Rifle. Magazine holds 20 Short, 16 Long or 15 Long Rifle. 25-inch barrel. Weight, 5¾ pounds. Peep or open rear sight, bead front sight. Plain pistol-grip stock. Made from 1938 to 1959.

Winchester Model 74 Self-Loading Rifle $75

Takedown. Calibers: 22 Short only, 22 Long Rifle only. Tubular magazine in butt stock holds 20 Short, 14 Long Rifle. 24-inch barrel. Weight, 6¼ pounds. Open rear sight, bead front sight. Plain pistol-grip stock, one-piece. Made from 1939 to 1955.

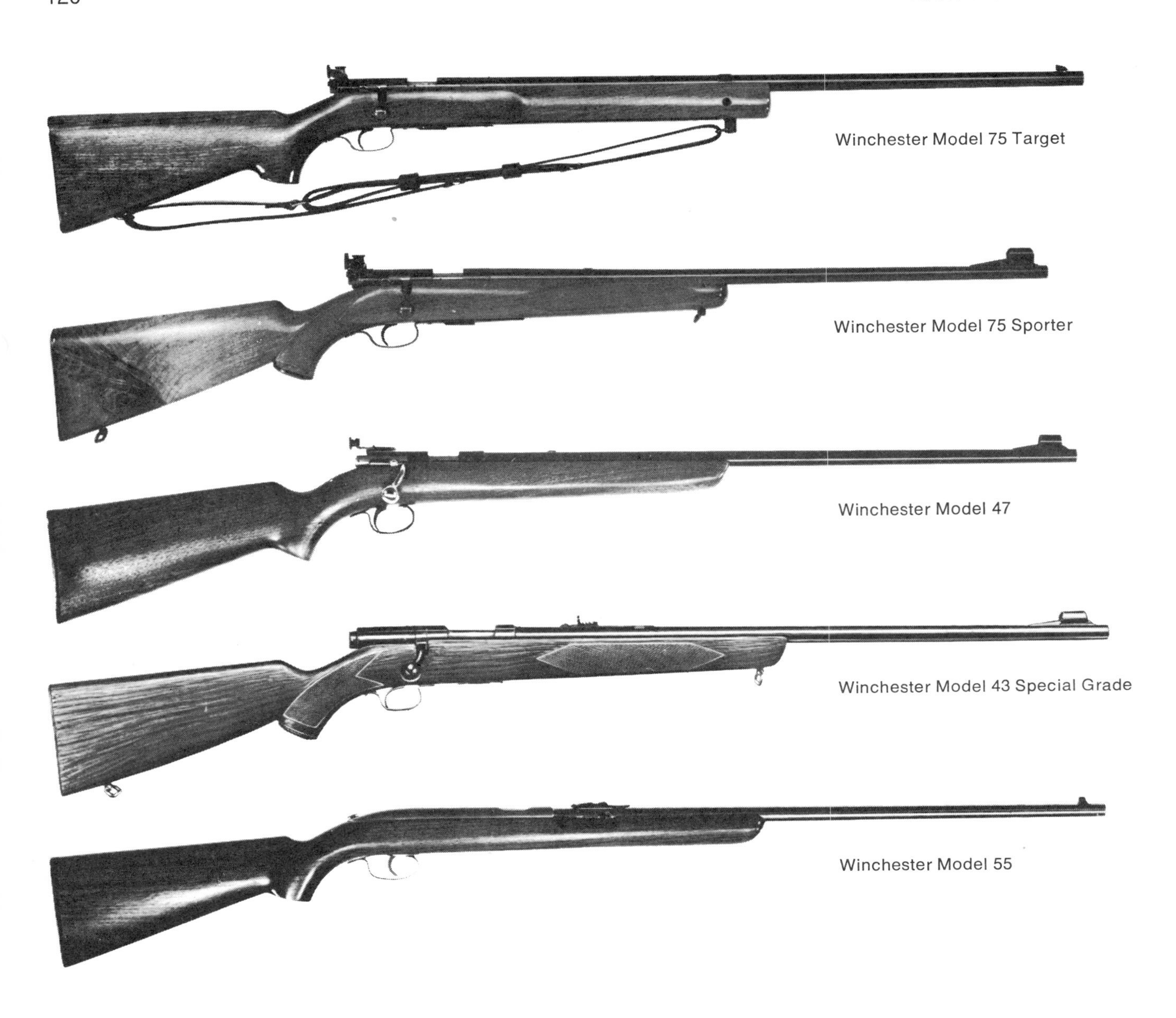
Winchester Model 75 Target

Winchester Model 75 Sporter

Winchester Model 47

Winchester Model 43 Special Grade

Winchester Model 55

Winchester Model 75 Bolt Action Target Rifle $135

Caliber, 22 Long Rifle. 5 or 10-shot box magazine. 28-inch barrel. Weight, 8¾ pounds. Target sights (Lyman, Redfield or Winchester). Target stock with pistol grip and semi-beavertail forearm, swivels and sling. Made from 1938 to 1959.

Winchester Model 75 Sporting Rifle $150

Same as Model 75 Target, except has 24-inch barrel, checkered sporter stock, open rear sight and bead front sight on hooded ramp, weighs 5½ pounds.

Winchester Model 47 Bolt Action Single Shot Rifle . . $40

Caliber, 22 Short, Long, Long Rifle. 25-inch barrel. Weight, 5½ pounds. Peep or open rear sight, bead front sight. Plain pistol-grip stock. Made from 1949 to 1954.

Winchester Model 43 Bolt Action Sporting Rifle . $170

Standard Grade. Calibers: 218 Bee, 22 Hornet, 25-20, 32-20. (latter two discontinued 1950). 3-shot detachable box magazine. 24-inch barrel. Weight, 6 pounds. Open rear sight, bead front sight on hooded ramp. Plain pistol-grip stock with swivels. Made from 1949 to 1957.

Winchester Model 43 Special Grade $195

Same as Standard Model 43, except has checkered pistol grip and forearm, grip cap.

Winchester Model 55 "Automatic" Single Shot Rifle $75

Caliber, 22 Short, Long, Long Rifle. 22-inch barrel. Open rear sight, bead front sight. One-piece walnut stock. Weight, about 5½ pounds. Made from 1958 to 1960.

Winchester Model 88

Winchester Model 77 Clip Type

Winchester Model 77 Tubular Magazine

Winchester Model 100

Winchester Model 250 Standard

Winchester Model 88 Lever Action Rifle $180

Hammerless. Calibers: 243 Win., 284 Win., 308 Win., 358 Win. 4-shot box magazine. 3-shot in pre-1963 models and in current 284. 22-inch barrel. Weight, about 7¼ pounds. One-piece walnut stock with pistol grip, swivels (1965 and later models have basket-weave ornamentation instead of checkering). Made from 1955 to 1973. *Note:* 243 and 358 introduced 1956, latter discontinued 1964; 284 introduced 1963.

Winchester Model 77 Semi-Automatic Rifle, Clip Type $75

Solid frame. Caliber, 22 Long Rifle. 8-shot clip magazine. 22-inch barrel. Weight, about 5½ pounds. Open rear sight, bead front sight. Plain, one-piece stock with pistol grip. Made from 1955 to 1963.

Winchester Model 77, Tubular Magazine Type $75

Same as Model 77 — clip type, except has tubular magazine holding 15 rounds. Made from 1955 to 1963.

Winchester Model 100 Autoloading Rifle $165

Gas-operated semi-automatic. Calibers: 243, 284, 308 Win. 4-shot clip magazine (3-shot in 284). 22-inch barrel. Weight, 7¼ pounds. Open rear sight, hooded ramp front sight. One-piece stock with pistol grip, basket-weave checkering, grip cap, sling swivels. Made from 1961 to 1973.

Winchester Model 250 Standard Lever Action Rifle $50

Hammerless. Caliber, 22 Short, Long or Long Rifle. Tubular magazine holds 21 Short, 17 Long, 15 L.R. 20½ inch barrel. Open rear sight, ramp front sight. Weight, about 5 pounds. Plain stock and forearm on early production; later model has checkering. Made from 1963 to 1973.

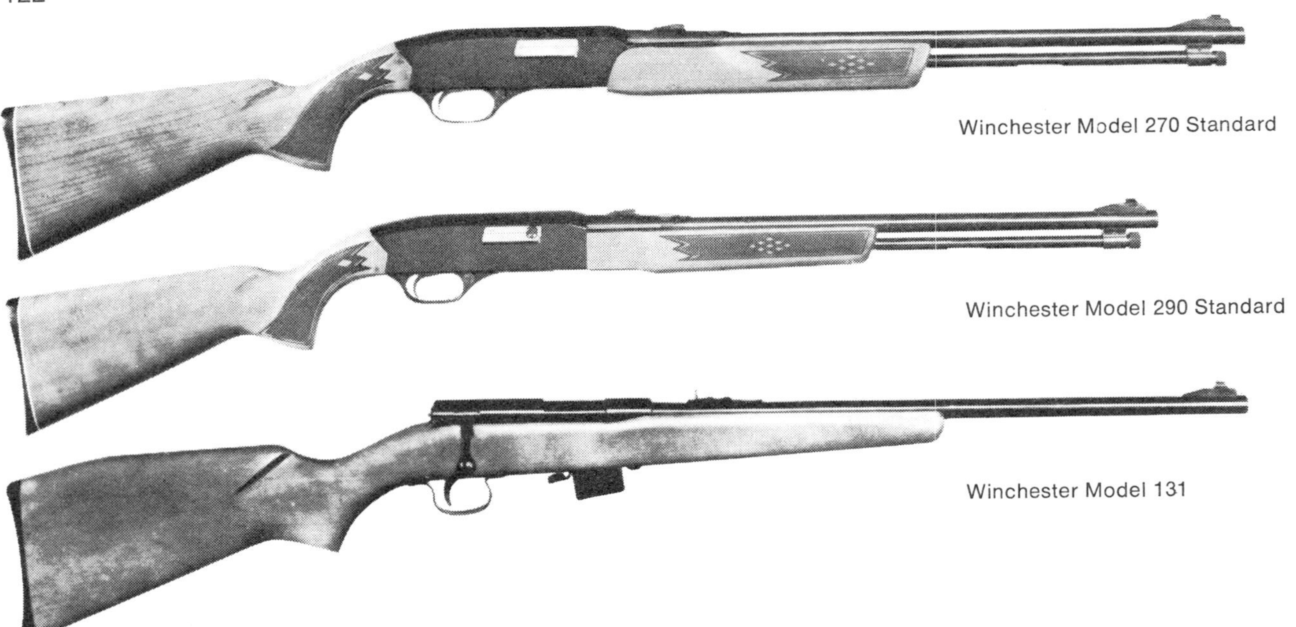

Winchester Model 270 Standard

Winchester Model 290 Standard

Winchester Model 131

Winchester Model 255 Standard Rifle **$60**

Same as Model 250 Standard Rifle, except chambered for 22 Win. Magnum R.F. cartridge. Magazine holds 11 rounds. Made from 1964 to 1970.

Winchester Model 250 De Luxe Rifle **$65**

Same as Model 250 Standard Rifle, except has fancy walnut Monte Carlo stock and forearm, sling swivels. Made from 1965 to 1971.

Winchester Model 255 De Luxe Rifle **$75**

Same as Model 250 DeLuxe Rifle, except chambered for 22 Win. Magnum R.F. cartridge. Magazine holds 11 rounds. Made from 1965 to 1973.

Winchester Model 270 Standard Slide Action Rifle $50

Hammerless. Caliber, 22 Short, Long, or Long Rifle. Tubular magazine holds 21 Short, 17 Long, 15 L.R. 20½ inch barrel. Open rear sight, ramp front sight. Weight, about 5 pounds. Early production had plain walnut stock and forearm (slide handle); latter also furnished in plastic (Cycolac); current model has checkering. Made from 1963 to 1973.

Winchester Model 275 Standard Rifle **$60**

Same as Model 270 Standard Rifle, except chambered for 22 Win. Magnum R.F. cartridge. Magazine holds 11 rounds. Made from 1964 to 1970.

Winchester Model 270 De Luxe Rifle **$65**

Same as Model 270 Standard Rifle, except has fancy walnut Monte Carlo stock and forearm. Made from 1965 to date.

Winchester Model 275 De Luxe Rifle **$75**

Same as Model 270 DeLuxe Rifle, except chambered for 22 Win. Magnum R.F. cartridge. Magazine holds 11 rounds. Made from 1965 to 1970.

Winchester Model 290 Standard Semi-Automatic Rifle $55

Caliber, 22 Long or Long Rifle. Tubular magazine holds 17 Long, 15 L.R. 20½-inch barrel. Open rear sight, ramp front sight. Weight, about 5 pounds. Plain stock and forearm on early production; current model has checkering. Made from 1963 to date.

Winchester Model 290 De Luxe Rifle **$70**

Same as Model 290 Standard Rifle, except has fancy walnut Monte Carlo stock and forearm. Made from 1965 to 1973.

Winchester Model 131 Bolt Action Repeating Rifle .. **$40**

Caliber, 22 Short, Long or Long Rifle. 7-shot clip magazine. 20¾-inch barrel. Weight, 5 pounds. Open rear sight, ramp front sight. Plain Monte Carlo stock. Made from 1967 to 1970.

Winchester Model 135 .... **$50**

Same as Model 131, except chambered for 22 Win. Magnum R.F. cartridge. Magazine holds 5 rounds. Made in 1967.

Winchester Model 145 .... **$50**

Same as Model 131, except tubular magazine (9-round) and chambered for 22 Win. Magnum R.F. cartridge. Made in 1967.

Z-B Rifle manufactured by Ceska Zbrojovka, Brno, Czechoslovakia

Z-B Mauser Varmint Rifle **$400**

Same as Brno Hornet Rifle. See listing of that rifle for specifications.

Section II
SHOTGUNS

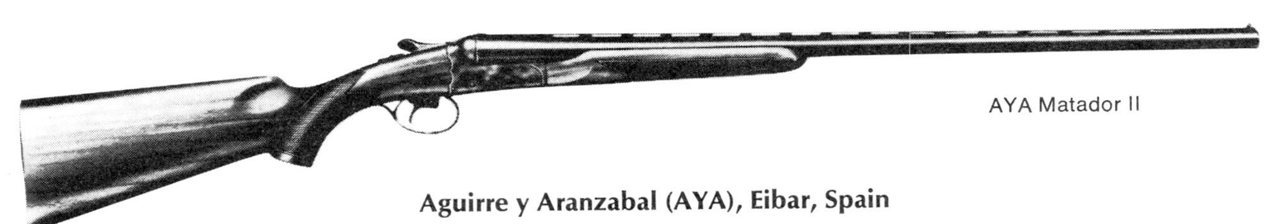
AYA Matador II

Aguirre y Aranzabal (AYA), Eibar, Spain

AYA Matador Hammerless Double Barrel Shotgun $175

Anson & Deeley box lock. Selective automatic ejectors. Selective single trigger. Gauges: 12, 16, 20, 20 Magnum (3"). Barrels: 26, 28, 30-inch; any standard choke combination. Weights: from 6½ to 7½ pounds, depending upon gauge and barrel length. Checkered pistol-grip stock and beavertail fore-end. *Note:* This model, prior to 1956, was designated F. I. Model 400E by the U.S. importer, Firearms International Corp., Washington, D.C. Made from 1955 to 1963.

AYA Matador II $210

Improved version of Matador with same general specifications, except has ventilated rib barrels. Made from 1964 to date.

AYA Bolero Hammerless Double Barrel Shotgun . . $140

Same general specifications as "Matador" except non-selective single trigger and extractors. Gauges: 12, 16, 20, 20 Magnum (3"), 410 (3"). *Note:* This model, prior to 1956, was designated F. I. Model 400 by the importer. Made from 1955 to 1963.

AYA Model 37 Super Over-and-Under Shotgun . . $1,100

Side lock. Automatic ejectors. Selective single trigger. Made in all gauges, barrel lengths and chokes. Ventilated rib barrels. Elaborately engraved. Checkered stock (with straight or pistol grip) and fore-end. Currently manufactured.

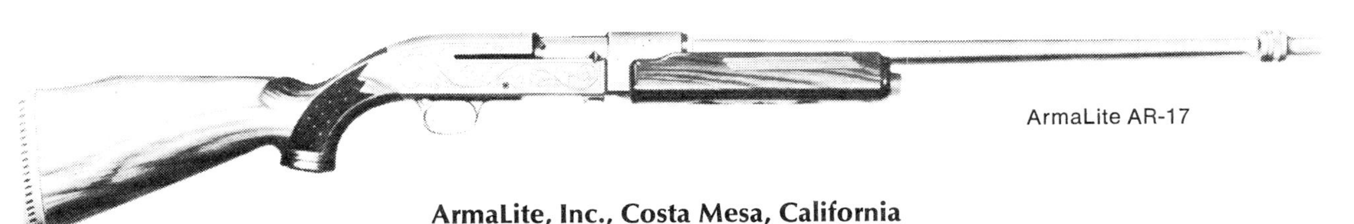
ArmaLite AR-17

ArmaLite, Inc., Costa Mesa, California

Armalite AR-17 Golden Gun $300

Recoil-operated semi-automatic. High-test aluminum barrel and receiver housing. 12 gauge only. 2-shot. 24-inch barrel with interchangeable choke tubes: improved cylinder, modified, and full. Weight, 5.6 pounds. Polycarbonate stock and forearm, recoil pad. Gold anodized finish standard; also made with black finish. Made from 1964 to 1965. Less than 2,000 produced.

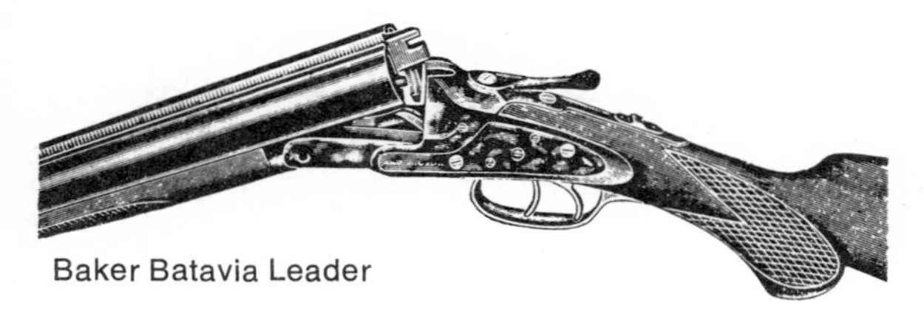
Baker Batavia Leader

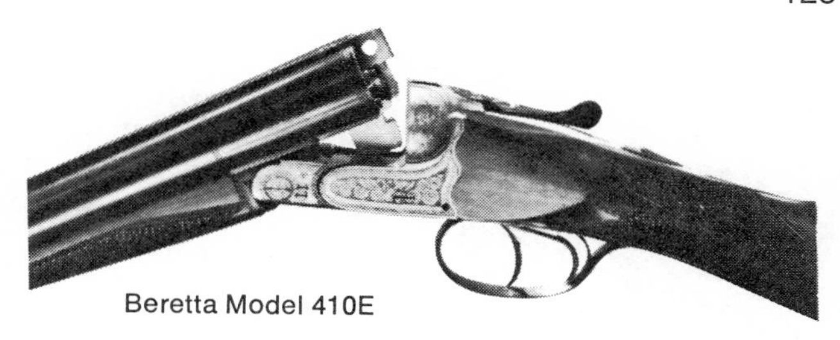
Beretta Model 410E

Baker Gun Company, Batavia, N.Y.

Baker Batavia Leader Hammerless Double Barrel Shotgun

Side Lock. Plain extractors or automatic ejectors. Double triggers. Gauges: 12, 60, 20. Barrels: 26 to 32-inch; any standard boring. Weight, about 7¾ pounds (12 gauge with 30-inch barrels). Checkered pistol-grip stock and forend. Discontinued c. 1930.
With plain extractors **$185**
With automatic ejectors **$250**

Baker Black Beauty Special

Same general specifications as the Batavia Leader, except higher quality and finer finish throughout. Discontinued c. 1930.
With plain extractors **$400**
With automatic ejectors **$500**

Pietro Beretta, Brescia, Italy

Beretta Silver Hawk Featherweight Hammerless Double Barrel Shotgun

Box lock. Double triggers or non-selective single trigger. Plain extractor. Gauges: 12, 16, 20, 28, 12 Mag. 26 to 32-inch barrels with high matted rib; all standard choke combinations. Weight, 12 ga. with 26-inch barrels, 7 pounds. Checkered walnut stock with beavertail forearm. Discontinued.
With double triggers **$250**
Extra for non-selective single trigger .... **$ 40**
Extra for Magnum Model .... **$ 50**

Beretta Model 409PB

Beretta Model 409PB Hammerless Double Barrel Shotgun $350

Box lock. Double triggers. Plain extractors. Gauges: 12, 16, 20, 28. Barrels: 27½, 28½ and 30-inch; improved cylinder and modified choke or modified and full choke. Weight, from 5½ to 7¾ pounds depending upon gauge and barrel length. Straight or pistol-grip stock and beavertail forearm, checkered. Made from 1934 to 1964.

Beretta Model 410E $450

Same general specifications as Model 409PB except has automatic ejectors and is of high quality throughout. Made from 1934 to 1964.

Beretta Model 410, 10 Gauge Magnum $400

Same as Model 410E, except heavier construction, plain extractors, double triggers, stock with recoil pad, weighs about 10½ pounds. Chambered for 10 gauge Magnum (3½"). Made from 1934 to 1964.

Beretta Model 411E $600

Same general specifications as Model 409PB except has sideplates, automatic ejectors and is of higher quality throughout. Made from 1934 to 1964.

Beretta Silver Snipe Over-And-Under Shotgun

Box lock. Non-selective or selective single trigger. Plain extractor. Gauges: 12, 20, 12 Mag., 20 Mag. Barrels: 26, 28, 30-inch; plain or ventilated rib; improved cylinder and modified choke, modified and full choke, Skeet chokes #1 and #2, full and full. Weight, from about 6 pounds in 20 ga. to 8½ pounds in 12 ga. (trap gun). Checkered walnut pistol-grip stock and forearm. Made from 1955 to 1967.
With plain barrel, non-selective trigger **$250**
With ventilated rib barrel, non-selective single trigger **$275**
Extra for selective single trigger .... **$ 40**

Beretta Golden Snipe Over-And-Under

Same as Silver Snipe, except has automatic ejectors, ventilated rib is standard feature. Made from 1955 to date.
With non-selective single trigger **$350**
Extra for selective single trigger .... **$ 40**

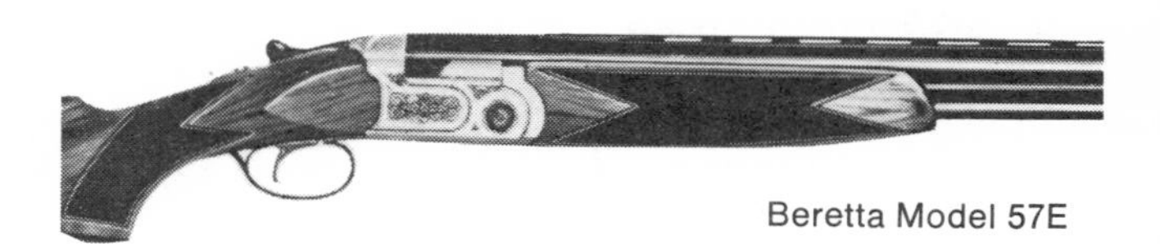
Beretta Model 57E

Beretta Model 57E Over-And-Under

Same general specifications as Golden Snipe, but higher quality throughout. Made from 1955 to 1967.
With non-selective single trigger **$500**
With selective single trigger **$550**

Beretta FS-1

Beretta Model Asel Over-And-Under Shotgun . . . $700
Box lock. Single non-selective trigger. Selective automatic ejectors. Gauges: 12, 20. Barrels: 26, 28, 30-inch, improved cylinder and modified choke or modified and full choke. Weights: 20 gauge—about 5¾ pounds, 12 gauge—about 7 pounds. Checkered pistol-grip stock and forearm. Made from 1947 to 1964.

Beretta Grade 100 Over-And-Under Shotgun $700
Side lock. Double triggers. Automatic ejectors, 12 gauge only. Barrels: 26, 28, 30-inch; any standard boring. Weight, about 7½ pounds. Checkered stock and fore-end, straight grip or pistol grip. Discontinued.

Beretta Grade 200 . . . . $850
Same general specifications as Grade 100 except higher quality, bores and action parts hard chrome plated.

Beretta Model SO2 Over-And-Under Shotgun . . $1,200
Holland & Holland sidelock system. Single non-selective trigger. Selective automatic ejectors. 12 gauge only. Barrels: 26, 28, 30-inch; ventilated rib; full and modified choke or improved cylinder and modified choke; bores hard chromed. Checkered pistol-grip stock and forearm. Weight, about 7 pounds. Currently manufactured.

Beretta Model SO3EL $1,500
Same general specifications as Model SO2, except higher grade with de luxe engraving, stainless steel barrels, stock and forearm of finest European walnut. Currently manufactured.

Beretta FS-1 Folding Single Barrel Shotgun $50
Formerly "Companion." Folds to length of barrel. Hammerless. Underlever. Gauges: 12, 16, 20, 28, 140. Barrels: 30-inch in 12 ga., 28-inch in 16 and 20 ga., 26-inch in 28 and 410 ga.; all full choke. Checkered semi-pistol-grip stock and forearm. Weight, 4½ to 5½ pounds depending upon gauge. Currently manufactured.

Vincenzo Bernardelli, Gardone V. T. (Brescia), Italy

Bernardelli Roma Hammerless Double Barrel Shotguns
Anson & Deeley system. Side plates. Non-ejector or ejector. Double triggers. Gauges: 12, 16, 20 (in Roma 3 Model, 12 gauge only in others). Barrels: 27½ or 29½-inch, modified and full choke standard. Weight, from 5½ to 7½ pounds depending upon barrel length and gauge. Checkered stock and forend, straight or pistol grip. Made in three models—Roma 3, Roma 4, Roma 6—which differ chiefly in overall quality, type of engraving, grade of wood, checkering, etc., general specifications are the same.
Roma 3 . . . . $400
Roma 4 . . . . $485
Roma 6 . . . . $600
Automatic ejectors, extra . . . . $ 75

Bernardelli St. Uberto F.S. Hammerless Double Barrel Shotgun $450
Box lock. Automatic ejectors. Double triggers. Gauges: 12, 16. Any barrel length, chokes. Checkered stock (straight or pistol-grip) and forearm.

Bernardelli V.B. Holland Hammerless Double Barrel Shotgun $1,000
Holland & Holland-type sidelock action. Automatic ejectors. Double triggers. 12 gauge only. Any barrel length, chokes. Checkered stock (straight or pistol grip) and forearm.

Bernardelli De Luxe V.B. Holland Model $1,100
Same as V.B. Holland Model except has hunting scene engraving and beavertail forearm.

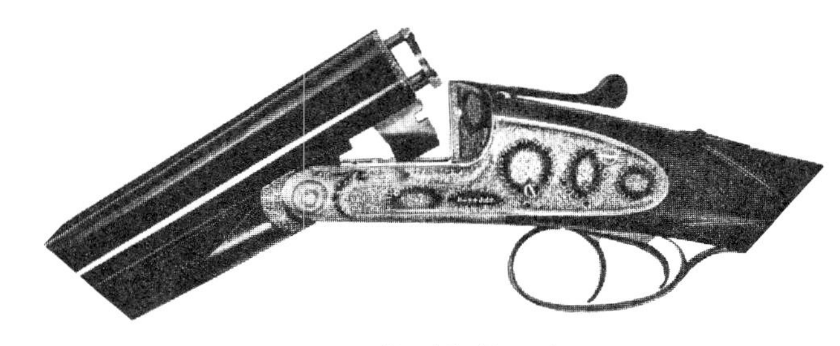
Boss Double Barrel

Boss & Co., London, England

Boss Hammerless Double Barrel Shotgun
Side lock. Automatic ejectors. Double triggers, non-selective or selective single trigger. Made in all gauges, barrel lengths and chokes. Checkered stock and fore-end, straight or pistol grip.
With double triggers or non-selective single trigger . . . $4,000
Selective single trigger, extra . . . . $ 500
Extra pair of barrels without forend $1,300

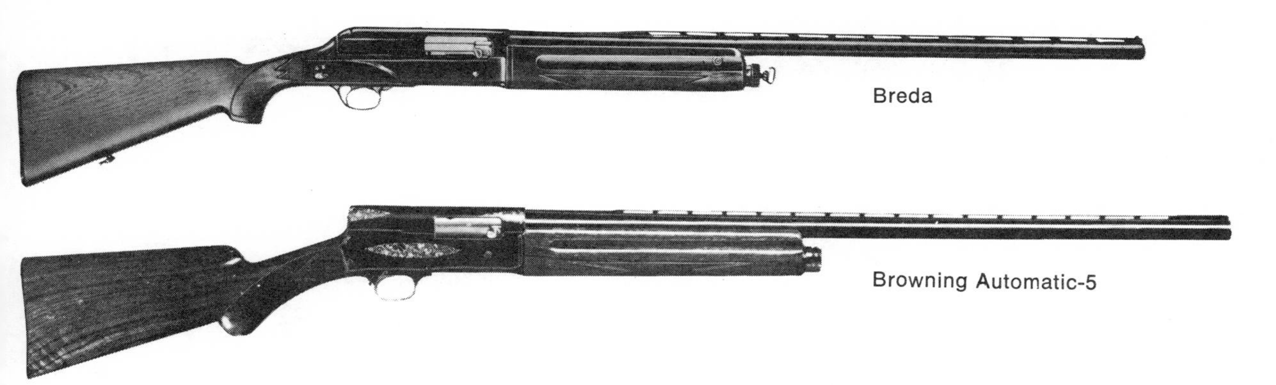

Breda

Browning Automatic-5

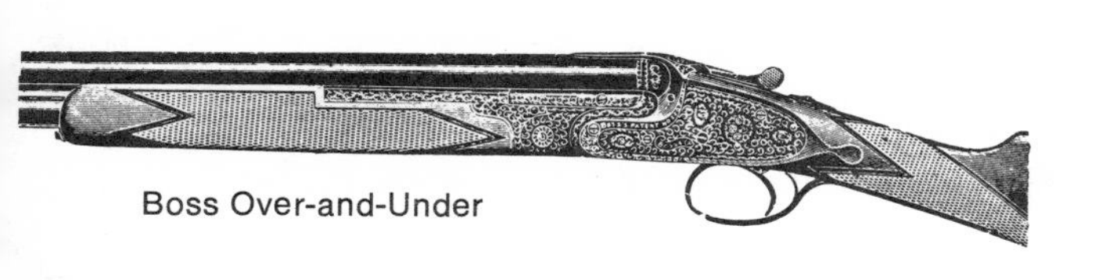

Boss Over-and-Under

Boss Hammerless Over And Under Shotgun

Side lock. Automatic ejectors. Double triggers, non-selective or selective trigger. Made in all gauges, barrel lengths and chokes. Checkered stock and forend, straight or pistol grip.
With double triggers or non-selective single trigger **$5,000**
Selective single trigger, extra . . . . **$ 500**
Extra pair of barrels without forend **$1,500**

Ernesto Breda, Milan, Italy

Breda Autoloading Shotgun

Five-shot. Hammerless. Takedown. 12 gauge only. 4-shell tubular magazine. Barrels: 25½ and 27½-inch, plain or matted rib, tapered choke, bore hard chromed. Weight, about 7¼ pounds. Checkered straight or pistol grip stock and forearm. Also available with engraved and chrome-plated receivers in three grades. Currently manufactured.
With plain barrel **$195**
With ribbed barrel **$210**
With Grade 1 engraving **$390**
With Grade 2 engraving **$470**
With Grade 3 engraving **$500**

Breda 12 Magnum Autoloader

Same general specifications as standard model, except chambered for 12 gauge 3″ Magnum. Currently manufactured.
With plain barrel **$200**
With ventilated rib barrel **$215**

American Browning Shotguns distributed by Browning Arms Company, St. Louis, Mo.; manufactured by Remington Arms Company, Ilion, N.Y. These Browning models are almost identical to the Remington Model 11A and Sportsman.

American Browning Grade I Three or Five Shot Autoloading Shotgun $125

Takedown. Gauges: 12, 16, 20. 2 or 4-shell tubular magazine. Plain barrel, 26 to 32-inch, any standard boring. Weight, from about 6⅞ (20 gauge) to 8 pounds (12 gauge). Checkered pistol-grip stock and forearm. Made from 1940 to 1949.

American Browning Special

Same general specifications as Grade I except supplied with raised matted rib or ventilated rib. Discontinued in 1949.
With raised matted rib **$140**
With ventilated rib **$160**

American Browning Special Skeet Model $175

Same general specifications as Grade I except has 26-inch barrel with ventilated rib and Cutts Compensator. Discontinued in 1949.

American Browning Utility Field Gun $135

Same general specifications as Grade I except has 28-inch plain barrel with Poly Choke. Discontinued in 1949.

Belgian Browning Shotguns distributed by Browning, Morgan, Utah; manufactured by Fabrique Nationale D'Armes de Guerre, Herstal, Belgium. F.N. also produces Browning design autoloading and superposed shotguns for sale under its own trademark.

Browning Automatic-5, Standard (Grade I)

Gauges: 12 and 16 (16 gauge guns made prior to World War II were chambered for 2-9/16-inch shells; standard 16 discontinued 1964). 4-shell magazine in five-shot model, prewar guns were also available in three-shot model. Barrels: 26 to 32-inch; plain, raised matted rib (discontinued), ventilated rib; choice of standard chokes. Weights: about 8 pounds in 12 gauge, 7¼ pounds in 16 gauge. Checkered pistol-grip stock and forearm. (*Note:* Browning Special, discontinued about 1940, is Grade I gun with either ventilated or raised matted rib). Made from 1900 to 1973.
Grade I, plain barrel **$235**
Grade I or Browning Special, raised matted rib . . **$250**
Grade I or Browning Special, ventilated rib **$275**

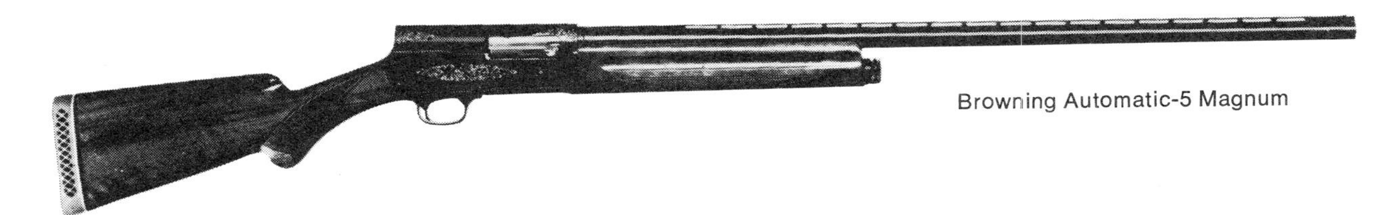
Browning Automatic-5 Magnum

Browning Autoloading Shotguns, Grade III and IV

These higher grade models differ from the Standard or Grade I in general quality, grade of wood, checkering, engraving, etc., otherwise specifications are the same. Grade IV guns, sometimes called Midas Grade, are inlaid with yellow and green gold. Discontinued in 1940.
Grade III, plain barrel **$600**
Grade IV, plain barrel **$900**
Extra for raised matted rib .... **$ 15**
Extra for ventilated rib .... **$ 50**

Browning Automatic-5, Trap Model **$285**

12 gauge only. Same general specifications as Standard Model, except has trap-style stock, 30-inch ventilated rib barrel, full choke; weighs 8½ pounds.

Browning Automatic-5, Magnum 12 Gauge

Same general specifications as Standard Model. Chambered for 3″ Magnum 12 gauge shell. Barrels: 28″ modified and full, 30″ or 32″ full and full; plain or ventilated rib. Buttstock has recoil pad. Weight, from 8½ to 9 pounds depending upon barrel. Made from 1958 to date.
With plain barrel **$245**
With ventilated rib barrel **$285**

Browning Sweet 16 Automatic-5

16 gauge only. Same general specifications as Standard Model except lightweight (about 6¾ pounds), has gold-plated trigger and guns without rib have striped matting on top of barrel. Made from 1937 to date.
With plain barrel **$245**
With raised matted rib **$260**
With ventilated rib **$285**

Browning Light 12 Automatic-5

12 gauge only. Same general specifications as Standard Model except lightweight (about 7¼ pounds), has gold plated trigger and guns without rib have striped matting on top of barrel. Made from 1948 to date.
With plain barrel **$245**
With raised matted rib **$260**
With ventilated rib **$285**

Browning Automatic-5, Skeet Model

12 gauge only. Same general specifications as Light 12; barrels: 26 or 28-inch, plain or ventilated rib, Skeet choke; weighs from 7 lbs. 5 oz. to 7 lbs. 10 oz., depending upon barrel.
With plain barrel **$245**
With ventilated rib barrel **$285**

Browning Light 20 Automatic-5

Same general specifications as Standard Model, except light-weight and 20 gauge. Barrels: 26 or 28-inch; plain or ventilated rib. Weight, from about 6¼ to 6½ pounds, depending upon barrel. Made from 1958 to date.
With plain barrel **$245**
With ventilated rib barrel **$285**

Browning Superposed (Overunder) Shotgun

Browning action. Automatic selective ejectors. Single selective trigger; earlier models were supplied with double triggers, twin single triggers or non-selective single trigger. Gauges: 12 and 20, the latter introduced in 1949. Barrels: 26½, 28, 30, 32-inch: ventilated or raised matted rib, prewar Lightning Model made without rib, now supplied only with ventilated rib; any combination of standard chokes. Weights: from 6½ pounds (20 gauge, 26½-inch barrels) to 7¾ pounds (12 gauge, 30-inch barrels); Lightning about ½ pound lighter. Checkered pistol-grip stock and forend, two styles: field/skeet, trap. Higher grade models—Pigeon, Pointer, Diana, Midas—differ from standard grades in general quality, grade of wood, checkering, engraving, etc.; otherwise, specifications are the same. Midas grade guns are richly inlaid with gold. Made from 1931 to date. *Note:* Prewar models may be considered as discontinued in 1940 when Belgium was occupied by Germany. Pointer grade discontinued in 1966, Standard Model in 1973, Pigeon grade in 1974. Values shown are for guns with selective single trigger; deduct 25% if this feature is lacking.

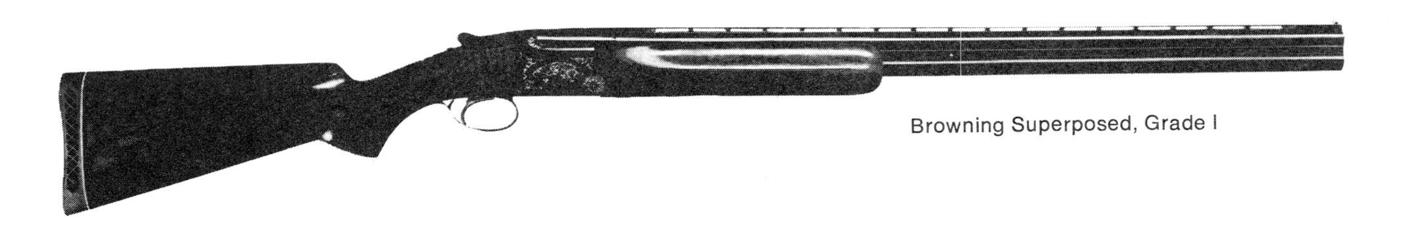
Browning Superposed, Grade I

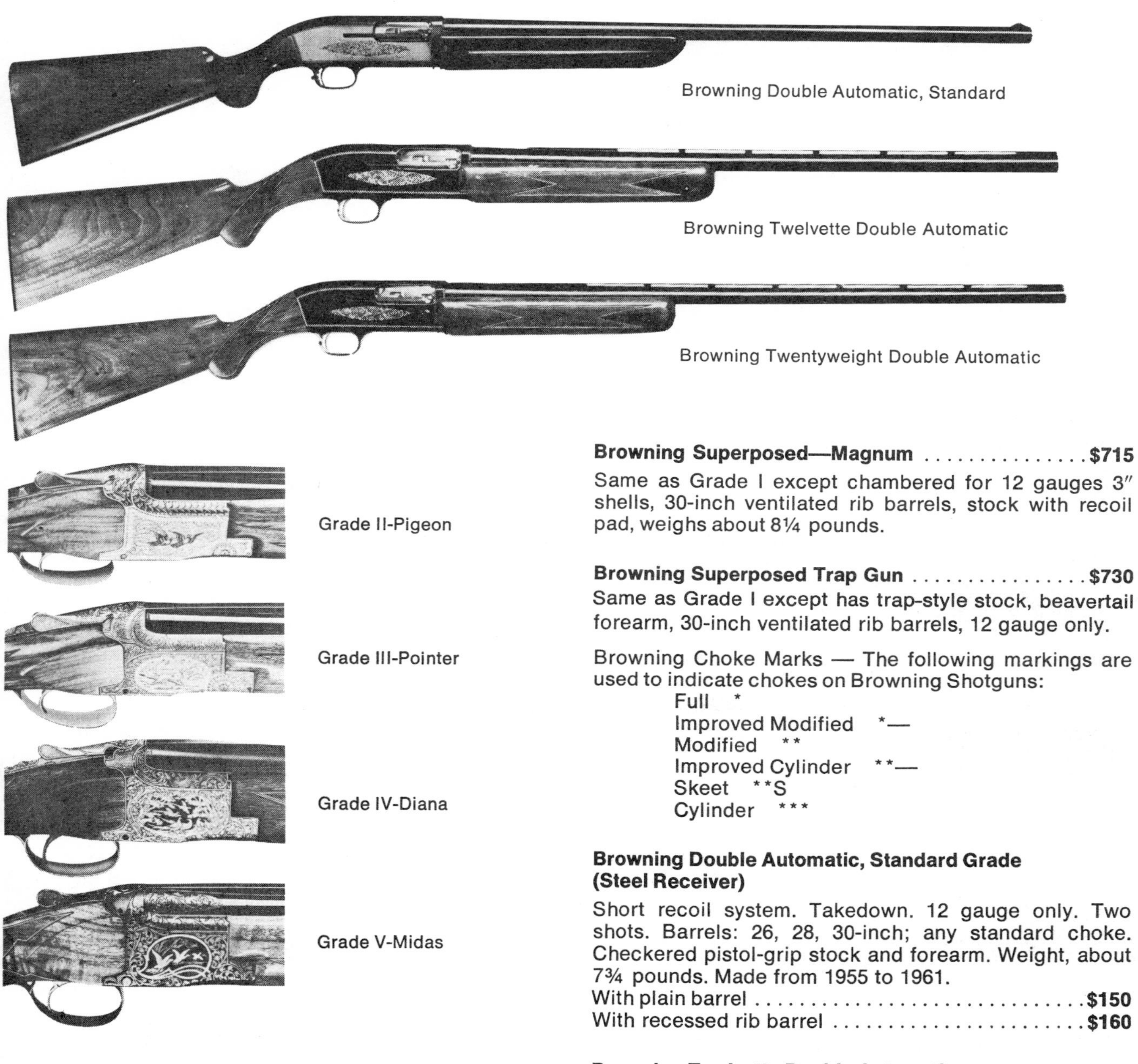

Browning Double Automatic, Standard

Browning Twelvette Double Automatic

Browning Twentyweight Double Automatic

Grade II-Pigeon

Grade III-Pointer

Grade IV-Diana

Grade V-Midas

Browning Superposed (Overunder) Shotgun

Grade I Standard Model, raised matted rib . . . . . . **$ 650**
Grade I Lightning Model, ventilated rib . . . . **$ 715**
Grade I Standard Model, ventilated rib . . . . **$ 700**
Grade I Lightning Model (prewar), matted barrel
without rib . . . . **$ 700**
Pigeon Grade, raised matted rib (prewar) **$1,000**
Pigeon Grade, ventilated rib (prewar) **$1,100**
Diana Grade, raised matted rib (prewar) **$1,300**
Diana Grade, ventilated rib (prewar) **$1,400**
Midas Grade, raised matted rib (prewar) **$1,800**
Midas Grade, ventilated rib (prewar) **$1,900**
Grade II-Pigeon (postwar) **$1,000**
Grade III-Pointer (postwar) **$1,150**
Grade IV-Diana (postwar) **$1,275**
Grade V-Midas (postwar) **$1,725**

Browning Superposed—Magnum $715

Same as Grade I except chambered for 12 gauges 3″ shells, 30-inch ventilated rib barrels, stock with recoil pad, weighs about 8¼ pounds.

Browning Superposed Trap Gun $730

Same as Grade I except has trap-style stock, beavertail forearm, 30-inch ventilated rib barrels, 12 gauge only.

Browning Choke Marks — The following markings are used to indicate chokes on Browning Shotguns:

Full *
Improved Modified *—
Modified **
Improved Cylinder **—
Skeet **S
Cylinder ***

Browning Double Automatic, Standard Grade (Steel Receiver)

Short recoil system. Takedown. 12 gauge only. Two shots. Barrels: 26, 28, 30-inch; any standard choke. Checkered pistol-grip stock and forearm. Weight, about 7¾ pounds. Made from 1955 to 1961.
With plain barrel **$150**
With recessed rib barrel **$160**

Browning Twelvette Double Automatic

Lightweight version of Double Automatic with same general specifications except aluminum receiver. Barrel with plain matted top or ventilated rib. Weight, from about 6¾ to 7 pounds, depending upon barrel. Receiver is finished in black with gold engraving; from 1956 to 1961, receivers were also anodized in grey, brown, and green with silver engraving. Made from 1955 to 1971.
With plain barrel **$200**
With ventilated rib barrel **$235**

Browning Twentyweight Double Automatic

Same as Twelvette but ¾ pound lighter. 26½-inch barrel only. Made from 1956 to 1971.
With plain barrel **$215**
With ventilated rib barrel **$250**

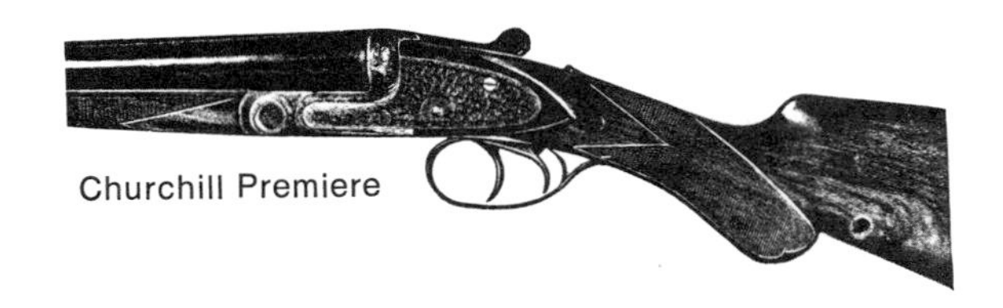
Churchill Premiere

E. J. Churchill, Ltd., London, England

Churchill Premiere Quality Hammerless Double Barrel Shotgun

Side lock. Automatic ejectors. Double triggers or selective single trigger. Gauges: 12, 16, 20, 28. Barrels: 25, 28, 30, 32-inch; any degree of boring. Weight, from 5 to 8 pounds depending upon gauge and barrel length. Checkered stock and forend, straight or pistol grip.
With double triggers **$3,000**
Selective single trigger, extra .... **$ 400**

Churchill Field Model Hammerless Double Barrel Shotgun

Side lock hammerless ejector gun with same general specifications as Premiere Model but of lower quality.
With double triggers **$2,000**
Selective single trigger, extra .... **$ 400**

Churchill Utility Model Hammerless Double Barrel Shotgun

Anson & Deeley box lock action. Double triggers or single trigger. Gauges: 12, 16, 20, 28, 410. Barrels: 25, 28, 30, 32-inch; any degree of boring. Weight from 4½ to 8 pounds depending upon gauge and barrel length. Checkered stock and forend, straight or pistol grip.
With double triggers **$1,300**
Selective single trigger, extra .... **$ 400**

Churchill Premiere Quality Under-And-Over Shotgun

Side lock. Automatic ejectors. Double triggers or selective single trigger. Gauges: 12, 16, 20, 28. Barrels: 25, 28, 30, 32-inch; any degree of boring. Weight, from 5 to 8 pounds depending upon gauge and barrel length. Checkered stock and forend, straight or pistol grip.
With double triggers **$4,500**
Selective single trigger, extra .... **$ 400**
Raised ventilated rib, extra .... **$ 400**

Cogswell & Harrison, Ltd., London, England

Cogswell & Harrison Best Quality Hammerless Side Lock Double Barrel Shotgun

Hand detachable locks. Automatic ejectors. Double triggers or single trigger (selective or non-selective). Gauges: 12, 16, 20. Barrels: 25, 26, 27½, 30-inch; any choke combination. Checkered stock and forend, straight grip standard. Made in two models Victor and Primic, the latter being of plainer finish, otherwise the same.
Victor Model **$3,000**
Primic Model **$2,000**
Single trigger, non selective, extra **$225**
Single trigger, selective, extra **$300**

Cogswell & Harrison Huntic Model Hammerless Double Barrel Shotgun

Side lock. Automatic ejectors. Double triggers or single trigger (selective or non-selective). Gauges: 12, 16, 20. Barrels: 25, 27½, 30-inch; any choke combination. Checkered stock and forend, straight grip standard.
With double triggers **$1,450**
Single trigger, non-selective, extra .... **$ 225**
Single trigger, selective, extra .... **$ 300**

Cogswell & Harrison Avant Tout Series Hammerless Double Barrel Shotguns

Box lock. Side plates (except Avant Tout III Grade). Automatic ejectors. Double triggers or single trigger (selective or non-selective). Gauges: 12, 16, 20. Barrels: 25, 27½, 30-inch; any choke combination. Checkered stock and forend, straight grip standard. Made in three models — Avant Tout I or Konor, Avant Tout II or Sandhurst, Avant Tout III or Rex — which differ chiefly in overall quality, engraving, grade of wood, checkering, etc., general specifications are the same. Values shown are for guns of recent production.
Avant Tout I **$1,300**
Avant Tout II **$1,200**
Avant Tout III .... **$ 900**
Single trigger, non-selective, extra .... **$ 225**
Single trigger, selective, extra .... **$ 300**

Cogswell & Harrison Markor Hammerless Double Barrel Shotgun

Box lock. Non-ejector or ejector. Double triggers. Gauges: 12, 16, 20. Barrels: 27½ or 30-inch; any choke combination. Checkered stock and forend, straight grip standard.
Non-ejector Model **$750**
Ejector Model **$850**

Colt's Firearms Division, Hartford, Connecticut

Colt Custom Double Barrel Hammerless Shotgun . . $200

Box lock. Double triggers. Automatic ejectors. Gauges: 12 Mag., 16. Barrels: 26-inch improved cylinder and modified, 28-inch modified and full, 30-inch full and full. Weight (12 ga.), about 7½ pounds. Checkered pistol-grip stock and beavertail forearm. Made in 1961.

Coltsman Standard Pump Shotgun $100

Takedown. Gauges: 12, 16, 20. Magazine holds 4 shells. Barrels: 26-inch improved cylinder, 28-inch modified or full choke, 30-inch full choke. Weight, about 6 pounds. Plain pistol-grip stock and forearm. Made from 1961 to 1965 by Manufrance.

Coltsman Custom Pump $140

Same as Standard Pump except has checkered stock, ventilated rib barrel, weighs about 6½ pounds. Made from 1961 to 1963.

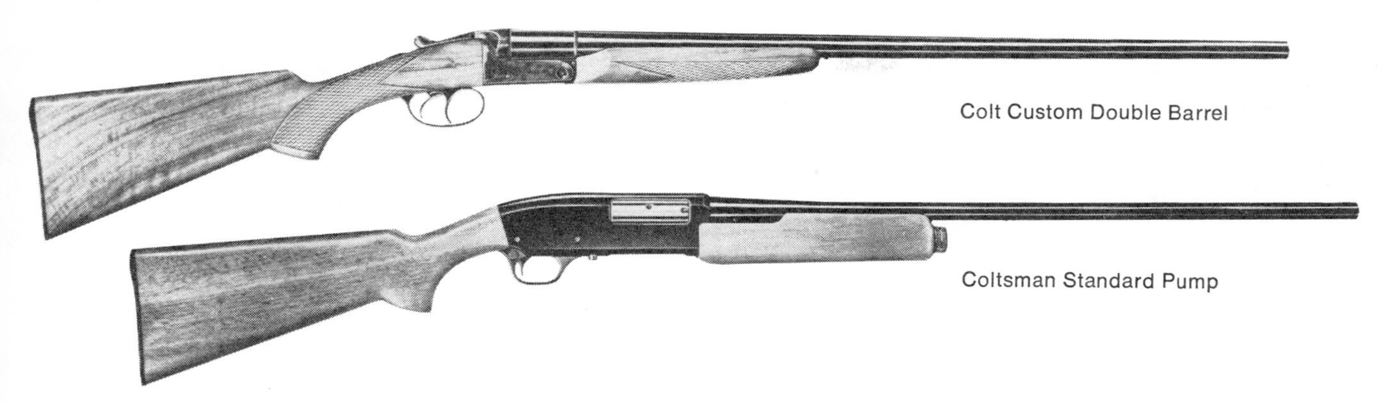

Colt Custom Double Barrel

Coltsman Standard Pump

Colt's Ultra Light Auto Shotgun—Standard

Takedown. Alloy receiver. Gauges: 12, 20. Magazine holds 4 shells. Barrels: plain, solid rib, ventilated rib; chrome-lined; 26-inch improved cylinder or modified choke, 28-inch modified or full choke, 30-inch full choke, 32-inch full choke. Weight (12 ga.), about 6¼ pounds. Checkered pistol-grip stock and forearm. Made from 1964 to 1966 by Franchi.
With plain barrel **$175**
With solid rib barrel **$185**
With ventilated rib barrel **$195**

Daly Regent Diamond Double Barrel

Colt's Ultra Light Auto—Custom

Same as Standard Auto except has engraved receiver, select walnut stock and forearm. Made from 1964 to 1966.
With solid rib barrel **$215**
With ventilated rib barrel **$225**

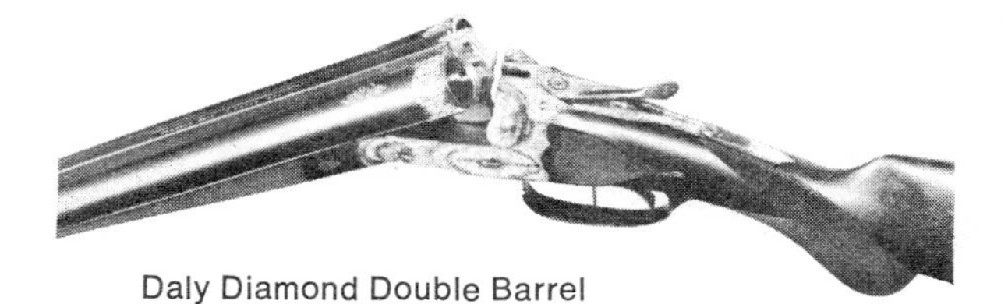

Daly Diamond Double Barrel

Colt's Magnum Auto Shotgun

Same as Standard Auto except steel receiver, handles 3″ Magnum shells, 30 and 32-inch barrels in 12 gauge, 28 inch in 20 gauge; weight (12 ga.), about 8¼ pounds. Made from 1964 to 1966.
With plain barrel **$215**
With solid rib barrel **$225**
With ventilated rib barrel **$235**

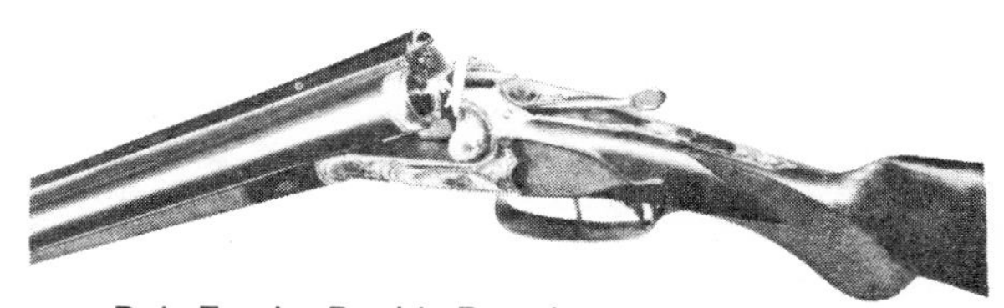

Daly Empire Double Barrel

Colt's Magnum Auto—Custom

Same as Magnum except has engraved receiver, select walnut stock and forearm. Made from 1964 to 1966.
With solid rib barrel **$255**
With ventilated rib barrel **$265**

Charles Daly, Inc., New York City

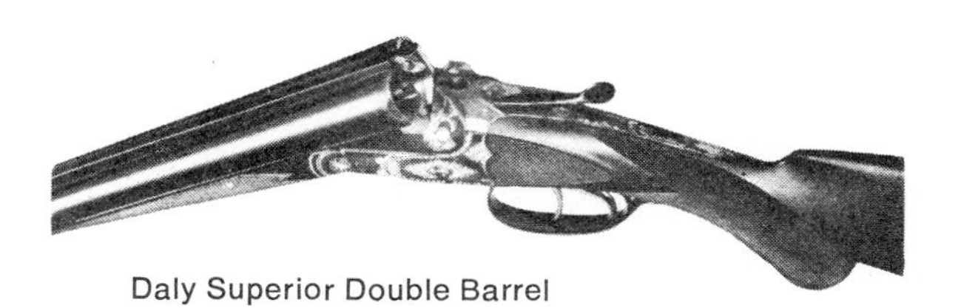

Daly Superior Double Barrel

Charles Daly Hammerless Double Barrel Shotgun

Daly pattern Anson & Deeley system box lock action. Automatic ejectors — except "Superior Quality" is non-ejector. Double triggers. Gauges: 10, 12, 16, 20, 28, 410. Barrels: 26 to 32-inch, any combination of chokes. Weight, from 4 pounds to 8½ pounds depending upon gauge and barrel length. Checkered pistol-grip stock and forend. The four grades — Regent Diamond, Diamond, Empire, Superior — differ in general quality, grade of wood, checkering, engraving, etc., otherwise specifications are the same. Discontinued about 1933.

Regent Diamond Quality **$2,000**
Diamond Quality **$1,500**
Empire Quality . . . . **$ 750**
Superior Quality . . . . **$ 500**

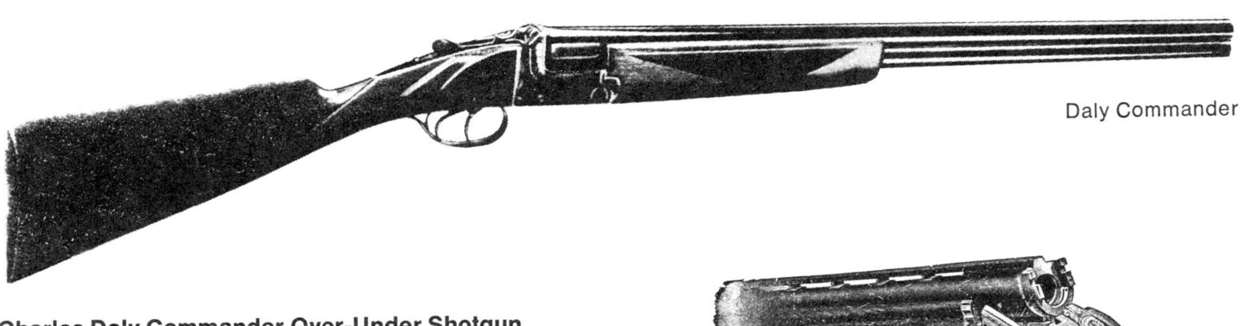

Daly Commander

Charles Daly Commander Over-Under Shotgun

Daly pattern Anson & Deeley system box lock action. Automatic ejectors. Double triggers or Miller single selective trigger. Gauges: 12, 16, 20, 28, 410. Barrels: 26 to 30-inch, improved cylinder and modified or modified and full choke. Weight, from 5¼ to 7¼ pounds depending upon gauge and barrel length. Checkered stock and forend, straight or pistol grip. The two models, 100 and 200, differ in general quality, grade of wood, checkering, engraving, etc., otherwise specifications are the same. Made prior to World War II.

Model 100 .... **$350**
Model 200 .... **$500**
Miller single trigger, extra .... **$ 75**

Daly Diamond Over-and-Under

Charles Daly Over-And-Under Shotgun

Daly pattern Anson & Deeley system box lock action. Automatic ejectors. Double triggers. Gauges: 12, 16, 20. Supplied in various barrel lengths and weights. Checkered pistol-grip stock and forend. The two grades —Diamond and Empire—differ in general quality, grade of wood, checkering, engraving, etc., otherwise specifications are the same. Discontinued about 1933.

Diamond Quality **$2,000**
Empire Quality **$1,500**

Daly Single Barrel Trap

Charles Daly Single Barrel Trap Gun $2,500

Daly pattern Anson & Deeley system box lock action. Automatic ejector. 12 gauge only. Barrels: 30, 32, 34-inch, ventilated rib. Weight, from 7½ to 8¼ pounds. Checkered pistol-grip stock and forend. This model was made in "Empire Quality" only. Discontinued about 1933.

Daly Sextuple Trap

Charles Daly Sextuple Model Single Barrel Trap Gun

Daly pattern Anson & Deeley system box lock action. Six locking bolts. Automatic ejector. 12 gauge only. Barrels: 30, 32, 34-inch, ventilated rib. Weight, from 7½ to 8¼ pounds. Checkered pistol grip stock and forend. This model was made in two grades, "Empire" and "Regent Diamond"; the guns differ in general quality, grade of wood, checkering, engraving, etc., otherwise specifications are the same. Discontinued about 1933.

Regent Diamond Quality **$3,000**
Empire Quality **$2,000**

Charles Daly Hammerless Drilling (Three Barrel Gun)

Daly pattern Anson & Deeley system box lock action. Plain extractors. Double triggers, front single set for rifle barrel. Gauges: 12, 16, 20; 25-20, 25-35, 30-30 rifle barrel. Supplied in various barrel lengths and weights. Checkered pistol-grip stock and forend. Automatic rear sight operated by rifle barrel selector. The three grades — Regent Diamond, Diamond, Superior — differ in general quality, grade of wood, checkering, engraving, etc., otherwise specifications are the same. Discontinued about 1933.

Regent Diamond Quality **$3,000**
Diamond Quality **$2,000**
Superior Quality **$1,000**

Charles Daly Field Grade Over-Under Shotgun . . . $315

Box lock action. Scroll-engraved receiver. Selective single trigger. Automatic safety/barrel selector. Automatic selective ejectors. Gauges: 12, 12 Mag., 20, 20 Mag., 28, 410. Barrel lengths: 26, 28, 30 inch; chokes: skeet & skeet, improved cylinder & modified, modified & full, full & full. Ventilated rib. Weight, from 6 lbs. 2 oz. (28 ga.) to 8 pounds (12 ga. Magnum). Select walnut stock with pistol grip, fluted forend, checkered, recoil pad in 12 ga. Magnum. Made from 1963 to date; 28 and 410 gauges introduced in 1965.

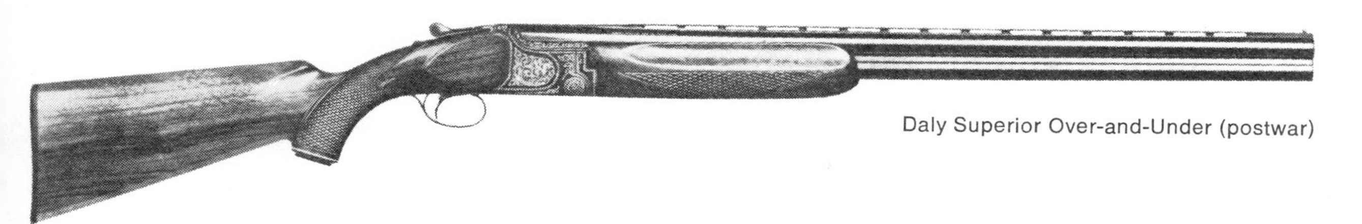
Daly Superior Over-and-Under (postwar)

Daly Regent Diamond Drilling

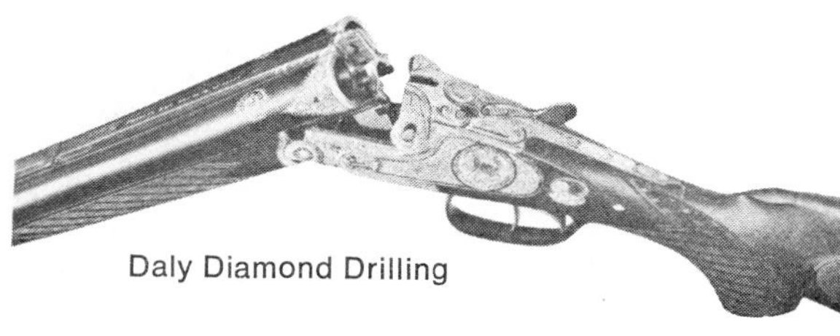
Daly Diamond Drilling

Daly Superior Drilling

Charles Daly Superior Grade Over-Under $350

Field and Skeet Models. Same general specifications as Field Grade, but with higher grade engraving and wood.

Note: Prewar Charles Daly guns—except "Commander" which was made in Liege, Belgium—were produced in Suhl, Germany. Postwar models are of Japanese manufacture.

Etablissements Darne
Saint-Etienne, France

Darne Bird-Hunter Double Barrel Shotgun $300

Sliding-breech action. Automatic selective ejection. Double triggers. 12 and 20 gauge. 25½-inch barrels, raised rib; improved cylinder and modified choke. Weights: 12 gauge, 6 lb. 4 oz.; 20 gauge, 5 lb. 10 oz. Deluxe walnut stock with semi-pistol grip, matching forend, checkered. Currently manufactured.

Darne Pheasant-Hunter De Luxe $400

Same as Bird-Hunter model, except has highly engraved receiver and fancy walnut stock and forend; 12 gauge also available with 28-inch barrels, modified and full choke.

Darne Quail-Hunter Supreme $525

Same as Bird-Hunter model, except has premium grade engraving and wood; made in 20 and 28 gauges only; 25½-inch barrels, improved cylinder and modified choke; weight, about 5½ pounds.

Davidson Guns manufactured by Fabrica de Armas ILJA, Eibar, Spain; distributed by Davidson Firearms Co., Greensboro, N.C.

Davidson Model 63B Double Barrel Shotgun $125

Anson & Deeley box lock action. Frame engraved and nickel plated. Plain extractors. Automatic safety. Double triggers. Gauges: 12, 16, 20, 28, 410. Barrel lengths: 25 (410 only), 26, 28, 30 inch (latter 12 ga. only); chokes: improved cylinder & modified, modified & full, full & full. Weights, from 5 lb. 11 oz. (410) to 7 pounds (12 ga.). Pistol-grip stock and forearm of European walnut, checkered. Made from 1963 to date.

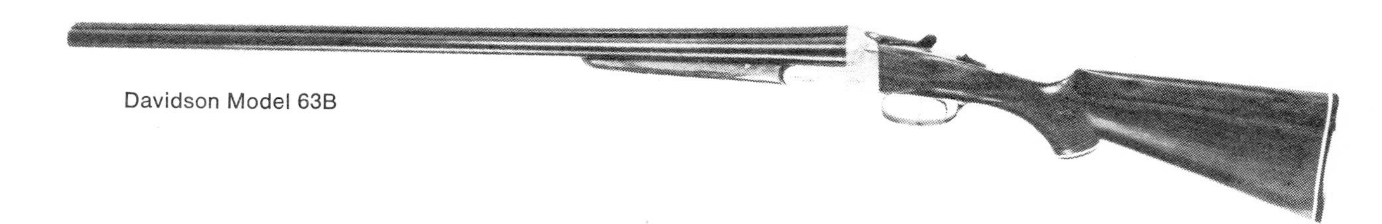
Davidson Model 63B

Davidson Model 63B Magnum

Similar to standard Model 63B, except chambered for 10 ga. 3½", 12 and 20 ga. 3" Magnum shells; 10 gauge has 32-inch barrels, choked full & full, weighs 10 lb. 10 oz. Made from 1963 to date.
12 and 20 gauge Magnum **$130**
10 gauge Magnum **$145**

Davidson Model 69SL Double Barrel Shotgun ... **$135**

Sidelock action with detachable sideplates, engraved and nickel plated. Plain extractors. Automatic safety. Double triggers. 12 and 20 gauge. Barrels: 26-inch improved cylinder & modified, 28-inch modified & full. Weights: 12 ga., 7 pounds; 20 ga., 6½ pounds. Pistol-grip stock and forearm of European walnut, checkered. Made from 1963 to date.

A. H. Fox Gun Company, Philadelphia, Pa. This firm was bought by Savage Arms Corporation in 1930 and the manufacturing facilities moved to Utica, N.Y.

Production of Fox Shotguns, with the exception of Model B which is still manufactured by Savage Arms Corporation, was discontinued about 1942.

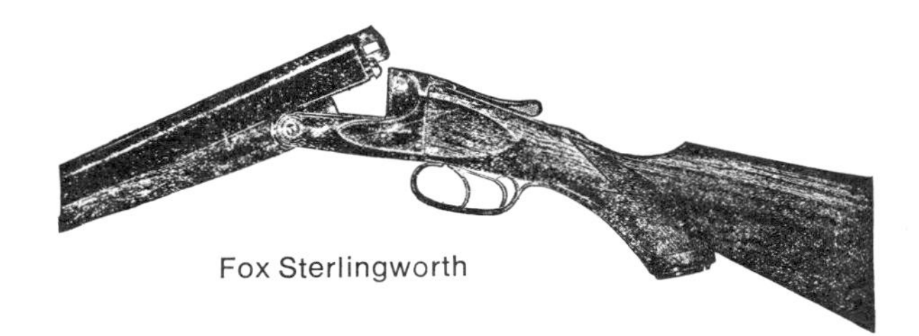
Fox Sterlingworth

Fox Sterlingworth Hammerless Double Barrel Shotgun

Box lock. Double triggers (Fox-Kautzky selective single trigger extra). Plain extractors (automatic ejectors extra). Gauges: 12, 16, 20. Barrel lengths: 26, 28, 30-inch; chokes: full and full, modified and full, cylinder and modified (any combination of cylinder to full choke borings was available at no extra cost). Weights: 12 gauge — 6⅞ to 8¼ pounds, 16 gauge — 6 to 7 pounds, 20 gauge — 5¾ to 6¾ pounds. Checkered pistol-grip stock and forearm.
With plain extractors **$200**
With automatic ejectors **$300**
Selective single trigger, extra .... **$ 75**

Fox Sterlingworth Deluxe

Same general specifications as Sterlingworth except 32-inch barrel was also available, has recoil pad, ivory bead sights.
With plain extractors **$250**
With automatic ejectors **$350**

Fox Sterlingworth Skeet and Upland Game Gun

Same general specifications as the standard Sterlingworth except has 26 or 28-inch barrels with skeet boring only, straight grip stock; weighs 7 pounds in 12 gauge model.
With plain extractors **$250**
With automatic ejectors **$350**

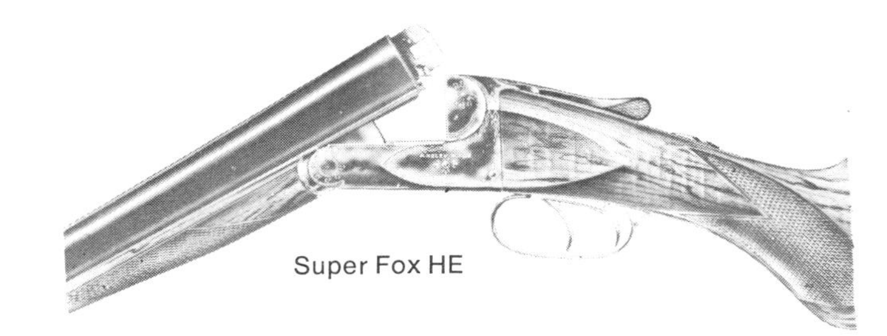
Super Fox HE

Fox Hammerless Double Barrel Shotgun, Super Fox HE Grade **$450**

Long Range Gun made in 12 gauge only (chambered for 3-inch shells on order), 30 or 32-inch full choke barrels, weighs 8¾ to 9¾ pounds, automatic ejectors standard. General specifications same as standard Sterlingworth.

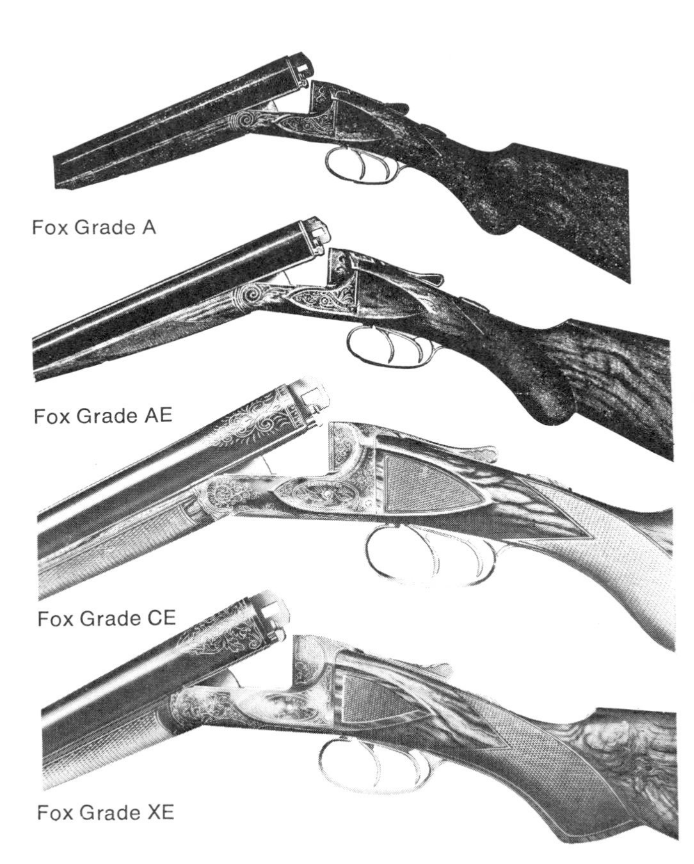
Fox Grade A
Fox Grade AE
Fox Grade CE
Fox Grade XE

Fox Hammerless Double Barrel Shotguns in the higher grades have the same general specifications as given for the standard Sterlingworth model. Differences are chiefly in workmanship and materials; the higher grade models are stocked in fine selected walnut and quantity and quality of engraving increases with price. With the exception of Grade A, all are equipped with automatic ejectors. Fox-Kautzky selective single trigger extra.
Grade A .... **$ 425**
Grade AE .... **$ 500**
Grade CE .... **$ 750**
Grade XE **$1,100**
Selective single trigger, extra on all grades ... **$ 75**
Ventilated rib, extra on all grades .... **$ 150**

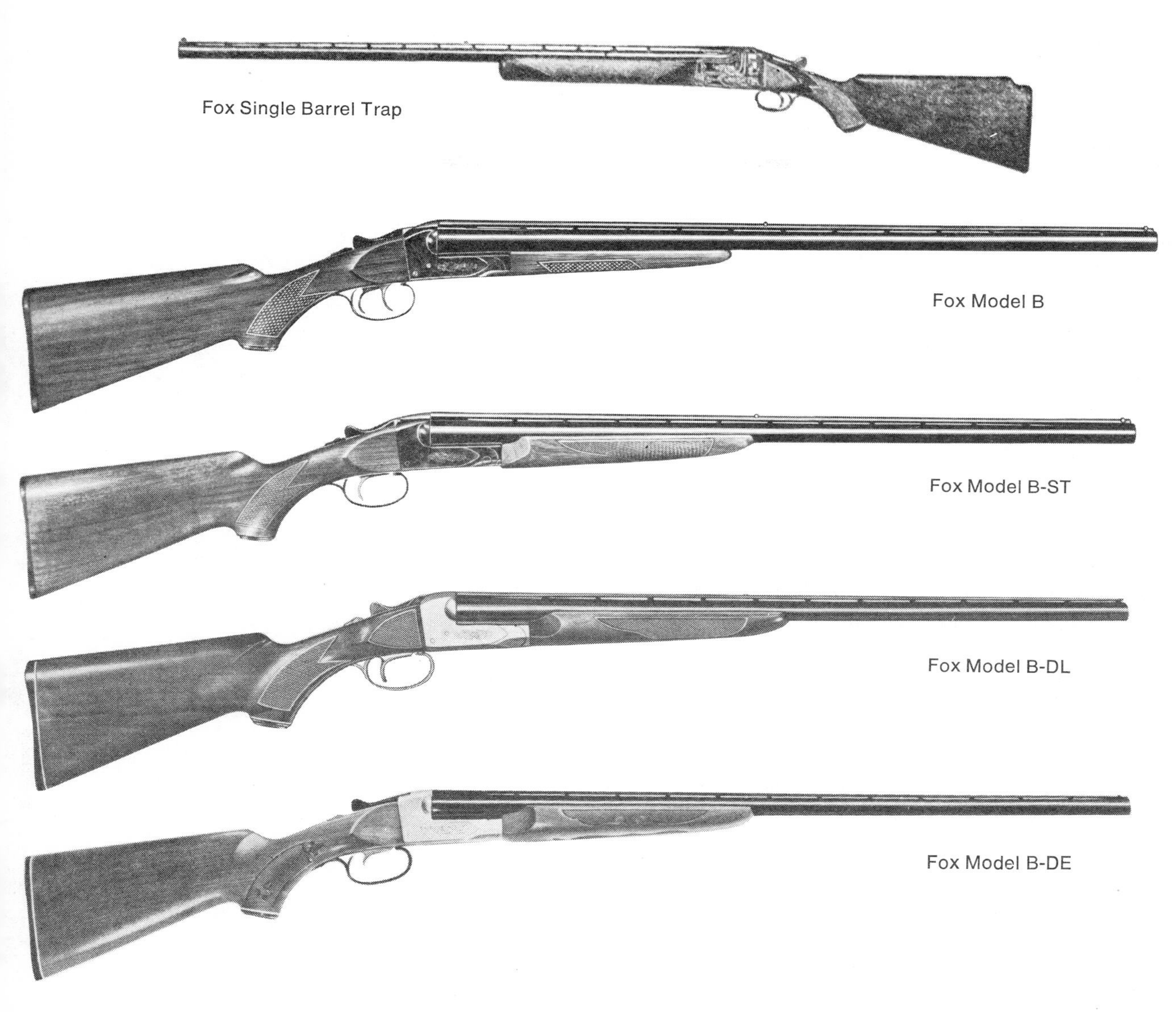

Fox Single Barrel Trap

Fox Model B

Fox Model B-ST

Fox Model B-DL

Fox Model B-DE

Fox Single Barrel Trap Guns

Box Lock. Automatic ejector. 12 gauge only. 30 or 32-inch ventilated rib barrel. Weight, from 7½ to 8 pounds. Trap-style stock and forearm of selected walnut, checkered, recoil pad optional. The four grades differ chiefly in quality of wood and engraving; Grade ME guns, built to order, have finest Circassian Walnut stock and are elaborately engraved and inlaid with gold. *Note:* In 1932 the Fox trap gun was redesigned and those manufactured after that date have an improved stock with full pistol grip and Monte Carlo comb; at the same time frame was changed to permit the rib line to extend across it to the rear. Values shown are for the 1932 and later models; for pre-1932 guns deduct about 25%.

Grade JE **$1,400**
Grade KE **$1,500**
Grade LE **$1,800**
Grade ME **$3,500**

Fox Model B Hammerless Double Barrel Shotgun . $115

Box lock. Double triggers. Plain extractor. Gauges: 12, 16, 20, 410. 26 to 30-inch barrels; ventilated rib on current production; chokes: modified and full, cylinder and modified, both full (410 only). Weight, about 7½ pounds in 12 gauge. Checkered pistol-grip stock and forearm. Made from about 1940 to date.

Fox Model B-ST $135

Same as Model B except has non-selective single trigger. Made from 1955 to 1966.

Fox Model B-DL $175

Same as Model B-ST except frame finished in satin chrome, select walnut buttstock with checkered pistol grip, side panels, beavertail forearm. Made from 1962 to 1965.

Fox Model B-DE $160

Same as Model B-ST except frame finished in satin chrome, select walnut buttstock with checkered pistol grip and beavertail forearm. Made from 1965 to 1966.

S. A. Luigi Franchi, Brescia, Italy

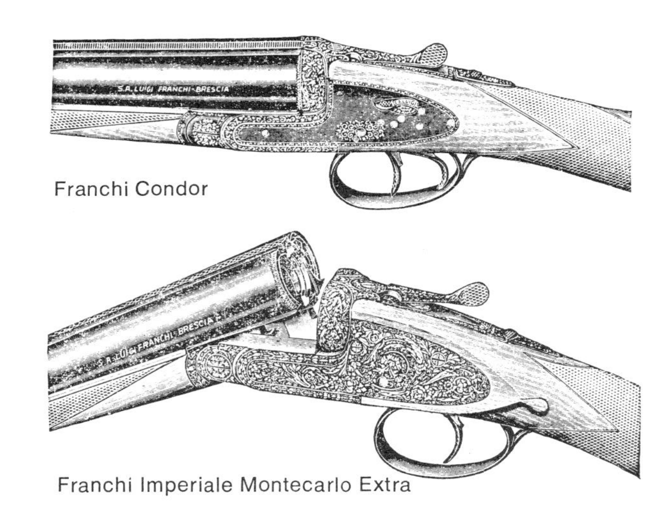
Franchi Condor

Franchi Imperiale Montecarlo Extra

Franchi Hammerless Side Lock Double Barrel Shotguns

Automatic ejectors. Hand-detachable locks, self-opening action optional. Double triggers or single trigger. Gauges: 12, 16, 20, 24. Barrel lengths, chokes, weights according to customer's specifications. Checkered stock and forend, straight or pistol grip. Made in six grades — Condor, Imperiale, Imperiale S, Imperiale Montecarlo No. 5, Imperiale Montecarlo No. 11, Imperiale Montecarlo Extra — which differ chiefly in overall quality, engraving, grade of wood, checkering, etc., general specifications are the same. Currently manufactured.

Condor Grade .... $ 475
Imperiale, Imperiale S Grades .... $ 625
Imperiale Montecarlo Grades No. 5, 11 .... $ 950
Imperiale Montecarlo Extra $1,150
Single trigger, extra .... $ 85
Self-opening action, extra .... $ 125

Franchi Standard Model Autoloader

Gauges: 12, 20. 4-shot magazine. Barrels: 26, 28, 30-inch; plain, solid rib, ventilated rib; improved cylinder, modified, full choke. Weights: 12 ga. — about 6¼ pounds, 20 ga. — 5⅛ pounds. Checkered pistol-grip stock and forearm. Made from 1950 to date.

With plain barrel $175
With solid rib $185
With ventilated rib $195

Franchi Standard Model Magnum Autoloader $215

Same general specifications as Standard Model except chambered for 12 gauge 3-inch Magnum; 32-inch plain full choke barrel, recoil pad; weighs about 8¼ pounds.

Franchi Hunter Model Autoloader

Same general specifications as Standard Model except higher grade with engraved receiver; furnished with ribbed barrel only. Made from 1950 to date.

With hollow matted rib $215
With ventilated rib $225

Franchi Hunter Model Magnum Autoloader $265

Same general specifications as Hunter Model except chambered for 12 gauge 3-inch Magnum; 32-inch ventilated rib full choke barrel, recoil pad; weighs about 8¼ pounds. Made from 1954 to 1973.

Franchi Eldorado Model Autoloader $280

Same general specifications as Standard Model except highest grade with gold-filled engraving, stock and forearm of selected walnut; furnished with ventilated rib barrel only. Made from 1954 to date.

Franchi Falconet Over-Under Shotgun

Box lock. Automatic ejectors. Selective single trigger. Gauges: 12, 16, 20, 28, 410. Barrels: 24, 26, 28, 30-inch; ventilated rib. Chokes: cylinder & improved cylinder, improved cylinder & modified, modified & full, skeet 1 & 2. Weight, about 6¼ pounds, except Skeet and Trap Models about 8 pounds. Engraved receiver; light-colored in Buckskin Model, blued in Ebony Model, pickled silver in Silver Model, color casehardened in Skeet and Trap Models. Checkered walnut stock and forearm. Made from 1968 to date.

Buckskin or Ebony Model $325
Silver Model $390
Trap or Skeet Model $615

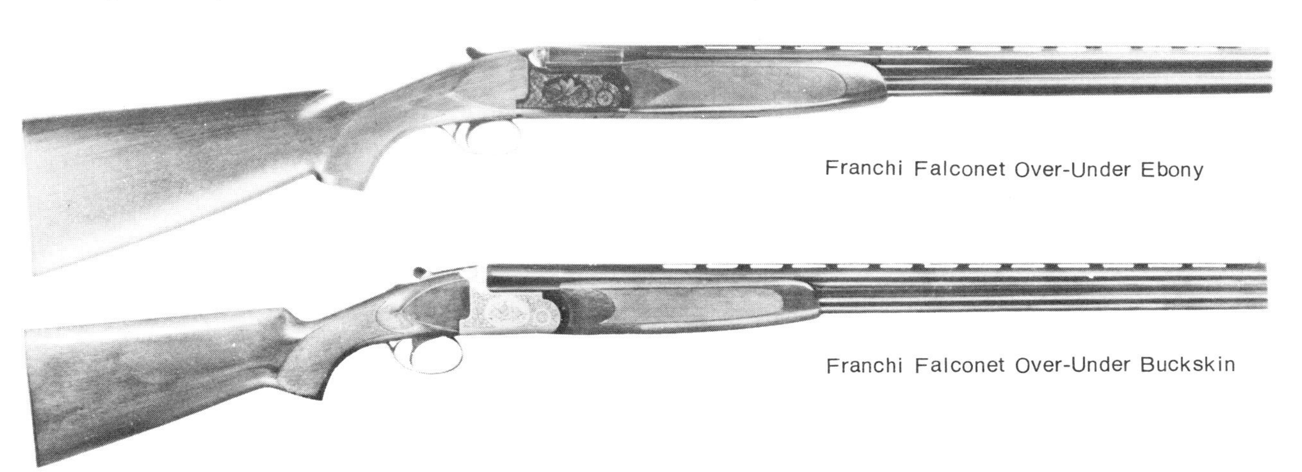
Franchi Falconet Over-Under Ebony

Franchi Falconet Over-Under Buckskin

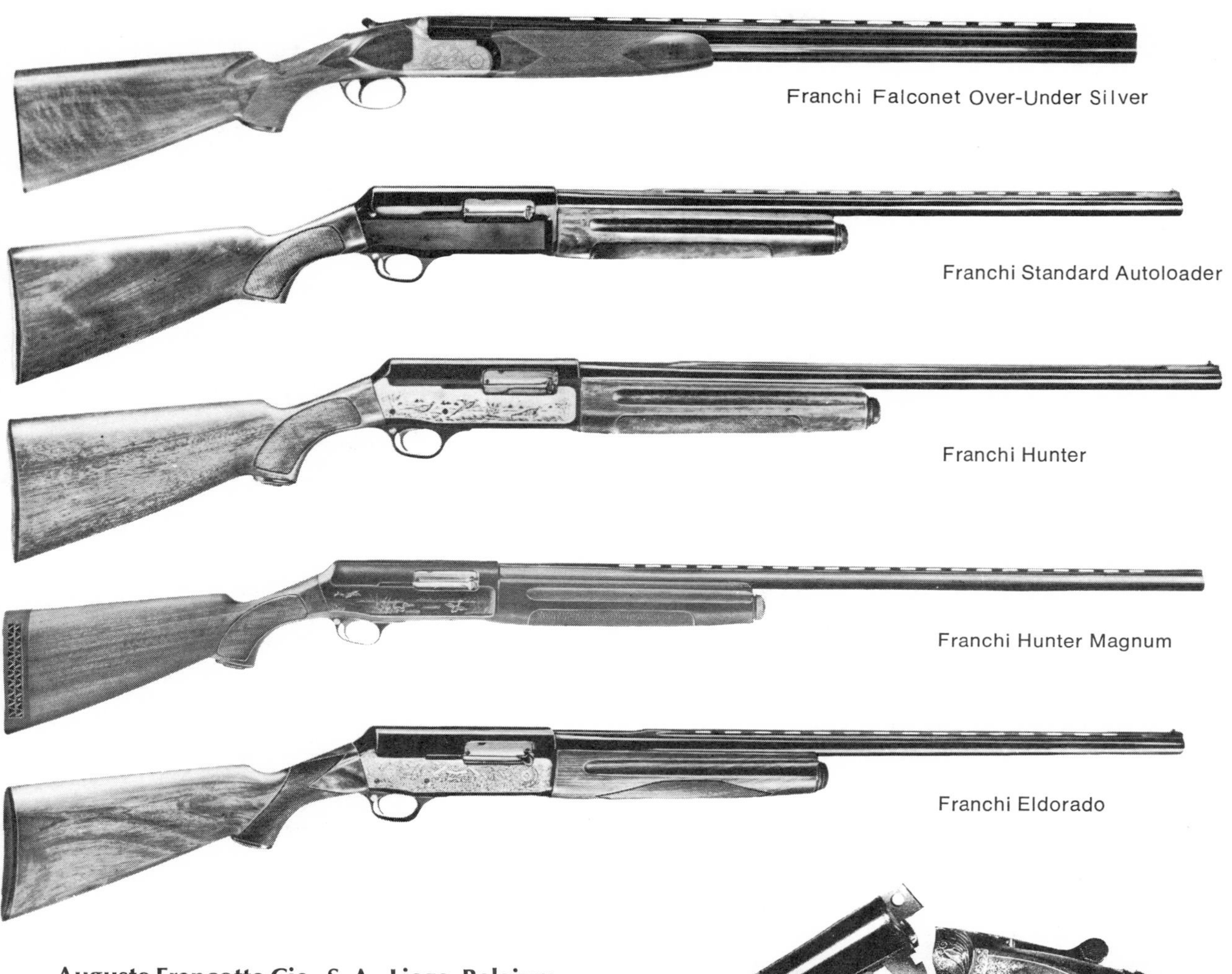
Franchi Falconet Over-Under Silver

Franchi Standard Autoloader

Franchi Hunter

Franchi Hunter Magnum

Franchi Eldorado

Auguste Francotte Cie., S. A., Liege, Belgium

Francotte shotguns for many years were distributed in the United States by the Abercrombie & Fitch Company of New York City. This firm has used a series of model designations for Francotte guns which do not correspond to those of the manufacturer. Because so many Francotte owners refer to their guns by the A & F model names and numbers, the A & F series is included in a listing separate from that of the standard Francotte numbers.

Francotte Hammerless Double Barrel Shotguns

A & F Series. Box lock, Anson & Deeley type. Crossbolt. Sideplates on all except Knockabout Model. Side clips Automatic ejectors. Double triggers. Gauges: 12, 16, 20, 28, 410. Barrels: 26 to 32-inch in 12 gauge, 26 and 28-inch in other gauges; any boring. Weight, 4¾ to 8 pounds depending upon gauge and barrel length. Checkered stock and forend; straight, half or full pistol grip. The seven grades — No. 45 Eagle Grade, No. 30, No. 25, No. 20, No. 14, Jubilee Model, Knockabout Model — differ chiefly in overall quality, engraving, grade of wood, checkering, etc., general specifications are the same. Discontinued.

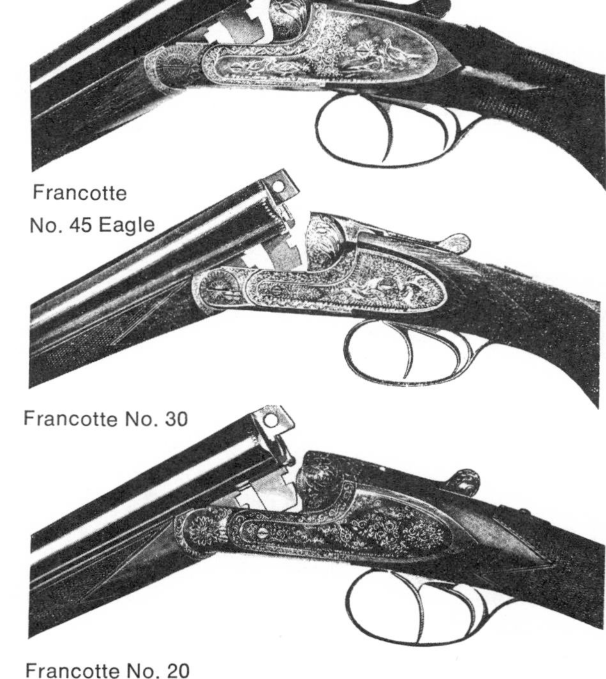
Francotte No. 45 Eagle

Francotte No. 30

Francotte No. 20

No. 45 Eagle Grade **$2,500**
No. 30 .... **$2,000**
No. 25 .... **$1,900**
No. 20 .... **$1,600**
No. 14 .... **$1,400**
Jubilee Model **$1,400**
Knockabout Model **$1,000**

Francotte Knockabout

Francotte Hammerless Boxlock Double Barrel Shotguns

Anson & Deeley system. Side clips. Greener cross bolt on Models 6886, 8446, 4996 and 9261; square cross bolt on Model 6930; Greener-Scott cross bolt on Model 8457; Purdey bolt on Models 11/18E and 10/18E/628. Automatic ejectors. Double triggers. Made in all standard gauges, barrel lengths, chokes, weights. Checkered stock and forend, straight or pistol grip. The eight models listed vary chiefly in fastening as described above, finish, and engraving, etc., general specifications are the same. All except Model 10/18E/628 have been discontinued.
Model 6886 .... **$1,100**
Models 8446 ("Francotte Special"), 6930, 4996 ... **$1,200**
Models 8457, 9261 ("Francotte Original"), 11/18E **$1,400**
Model 10/18E/628 .... **$2,000**

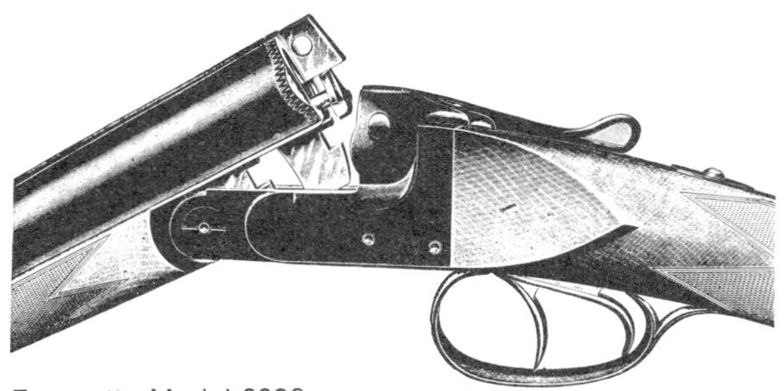
Francotte Model 6886

Francotte Hammerless Boxlock Double Barrel Shotguns With Sideplates

Anson & Deeley system. Reinforced frame with side clips. Purdey-type bolt except on Model 8455 which has Greener cross bolt. Automatic ejectors. Double triggers. Made in all standard gauges, barrel lengths, chokes, weights. Checkered stock and forend, straight or pistol grip. Models 10594, 8455 and 6982 are of equal quality, differ chiefly in style of engraving; Model 9/40E/38321 is a higher grade gun in all details and has fine English style engraving. Currently manufactured.
Models 10594, 8455, 6982 .... **$1,500**
Model 9/40E/38321 .... **$2,000**

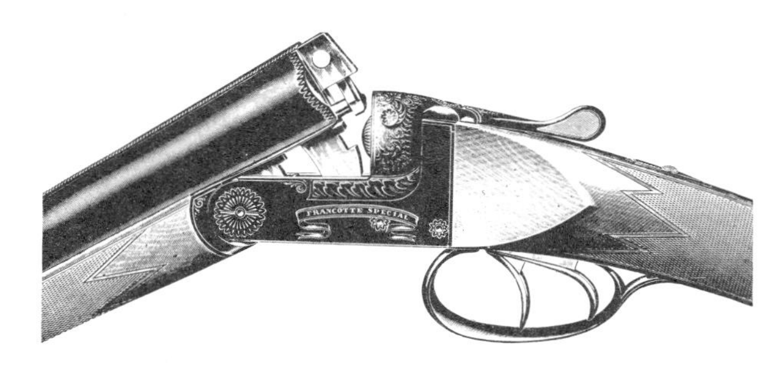

Francotte Model 8446

Francotte Fine Hammerless Sidelock Double Barrel Shotgun **$4,000**

Model 120.HE/328 Automatic ejectors. Double triggers. Made in all standard gauges; barrel length, boring, weight to order. Checkered stock and forend, straight or pistol grip. Currently manufactured.

Francotte Model 9261

Francotte Half-Fine Over-And-Under Shotgun ..**$3,000**

Model SOB.E/11082. Box lock, Anson & Deeley system. Automatic ejectors. Double triggers. Made in all standard gauges; barrel length, boring to order. Checkered stock and forend, straight or pistol grip.

Note: This model is quite similar to No. 9/40.SE except general quality is not as high and frame is not fully engraved or scalloped. Discontinued.

Francotte Fine Over-And-Under Shotgun **$4,000**

Model 9/40.SE. Box lock, Anson & Deeley system. Automatic ejectors. Double triggers. Made in all standard gauges; barrel length, boring to order. Weight, about 6¾ pounds in 12 gauge. Checkered stock and forend, straight or pistol grip. Currently manufactured.

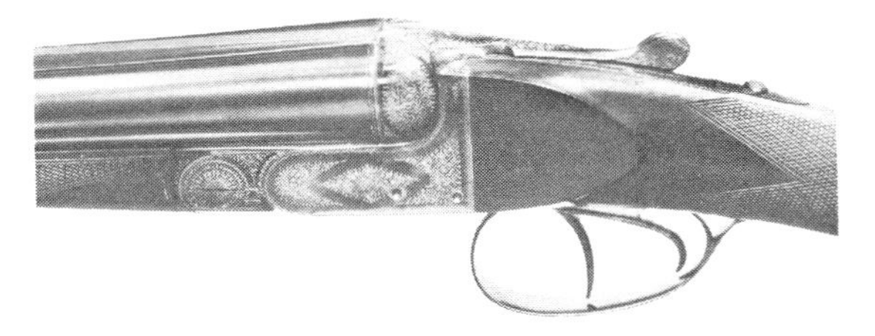
Francotte Model 10/18E/628

Francotte Model 6982

Greener Royal

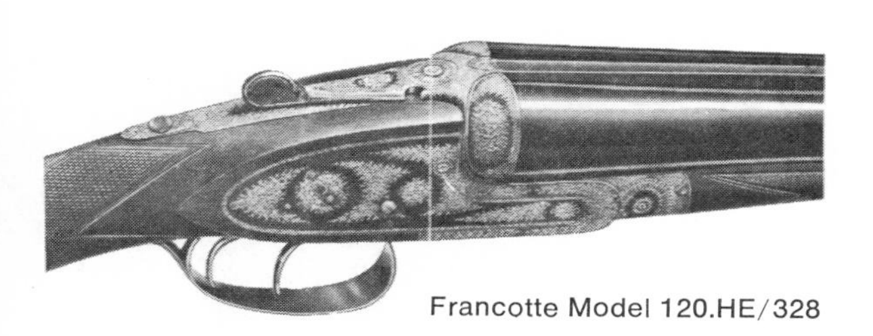

Francotte Model 120.HE/328

Greener Sovereign

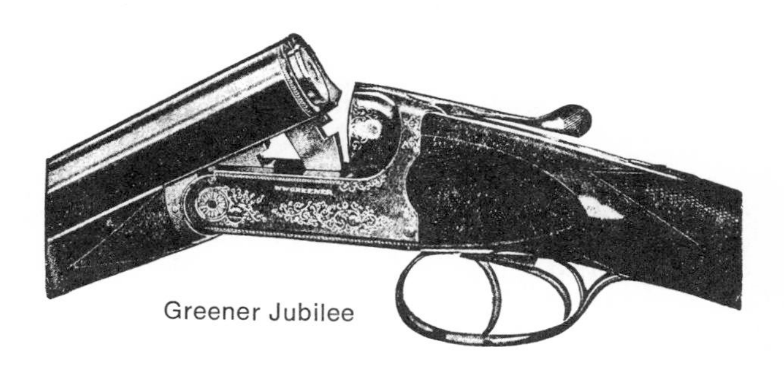

Greener Jubilee

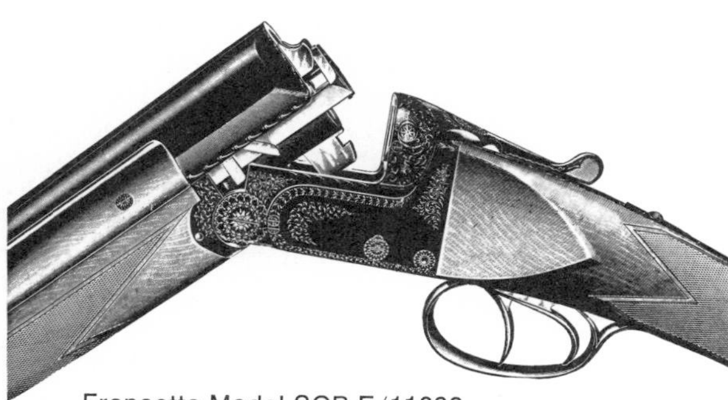

Francotte Model SOB.E/11082

Francotte Model 9/40.SE

W. W. Greener, Ltd., Birmingham, England

Greener Hammerless Ejector Double Barrel Shotguns

Box lock. Automatic ejectors. Double triggers, non-selective or selective single trigger. Gauges: 12, 16, 20, 28, 410 (two latter gauges not supplied in Grades DH40 and DH35). Barrels: 26, 28, 30-inch; any choke combination. Weight, from 4¾ to 8 pounds depending upon gauge and barrel length. Checkered stock and forend, straight or half-pistol grip. The Royal, Crown, Sovereign and Jubilee Models differ in quality, engraving, grade of wood, checkering, etc. General specifications are the same.

Royal Model Grade DH75 .... **$1,500**
Crown Model Grade DH55 .... **$1,300**
Sovereign Model Grade DH40 .... **$1,000**
Jubilee Model Grade DH35 .... **$ 900**
Selective single trigger, extra .... **$ 150**
Non-selective single trigger, extra .... **$ 75**

Greener Far-Killer

Greener Far-Killer Model Grade F35 Hammerless Double Barrel Shotgun

Box lock. Non-ejector or with automatic ejectors. Double triggers. Gauges: 12 (2¾-inch or 3-inch), 10, 8. Barrels: 28, 30 or 32-inch. Weight, from 7½ to 9 pounds in 12 gauge. Checkered stock and forend, straight or half pistol grip.
Non-ejector or half pistol grip .... **$ 900**
Ejector, 12 gauge **$1,300**
Non-ejector, 10 or 8 gauge **$1,000**
Ejector, 10 or 8 gauge **$1,400**

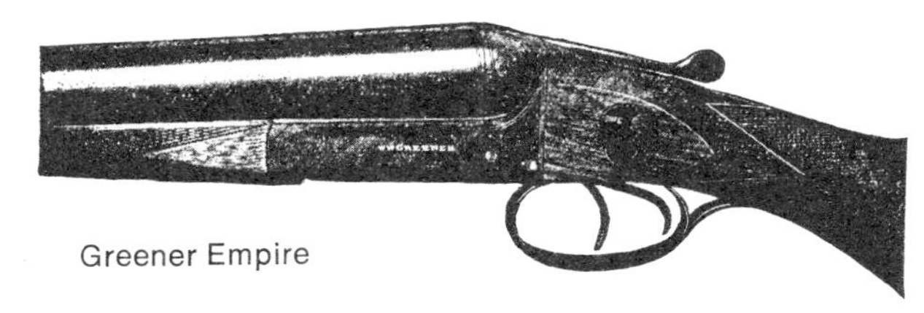
Greener Empire

Greener Empire Model Hammerless Double Barrel Shotgun

Box lock. Non-ejector or with automatic ejectors. Double triggers. 12 gauge only (2¾-inch or 3-inch chamber). Barrels: 28 to 32-inch; any choke combination. Weight, from 7¼ to 7¾ pounds depending upon barrel length. Checkered stock and forend, straight or half pistol grip. Also furnished in "Empire DeLuxe Grade"; this model has same general specifications but in deluxe finish. Currently manufactured.
Empire Model, non-ejector **$575**
Empire Model, ejector **$675**
Empire DeLuxe Model, non-ejector **$650**
Empire DeLuxe Model, ejector **$675**

Greener G. P. (General Purpose) Single Barrel Shotgun **$150**

Greener Improved Martini Lever Action. Takedown. Ejector. 12 gauge only. Barrel lengths: 26, 30, 32-inch. Modified or full choke. Weight, from 6¼ to 6¾ pounds depending upon barrel length. Checkered straight grip stock and forearm. Currently manufactured.

Greifelt & Co., Suhl, Germany

Greifelt Model 103 Hammerless Double Barrel Shotgun **$600**

Anson & Deeley box lock. Plain extractors. Double triggers. Gauges: 12 and 16. Barrels: 28 or 30-inch, modified and full choke. Checkered stock and forend, pistol grip and cheekpiece standard, English-style stock also supplied. Manufactured since World War II.

Greifelt Model 103E Hammerless Double Barrel Shotgun **$750**

Same as Model 103 except has automatic ejectors.

Greifelt Model 22 Hammerless Double Barrel Shotgun **$700**

Anson & Deeley box lock, sideplates. Plain extractors. Double triggers. Gauges: 12 and 16. Barrels: 28 or 30-inch, modified and full choke. Checkered stock and forend, pistol grip and cheekpiece standard, English style stock also supplied. Manufactured since World War II.

Greifelt Model 22 E Hammerless Double Barrel Shotgun **$900**

Same as Model 22 except has automatic ejectors.

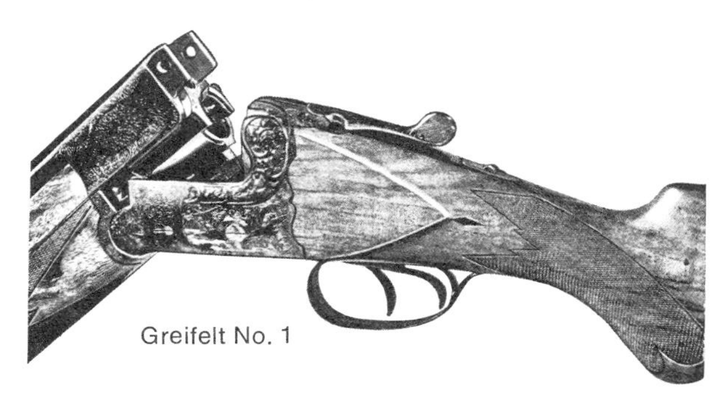
Greifelt No. 1

Greifelt Grade No. 1 Over-And-Under Shotgun

Anson & Deeley box lock, Kersten fastening. Automatic ejectors. Double triggers or single trigger. Elaborately engraved. Gauges: 12, 16, 20, 28, 410. Barrels: 26 to 32-inch, any combination of chokes, ventilated or solid matted rib. Weight, from 4¼ to 8¼ pounds depending upon gauge and barrel length. Straight or pistol grip stock, Purdey-type forend, both checkered. Manufactured prior to World War II.
With solid matted rib barrel, in all gauges except 410 **$2,200**
With solid matted rib barrel, 410 gauge **$2,600**
Extra for ventilated rib .... **$ 120**
Extra for single trigger .... **$ 150**

Greifelt Grade No. 3 Over-And-Under Shotgun

Same general specifications as Grade No. 1 except not as fancy engraving. Manufactured prior to World War II.
With solid matted rib barrel, in all gauges except 410 **$1,400**
With solid matted rib barrel, 410 gauge **$1,800**
Extra for ventilated rib .... **$ 120**
Extra for single trigger .... **$ 150**

Greifelt Model 143E Over-And-Under Shotgun

General specifications same as prewar Grade No. 1 Over-and-Under except this model is not supplied in 28 and 410 gauge or with 32-inch barrels. Model 143E is not as high quality as the Grade No. 1 gun. Manufactured since World War II.
With raised matted rib, double triggers **$1,100**
With ventilated rib, single selective trigger **$1,275**

Greifelt Over-And-Under Combination Gun

Similar in design to this maker's over-and-under shotguns. Gauges: 12, 16, 20, 28, 410; rifle barrel in any caliber adapted to this type of gun (*Note:* values shown are for guns chambered for cartridges readily obtainable; if rifle barrel is an odd foreign caliber, value will be considerably less). Barrels: 24 or 26-inch, solid matted rib. Weight, from 4¾ to 7¼ pounds. Folding rear sight. Manufactured prior to World War II.
With non-automatic ejector **$2,000**
With automatic ejector **$2,500**

Greifelt Hammerless Drilling (Three Barrel Combination Gun) **$2,000**

Box lock. Plain extractors. Double triggers, front single set for rifle barrel. Gauges: 12, 16, 20; rifle barrel in any caliber adapted to this type of gun (*Note:* value shown is for guns chambered for cartridges readily obtainable; if rifle barrel is an odd foreign caliber, value will be considerably less). 26-inch barrels. Weight, about 7½ pounds. Automatic rear sight operated by rifle barrel selector. Checkered stock and forearm, pistol grip and cheekpiece standard. Manufactured prior to WW II.

Harrington & Richardson Arms Co., Worcester, Massachusetts

H&R No. 8

Harrington & Richardson No. 8 Standard Single Barrel Hammer Shotgun **$30**
Takedown. Automatic ejector. Gauges: 12, 16, 20, 24, 28, 410. Barrels: plain, 26 to 32-inch, full choke. Weight, from 5½ to 6½ pounds depending upon gauge and barrel length. Plain pistol-grip stock and forend. Made from 1908 to 1942.

H&R No. 6

Harrington & Richardson No. 6 Heavy Breech Single Barrel Hammer Shotgun **$35**
Takedown. Automatic ejector. Gauges: 10, 12, 16, 20. Barrels: plain, 28 to 36-inch, full choke. Weight, about 7 to 7¼ pounds. Plain stock and forend. Discontinued 1942.

H&R No. 7

Harrington & Richardson Bay State No. 7 or 9 Single Barrel Hammer Shotgun **$30**
Takedown. Automatic ejector. Gauges: 12, 16, 20, 410. Barrels: plain, 26 to 32-inch full choke. Weight, from 5½ to 6½ pounds depending upon gauge and barrel length. Plain pistol-grip stock and forend. Discontinued 1942.

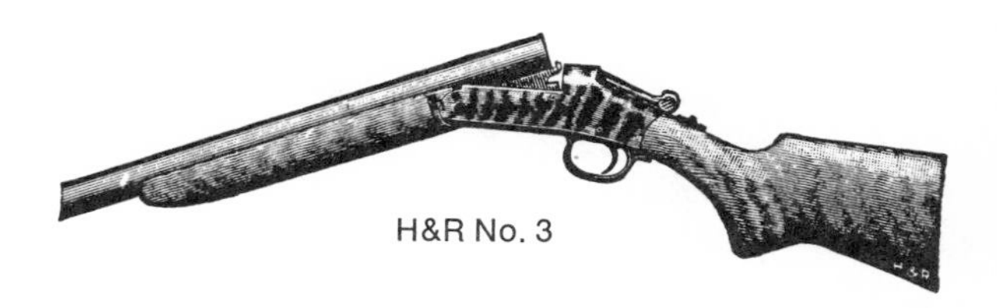
H&R No. 3

Harrington & Richardson No. 3 Hammerless Single Barrel Shotgun **$30**

Takedown. Automatic ejector. Gauges: 12, 16, 20, 410. Barrels: plain, 26 to 32-inch, full choke. Weight, from 6½ to 7¼ pounds depending upon gauge and barrel length. Plain pistol-grip stock and forend. Discontinued 1942.

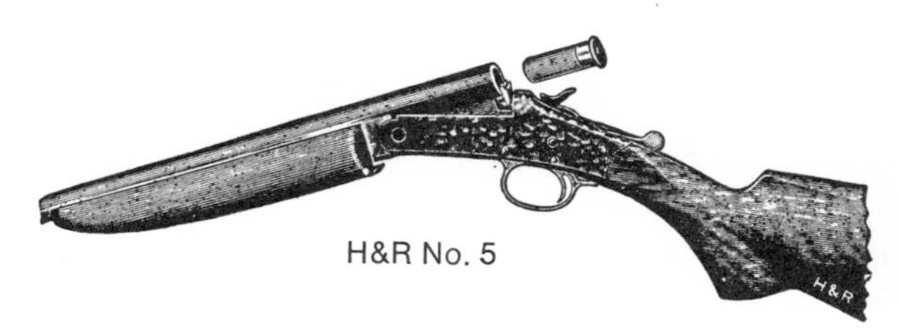

H&R No. 5

Harrington & Richardson Standard Light Weight No. 5 Hammer Single Barrel Shotgun **$30**

Takedown. Automatic ejector. Gauges: 24, 28, 410, 14mm. Barrels: 26 or 28-inch, full choke. Weight, about 4 to 4¾ pounds. Plain pistol-grip stock and forend. Discontinued 1942.

H&R Folding Gun

Harrington & Richardson Folding Gun **$35**

Single barrel hammer shotgun hinged at the front of the frame, the barrel folds down against the stock. Light Frame Model: gauges—28, 14mm, 410; 22-inch barrel; weight, about 4½ pounds. Heavy Frame Model: gauges—12, 16, 20, 28, 410; 26-inch barrel; weight, from 5¾ to 6½ pounds. Plain pistol-grip stock and forend. Discontinued 1942.

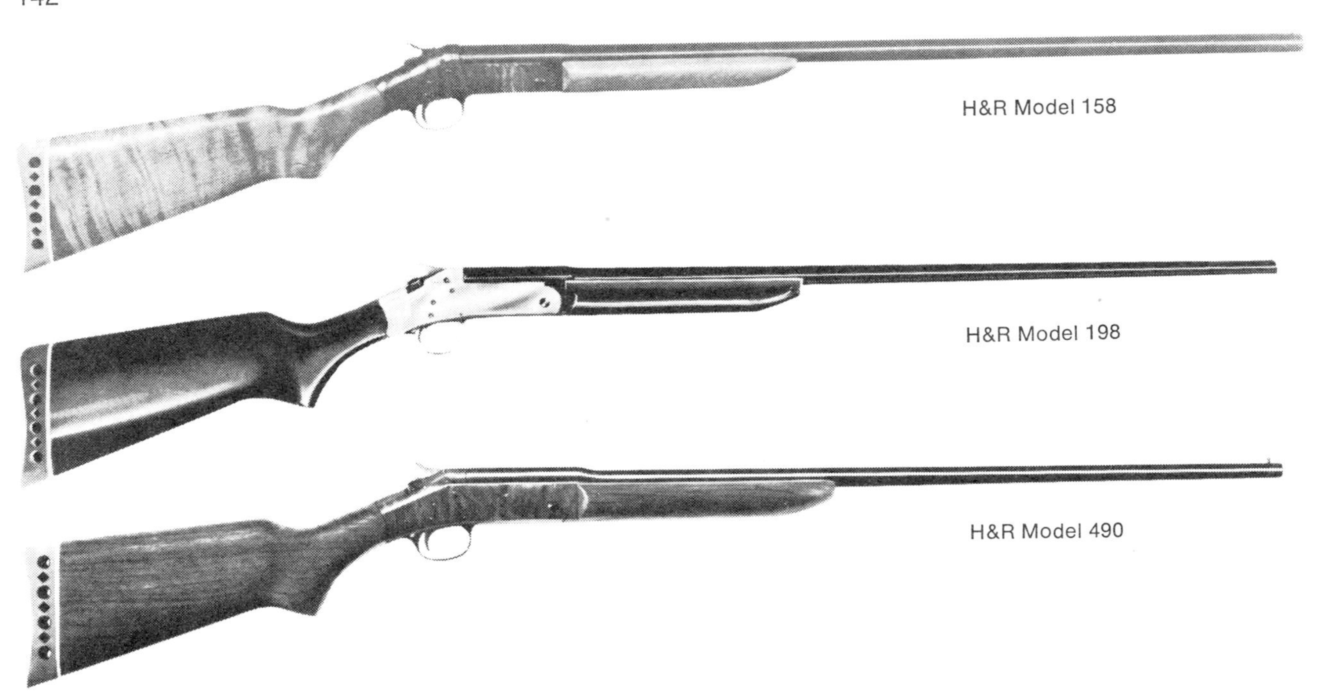

H&R Model 158

H&R Model 198

H&R Model 490

Harrington & Richardson No. 48 Topper Single Barrel Hammer Shotgun $30

Similar to old Model 8 Standard. Takedown. Top lever. Automatic ejector. Gauges: 12, 16, 20, 410. Barrels: plain, 26 to 30-inch, modified or full choke. Weight, 5½ to 6½ pounds depending upon gauge and barrel length. Plain pistol-grip stock and forend. Made from 1946 to 1957.

Harrington & Richardson No. 488 Topper De Luxe . . $30

Same as standard No. 48 Topper except chrome-plated frame, black lacquered stock and forend, recoil pad. Discontinued 1957.

Harrington & Richardson Topper Model 148 Single Barrel Hammer Shotgun $30

Takedown. Side lever. Automatic ejection. Gauges: 12, 16, 20, 410. Barrels: 12 ga., 30, 32 and 36-inch; 16 ga., 28 and 30 inch; 20 and 410 ga., 28 inch; full choke. Weight, 5 to 6½ pounds. Plain pistol-grip stock and forend, recoil pad. Made from 1958 to 1961.

Harrington & Richardson Topper De Luxe Model 188 $30

Same as standard Topper Model 148, except has chromed frame, stock and forend in black, red, yellow, blue, green, pink, or purple colored finish. 410 gauge only. Made from 1958 to 1961.

Harrington & Richardson Topper JR Model 480 . . $30

Similar to No. 48 Topper, except has youth size stock, 26-inch barrel, 410 gauge only. Made from 1958 to 1961.

Harrington & Richardson Topper JR Model 580 . . . $30

Same as Model 480 except has colored stocks as on Model 188. Made from 1958 to 1961.

Harrington & Richardson Model 158 Topper Single Barrel Hammer Shotgun $30

Takedown. Side lever. Automatic ejection. Gauges: 12, 20, 410 (2¾″ and 3″ shells); 16 (2¾″). Barrel length and choke combinations: 12 ga.—36″/full, 32″/full, 30″/full, 28″/full or modified; 16 ga.—28″/modified; 20 ga.—28″/full or modified; 410—28″/full. Weight, about 5½ pounds. Plain pistol-grip stock and forend, recoil pad. Made from 1962 to date.

Harrington & Richardson Model 198 Topper Deluxe $30

Same as Model 158, except has chrome-plated frame, black finished stock and forend; 20 and 410 gauges only. Made from 1962 to date.

Harrington & Richardson Model 490 Topper $30

Same as Model 158, except has youth size stock (3″ shorter), 26-inch barrel; 20 ga. (modified choke), 410 (full). Made from 1962 to date.

Harrington & Richardson Model 590 Topper $30

Same as Model 490, except has chrome-plated frame, black finished stock and forend. Made from 1962 to 1963.

H&R No. 48

H&R Model 159

Harrington & Richardson Model 159 Golden Squire Single Barrel Hammer Shotgun **$40**

Hammerless. Side lever. Automatic ejection. Gauges: 12, 20. Barrels: 30-inch in 12 ga., 28-inch in 20 ga., both full choke. Weight, about 6½ pounds. Straight-grip stock with recoil pad, forearm with schnabel. Made from 1964 to 1966.

Harrington & Richardson Model 459 Golden Squire Jr. **$40**

Same as Model 159, except gauges 20 and 410, 26-inch barrel, youth size stock. Made in 1964.

Harrington & Richardson Model 348 Gamester Bolt Action Shotgun **$30**

Takedown. 12 and 16 gauge. 2-shot tubular magazine. 28-inch barrel, full choke. Plain pistol-grip stock. Weight, about 7½ pounds. Made from 1949 to 1954.

Harrington & Richardson Model 349 Gamester De Luxe **$40**

Same as Model 348 except has 26-inch barrel with adjustable choke device, recoil pad. Made from 1953 to 1955.

Harrington & Richardson Model 351 Huntsman Bolt Action Shotgun **$40**

Takedown. 12 and 16 gauge. 2-shot tubular magazine. Push button safety. 26-inch barrel with H&R variable choke. Weight, about 6¾ pounds. Monte Carlo stock with recoil pad. Made from 1956 to 1958.

Harrington & Richardson Model 400 Pump Action Shotgun **$90**

Hammerless. Gauges: 12, 16, 20. Tubular magazine holds 5 shells. 28-inch barrel, full choke. Weight, about 7¼ pounds. Plain pistol-grip stock (recoil pad in 12 and 16 ga.), grooved slide handle. Made from 1955 to 1967.

Harrington & Richardson Model 401 . . . . **$95**

Same as Model 400, except has H&R variable choke. Made from 1956 to 1963.

Harrington & Richardson Model 402 . . . . **$95**

Similar to Model 400, except 410 gauge, weighs about 5½ pounds. Made from 1959 to 1967.

Harrington & Richardson Model 403 Autoloading Shotgun **$125**

Takedown. 410 gauge. Tubular magazine holds four shells. 26-inch barrel, full choke. Weight, about 5¾ pounds. Plain pistol-grip stock and forearm. Made in 1964.

Harrington & Richardson Model 404 Double Barrel Shotgun **$150**

Box lock. Plain extractors. Double triggers. Gauges: 12, 20, 410. Barrels: 28-inch modified & full choke in 12 ga., 26-inch in 20 ga. (improved cylinder & modified) and 410 (full & full). Weight, 5½ to 7¼ pounds. Plain walnut-finished hardwood stock and forend. Made in Brazil by Amadeo Rossi Cia.

Harrington & Richardson Model 404C **$165**

Same as Model 404, except has checkered stock and forend.

H&R Model 400

H&R Model 402

H&R Model 403

The High Standard Mfg. Corp., Hamden, Connecticut

High Standard Supermatic Field Autoloading Shotgun—12 Gauge $110

Gas-operated. Magazine holds four shells. Barrels: 26-inch improved cylinder, 28-inch modified or full choke, 30-inch full choke. Weight, about 7½ pounds. Plain pistol-grip stock and forearm. Made from 1960 to 1966.

High Standard Supermatic Special—12 Gauge $125

Same as Supermatic Field 12, except has 27-inch barrel with adjustable choke. Made from 1960 to 1966.

High Standard Supermatic Deluxe Rib—12 Gauge .. $135

Same as Supermatic Field 12, except ventilated rib barrel (28″ modified or full, 30″ full), checkered stock and forearm. Made from 1961 to 1966.

High Standard Supermatic Trophy—12 Gauge $150

Same as Supermatic Deluxe Rib 12, except has 27-inch ventilated rib barrel with adjustable choke. Made from 1961 to 1966.

High Standard Supermatic Duck—12 Gauge Magnum $120

Same as Supermatic Field 12, except chambered for 3″ Magnum shell, 30-inch full choke barrel, recoil pad. Made from 1961 to 1966.

High Standard Supermatic Duck Rib—12 Gauge Magnum $135

Same as Supermatic Duck 12 Magnum, except has ventilated rib barrel, checkered stock and forearm. Made from 1961 to 1966.

High Standard Supermatic Skeet—12 Gauge $135

Same as Supermatic Deluxe Rib 12, except 26-inch ventilated rib barrel bored Skeet choke. Made from 1962 to 1966.

High Standard Supermatic Trap—12 Gauge $135

Same as Supermatic Deluxe Rib 12, except 30″ ventilated rib barrel, full choke; special trap stock with recoil pad. Made from 1962 to 1966.

High Standard Supermatic Field Autoloading Shotgun—20 Gauge $110

Gas-operated. Chambered for 3″ magnum shells, also handles 2¾″. Magazine holds three shells. Barrels: 26-inch improved cylinder, 28-inch modified or full choke. Weight, about 7 pounds. Plain pistol-grip stock and forearm. Made from 1963 to 1966.

High Standard Supermatic Special—20 Gauge ... $125

Same as Supermatic Field 20, except has 27-inch barrel with adjustable choke. Made from 1963 to 1966.

High Standard Supermatic Deluxe Rib—20 Gauge $135

Same as Supermatic Field 20, except ventilated rib barrel (28-inch modified or full), checkered stock and forearm. Made from 1963 to 1966.

High Standard Supermatic Trophy—20 Gauge ... $150

Same as Supermatic Deluxe Rib 20, except has 27-inch ventilated rib barrel with adjustable choke. Made from 1963 to 1966.

High Standard Supermatic Skeet—20 Gauge $135

Same as Supermatic Deluxe Rib 20, except 26-inch ventilated rib barrel bored Skeet choke. Made from 1964 to 1966.

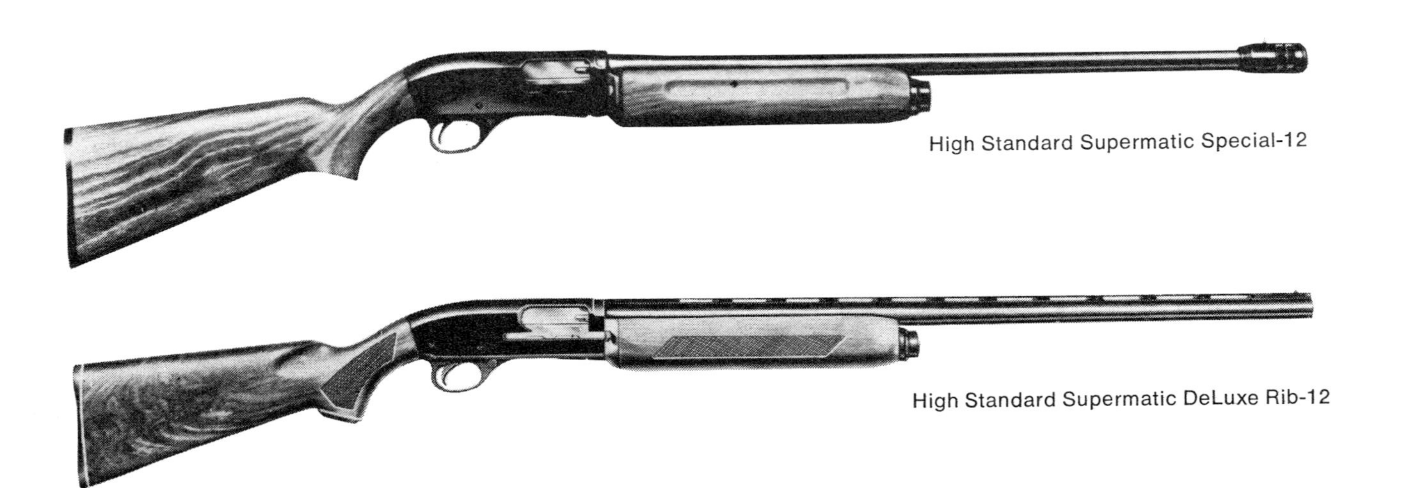

High Standard Supermatic Special-12

High Standard Supermatic DeLuxe Rib-12

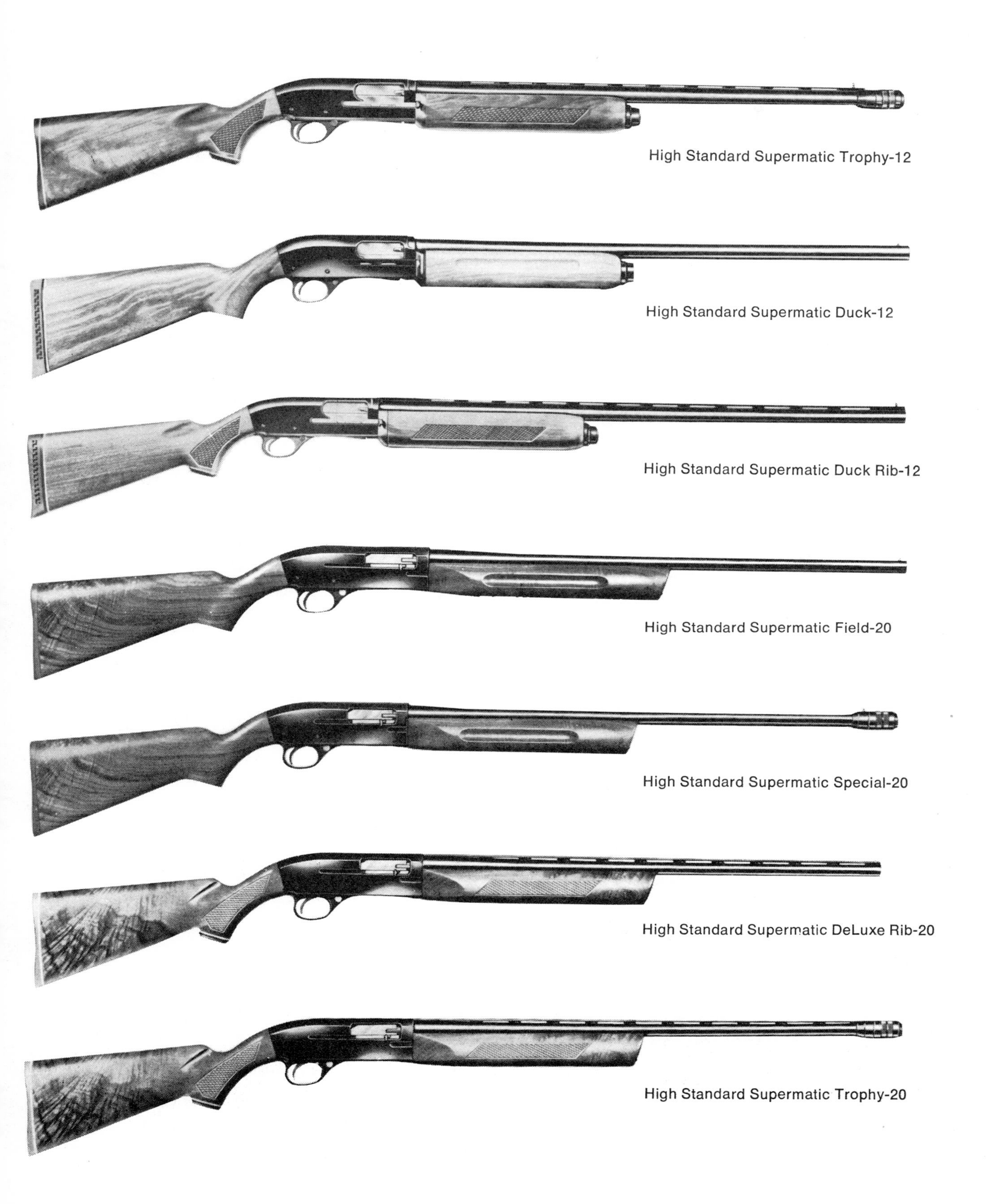

High Standard Supermatic Trophy-12

High Standard Supermatic Duck-12

High Standard Supermatic Duck Rib-12

High Standard Supermatic Field-20

High Standard Supermatic Special-20

High Standard Supermatic DeLuxe Rib-20

High Standard Supermatic Trophy-20

High Standard Flite-King Field Pump Shotgun— 12 Gauge $75

Hammerless. Magazine holds 5 shells. Barrels: 26-inch improved cylinder, 28-inch modified or full, 30-inch full choke. Weight, 7¼ pounds. Plain pistol-grip stock and slide handle. Made from 1960 to 1966.

High Standard Flite-King Special—12 Gauge $90

Same as Flite-King Field 12, except has 27-inch barrel with adjustable choke. Made from 1960 to 1966.

High Standard Flite-King Deluxe Rib—12 Gauge . . $100

Same as Flite-King Field 12, except ventilated rib barrel (28″ modified or full 30″ full), checkered stock and forearm. Made from 1961 to 1966.

High Standard Flite-King Trophy—12 Gauge $115

Same as Flite-King Deluxe Rib 12, except has 27-inch ventilated rib barrel with adjustable choke. Made from 1960 to 1966.

High Standard Flite-King Brush—12 Gauge $90

Same as Flite-King Field 12, except has 18 or 20-inch barrel (cylinder bore) with rifle sights. Made from 1962 to 1964.

High Standard Flite-King Skeet—12 Gauge $110

Same as Flite-King Deluxe Rib, except 26-inch ventilated rib barrel bored Skeet choke. Made from 1962 to 1966.

High Standard Flite-King Trap—12 Gauge $115

Same as Flite-King Deluxe Rib 12, except 30″ ventilated rib barrel, full choke; special trap stock with recoil pad. Made from 1962 to 1966.

High Standard Flite-King Pump Shotguns—16 Gauge

Same general specifications as Flite-King 12, except not available in Brush, Skeet, and Trap Models, or 30-inch barrel. Values same as for 12 gauge guns. Made from 1961 to 1965.

High Standard Flite-King Field Pump Shotgun— 20 Gauge $75

Hammerless. Chambered for 3″ Magnum shells, also handles 2¾″. Magazine holds four shells. Barrels: 26-inch improved cylinder, 28-inch modified or full choke. Weight, about 6 pounds. Plain pistol-grip stock and slide handle. Made from 1961 to 1966.

High Standard Flite-King Special—20 Gauge $90

Same as Flite-King Field 20, except has 27-inch barrel with adjustable choke. Made from 1961 to 1966.

High Standard Flite-King Deluxe Rib—20 Gauge . . $100

Same as Flite-King Field 20, except ventilated rib barrel (28-inch modified or full), checkered stock and slide handle. Made from 1962 to 1966.

High Standard Flite-King Trophy—20 Gauge $115

Same as Flite-King Deluxe Rib 20, except has 27-inch ventilated rib barrel with adjustable choke. Made from 1962 to 1966.

High Standard Flite-King Pump Shotguns—410 Gauge

Same general specifications as Flite-King 20, except not available in Special and Trophy Models, or with other than 26-inch full choke barrel. Values same as for 20 gauge guns. Made from 1962 to 1966.

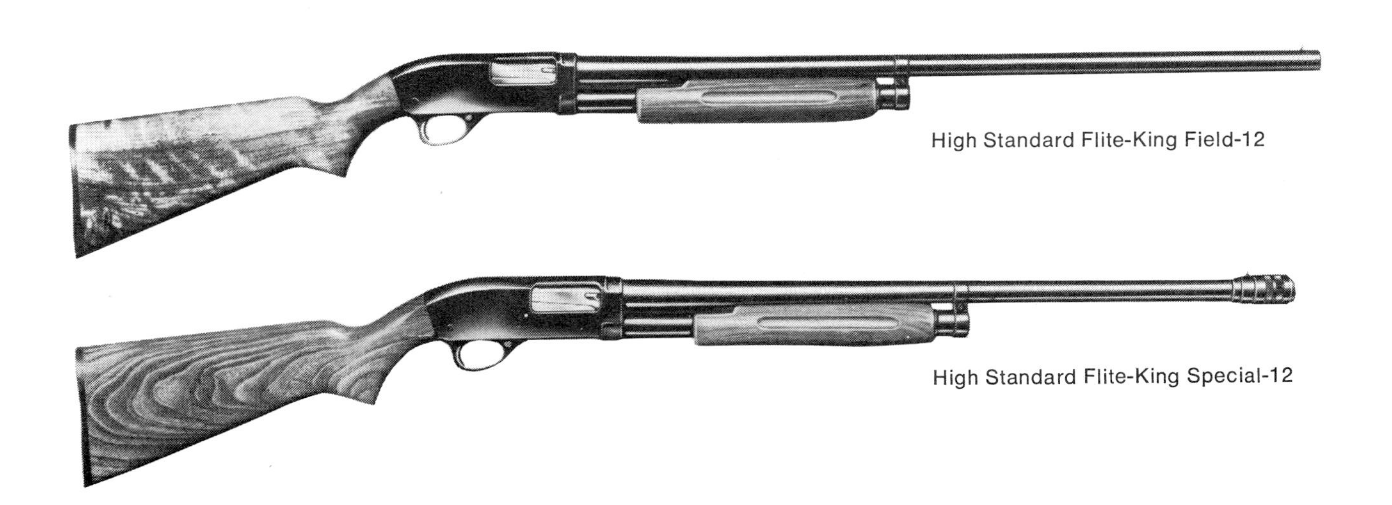

High Standard Flite-King Field-12

High Standard Flite-King Special-12

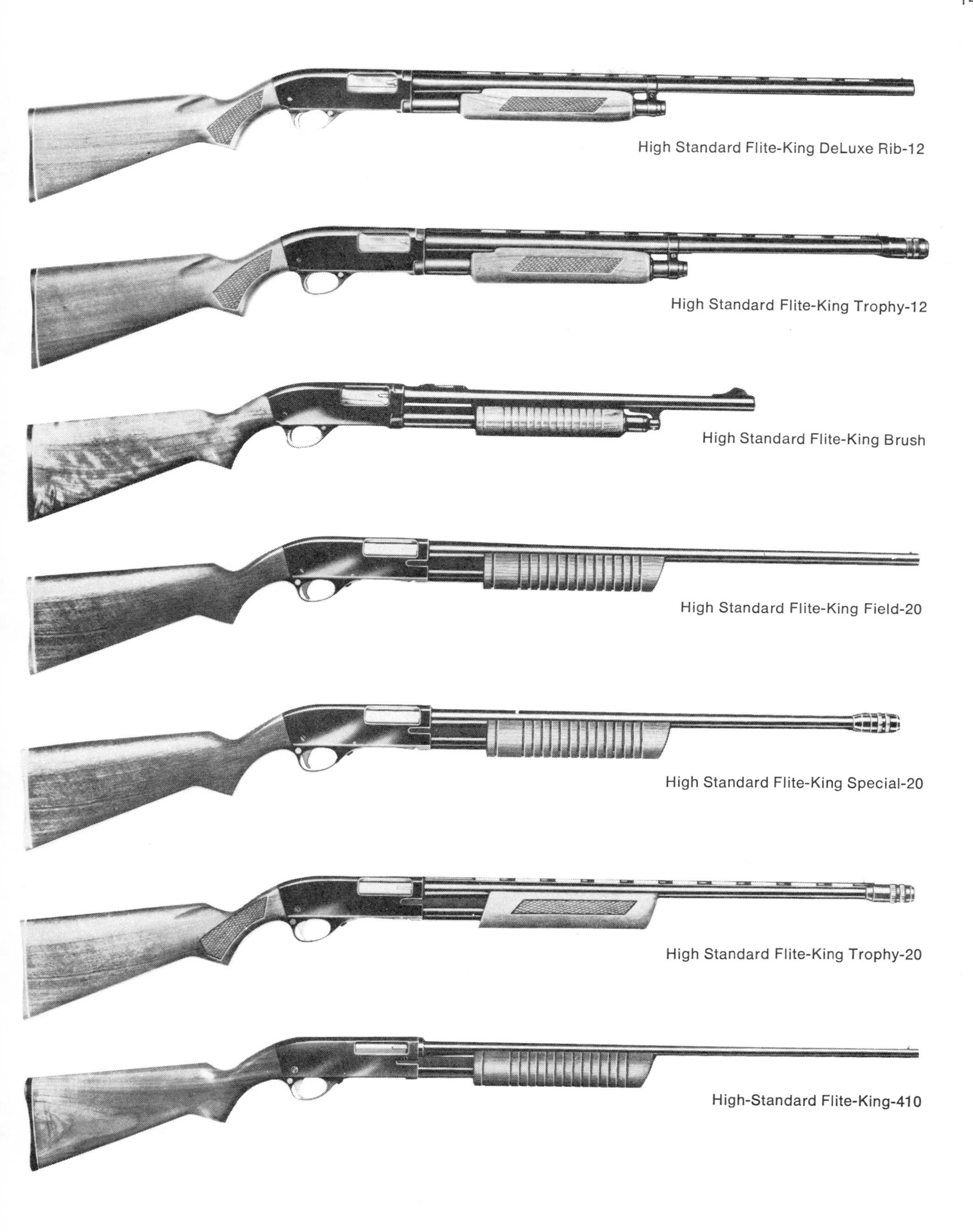

High Standard Flite-King DeLuxe Rib-12

High Standard Flite-King Trophy-12

High Standard Flite-King Brush

High Standard Flite-King Field-20

High Standard Flite-King Special-20

High Standard Flite-King Trophy-20

High-Standard Flite-King-410

Holland & Holland, Ltd., London, England

Holland & Holland Royal Model Under-And-Over Gun

Side locks, hand-detachable. Automatic ejectors. Double triggers or single trigger. 12 gauge. Built to customer's specifications as to barrel length, chokes, etc. Made as a Game Gun or Pigeon and Wildfowl Gun. Checkered stock and forend, straight grip standard. *Note:* In 1951 Holland & Holland introduced their New Model Under-and-Over Gun with an improved, narrower action body.
New Model with double triggers **$7,000**
New Model with single trigger **$7,500**
Old Model with double triggers **$5,500**
Old Model with single trigger **$6,000**

Holland & Holland Model De Luxe Hammerless Double Barrel Shotgun

Self-opening. Side locks, hand detachable. Automatic ejectors. Double triggers or single trigger. Gauges: 12, 16, 20, 28. Built to customer's specifications as to barrel length, chokes, etc. Made as a Game Gun or Pigeon and Wildfowl Gun, the latter having treble grip action and side clips. Checkered stock and forend, straight grip standard. Currently manufactured.
With double triggers **$4,500**
With single trigger **$4,900**

Holland & Holland Royal Model Hammerless Double Barrel Shotgun

General specifications same as Modele DeLuxe, differs from that grade in style of engraving. Made as a Game Gun ("Royal Brevis") or Pigeon and Wildfowl Gun. Currently manufactured.
With double triggers **$4,100**
With single trigger **$4,500**

Holland & Holland Badminton Model Hammerless Double Barrel Shotgun

General specifications same as Royal Model except without self-opening action. Made as a Game Gun or Pigeon and Wildfowl Gun. Currently manufactured.
With double triggers **$2,300**
With single trigger **$2,700**

Holland & Holland Riviera Model Pigeon Gun **$3,500**

Same as Badminton Model but supplied with two sets of barrels, double triggers. Currently manufactured.

Holland & Holland Dominion Model Hammerless Double Barrel Shotgun **$1,300**

Game Gun. Side lock. Automatic ejectors; Double triggers. Gauges: 12, 16, 20. Barrels: 25 to 30-inch, any standard boring. Checkered stock and forend, straight grip standard. Currently manufactured.

Holland & Holland Centenary Model Hammerless Double Barrel Shotgun

Lightweight (5½-pound). 12 gauge game gun designed for 2-inch shell. Made in four grades—Modele DeLuxe, Royal, Badminton, Dominion—values same as shown for standard guns in those grades.

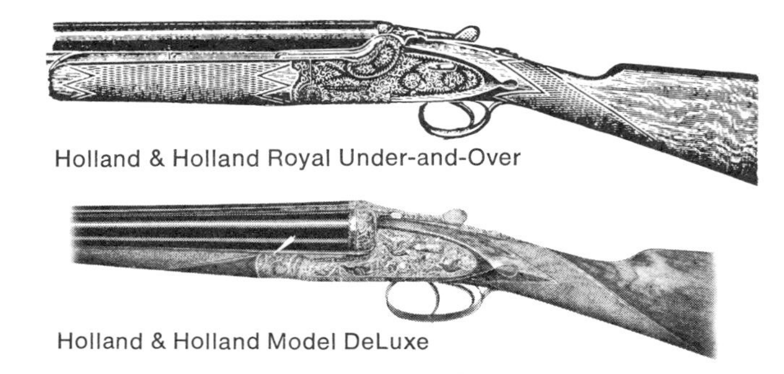

Holland & Holland Royal Under-and-Over

Holland & Holland Model DeLuxe

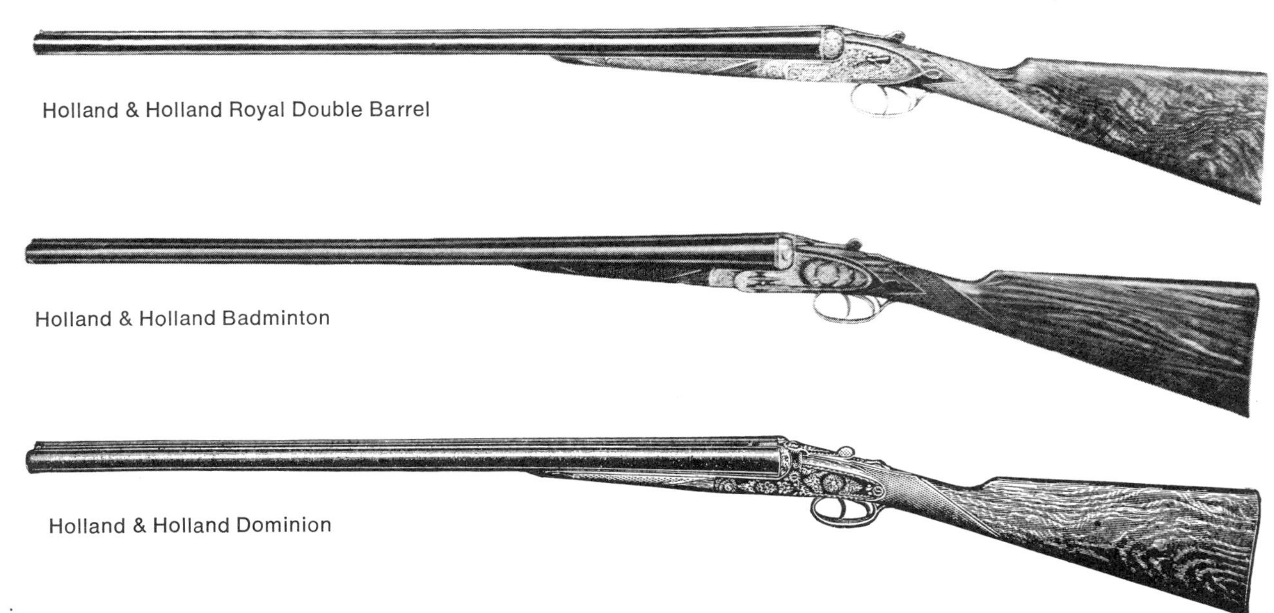

Holland & Holland Royal Double Barrel

Holland & Holland Badminton

Holland & Holland Dominion

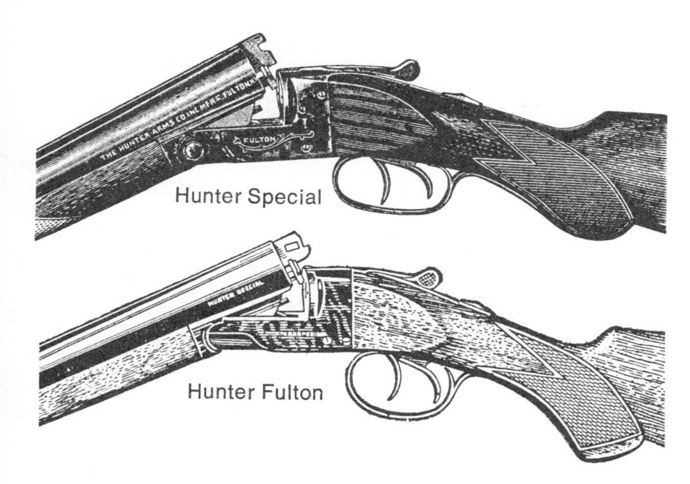

Hunter Special

Hunter Fulton

Hunter Arms Company, Fulton, N.Y.

Hunter Fulton Hammerless Double Barrel Shotgun

Box lock. Plain extractors. Double triggers or non-selective single trigger. Gauges: 12, 16, 20. Barrels: 26 to 32-inch, various choke combinations. Weight, about 7 pounds. Checkered pistol-grip stock and forearm. Discontinued 1948.

With double triggers **$300**
With single trigger **$375**

Hunter Special Hammerless Double Barrel Shotgun

Box lock. Plain extractors. Double triggers or non-selective single trigger. Gauges: 12, 16, 20. Barrels: 26 to 30-inch, various choke combinations. Weight, 6½ to 7¼ pounds depending upon barrel length and gauge. Checkered full pistol-grip stock and forearm. Discontinued 1948.

With double triggers **$425**
With single trigger **$500**

Ithaca Gun Company, Ithaca, N.Y.

Ithaca Hammerless Double Barrel Shotguns

Box lock. Plain extractors, automatic ejectors standard on the "E" grades. Double triggers, non-selective or selective single trigger extra. Gauges: Magnum 10, Magnum 12, 12, 16, 20, 28, 410. Barrels: 26 to 32-inch, any standard boring. Weight, 5¾ (410) to 10½ pounds (Magnum 10). Checkered pistol-grip stock and forearm standard. The higher grades differ from the Field Grade chiefly in quality of workmanship, grade of wood, checkering, engraving, etc.; general specifications are the same. Ithaca doubles made before 1926 had under bolts and a bolt through the rib extension (parts are no longer available for old Ithaca doubles numbered under 400,000). In 1926 the rotary bolt and a stronger frame were adopted. Values shown are for this latter type; earlier models bring prices about 50% under those of the more recent type. Ithaca double guns were discontinued in 1948.

Field Grade . . . . **$ 300**
No. 1 Grade . . . . **$ 350**
No. 2 Grade . . . . **$ 400**

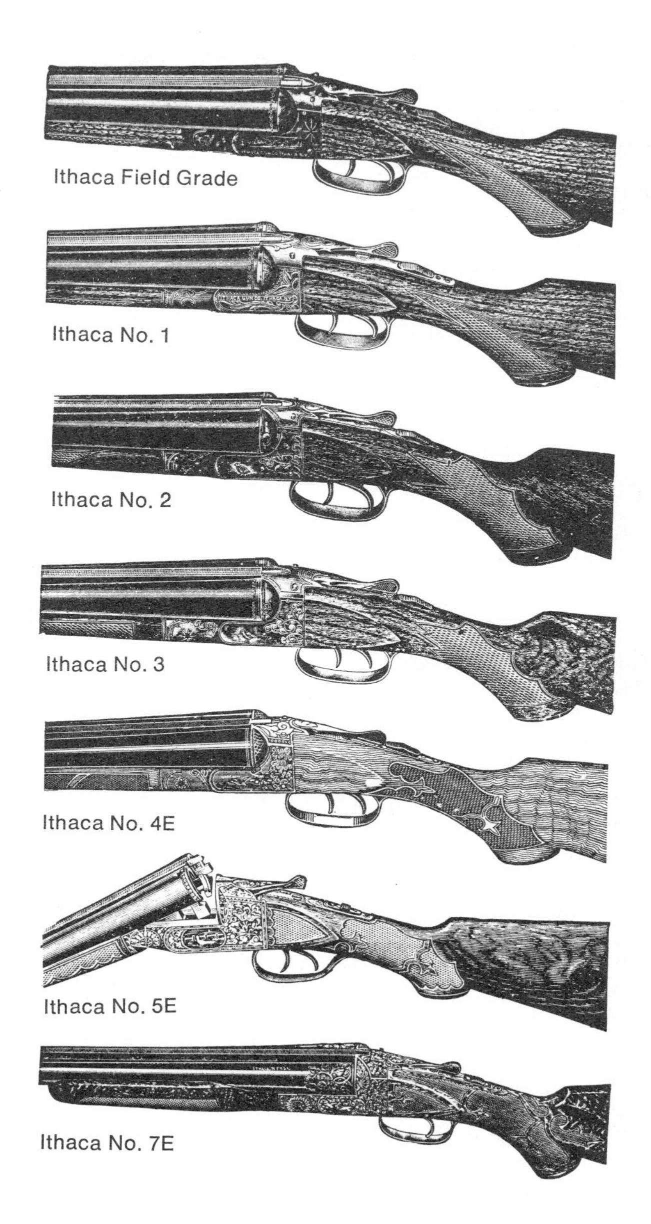
Ithaca Field Grade

Ithaca No. 1

Ithaca No. 2

Ithaca No. 3

Ithaca No. 4E

Ithaca No. 5E

Ithaca No. 7E

No. 3 Grade . . . . **$ 500**
No. 4-E Grade (ejector) . . . . **$ 750**
No. 5-E Grade (ejector) **$1,500**
No. 7-E Grade (ejector) **$3,000**
$2000 (pre-war $1,000) Grade (ejector and selective single trigger standard) **$4,500**

Extras:

Magnum 10 or 12 gauge (in other than the four highest grades), add . . . . **$ 100**
Automatic ejectors (Grades No. 1, 2, 3, with ejectors are designated No. 1E, 2E, 3E), add . . . . **$ 125**
Selective single trigger, add . . . . **$ 125**
Non-selective single trigger, add . . . . **$ 75**
Beavertail forend (Field, No. 1 or 2), add . . . . **$ 100**
Beavertail forend (No. 3 or 4), add . . . . **$ 125**
Beavertail forend (No. 5, 7 or $2000. Grade), add **$ 175**
Ventilated rib (No. 4, 5, 7 or $2000. Grade), add **$ 250**
Ventilated rib (lower grades), add . . . . **$ 175**

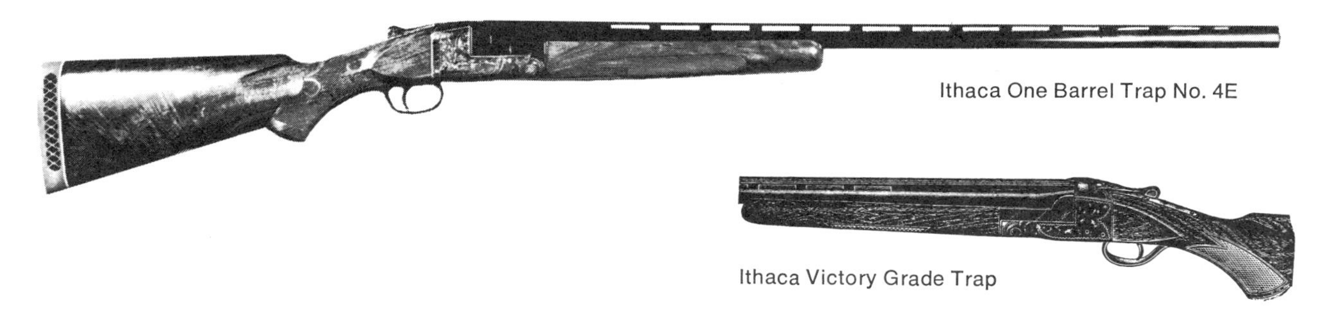

Ithaca One Barrel Trap No. 4E

Ithaca Victory Grade Trap

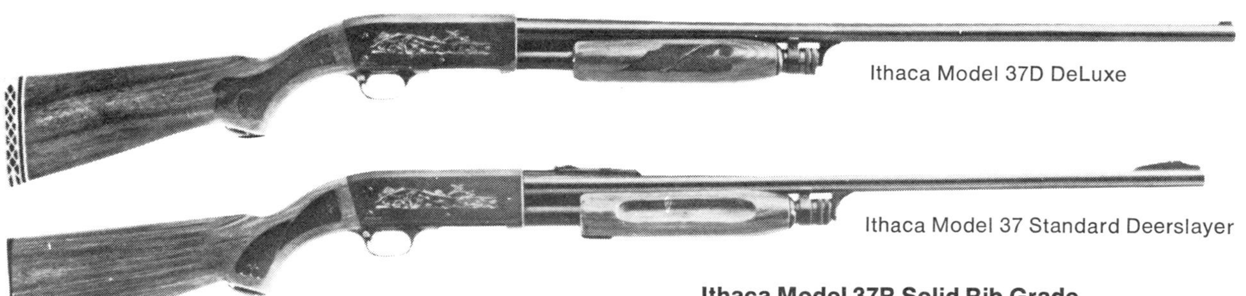

Ithaca Model 37D DeLuxe

Ithaca Model 37 Standard Deerslayer

Ithaca One Barrel Trap Guns

Box lock. Hammerless. Ejector. 12 gauge only. Barrel lengths: 30, 32, 34-inch (32-inch only in Victory Grade). Ventilated rib. Weight, about 8 pounds. Checkered pistol-grip stock and forend. The five grades differ only in quality of workmanship, grade of engraving, checkering, wood, etc. Victory Grade discontinued during late 1930's, other grades still manufactured.

Victory Grade .... **$ 700**
No. 4-E **$1,750**
No. 5-E **$2,450**
No. 7-E **$2,900**
$5,000 Grade (prewar $1,000 Grade) **$3,500**

Ithaca Model 37 Featherlight Standard Grade Slide Action Repeating Shotgun

Hammerless. Takedown. Gauges: 12, 16, 20. 4-shell tubular magazine. Barrel lengths: 26, 28, 30-inch (the latter in 12 gauge only); any standard choke. Weight, from 5¾ to 7½ pounds depending upon gauge and barrel length. Checkered pistol-grip stock and slide handle. Some guns made in the 1950's and 1960's have grooved slide handle; pistol grip on these may be plain or checkered.

(*Note:* The Ithaca Model 37 is an adaptation of the earlier Remington Model 17, a Browning design patented in 1915). Made from 1937 to date.

With checkered pistol-grip **$110**
With plain stock .... **$ 90**

Ithaca Model 37D Deluxe **$115**

Same as Model 37 Standard except checkered stock and beavertail forearm, recoil pad. Made from 1954 to date.

Ithaca Model 37R Solid Rib Grade

Same general specifications as the Model 37 Featherlight except has a raised solid rib, adding about ¼-pound of weight. Made from 1937 to 1967.

With checkered grip and slide handle **$125**
With plain stock **$100**

Ithaca Model 37R De Luxe Solid Rib **$150**

Same general specifications as Model 37R, except has fancy walnut stock and slide handle, checkered. Made from 1955 to 1961.

Ithaca Model 37S Skeet Grade **$220**

Same general specifications as the Model 37 Featherlight except has ventilated rib and large extension-type fore-end, weighs about ½-pound more than the Featherlight. Made from 1937 to 1955.

Ithaca Model 37T Trap Grade **$260**

Same general specifications as Model 37S except has straighter trap-style stock of selected walnut, recoil pad, weighs about ½-pound more than Model 37S. Made from 1937 to 1955.

Ithaca Model 37T Target Grade **$250**

Same general specifications as Model 37 Featherlight, except has ventilated rib barrel, checkered stock and slide handle of fancy walnut (choice of Skeet or Trap style stock). *Note:* This model replaced Model 37S Skeet and Model 37T Trap. Made from 1955 to 1961.

Ithaca Model 37 Standard Deerslayer **$125**

Same as Model 37 Standard except has 20 or 26-inch barrel bored for rifled slugs, rifle-type open rear sight and ramp front sight, weighs 5¾ to 6½ pounds depending upon gauge and barrel length. Made from 1959 to date.

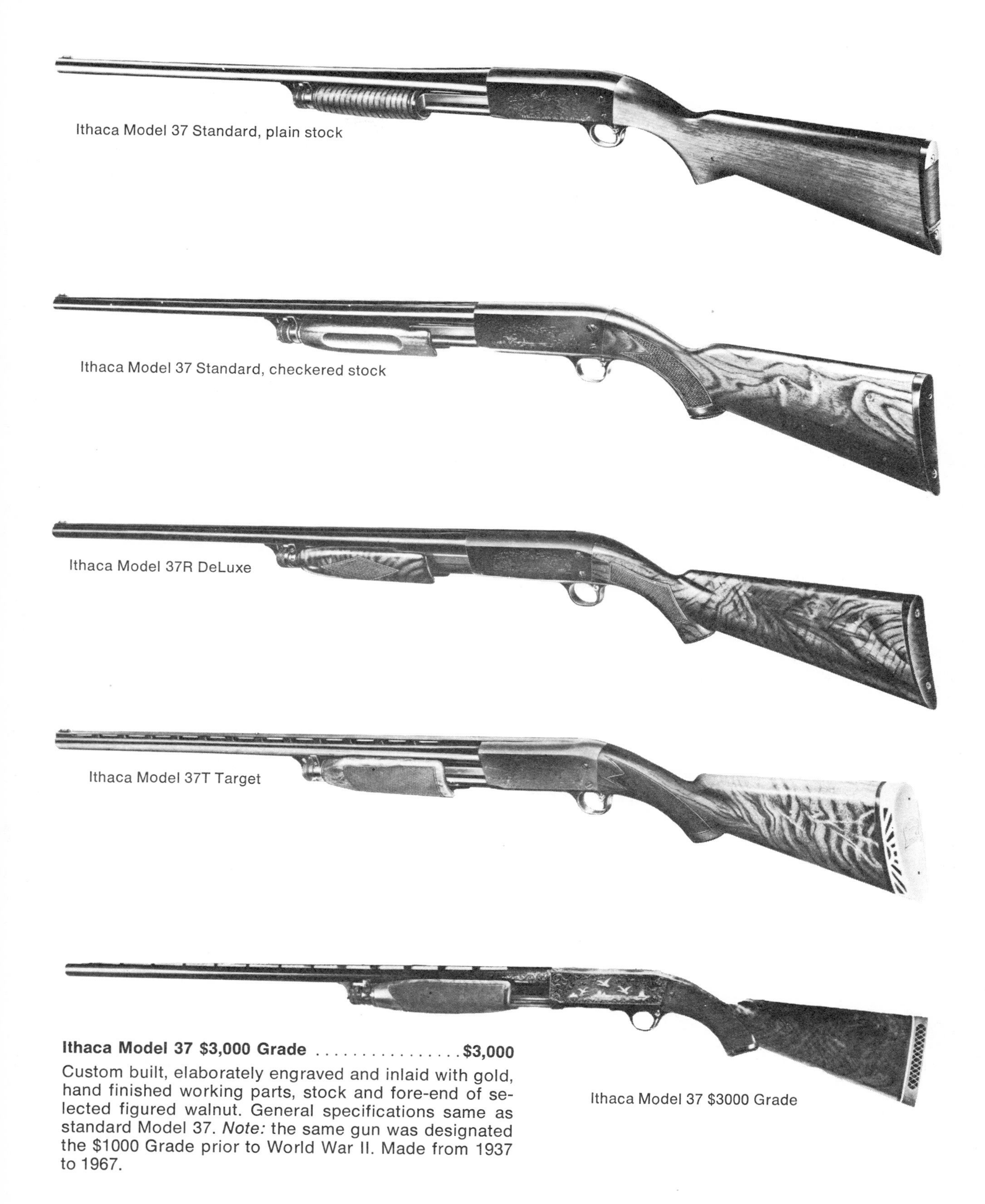

Ithaca Model 37 Standard, plain stock

Ithaca Model 37 Standard, checkered stock

Ithaca Model 37R DeLuxe

Ithaca Model 37T Target

Ithaca Model 37 $3000 Grade

Ithaca Model 37 $3,000 Grade $3,000

Custom built, elaborately engraved and inlaid with gold, hand finished working parts, stock and fore-end of selected figured walnut. General specifications same as standard Model 37. *Note:* the same gun was designated the $1000 Grade prior to World War II. Made from 1937 to 1967.

Ithaca Standard Model 66 Supersingle Lever Action Shotgun $40

Single shot. Hand-cocked hammer. Gauges: 12, 20, 410; 3-inch chambers. Barrels: 12 ga.—30″/full choke, 28″/full or modified; 20 ga.—28″/full or modified; 410—26″/full. Weight, about 7 pounds. Checkered straight-grip stock, plain forend. Made from 1964 to date.

Ithaca Youth Model 66 Supersingle $40

Same as Standard Model 66, except 26-inch barrel, shorter stock and recoil pad; 20 and 410 gauges only. Made from 1965 to date.

Ithaca-SKB Model 100 Side-By-Side Double Gun . . $195

Box lock. Plain extractors. Selective single trigger. Automatic safety. Gauges: 12 and 20; 2¾″ and 3″ chambers respectively. Barrels: 30″/full and full (12 ga. only), 28″/full and modified, 26″/improved cylinder and modified (12 ga. only), 25″/improved cylinder and modified choke (20 ga. only). Weights: 12 ga., about 7 pounds; 20 ga., about 6 pounds. Checkered stock and forend. Made from 1966 to date.

Ithaca-SKB Model 200E Field Grade Side-By-Side $275

Same as Model 100, except automatic selective ejectors, engraved and silver-plated frame, gold-plated nameplate and trigger, beavertail forearm. Made from 1966 to date.

Ithaca-SKB Model 200E Skeet Gun $285

Same as Model 200E Field Grade, except 26-inch (12 ga.) and 25-inch (20 ga./2¾″ chambers) barrels bored skeet choke; has non-automatic safety and recoil pad. Made from 1966 to date.

Ithaca-SKB Model 500 Field Grade Over-And-Under Gun $260

Box lock. Automatic selective ejectors. Single selective trigger. Non-automatic safety. Gauges: 12 and 20; 2¾″ and 3″ chambers respectively. Ventilated rib barrels: 30″/modified and full (12 ga. only), 28″/modified and full, 26″/improved cylinder and modified choke. Weights: 12 ga., about 7½ pounds; 20 ga., about 6½ pounds. Checkered stock and forearm. Made from 1966 to date.

Ithaca-SKB Model 600 Trap Grade Over-And-Under Gun $325

Same as Model 500, except 12 gauge only, 30 or 32-inch barrels bored full and full or full and improved modified choke, choice of Monte Carlo or straight stock, recoil pad, weight about 8 pounds. Made from 1966 to date.

Ithaca-SKB Model 600 Skeet Grade $325

Same as Model 500, except 26 or 28-inch barrels bored skeet choke, recoil pad; weights, 7¾ pounds in 12 ga., 7 pounds in 20 ga. Made from 1966 to date.

Note: Ithaca-SKB shotguns are manufactured in Japan.

Ithaca Model 66 Standard Supersingle

Ithaca-SKB Model 100

Ithaca-SKB Model 200E Skeet

Ithaca-SKB Model 500

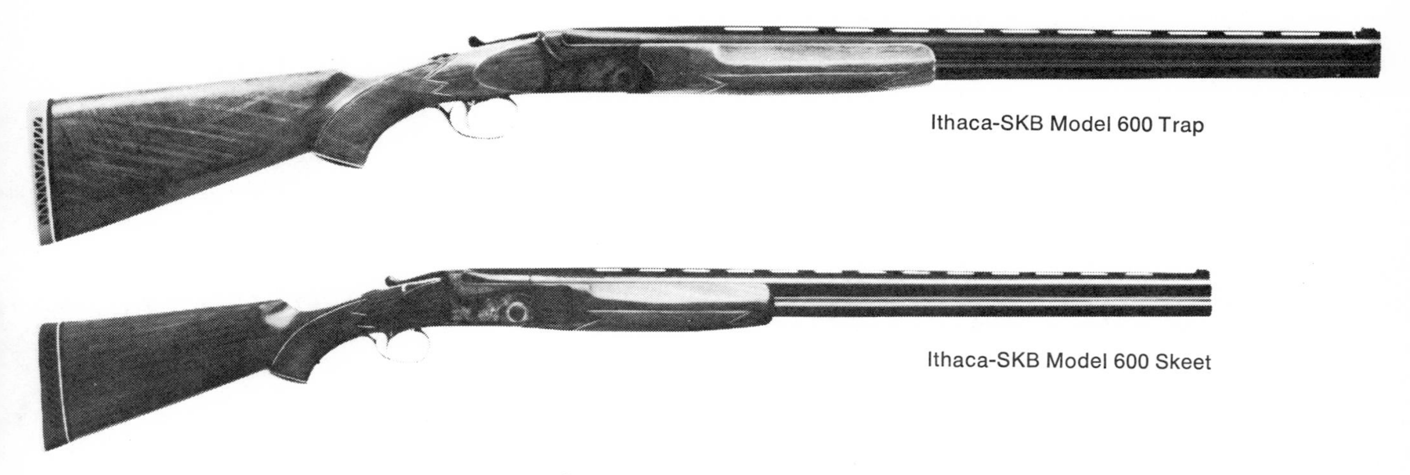

Ithaca-SKB Model 600 Trap

Ithaca-SKB Model 600 Skeet

Iver Johnson's Arms & Cycle Works, Fitchburg, Massachusetts

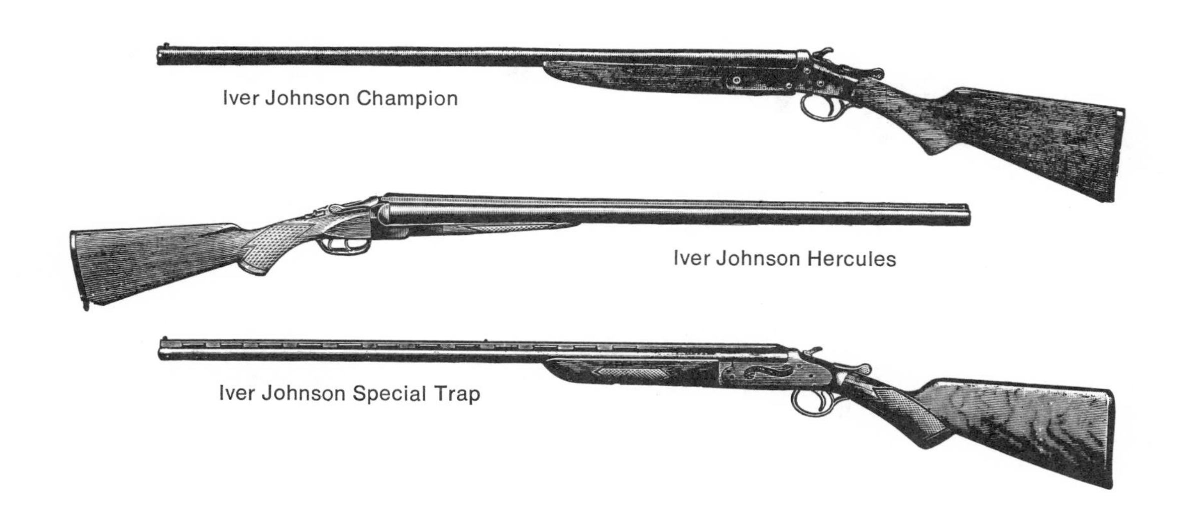

Iver Johnson Champion

Iver Johnson Hercules

Iver Johnson Special Trap

Iver Johnson Champion Grade Single Barrel Hammer Shotgun $40

Automatic ejector. Gauges: 12, 16, 20, 410. Barrels: 26 to 32-inch, full choke. Weight, from 5¾ to 6½ pounds depending upon gauge and barrel length. Plain pistol-grip stock and forend. Made from 1909 to date.

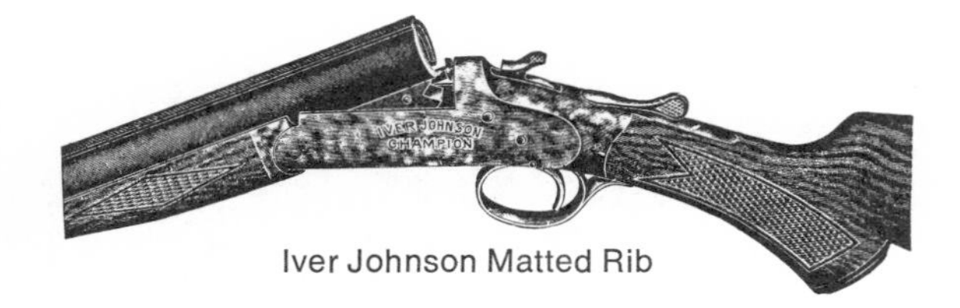

Iver Johnson Matted Rib

Iver Johnson Matted Rib Grade Single Barrel Hammer Shotgun $50

Same general specifications as Champion Grade except has solid matted top rib, checkered stock and forend, weighs about ¼-pound more. Discontinued 1948.

Iver Johnson Hercules Grade Hammerless Double Barrel Shotgun

Box lock. Plain extractors or automatic ejectors. Double triggers or Miller single trigger (selective or non-selective). Gauges: 12, 16, 20, 410. Barrel lengths: 26 to 32-inch, chokes both full or modified and full. Weight, from 5¾ to 7¾ pounds, depending upon gauge and barrel length and whether plain extractor or ejector model. Checkered straight or pistol-grip stock and forend. Discontinued 1948.

With double triggers, plain extractors **$180**
With double triggers, automatic ejectors **$225**
Extra for non-selective single trigger . . . . **$ 50**
Extra for selective single trigger . . . . **$ 75**

Iver Johnson Special Trap Single Barrel Hammer Shotgun $275

Automatic ejector. 12 gauge only. 32-inch barrel with ventilated rib, full choke. Weight, about 7½ pounds. Checkered pistol-grip stock and forend. Discontinued 1942.

Iver Johnson Skeeter

Iver Johnson Skeeter Model Hammerless Double Barrel Shotgun

Box lock. Plain extractors or automatic ejectors. Double triggers or Miller single trigger (selective or non-selective). Gauges: 12, 16, 20, 28, 410. 26 or 28-inch barrels, skeet boring standard. Weight, about 7½ pounds. Straight or pistol-grip stock, beavertail forend, both checkered. Discontinued 1942.
With double triggers, plain extractors **$325**
With double triggers, automatic ejectors **$375**
Extra for non-selective single trigger .... **$ 50**
Extra for selective single trigger .... **$ 75**

Iver Johnson Super Trap

Iver Johnson Super Trap Hammerless Double Barrel Shotgun

Box lock. Plain extractors. Double triggers or Miller single trigger (selective or non-selective), 12 gauge only. 32-inch full choke barrels, ventilated rib. Weight, about 8½ pounds. Checkered pistol-grip stock and beavertail forend, recoil pad. Discontinued 1942.
With double triggers **$450**
With non-selective single trigger **$500**
With selective single trigger **$600**

Kessler Arms Corp., Silver Creek, N.Y.

Kessler Three Shot Bolt Action Repeating Shotgun $25

Takedown. Gauges: 12, 16, 20. 2-shell detachable box magazine. Barrels: 28-inch in 12 and 16 gauge, 26-inch in 20 gauge, full choke. Weight, from 6¼ to 7¼ pounds depending upon gauge and barrel length. Plain one-piece pistol-grip stock, recoil pad. Made from 1951 to 1953.

Kessler Lever-Matic Repeating Shotgun $40

Lever action. Takedown. Gauges: 12, 16, 20, 3-shot magazine. Barrels: 26, 28, 30-inch; full choke. Plain pistol-grip stock, recoil pad. Weight, 7 to 7¾ pounds. Discontinued in 1953.

Lefever Arms Company, a division of the Ithaca Gun Company, Ithaca, N.Y.

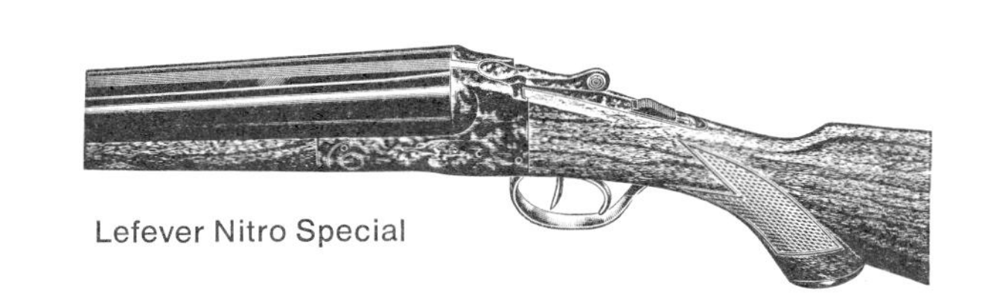
Lefever Nitro Special

Lefever Nitro Special Hammerless Double Barrel Shotgun

Box lock. Plain extractors. Double triggers or single trigger. Gauges: 12, 16, 20, 410. Barrels: 26 to 32-inch, standard chokes. Weight, about 7 pounds in 12 gauge. Checkered pistol-grip stock and forend. Made from 1921 to 1948.
With double triggers **$185**
With single trigger **$235**

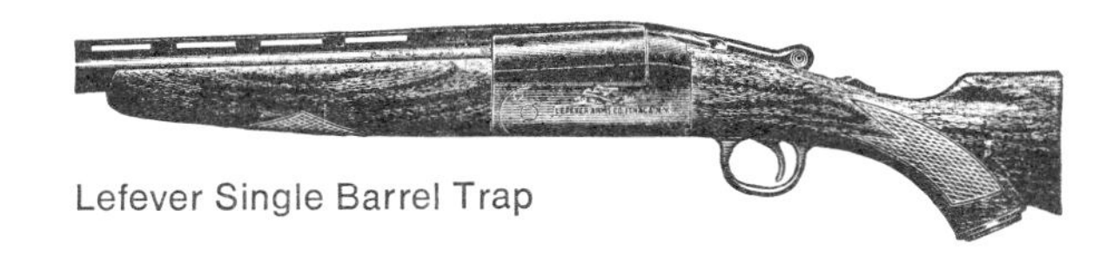
Lefever Single Barrel Trap

Lefever Hammerless Single Barrel Trap Gun $200

Box lock. Ejector. 12 gauge only. Barrel lengths: 30 or 32-inch. Ventilated rib. Weight, about 8 pounds. Checkered pistol-grip stock and forend, recoil pad. Discontinued 1942.

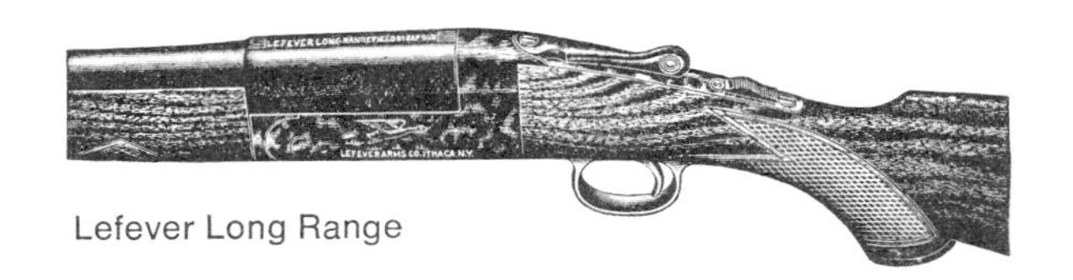
Lefever Long Range

Lefever Long Range Single Barrel Field Gun $85

Box lock. Plain extractor. Gauges: 12, 16, 20, 410. Barrel lengths: 26 to 32-inch. Weight, 5½ to 7 pounds depending upon gauge and barrel length. Checkered pistol-grip stock and forend. Discontinued 1942.

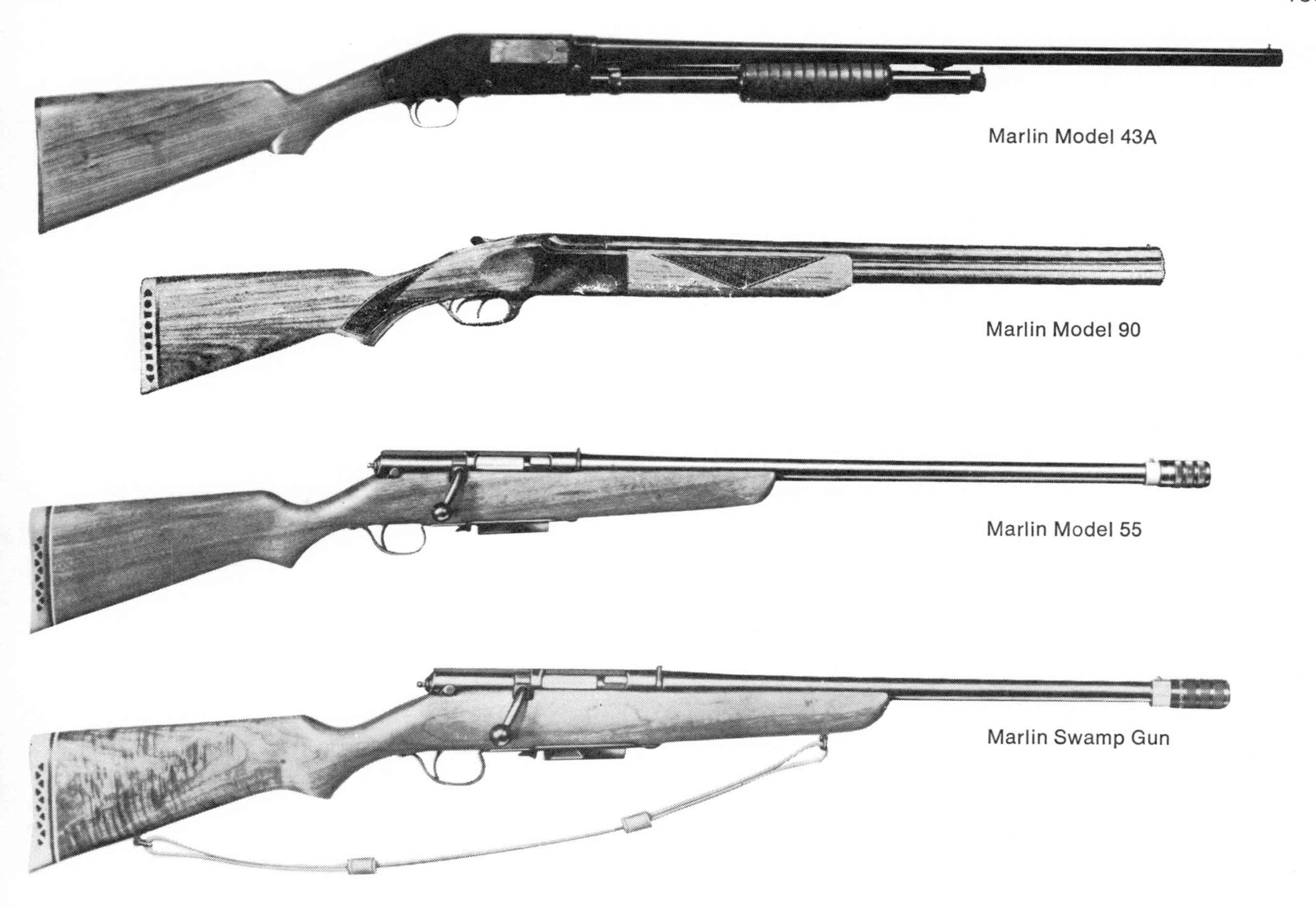

Marlin Model 43A

Marlin Model 90

Marlin Model 55

Marlin Swamp Gun

Marlin Firearms Co., New Haven, Connecticut

Marlin 42A Slide Action Repeating Shotgun $80

Visible hammer. Takedown. 12 gauge. 5-shell tubular magazine. Barrels: 26-inch cylinder bore, 28-inch modified, 30 or 32-inch full choke. Plain pistol-grip stock, grooved slide handle. Made from 1922 to 1934.

Marlin Model 43A Slide Action Hammerless Repeating Shotgun $90

Takedown. 12 gauge. 5-shell tubular magazine. Barrels: 26-inch cylinder bore, 28-inch modified, 30 or 32-inch full choke. Plain pistol-grip stock, grooved slide handle. Made from 1923 to 1930.

Marlin Model 44A Hammerless Slide Action Repeating Shotgun $125

Takedown. 20 gauge. 4-shell tubular magazine. Barrels: 25 or 28-inch; cylinder bore, modified or full choke. Plain pistol-grip stock, grooved slide handle. Made from 1923 to 1935.

Marlin Model 90 Standard Over-And-Under Shotgun

Hammerless. Box lock. Double triggers; non-selective single trigger was available as an extra on pre-war guns except 410. Gauges: 12, 16, 20, 410. Barrels: plain; 26, 28 or 30-inch; chokes improved cylinder and modified or modified and full; barrel design changed in 1949, eliminating full-length rib between barrels. Weights: 12 gauge about 7½ pounds, 16 and 20 gauge about 6¼ pounds. Checkered pistol-grip stock and forearm, recoil pad standard on pre-war guns. Postwar production: Model 90-DT (double trigger), Model 90-ST (single trigger). Made from 1937 to 1958.

With double triggers $250
With single trigger $325

Marlin Model 55 Hunter Bolt Action Shotgun

Takedown. Gauges: 12, 16, 20. 2-shot clip magazine. 28-inch barrel (26-inch in 20 ga.), full choke or with adjustable choke. Plain pistol-grip stock; 12 ga. has recoil pad. Weight, about 7¼ pounds (20 ga., 6½ lbs). Made from 1950 to 1965.

With plain barrel $40
With adjustable choke $45

Marlin Swamp Gun $50

Same as Model 55 except chambered for 12 gauge 3″ Magnum shell, has 20½-inch barrel with adjustable choke, sling swivels, weighs about 6½ pounds. Made from 1963 to 1965.

Marlin Model 59

Marlin Premier Mark I

Marlin Premier Mark II

Marlin Premier Mark IV

Marlin Model 59 Auto-Safe Bolt Action Single Shotgun **$35**

Takedown. Automatic thumb safety. 410 gauge. 24-inch barrel, full choke. Weight, about 5 pounds. Plain pistol-grip stock. Made from 1959 to 1961.

Marlin Premier Mark I Slide Action Repeating Shotgun **$100**

Hammerless. Takedown. 12 gauge. Magazine holds 3 shells. Barrels: 30-inch full choke, 28-inch modified, 26-inch improved cylinder or Skeet choke. Weight, about 6 pounds. Plain pistol-grip stock and forearm. Made in France from 1960 to 1963.

Marlin Premier Mark II **$140**

Same as Premier Mark I except engraved receiver, checkered stock and forearm. Made from 1960 to 1963.

Marlin Premier Mark IV

Same as Premier Mark II except more elaborate engraving, fancier wood. Made from 1960 to 1963.
With plain barrel **$190**
With ventilated rib barrel **$220**

Gebruder Merkel, Suhl, Germany

Merkel Model 100 Over-And-Under Shotgun

Hammerless. Box lock. Greener crossbolt. Plain extractor. Double triggers. Gauges: 12, 16, 20. Made with plain or ribbed barrels in various lengths and chokes. Plain finish, no engraving. Checkered forend and stock with pistol grip and cheekpiece or English style. Made prior to World War II.
With plain barrel **$500**
With ribbed barrel **$525**

Merkel Models 101 and 101E Over-And-Under Shotguns

Same as Model 100 except ribbed barrel standard, has separate extractors (ejectors on Model 101E), English engraving. Made prior to World War II.
Model 101 . . . . **$600**
Model 101E **$650**

Merkel Models 400, 400E, 401 and 401E Over-And-Under Shotguns

Similar to Model 101 except have Kersten double crossbolt, Arabesque engraving on Models 400 and 400E, hunting engraving on Models 401 and 401E, finer general quality. "E" models have Merkel ejectors, others have separate extractors. Made prior to World War II.

Model 400 .... $675
Model 400E $750
Model 401 .... $825
Model 401E $900

Merkel Models 200, 200E, 201, 201E, 202 and 202E Over-And-Under Shotguns

Hammerless. Box lock. Kersten double crossbolt. Scalloped frame. Sideplates on Models 202 and 202E. Arabesque engraving, hunting engraving also supplied on all except Models 200 and 200E. "E" models have ejectors, others have separate extractors. Signal pins. Double triggers. Gauges: 12, 16, 20, 24, 28, 32 (last three gauges are not available in post-war guns). Ribbed barrels in various lengths and chokes. Weight, from 5¾ to 7½ pounds depending upon barrel length and gauge. Checkered forend and stock with pistol grip and cheekpiece or English style. The three grades—200, 201, 202—differ in overall quality, engraving, wood, checkering, etc., aside from the dummy sideplates on Models 202 and 202E, general specifications are the same. Models 200, 201, 202, andl 202E, which were made before World War II, are not offered in the current catalogue; the other models are in production.

Model 200 .... $ 700
Model 200E .... $ 775
Model 201 .... $ 775
Model 201E .... $ 950
Model 202 .... $ 950
Model 202E $1,200

Merkel Models 300, 300E, 301, 301E and 302 Over-And-Under Shotguns

Merkel-Anson system box lock. Kersten double crossbolt. Two underlugs. Scalloped frame. Sideplates on Model 302. Arabesque or hunting engraving. "E" models and Model 302 have automatic ejectors, others have separate extractors. Signal pins. Double triggers. Gauges: 12, 16, 20, 24, 28, 32. Ribbed barrels in various lengths and chokes. Checkered forend and stock with pistol grip and cheekpiece or English style. The three grades—300, 301, 302—differ in overall quality, engraving, wood, checkering, etc., aside from the dummy sideplates on Model 302, general specifications are the same. Manufactured prior to World War II.

Model 300 .... $1,000
Model 300E $1,100
Model 301 .... $1,100
Model 301E $1,300
Model 302 .... $1,400

Merkel Model 203E Over-And-Under Shotgun $1,600

Hammerless. Hand detachable side locks. Kersten fastening. Automatic ejectors. Double triggers. Arabesque engraving standard, hunting engraving also supplied. Gauges: 12, 16, 20. Ribbed barrels in various lengths and chokes. Checkered forend and stock with pistol grip and cheekpiece or English style. Currently manufactured.

Merkel Model 204E Over-And-Under Shotgun $2,000

Similar to Model 203E. Has Merkel sidelocks, fine English engravings. Made prior to World War II.

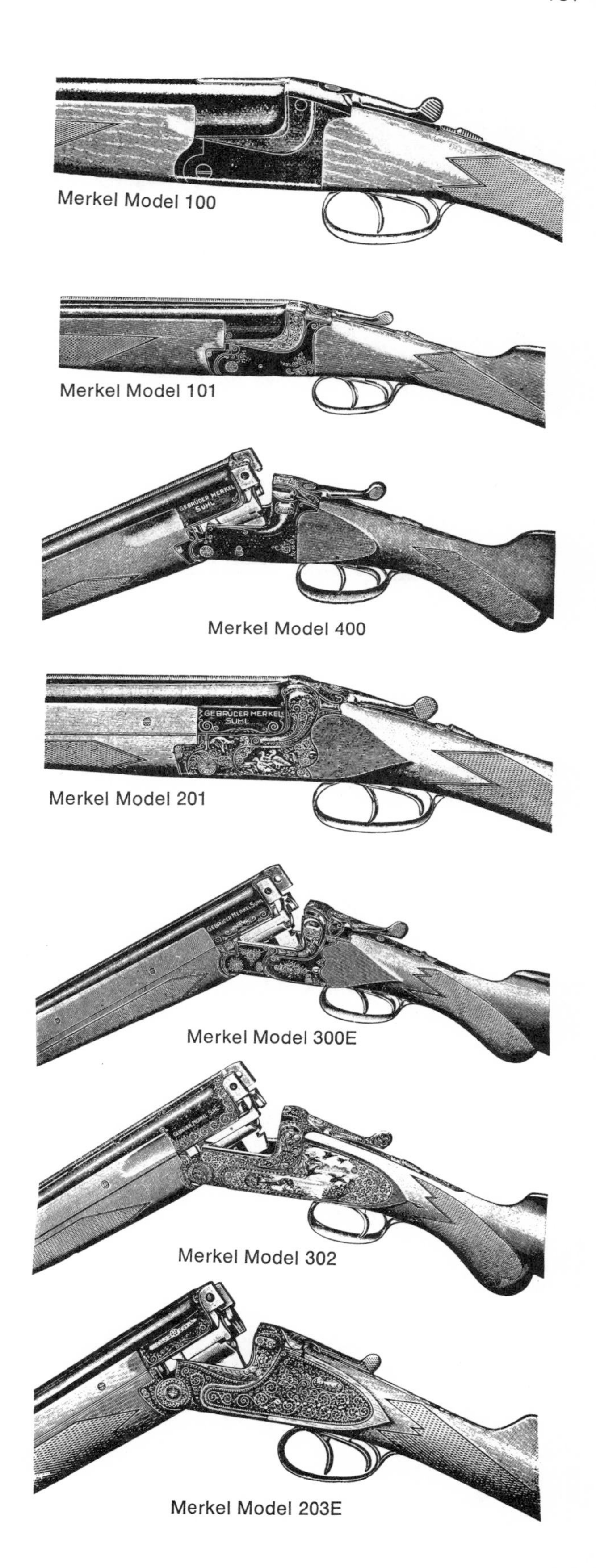

Merkel Model 100

Merkel Model 101

Merkel Model 400

Merkel Model 201

Merkel Model 300E

Merkel Model 302

Merkel Model 203E

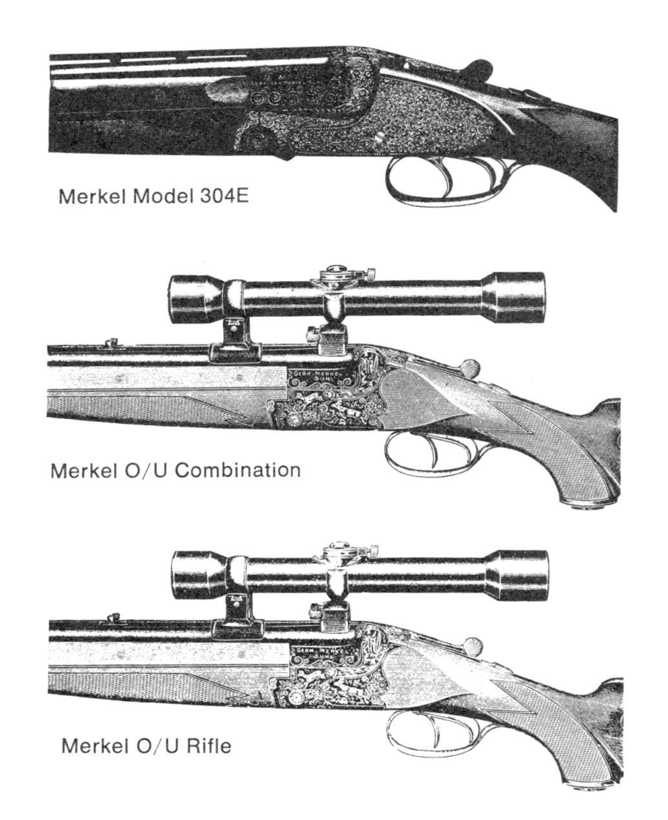
Merkel Model 304E

Merkel O/U Combination

Merkel O/U Rifle

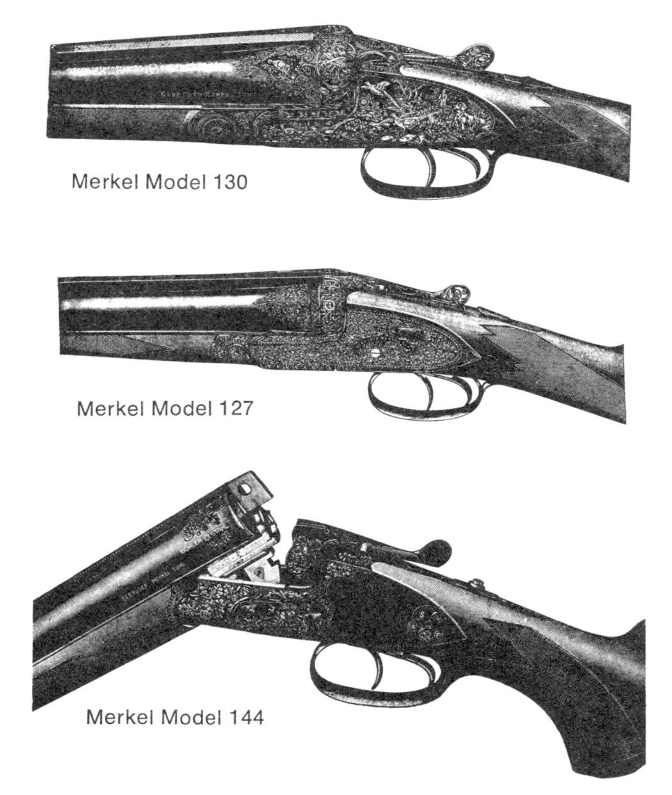
Merkel Model 130

Merkel Model 127

Merkel Model 144

Merkel Model 303E Over-And-Under Shotgun . . . $2,400

Similar to Model 203E. Has Kersten crossbolt, double underlugs, Holland & Holland-type hand-detachable sidelocks, automatic ejectors. This is a finer gun than Model 203E. Currently manufactured.

Merkel Model 304E Over-And-Under Shotgun . . $3,800

Special model of the Model 303E-type but higher quality throughout. This is the top grade Merkel Over-and-Under. Currently manufactured.

Merkel Over-And-Under Combination Guns ("Bock-Buchsflinten")

Shotgun barrel over, rifle barrel under. Gauges: 12, 16, 20; calibers: 5.6X35 Vierling, 7X57R, 8X57JR, 8X60R, Magnum, 9.3X53R, 9.3X72R, 9.3X74R and others. Various barrel lengths, chokes and weights. Other specifications and values correspond to those of Merkel Over-and-Under Shotguns listed below. Currently manufactured.

Models 410, 410E, 411E . . . . . . see shotgun Models 400, 400E, 401, 401E respectively
Models 210, 210E, 211, 211E, 212, 212E . . . . see shotgun Models 200, 200E, 201, 201E, 202, 202E respectively
Models 310, 310E, 311, 311E, 312 . . . . see shotgun Models 300, 300E, 301, 301E, 302 respectively
Model 213E . . . . see shotgun Model 203E
Model 214E . . . . see shotgun Model 204E
Model 313 . . . . see shotgun Model 303E
Model 314 . . . . see shotgun Model 304E

Merkel Over-And-Under Rifles ("Bock-Doppelbuchsen")

Calibers: 5.6X35 Vierling, 6.5X58R, 7X57R, 8X57JR, 8X 60R Magnum, 9.3X53R, 9.3X72R, 9.3X74R, 10.3X60R as well as most of the British calibers for African and Indian big game. Various barrel lengths, weights. In general, specifications correspond to those of Merkel Over-and-Under Shotguns listed below. Values of these over-and-under rifles (in calibers for which ammunition is obtainable) are about the same as those of comparable shotgun models. Currently manufactured.

Models 220, 220E, 221, 221E . . . . . . see shotgun Models 200, 200E, 201, 201E respectively
Models 320, 320E, 321, 321E, 322 . . . . see shotgun Models 300, 300E, 301, 301E, 302 respectively
Model 323 . . . . see shotgun Model 303E
Model 324 . . . . see shotgun Model 304E

Merkel Interchangeable Barrels

This manufacturer's over-and-under guns were often supplied with accessory barrels, interchangeable to convert the gun into an arm of another type; for example, a set might consist of one pair each of shotgun, rifle and combination gun barrels. Each pair of interchangeable barrels has a value of approximately one-third that of the gun with which they are supplied.

Merkel Model 130 Hammerless Box-Lock Double Barrel Shotgun $2,000

Anson & Deeley system. Side plates. Automatic ejectors.

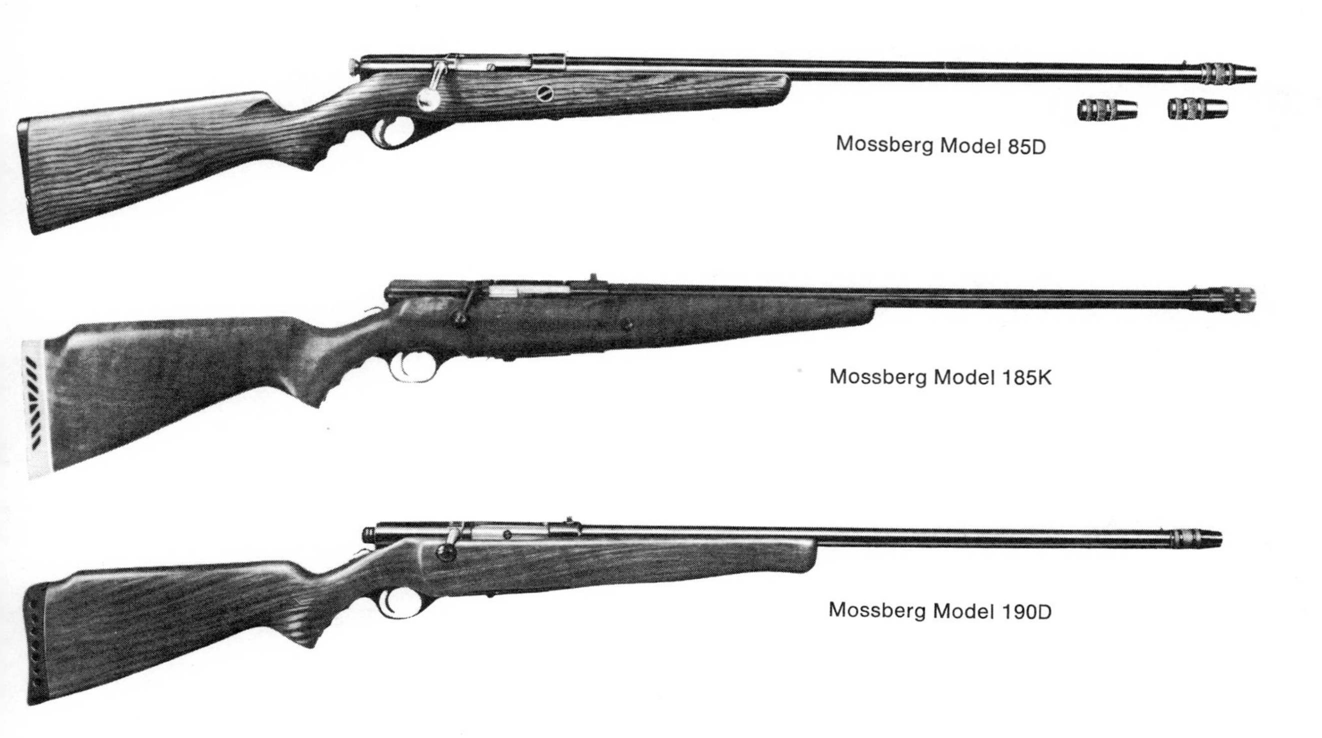

Mossberg Model 85D

Mossberg Model 185K

Mossberg Model 190D

Double triggers. Elaborate hunting scene engraving or Arabesque engraving. Made in all standard gauges, various barrel lengths and chokes. Checkered forend and stock with pistol grip and cheekpiece or English style. Manufactured prior to World War II.

Merkel Model 127 Hammerless Sidelock Double Barrel Shotgun $4,000

Holland & Holland system, hand detachable locks. Automatic ejectors. Double triggers. Made in all standard gauges, barrel lengths and chokes. Checkered forend and stock with pistol grip and cheekpiece or English style. This is a highest quality de luxe gun, elaborately engraved in Arabesque or hunting scene pattern. Manufactured prior to World War II.

Merkel Anson Drillings

Three-barrel combination guns; usually made with double shotgun barrels, over rifle barrel, although "Doppelbuchsdrillingen" were made with two rifle barrels over and shotgun barrel under. Hammerless. Box lock, Anson & Deeley system. Side clips. Plain extractors. Double triggers. Gauges: 12, 16, 20; rifle calibers: 7X57R, 8X57JR and 9.3X74R are most common but these guns were produced in other calibers from 5.6mm to 10.75mm. Barrels: standard drilling, 25.6 inches; short drilling, 21.6 inches. Checkered pistol-grip stock and forend. The three models listed differ chiefly in overall quality, grade of wood, etc., general specifications are the same. Manufactured prior to World War II.

Model 144 . . . . **$2,700**
Model 142 . . . . **$2,300**
Model 145 . . . . **$2,000**

O. F. Mossberg & Sons, Inc., New Haven, Connecticut

Mossberg Model 85D or 185D Bolt Action Repeating Shotgun $35

Takedown. 3-shot. 20 gauge only. 2-shell detachable box magazine. 25-inch barrel, three interchangeable choke tubes (full, modified, improved cylinder). Later production had 26-inch barrel with full and improved cylinder choke tubes. Weight, about 6¼ pounds. Plain, one-piece, pistol-grip stock. Originally designated Model 85D, changed in 1947 to Model 185D. Made from 1940 to 1971.

Mossberg Model 185K $40

Same as Model 185D except has variable C-Lect-Choke instead of interchangeable choke tubes. Made from 1950 to 1963.

Mossberg Model 195K $40

Same as Model 185K except in 12 gauge, weighs about 7½ pounds. Made from 1956 to 1963.

Mossberg Model 190D $35

Same as Model 185D except in 16 gauge, weighs about 6 pounds. Made from 1955 to 1971.

Mossberg Model 190K $40

Same as Model 185K except in 16 gauge, weighs about 6¾ pounds. Made from 1956 to 1963.

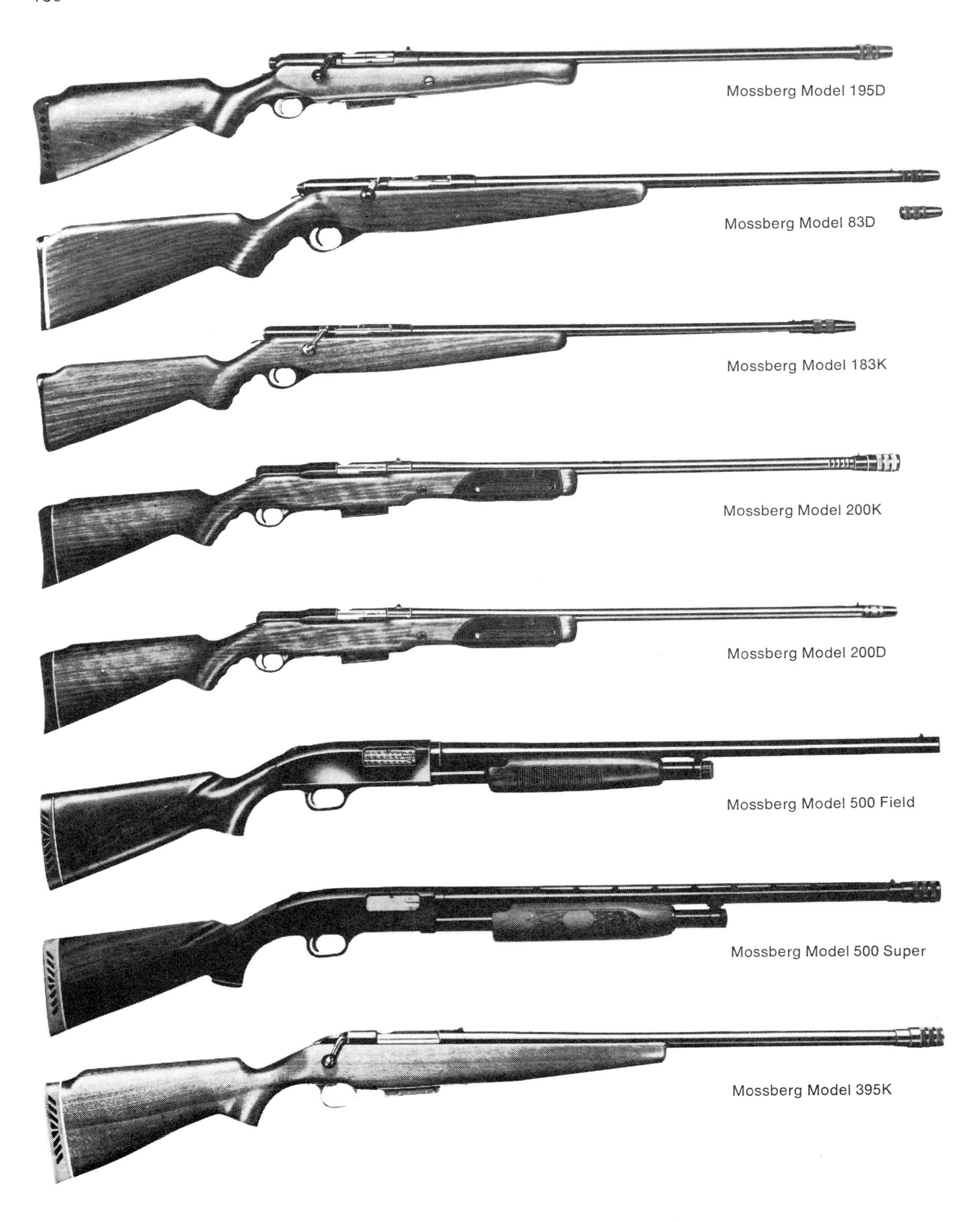

Mossberg Model 195D

Mossberg Model 83D

Mossberg Model 183K

Mossberg Model 200K

Mossberg Model 200D

Mossberg Model 500 Field

Mossberg Model 500 Super

Mossberg Model 395K

Mossberg Model 195D **$35**

Same as Model 185D except in 12 gauge, weighs about 6¾ pounds. Made from 1955 to 1971.

Mossberg Model 83D or 183D **$35**

3-shot. Takedown. 410-gauge only. 2-shell fixed, top-loading magazine. 23-inch barrel with two interchangeable choke tubes (modified, full). Later production had 24-inch barrel. Plain, one-piece, pistol-grip stock. Weight, about 5½ pounds. Originally designated Model 83D, changed in 1947 to Model 183D. Made from 1940 to 1971.

Mossberg Model 183K **$40**

Same as Model 183D except has variable C-Lect-Choke instead of interchangeable choke tubes. Made from 1953 to date.

Mossberg Model 200K Slide Action Repeater **$40**

12 gauge. 3-shot detachable box magazine. 28-inch barrel. C-Lect-Choke. Plain pistol-grip stock. Black nylon slide handle. Weight, about 7½ pounds. Made from 1955 to 1959.

Mossberg Model 200D **$35**

Same as Model 200K except with two interchangeable choke tubes instead of C-Lect-Choke. Made from 1955 to 1959.

Mossberg Model 500 Field Grade Pump Action Repeater

Hammerless. Takedown. Magazine holds six 2¾" or five 3" shells (12 and 20 ga. chambered for 3"). Gauges: 12, 16, 20. Barrels: 30" regular or heavy/full choke (12 ga. only), 28"/modified or full, 26"/improved cylinder or adjustable C-Lect-Choke, 24" Slugster with rifle-type sights (12 ga. only). Weights: 12 ga., 6¾ or 8 pounds (heavy magnum); 16 ga., 6½ pounds; 20 ga., 6 pounds. Plain pistol-grip stock with recoil pad, grooved slide handle. Made from 1961 to date.

With regular barrel **$90**

With C-Lect-Choke, heavy magnum, or Slugster barrel **$95**

Mossberg Model 500 Super Grade

Same as Model 500 Field Grade, except has ventilated rib barrel, checkered pistol-grip and slide handle. Made from 1961 to date.

With regular barrel **$100**

With C-Lect-Choke or heavy magnum barrel **$105**

Mossberg Model 500ATR Pigeon Grade Trap Gun $110

Same as Model 500 Field Grade, except has ventilated rib barrel—30" full choke; Monte Carlo stock with recoil pad, beavertail forearm (slide handle)—both checkered. Made from 1968 to 1971.

Mossberg Model 395K Bolt Action Repeating Shotgun **$40**

Takedown. 3-shot (detachable clip magazine holds two shells). 12 gauge (3" chamber). 28-inch barrel with C-Lect-Choke. Weight, about 6¾ pounds. Monte Carlo stock with recoil pad. Made from 1963 to date.

Mossberg Model 390K **$40**

Same as Model 395K, except 16 gauge (2¾"). Made from 1963 to date.

Mossberg Model 385K **$40**

Same as Model 395K, except 20 gauge (3"), 26-inch barrel with C-Lect-Choke; weight, about 6¼ pounds. Made from 1963 to date.

Noble Model 65

Noble Mfg. Co., Haydenville, Massachusetts

Noble Model 40 Hammerless Slide Action Repeating Shotgun **$55**

Solid frame. 12 gauge only. 5-shell tubular magazine. 28-inch barrel with ventilated Multi-Choke. Weight, about 7½ pounds. Plain pistol-grip stock, grooved slide handle. Made from 1950 to 1955.

Noble Model 50 .... **$50**

Same as Model 40, except without Multi-Choke. Modified or full choke barrel. Made from 1953 to 1955.

Noble Model 60 Hammerless Slide Action Repeating Shotgun **$60**

Solid frame. 12 and 16 gauge. 5-shot tubular magazine. 28-inch barrel with adjustable choke. Plain pistol-grip stock with recoil pad, grooved slide handle. Weight, about 7½ pounds. Made from 1955 to 1966.

Noble Model 65 .... **$55**

Same as Model 60, except without adjustable choke and recoil pad. Modified or full choke barrel. Made from 1955 to 1966.

Noble Model 70CLP Slide Action Repeating Shotgun $75

Hammerless. 410 gauge. Magazine holds 5 shells. 26-inch barrel with adjustable choke. Weight about 6 pounds. Checkered buttstock and forearm, recoil pad. Made from 1958 to date.

Noble Model 70XL **$65**
Same as Model 70CLP except without adjustable choke and checkering on buttstock. Made from 1958 to 1970.

Noble Model 420 Hammerless Double Barrel Shotgun **$125**
Box lock. Plain extractors. Double triggers. Gauges: 12 ga. 3" Mag., 16 ga., 20 ga. 3" Mag., 410 ga. Barrels: 28-inch, except 410 in 26-inch, modified and full choke. Weight about 6¾ pounds. Engraved frame. Checkered walnut stock and forearm. Made from 1958 to 1970.

Parker Brothers, Meriden, Conn. This firm was taken over by Remington Arms Company in 1934 and its production facilities removed to Remington's Ilion, N.Y. plant

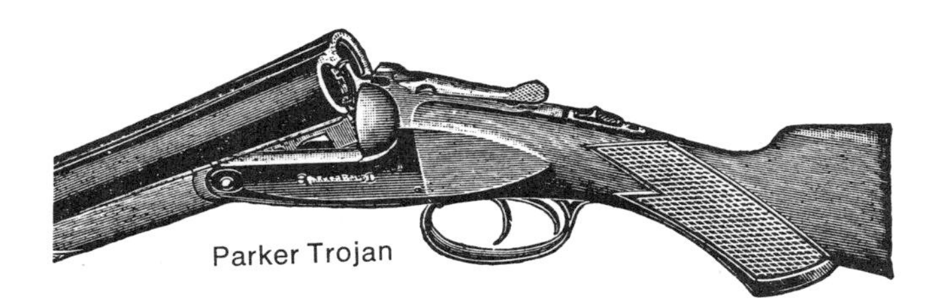
Parker Trojan

Parker Trojan Hammerless Double Barrel Shotgun
Box lock. Plain extractors. Double trigger or single trigger. Gauges: 12, 16, 20. Barrels: 30-inch both full choke (12 gauge only), 26 or 28-inch modified and full choke. Weight, 6¼ to 7¾ pounds depending upon gauge and barrel length. Checkered pistol-grip stock and forearm. Discontinued in 1939.
With double triggers **$500**
With single trigger **$600**
Values of 20 gauge guns about 50% higher.

Parker Hammerless Double Barrel Shotguns
Grades V.H.E. through A-1 Special. Box lock. Automatic ejectors. Double triggers or selective single trigger. Gauges: 10, 12, 16, 20, 28, 410. Barrels: 26 to 32-inch, any standard boring. Weight, 6⅞ to 8½ pounds in 12 gauge. Stock and forearm of select walnut, checkered; straight, half or full pistol grip. The various grades differ only in quality of workmanship, grade of wood, engraving, checkering, etc.; general specifications are the same for all. Manufacture of Parker guns was discontinued about 1940. Values shown are for guns with double triggers, automatic ejectors; non-ejector models are worth about 1/3 less; smaller gauge guns bring up to 50% more than 12 and 16 gauge; add 20% for serial number over 200,000. Set of interchangeable Barrels add about ⅓ of gun value.

V.H.E. Grade **$1,000**
G.H.E. Grade **$1,500**
D.H.E. Grade **$1,800**
C.H.E. Grade **$2,000**
B.H.E. Grade **$3,000**
A.H.E. Grade **$4,000**
A.A.H.E. Grade **$5,000**
A-1 Special Grade **$6,000**
Extras:
Selective Single Trigger **$150**
Raised Ventilated Rib,
V.H.E., G.H.E., D.H.E. Grades **$200**
C.H.E., B.H.E., A.H.E. Grades **$200**
A.A.H.E., A-1 Special Grades **$225**
Beavertail Forearm,
V.H.E., G.H.E. Grades **$100**
D.H.E. Grade **$100**
C.H.E. Grade **$100**
B.H.E., A.H.E. Grade **$150**
A.A.H.E. Grade **$150**
A-1 Special Grade **$200**

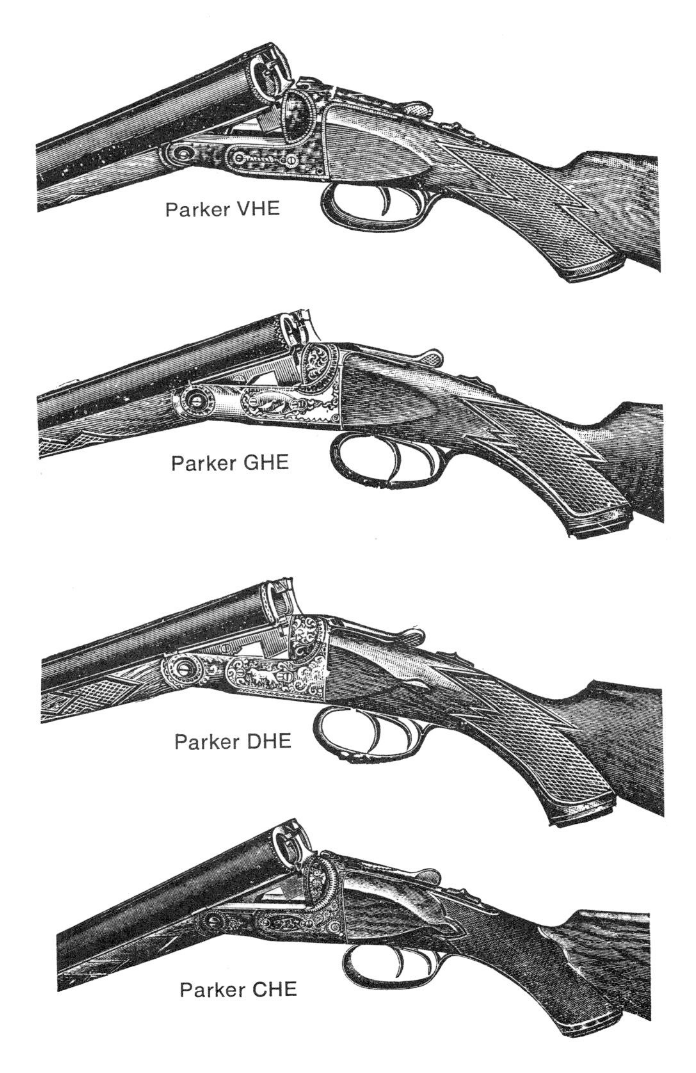
Parker VHE
Parker GHE
Parker DHE
Parker CHE

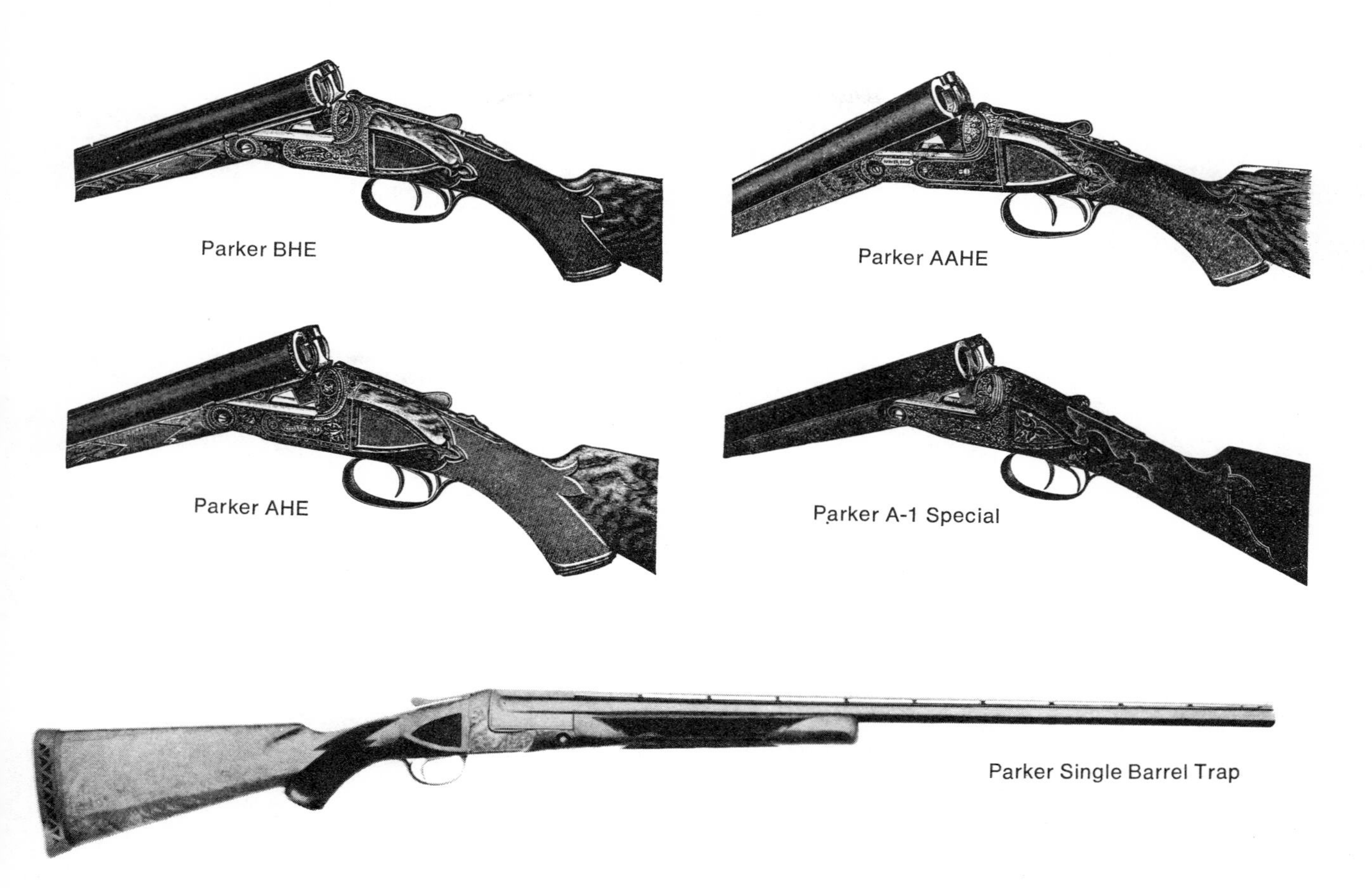
Parker BHE

Parker AAHE

Parker AHE

Parker A-1 Special

Parker Single Barrel Trap

Parker Single Barrel Trap Guns

Hammerless. Box lock. Ejector. 12 gauge only. Barrel lengths: 30, 32, 34-inch; any boring. Ventilated rib. Weight, 7½ to 8½ pounds. Stock and forearm of select walnut, checkered; straight, half or full pistol grip. The five grades differ only in quality of workmanship, grade of wood, checkering, engraving, etc., general specifications same for all. Discontinued about 1942.

S.C. Grade **$1,100**
S.B. Grade **$1,700**
S.A. Grade **$2,300**
S.A.A. Grade **$3,000**
S.A.1 Special **$5,000**

James Purdey & Sons, Ltd., London, England

Purdey Hammerless Double Barrel Shotgun

Side lock. Automatic ejectors. Double triggers or single trigger. Gauges: 12, 16, 20. Barrels: 26, 27, 28, 30-inch (latter in 12 gauge only); any boring, any shape or style of rib. Weight, from 5¼ to 6½ pounds depending upon model, gauge and barrel length. Checkered stock and forearm, straight grip standard, pistol grip also available. Purdey guns of this type have been made from about 1880 to date. Models include: Game Gun, Featherweight Game Gun, Two-Inch Gun (chambered for 12 gauge 2-inch shells), Pigeon Gun (with 3rd fastening and side clips); values of all models are the same.

With double triggers **$4,500**
With single trigger **$5,000**
Extra pair of barrels without forend **$1,200**

Purdey Double Barrel

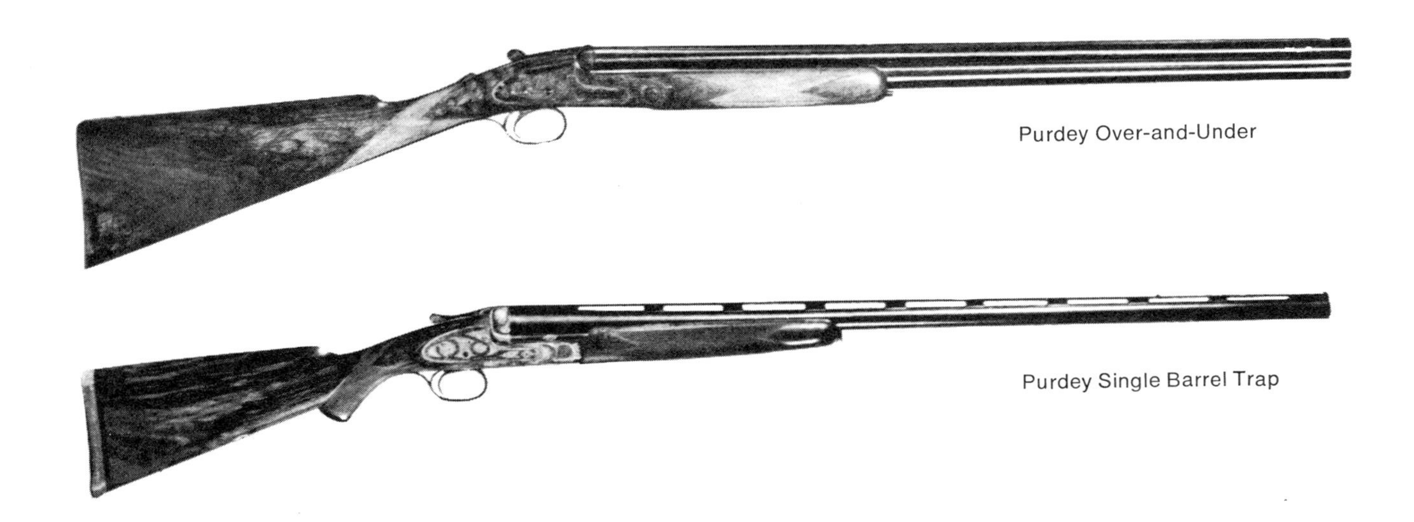
Purdey Over-and-Under

Purdey Single Barrel Trap

Purdey Over-And-Under Gun

Side lock. Automatic ejectors. Double triggers and single trigger. Gauges: 12, 16, 20. Barrels: 26, 27, 28, 30-inch (latter in 12 gauge only); any boring, any style rib. Weight, from 6 to 7½ pounds depending upon gauge and barrel length. Checkered stock and forend, straight or pistol grip. Prior to World War II, the Purdey Over-and-Under Gun was made with a Purdey action; since the war James Purdey & Sons have acquired the business of James Woodward & Sons and all Purdey Over-and-Under Guns are now built on the Woodward principle. General specifications of both types are the same.
With Purdey action, double triggers $6,000
With Woodward action, double triggers $8,000
Extra pair of barrels without forend $2,000
Single trigger, extra .... $ 500

Purdey Single Barrel Trap Gun $6,000

Side lock. Mechanical features similar to those of the over-and-under model with Purdey action. 12 gauge only. Built to customer's specifications. Made prior to World War II.

Remington Arms Co., Ilion, N.Y.

Remington New Model 1882 Hammer Double Barrel Shotgun $225

Gauges: 16, 12, 10. Plain or Damascus barrels, 28 to 32-inch. Weight, 6¾ to 10¼ pounds, depending upon gauge and barrel length. Checkered pistol-grip stock and forearm. Made from 1882 to 1910. *Note:* Value shown is for standard grade; this model was made in six higher grades, varying in quality of workmanship, engraving, grade of wood, etc.

Remington Model 1889 Hammer Double Barrel Shotgun $375

Gauges: 16, 12, 10. Steel or Damascus barrels, 28 to 32-inch. Weight, 7 to 10 pounds, depending upon gauge and barrel length. Checkered pistol-grip stock and forearm. Made from 1889 to 1908.

Remington Rider No. 3 Single Barrel Shotgun $100

Semi-hammerless. Gauges: 28, 24, 20, 16, 12, 10. Plain barrel, 30 to 32-inch. Weight, about 6 pounds. Plain pistol-grip stock and forearm. Made from 1893 to 1903.

Remington Rider No. 9 Single Barrel Shotgun $100

Improved version of No. 3 Single; same general specifications except has automatic ejector. Made from 1902 to 1910.

Remington Model 1894 Hammerless Double Barrel Shotgun $375

Box lock. Automatic ejector. Double triggers. Gauges: 16, 12, 10. Ordnance steel barrels, 28 to 32-inch. Weight, 7 to 10 pounds, depending upon gauge and barrel length. Checkered stock and forearm. Made from 1894 to 1910. *Note:* This model was made in seven higher grades, including a trap gun; these, of course, have a higher value than the standard grade for which valuation is given. Guns with Damascus barrels have about 50% lower value.

Remington Model 1900 Hammerless Double Barrel Shotgun $400

Improved version of Model 1894. Same general specifications as that model. Made from 1900 to 1910. Value shown is for standard grade with ordnance steel barrels; see note under Model 1894.

Remington Model 10A Standard Grade Slide Action Repeating Shotgun $150

Hammerless. Takedown. 6-shot. 12 gauge only. 5-shell tubular magazine. Barrels: plain, 26 to 32-inch; chokes: full, modified or cylinder bore. Weight, about 7½ pounds. Plain pistol-grip stock, grooved slide handle. Made from 1907 to 1929.

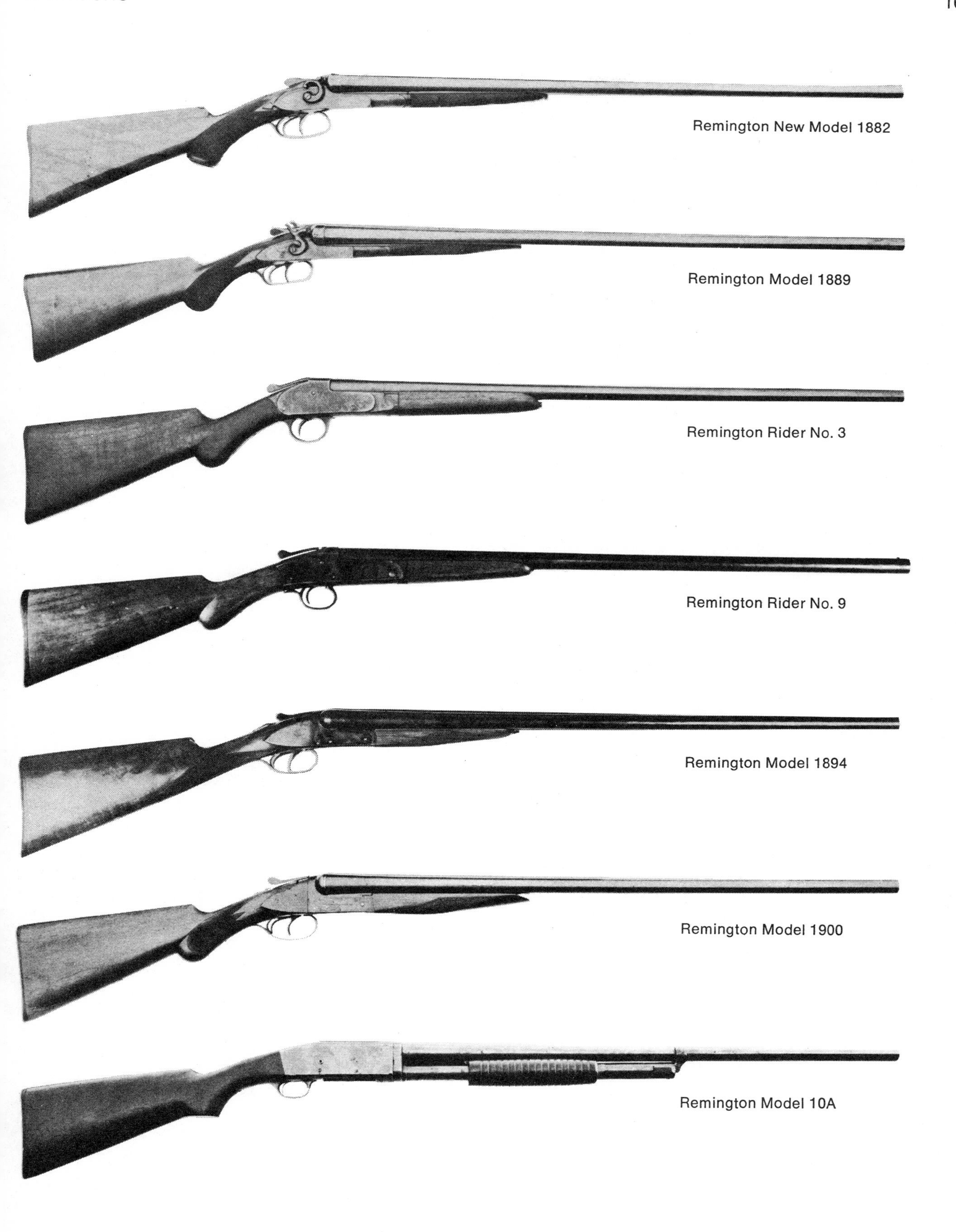

Remington New Model 1882

Remington Model 1889

Remington Rider No. 3

Remington Rider No. 9

Remington Model 1894

Remington Model 1900

Remington Model 10A

Remington Model 11A

Remington Sportsman

Remington Model 17A

Remington Model 29A

Remington Model 31A

Remington Model 32A

Remington Model 11A Standard Grade 5-Shot Autoloader

Hammerless. Browning type. Takedown. Gauges: 12, 16, 20. Tubular magazine holds four shells. Barrels: plain, solid rib or ventilated rib; lengths from 26 inches to 32 inches; full, modified, improved cylinder, cylinder bore, skeet choke. Weights: about 8 pounds in 12 gauge, about 7½ pounds in 16 gauge, about 7¼ pounds in 20 gauges. Checkered pistol grip and forend. Made from 1905 to 1949.
With plain barrel **$125**
With solid rib barrel **$140**
With ventilated rib barrel **$160**

Remington Model 11R Riot Gun $115

Same as Model 11A Standard Grade except has 20-inch plain barrel, 12 gauge only.

Remington Model 11 Special, Tournament, Expert and Premier Grade Guns

These higher grade models differ from the Model 11A in general quality, grade of wood, checkering, engraving, etc. General specifications are the same.
Model 11B Special Grade **$175**
Model 11D Tournament Grade **$400**
Model 11E Expert Grade **$575**
Model 11F Premier Grade **$775**

Remington "Sportsman" A Standard Grade 3-Shot Autoloader

Same general specifications as Model 11A except magazine holds two shells. Also available in "B" Special Grade, "D" Tournament Grade, "E" Expert Grade, "F" Premier Grade. Made from 1931 to 1948. Prices same as shown for Model 11A, etc.

Remington "Sportsman" Skeet Gun

Same general specifications as the "Sportsman" A except has 26-inch barrel (plain, solid rib or ventilated rib), skeet boring, beavertail fore-end. Discontinued 1949.
With plain barrel **$140**
With solid rib barrel **$160**
With ventilated rib barrel **$170**

Remington Model 17A Standard Grade Slide Action Repeating Shotgun $200

Hammerless. Takedown. 5-shot. 20 gauge only. 4-shell tubular magazine. Barrels: plain, 26 to 32-inch; chokes: full, modified or cylinder bore. Weight, about 5¾ pounds. Plain pistol-grip stock, grooved slide handle. Made from 1921 to 1933. *Note:* The present Ithaca Model 37 is an adaptation of this Browning design.

Remington Model 29A Standard Grade Slide Action Repeating Shotgun $175

Hammerless. Takedown. 6-shot. 12 gauge only. 5-shell tubular magazine. Barrels: plain, 26 to 32-inch; chokes: full, modified or cylinder bore. Weight, about 7½ pounds. Checkered pistol-grip stock and slide handle. Made from 1929 to 1933.

Remington Model 29T Target Grade $250

Same general specifications as Model 29A except has trap-style stock with straight grip, extension slide handle, ventilated rib barrel. Discontinued 1933.

Remington Model 31A Standard Grade Slide Action Repeater

Hammerless. Takedown. 3-shot or 5-shot. Gauges: 12, 16, 20. Tubular magazine holds two or four shells. Barrels: plain, solid rib or ventilated rib; lengths from 26 inches to 32 inches; full, modified, improved cylinder, cylinder bore, skeet choke. Weights: about 7½ pounds in 12 gauge, 6¾ pounds in 16 gauge, 6½ pounds in 20 gauge. Earlier models have checkered pistol-grip stock and slide handle: later models have plain stock and grooved slide handle. Made from 1931 to 1949.
With plain barrel **$150**
With solid rib barrel **$175**
With ventilated rib barrel **$200**

Remington Model 31R Riot Gun $135

Same as Model 31A except has 20-inch plain barrel, 12 gauge only.

Remington Model 31 Special, Tournament, Expert and Premier Grade Guns

These higher grade models differ from the Model 31A in general quality, grade of wood, checkering, engraving, etc. General specifications are the same.
Model 31B Special Grade **$225**
Model 31D Tournament Grade **$500**
Model 31E Expert Grade **$750**
Model 31F Premier Grade **$900**

Remington Model 31TC Trap Grade $375

Same general specifications as Model 31A except 12 gauge only, has 30 or 32-inch ventilated rib barrel, full choke, trap stock with full pistol-grip and recoil pad, extension beavertail fore-end, both checkered, weighs about 8 pounds.

Remington Model 31S Trap Special $350

Same general specifications as Model 31TC except has solid rib barrel, half-pistol-grip stock and forend of standard walnut.

Remington Model 31H Hunters' Special $325

Same as Model 31S except has sporting-style stock (shorter and with more drop).

Remington Model 31 Skeet Grade

Same general specifications as Model 31A except has 26-inch barrel with raised solid rib or ventilated rib, skeet boring, checkered pistol-grip stock and beavertail forend, weighs about 8 pounds in 12 gauge.
With raised solid rib **$275**
With ventilated rib **$350**

Remington Model 32A Standard Grade Over-and-Under Gun

Hammerless. Takedown. Automatic ejectors. Early model had double triggers, later built with selective single trigger only. 12 gauge only. Barrels: plain, raised matted solid rib, ventilated rib; 26, 28, 30, 32-inch; full and modified choke standard, option of any combination of full, modified, improved cylinder, cylinder, skeet boring. Weight, about 7¾ pounds. Checkered pistol-grip stock and forend. Made from 1932 to 1942.
With double triggers **$550**
With selective single trigger **$750**
Extra for raised solid rib .... **$ 50**
Extra for ventilated rib **$100**

Remington Model 32 Tournament, Expert and Premier Grade Guns

These higher grade models differ from the Model 32A in general quality, grade of wood, checkering, engraving, etc. General specifications are the same. Made from 1932 to 1942.
Model 32D Tournament Grade **$1,500**
Model 32E Expert Grade **$2,200**
Model 32F Premier Grade **$2,500**

Remington Model 32 Skeet Grade

Same general specifications as Model 32A except 26 or 28-inch barrel, skeet boring, beavertail forend, weighs about 7½ pounds, selective single trigger only. Made from 1932 to 1942.
With plain barrels .... **$ 900**
With raised solid rib .... **$ 950**
With ventilated rib **$1,000**

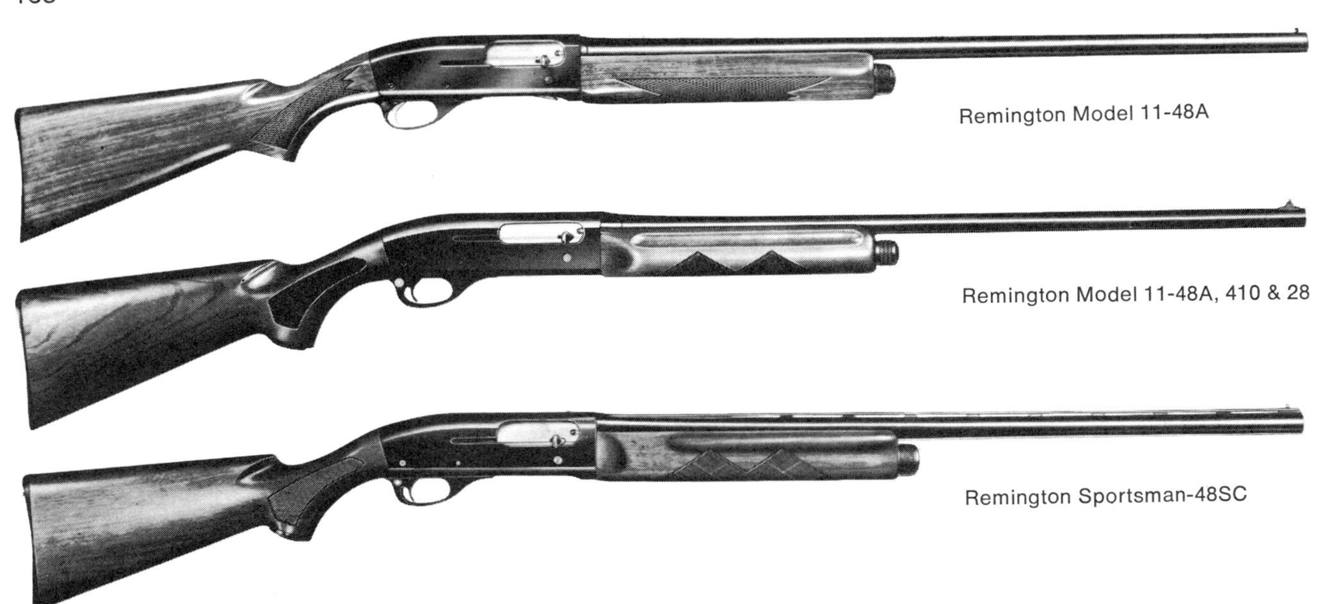
Remington Model 11-48A

Remington Model 11-48A, 410 & 28

Remington Sportsman-48SC

Remington Model 32TC Target (Trap) Grade

Same general specifications as Model 32A except 30 or 32-inch ventilated rib barrel, full choke, trap-style stock with checkered pistol-grip and beavertail forend, weighs about 8 pounds. Made from 1932 to 1942.
With double triggers . . . . **$ 900**
With selective single trigger **$1,000**

Remington Sportsman-48A Standard Grade 3-Shot Autoloader

Streamlined receiver. Hammerless. Takedown. Gauges: 12, 16, 20. Tubular magazine holds two shells. Barrels: plain, matted top surface or ventilated rib; 26-inch improved cylinder, 28-inch modified or full choke, 30-inch full choke (12 gauge only). Weights: about 7½ pounds in 12 gauge, about 6¾ pounds in 16 gauge, about 6½ pounds in 20 gauge. Pistol-grip stock, grooved forend, both checkered. Made from 1949 to 1959.
With plain barrel **$125**
With matted top surface barrel **$140**
With ventilated rib barrel **$165**

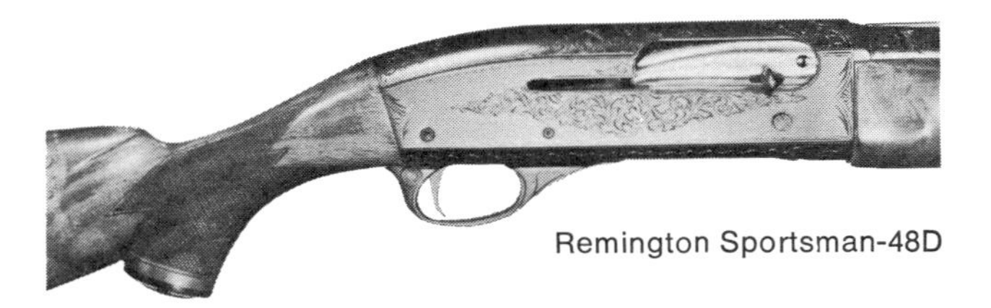
Remington Sportsman-48D

Remington Sportsman-48 Special, Tournament and Premier Grade Guns

These higher grade models differ from the Sportsman-48A in general quality, grade of wood, checkering, engraving, etc. General specifications are the same. Made from 1949 to 1959.
Sportsman-48B Special Grade **$135**
Sportsman-48D Tournament Grade **$475**
Sportsman-48F Premier Grade **$900**

Remington Model 11-48A Standard Grade 5-Shot Autoloader

Same general specifications as Sportsman-48A except magazine holds four shells, forend not grooved. Also available in Special Grade (11-48B), Tournament Grade (11-48D) and Premier Grade (11-48F). Made from 1949 to 1969.
Prices same as shown for Sportsman-48A, etc.

Remington Model 11-48A Standard Grade 4-Shot Autoloader, 410 & 28 Gauge

Same general specifications as Sportsman-48A, except gauge, 3-shell magazine, 25-inch barrel, weighs about 6¼ pounds. 28 gauge introduced 1952, 410 in 1954. Discontinued in 1969.
Prices same as shown for Sportsman-48A.

Remington Model 11-48A Riot Gun $115

Same as Model 11-48A except 20-inch plain barrel and 12 gauge only. Discontinued in 1969.

Remington Sportsman-48SA Skeet Gun

Same general specifications as Sportsman-48A except has 26-inch barrel with matted top surface or ventilated rib, skeet choke, ivory bead front sight, metal bead rear sight. Made from 1949 to 1960.
With matted top surface barrel . . . . **$ 140**
With ventilated rib barrel . . . . **$ 175**
Sportsman-48SC Skeet Target Grade . . . . **$ 225**
Sportsman-48SD Skeet Tournament Grade . . . . . **$ 500**
Sportsman-48SF Skeet Premier Grade **$1,000**

Remington Model 11-48SA 28 Gauge Skeet Gun . . . $185

Same general specifications as Model 11-48A 28 Gauge except has 25-inch ventilated rib barrel, skeet choke. 28 gauge introduced 1952, 410 in 1954.

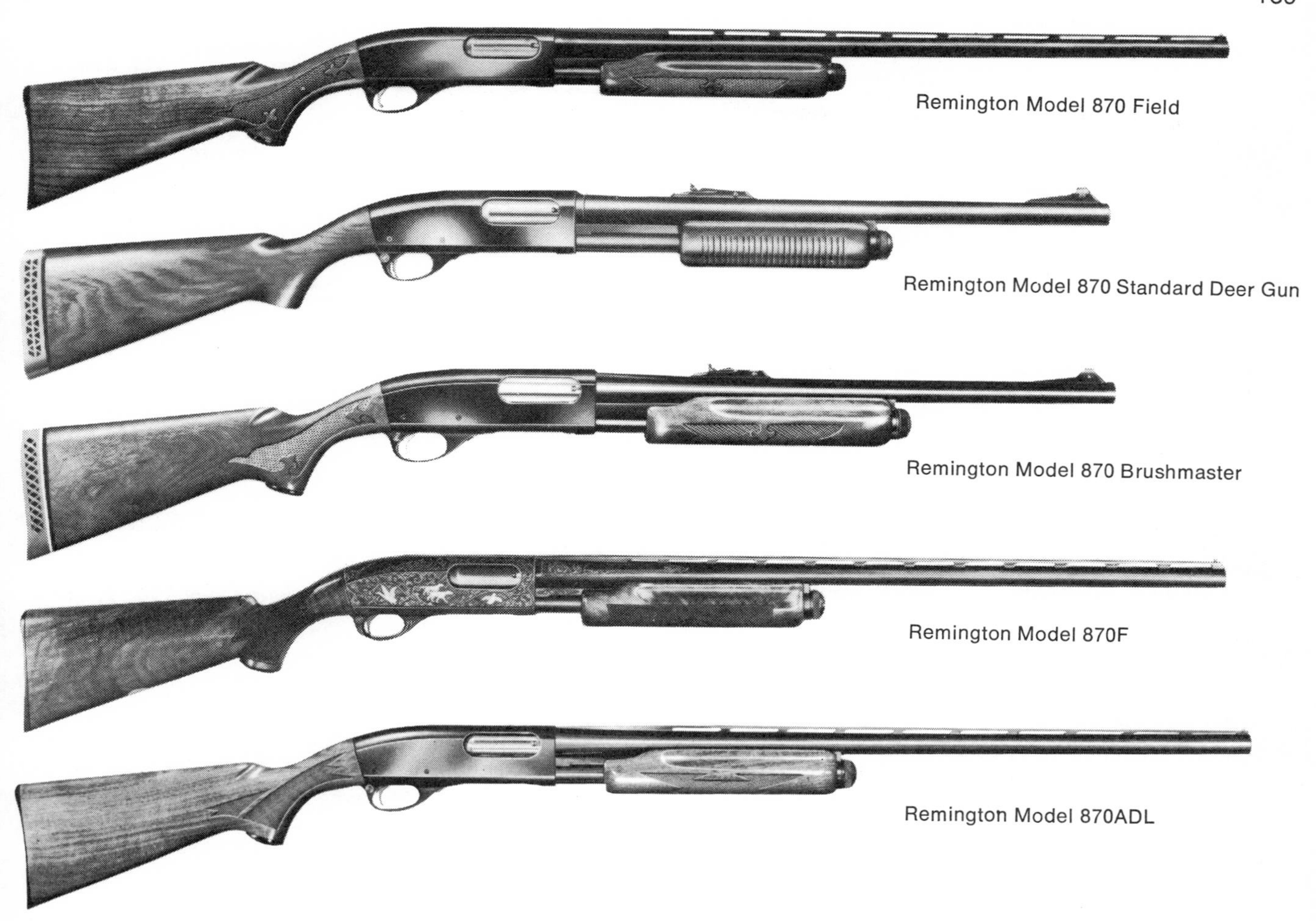

Remington Model 870 Field

Remington Model 870 Standard Deer Gun

Remington Model 870 Brushmaster

Remington Model 870F

Remington Model 870ADL

Remington Wingmaster Model 870AP Standard Grade 5-Shot Slide Action Repeater

Hammerless. Takedown. Gauges: 12, 16, 20. Tubular magazine holds four shells. Barrels: plain, matted top surface or ventilated rib; 26-inch improved cylinder, 28-inch modified or full choke, 30-inch full choke (12 gauge only). Weights: about 7 pounds in 12 gauge, about 6¾ pounds in 16 gauge, about 6½ pounds in 20 gauge. Plain pistol-grip stock, grooved forend. Made from 1950 to 1963.

With plain barrel . . . . $ 85
With matted top surface barrel . . . . $ 90
With ventilated rib barrel $105

Remington Model 870 Wingmaster Field Gun

Same general specifications as Model 870AP except checkered stock and forend. Made from 1964 to date.

With plain barrel $110
With ventilated rib barrel $125

Remington Wingmaster Model 870R Riot Gun

Same as Model 870AP except 20-inch barrel, improved cylinder, 12 gauge only.

Remington Model 870 Standard Deer Gun $100

Same as Model 870 Riot Gun, except has rifle-type sights.

Remington Model 870 Brushmaster Deluxe Deer Gun $125

Same as Model 870 Standard Deer Gun, except available in 20 gauge as well as 12 gauge, has checkered stock and forend, recoil pad.

Remington Wingmaster Model 870 Tournament and Premier Grade Guns

These higher grade models differ from the Model 870 AP in general quality, grade of wood, checkering, engraving, etc. General specifications are the same. Made from 1950 to date.

Model 870D Tournament Grade . . . . $ 520
Model 870F Premier Grade $1,000
Model 870F Premier Grade with gold inlay $1,500

Remington Wingmaster Model 870ADL Deluxe Grade

Same general specifications as Model 870AP except has pistol-grip stock and extension beavertail forend, both finely checkered; matted top surface or ventilated rib barrel. Made from 1950 to 1963.

With matted top surface barrel $100
With ventilated rib barrel $120

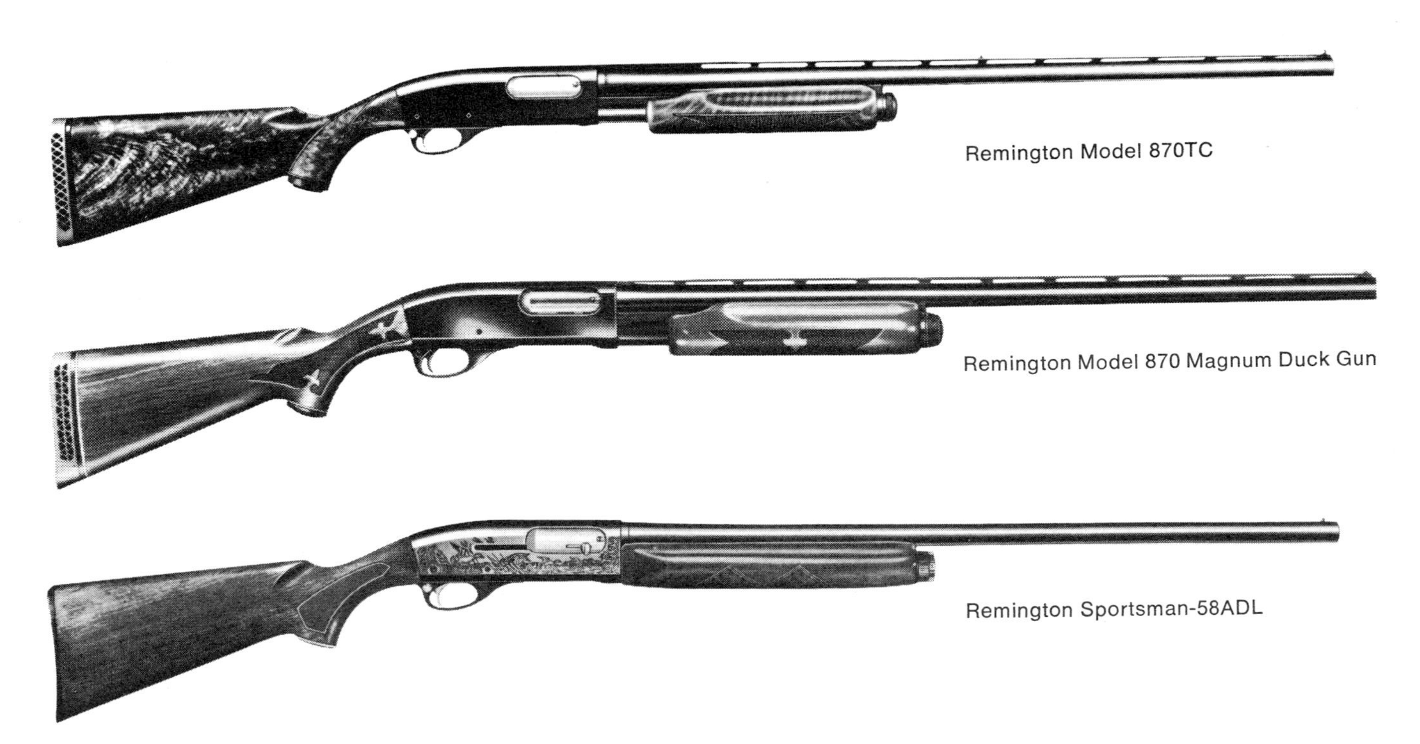

Remington Model 870TC

Remington Model 870 Magnum Duck Gun

Remington Sportsman-58ADL

Remington Wingmaster Model 870BDL Deluxe Special Grade

Same as Model 870ADL except selected American walnut stock and forend. Made from 1950 to 1963.
With matted top surface barrel $110
With ventilated rib barrel $130

Remington Wingmaster Model 870SA Skeet Gun

Same general specifications as Model 870AP except has 26-inch ventilated rib barrel, skeet boring, ivory bead front sight, metal bead rear sight, pistol-grip stock and extension beavertail forend, both finely checkered, weighs 6¾ to 7½ pounds depending upon gauge. Made from 1950 to date.

Model 870SA Skeet Grade . . . . $ 130
Model 870SC Skeet Target Grade . . . . $ 180
Model 870SD Skeet Tournament Grade . . . . $ 520
Model 870SF Skeet Premier Grade $1,000

Remington Wingmaster Model 870TB Trap Special $145

Same general specifications as Model 870AP except has 28 or 30-inch ventilated rib barrel, full choke, metal bead front sight, no rear sight, "Special" grade trap-style stock and forend, both checkered, recoil pad, weighs about 8 pounds. Made from 1950 to date.

Remington Wingmaster Model 870TC Trap Grade

Same as Model 870TB except higher grade walnut in stock and forend, has both front and rear sights. Made from 1950 to date.
Model 870TC Trap Grade . . . . $ 200
Model 870TD Trap Tournament Grade . . . . $ 520
Model 870TF Trap Premier Grade $1,000

Remington Wingmaster Model 870 Magnum Standard Grade $100

Same as Model 870AP, except chambered for 12 gauge 3-inch magnum, 30-inch full choke barrel, recoil pad, weighs about 8¼ pounds. Made from 1955 to 1963.

Remington Wingmaster Model 870 Magnum De Luxe Grade $120

Same as Model 870 Magnum Standard Grade, except has checkered stock and extension beavertail forearm, barrel with matted top surface. Discontinued in 1963.

Remington Model 870 Magnum Duck Gun

Same as Model 870 Field Gun, except has 3-inch chamber, 12 and 20 gauge Magnum only. 28 or 30-inch barrel, plain or ventilated rib, modified or full choke; recoil pad; weight, about 7½ or 6¾ pounds. Made from 1964 to date.
With plain barrel $120
With ventilated rib barrel $135

Remington Sportsman-58ADL Autoloader

De Luxe Grade. Gas-operated. 12 gauge. 3-shot magazine. Barrels: plain or ventilated rib; 26, 28 or 30-inch; improved cylinder, modified choke, full choke, Remington Special Skeet boring. Weight, about 7 pounds. Checkered pistol-grip stock and forearm. Made from 1956 to 1964.
With plain barrel $140
With ventilated rib barrel $165

Remington Sportsman-58BDL De Luxe Special Grade

Same as Model 58ADL, except select grade wood.
With plain barrel $165
With ventilated rib barrel $190

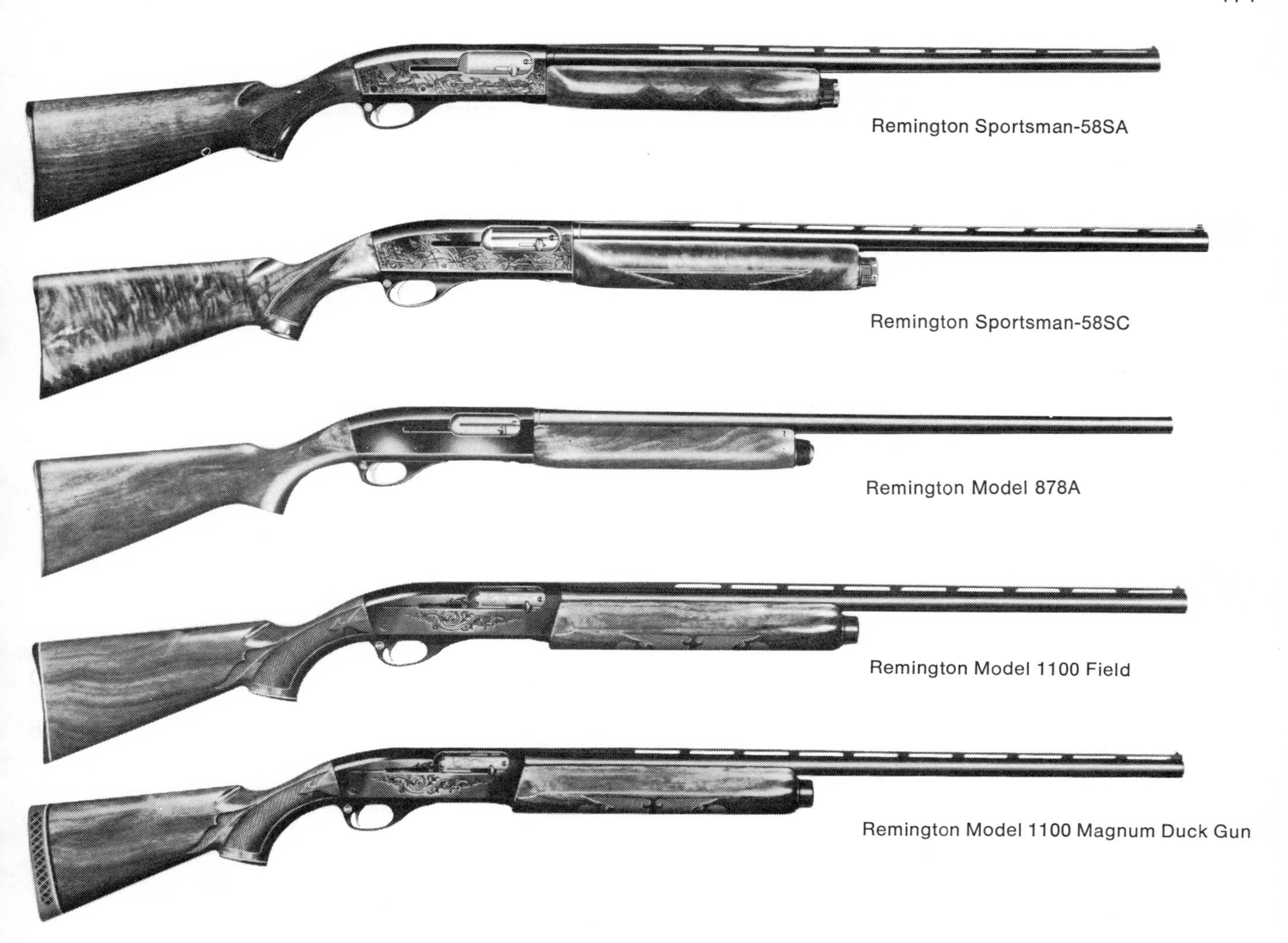

Remington Sportsman-58SA

Remington Sportsman-58SC

Remington Model 878A

Remington Model 1100 Field

Remington Model 1100 Magnum Duck Gun

Remington Sportsman-58 Tournament and Premier Grades

These higher grade models differ from the Sportsman-58ADL with ventilated rib barrel in general quality, grade of wood, checkering, engraving, etc. General specifications are the same.
Sportsman-58D Tournament Grade **$475**
Sportsman-58F Premier Grade **$975**

Remington Sportsman-58SA Skeet Grade $165

Same general specifications as Model 58ADL with ventilated rib barrel, except special Skeet stock and forearm.

Remington Sportsman-58 Skeet Target, Tournament and Premier Grades

These higher grade models differ from the Sportsman-58SA in general quality, grade of wood, checkering, engraving, etc. General specifications are the same.
Sportsman-58SC Skeet Target Grade **$275**
Sportsman-58D Skeet Tournament Grade **$475**
Sportsman-58SF Skeet Premier Grade **$975**

Remington Model 878A Automaster Autoloader $90

Gas-operated. 12 gauge. 3-shot magazine. Barrels: 26-inch improved cylinder, 28-inch modified choke, 30″ full choke. Weight, about 7 pounds. Plain pistol-grip stock and forearm. Made from 1959 to 1962.

Remington Model 1100 Automatic Field Gun

Gas-operated. Hammerless. Takedown. Gauges: 12, 16, 20. Barrels: plain or ventilated rib; 30″/full, 28″/modified or full, 26″/improved cylinder. Weights, average 7¼ to 7½ pounds, depending upon gauge and barrel length. Checkered pistol-grip stock and forearm. Made from 1963 to date.
With plain barrel **$145**
With ventilated rib barrel **$165**

Remington Model 1100 Magnum Duck Gun

Same as Model 1100 Field Gun, except has 3-inch chamber, 12 and 20 gauge Magnum only. 30-inch plain or ventilated-rib barrel in 12 gauge, 28-inch in 20 gauge; modified or full choke. Recoil pad. Weight, about 7¾ pounds. Made from 1963 to date.
With plain barrel **$155**
With ventilated rib barrel **$175**

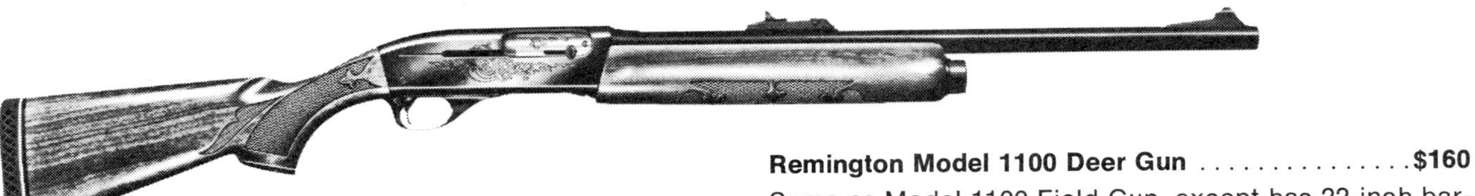

Remington Model 1100 Deer Gun

Remington Model 1100 Deer Gun **$160**

Same as Model 1100 Field Gun, except has 22-inch barrel, improved cylinder, with rifle-type sights; 12 and 20 gauge only; recoil pad; weighs about 7¼ pounds. Made from 1963 to date.

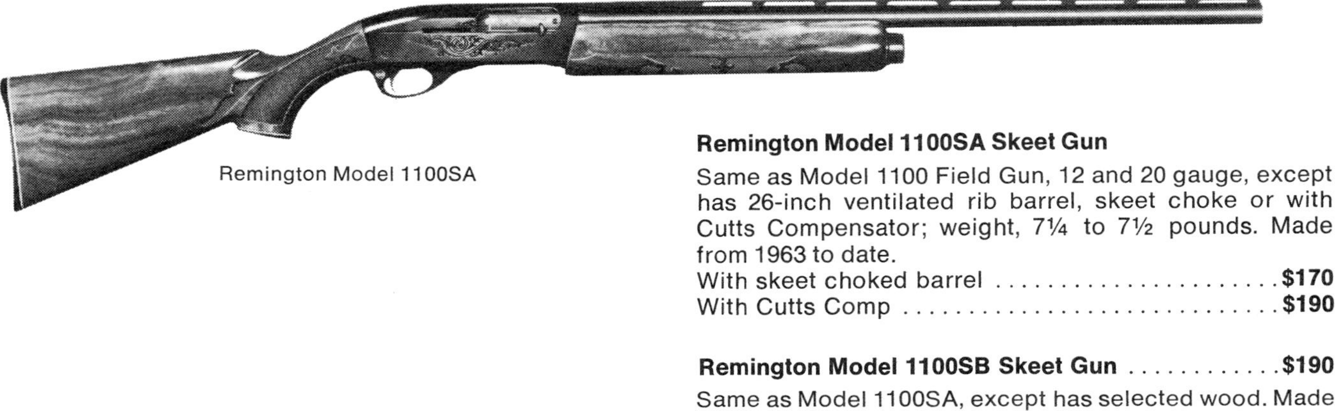

Remington Model 1100SA

Remington Model 1100SA Skeet Gun

Same as Model 1100 Field Gun, 12 and 20 gauge, except has 26-inch ventilated rib barrel, skeet choke or with Cutts Compensator; weight, 7¼ to 7½ pounds. Made from 1963 to date.
With skeet choked barrel **$170**
With Cutts Comp **$190**

Remington Model 1100SB Skeet Gun **$190**

Same as Model 1100SA, except has selected wood. Made from 1963 to date.

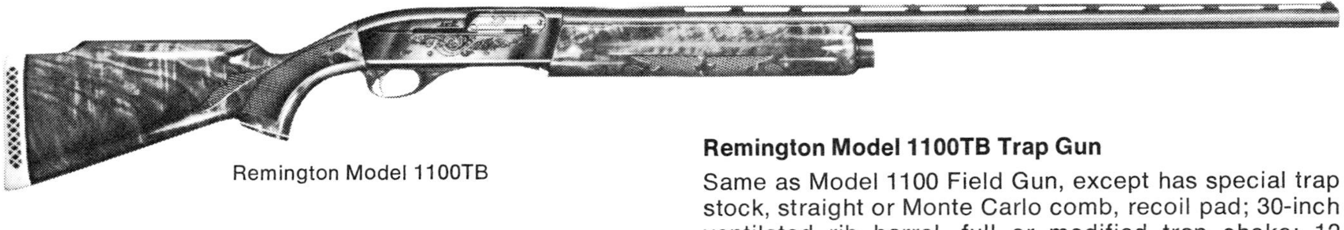

Remington Model 1100TB

Remington Model 1100TB Trap Gun

Same as Model 1100 Field Gun, except has special trap stock, straight or Monte Carlo comb, recoil pad; 30-inch ventilated rib barrel, full or modified trap choke; 12 gauge only; weight, 8¼ pounds. Made from 1963 to date.
With straight stock **$195**
With Monte Carlo stock **$205**

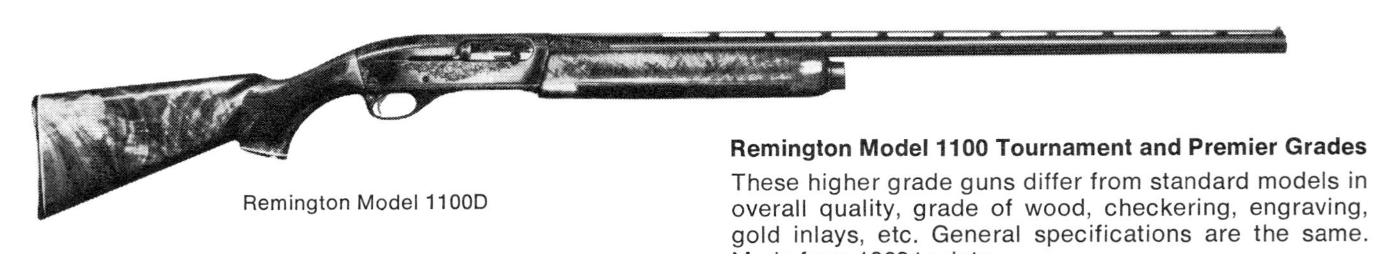

Remington Model 1100D

Remington Model 1100 Tournament and Premier Grades

These higher grade guns differ from standard models in overall quality, grade of wood, checkering, engraving, gold inlays, etc. General specifications are the same. Made from 1963 to date.
Model 1100D Tournament . . . . **$ 520**
Model 1100F Premier **$1,000**
Model 1100F Premier with gold inlay **$1,500**

Richland Model 200

Richland Model 202

Richland Shotguns are manufactured in Italy and Spain for Richland Arms Company, Blissfield, Michigan

Richland Model 200 Field Grade Double Barrel Shotgun $150

Hammerless, box lock, Anson & Deeley type. Plain extractors. Double triggers. Gauges: 12, 16, 20, 28, 410 (3-inch chambers in 20 and 410; others have 2¾-inch). Barrels: 28-inch modified and full choke, 26-inch improved cylinder and modified; 410 with 26-inch modified and full only; 22-inch improved cylinder and modified in 20 gauge only. Weights: 6 lb. 2 oz. to 7 lb. 4 oz. Checkered walnut stock with cheekpiece, pistol grip, recoil pad; beavertail forend; both checkered. Made in Spain 1963 to date.

Richland Model 202 All-Purpose Field Gun $215

Same as Model 200, except has two sets of barrels same gauge. 12 gauge: 30-inch barrels full and full, 3-inch chambers; 26-inch barrels improved cylinder and modified, 2¾-inch chambers. 20 gauge: 28-inch barrels modified and full; 22-inch barrels improved cylinder and modified; 3-inch chambers. Made from 1963 to date.

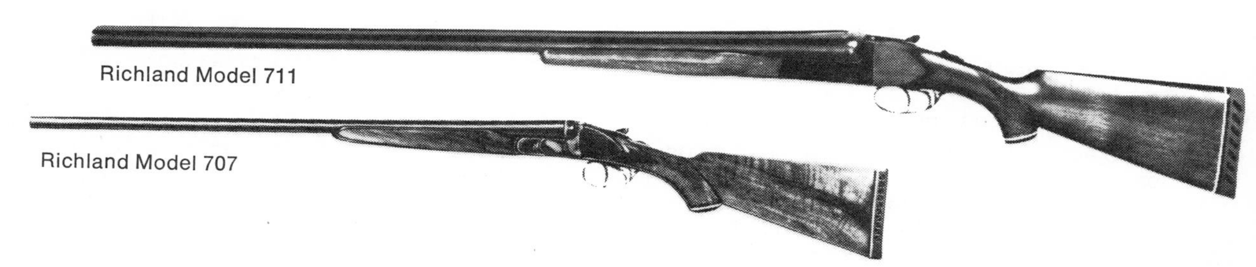
Richland Model 711

Richland Model 707

Richland Model 711 Long Range Waterfowl Magnum Double Barrel Shotgun $180

Hammerless, box lock, Anson & Deeley type, Purdey triple lock. Plain extractors. Double triggers. Automatic safety. Gauges: 10 gauge (3½-inch chambers), 12 gauge (3-inch chambers). Barrels: 10 gauge, 32-inch; 12 gauge, 30-inch; full and full. Weights: 10 gauge, 11 pounds; 12 gauge, 7¾ pounds. Checkered walnut stock and beavertail forend; recoil pad. Made in Spain 1963 to date.

Richland Model 707 Deluxe Field Gun $225

Hammerless, box lock, triple bolting system. Plain extractors. Double triggers. Gauges: 12 (2¾-inch chambers), 20 (3-inch chambers). Barrels: 12 gauge—28-inch modified and full, 26-inch improved cylinder and modified; 20 gauge—30-inch full and full, 28-inch modified and full, 26-inch improved cylinder and modified. Weights: 6 lb. 4 oz. to 6 lb. 15 oz. Checkered walnut stock and forend, recoil pad. Made from 1963 to 1972.

Richland Model 808

Richland Model 808 Over-and-Under Gun $260

Box lock. Plain extractors. Non-selective single trigger. 12 gauge only. Barrels (Vickers steel): 30-inch full and full, 28-inch modified and full, 26-inch improved cylinder and modified. Weight, 6 lb. 12 oz. to 7 lb. 3 oz. Checkered walnut stock and forend. Made in Italy from 1963 to 1968.

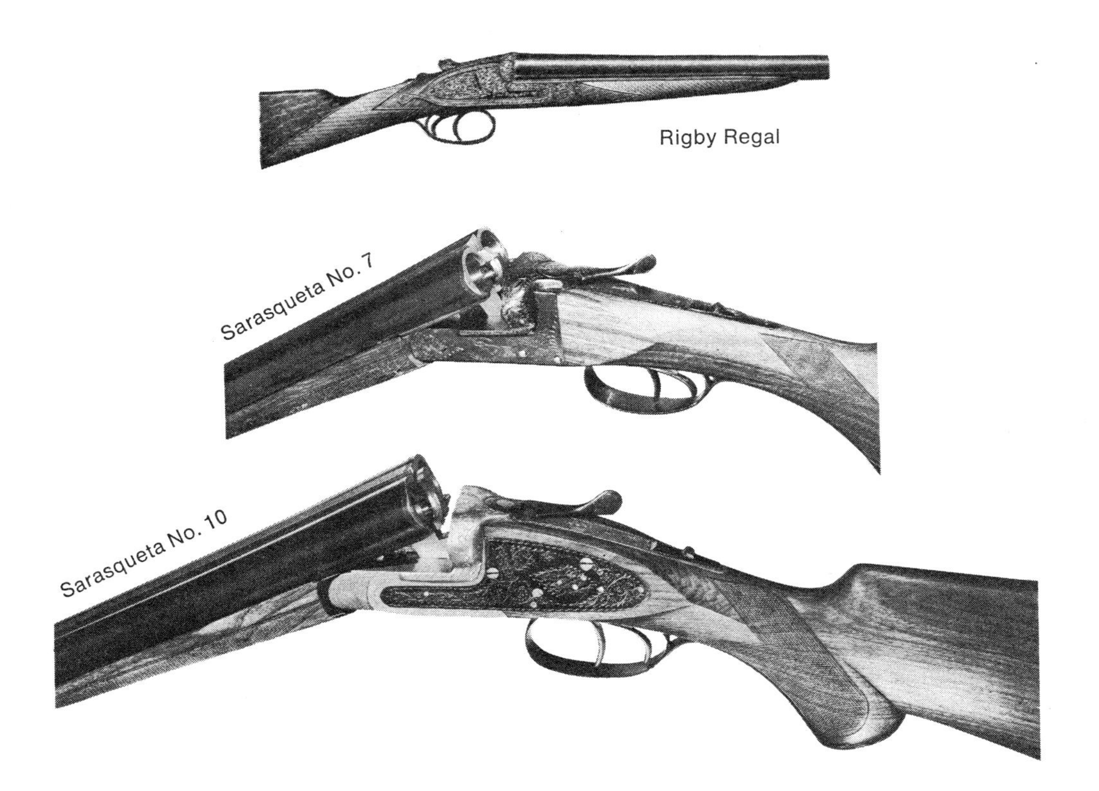

John Rigby & Co., London, England

Rigby Hammerless Side Lock Double Barrel Shotgun

Automatic ejectors. Double triggers. Made in all gauges, barrel lengths and chokes. Checkered stock and forend, straight grip standard. Made in two grades: Regal (best quality) and Sandringham; these guns differ in general quality, engraving, etc.; specifications are the same.
Regal Grade **$3,375**
Sandringham Grade **$2,250**

Rigby Hammerless Box Lock Double Barrel Shotgun

Automatic ejectors. Double triggers. Made in all gauges, barrel lengths and chokes. Checkered stock and forend, straight grip standard. Made in two grades: Sackville and Chatsworth; these guns differ in general quality, engraving, etc., specifications are the same.
Sackville Grade **$1,250**
Chatsworth Grade . . . . **$ 950**

Victor Sarasqueta, Eibar, Spain

Sarasqueta Hammerless Box Lock Double Barrel Shotguns **$140**

Plain extractors. Double triggers. Gauges: 12, 16, 20, 24. Made in various barrel lengths, chokes and weights. Checkered stock and forend, straight grip standard. The two models, No. 2 and No. 3, differ chiefly in that the former has Greener cross bolt, otherwise differences are only in style of engraving. Currently manufactured. Price same for either model.

Sarasqueta Hammerless Side Lock Double Barrel Shotguns

Automatic ejectors (except on Nos. 6 and 7 which are non-ejector models). Double triggers. Gauges: 12, 16, 20, 24. Barrel lengths, chokes and weights made to order. Checkered stock and forend, straight grip standard. There are 13 grades—No. 4, 4E, 5, 5E, 6, 6E, 7, 7E, 8, 9, 10, 11, 12—which differ chiefly in overall quality, engraving, grade of wood, checkering, etc., general specifications are the same. These guns range in degree of decoration from a simple engraved border on No. 4 to the elaborate relief engraving of No. 12. Currently manufactured.
No. 4 . . . . **$190**
No. 4E **$240**
No. 5 . . . . **$230**
No. 5E **$280**
No. 6 . . . . **$245**
No. 6E **$295**
No. 7 . . . . **$280**
No. 7E **$330**
No. 8 . . . . **$450**
No. 9 . . . . **$560**
No. 10 . . . . **$560**
No. 11 . . . . **$595**
No. 12 . . . . **$725**

Sarasqueta Super De Luxe Over-and-Under Shotgun **$650**

Hammerless. Side lock. Automatic ejectors. Double triggers. 12 gauge only. Barrel lengths, chokes, weights made to order. Checkered stock and forend, pistol grip standard. Currently manufactured.

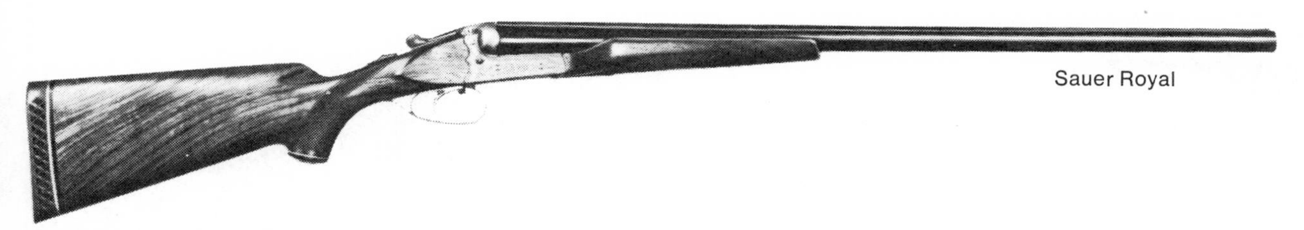
Sauer Royal

J. P. Sauer & Sohn, formerly located in Suhl, now in Eckernforde, West Germany

Sauer "Royal" Double Barrel Shotgun $450
Anson & Deeley action (box lock) with Greener cross bolt, double underlugs, signal pins, single selective trigger, selective automatic ejectors, automatic safety. Scalloped frame with arabesque engraving. Krupp-Special steel barrels. Gauges: 12 (2¾″ chambers, 20 (3″ chambers). Barrels: 30-inch (12 ga. only) and 28-inch, modified and full; 26-inch (20 ga. only), improved cylinder and modified. Weights: 12 ga., about 6½ pounds; 20 ga., about 6 pounds. Checkered walnut pistol-grip stock and beavertail forend; recoil pad. Currently manufactured.

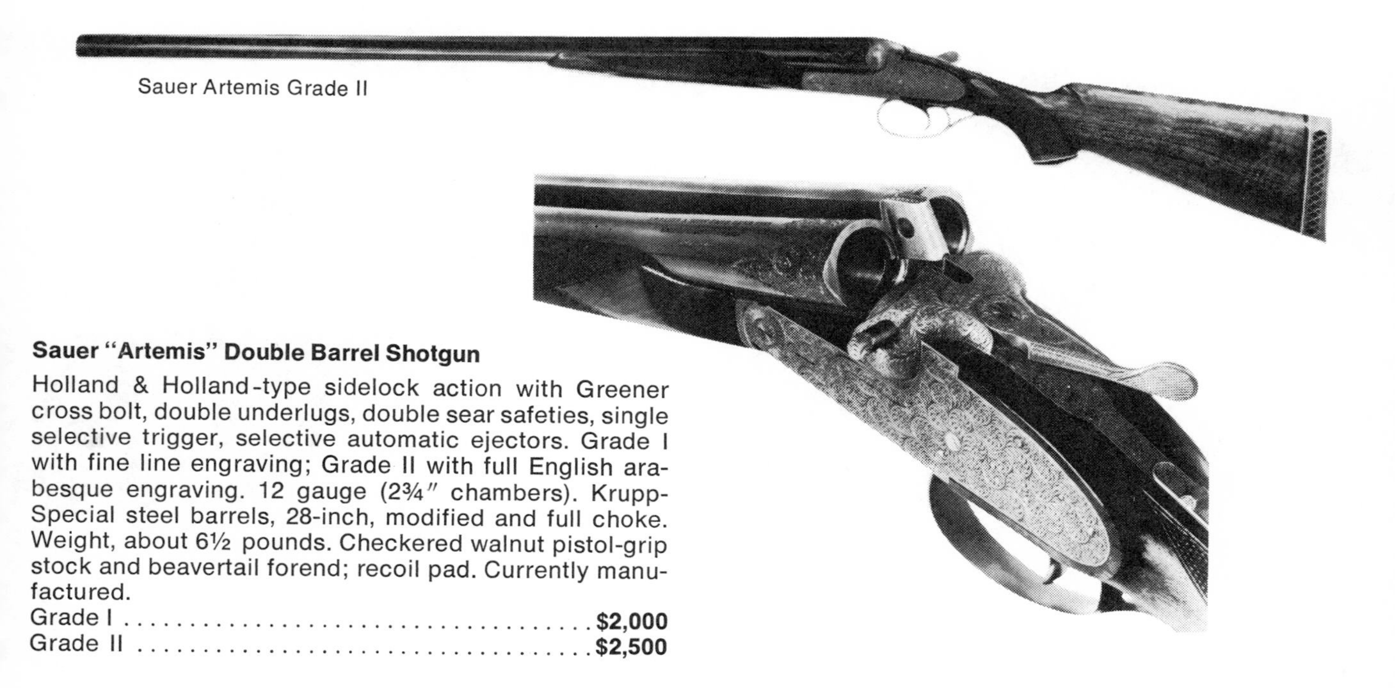
Sauer Artemis Grade II

Sauer "Artemis" Double Barrel Shotgun

Holland & Holland-type sidelock action with Greener cross bolt, double underlugs, double sear safeties, single selective trigger, selective automatic ejectors. Grade I with fine line engraving; Grade II with full English arabesque engraving. 12 gauge (2¾″ chambers). Krupp-Special steel barrels, 28-inch, modified and full choke. Weight, about 6½ pounds. Checkered walnut pistol-grip stock and beavertail forend; recoil pad. Currently manufactured.
Grade I **$2,000**
Grade II **$2,500**

Sauer Model 66 Field Grade I

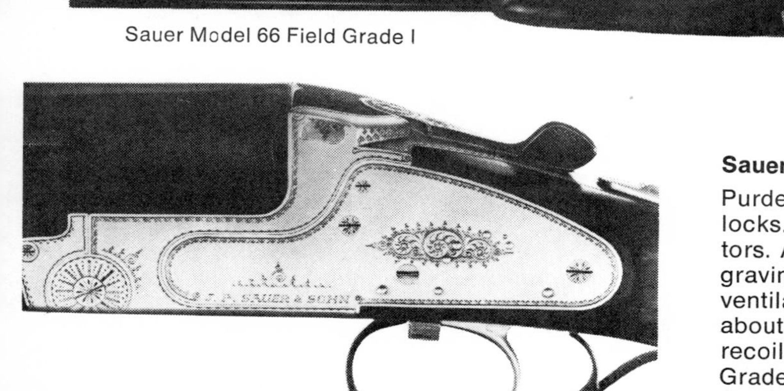

Sauer Model 66 Over-and-Under Field Gun

Purdey system action with Holland & Holland-type sidelocks. Single selective trigger. Selective automatic ejectors. Automatic safety. Available in three grades of engraving. 12 gauge only. Krupp-Special steel barrels with ventilated rib, 28-inch, modified and full choke. Weight, about 7¼ pounds. Checkered walnut stock and forend; recoil pad. Currently manufactured.
Grade I . . . . **$ 725**
Grade II . . . . **$ 850**
Grade III **$1,350**

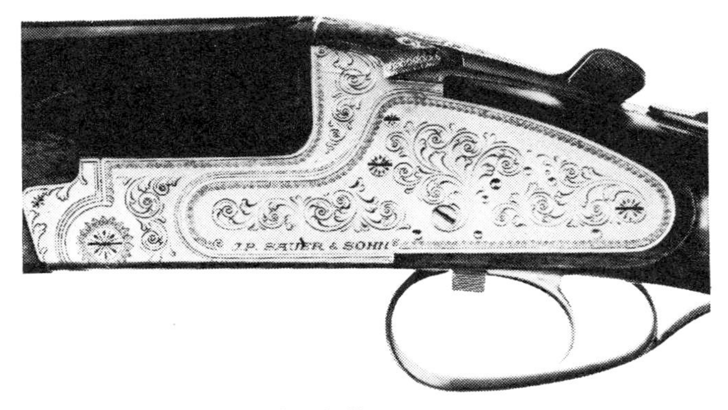

Sauer Model 66 Field Grade II

Sauer Model 66 Field Grade III

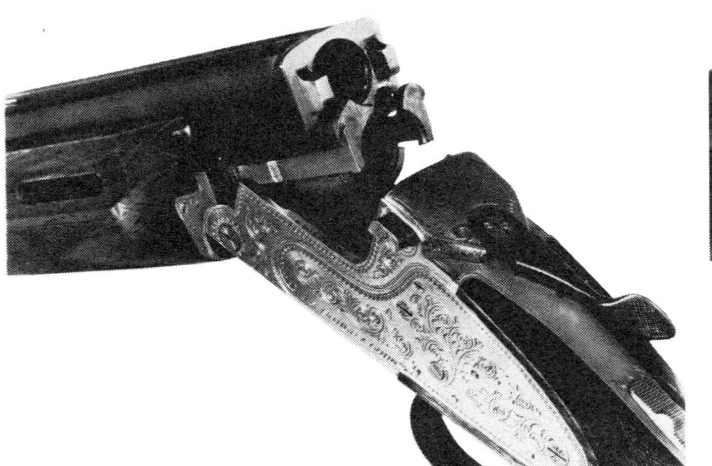

Sauer Model 66 Over-and-Under Skeet Gun

Same as Model 66 Field Gun, except 26-inch barrels with wide ventilated rib, skeet choked; skeet-style stock and ventilated beavertail forearm; non-automatic safety. Currently manufactured.

Grade I	$ 800
Grade II	$ 900
Grade III	$1,400

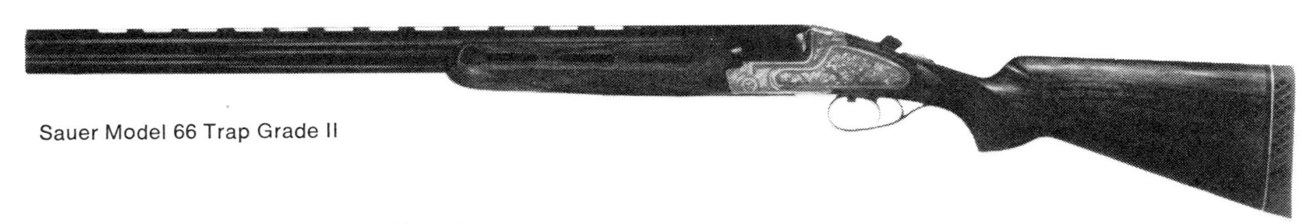

Sauer Model 66 Trap Grade II

Sauer Model 66 Over-and-Under Trap Gun

Same as Model 66 Skeet Gun, except has 30-inch barrels bored full and full or modified and full; trap-style stock. Currently manufactured. Values same as for Skeet Model.

Sauer Model 3000E Drilling, Standard

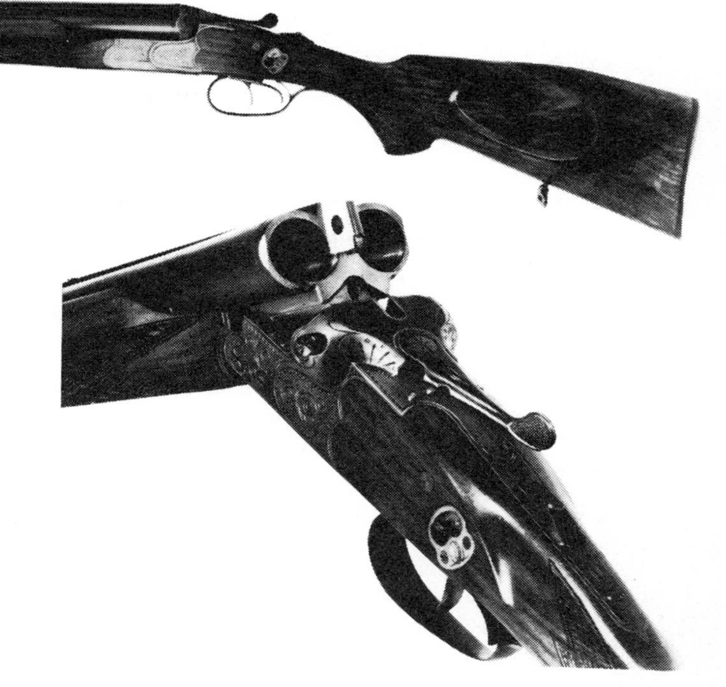

Sauer Model 3000E Drilling

Combination rifle and double barrel shotgun. Blitz action with Greener cross bolt, double underlugs, separate rifle cartridge extractor, front set trigger, firing pin indicators, Greener side safety, sear slide selector locks right shotgun barrel for firing rifle barrel. Gauge/calibers: 12 gauge (2¾″ chambers); 222, 243, 30-06, 7x65R. 25-inch Krupp-Special steel barrels; modified and full choke, automatic folding leaf rear rifle sight. Weight, 6½ to 7¼ pounds depending on rifle caliber. Checkered walnut stock and forend; pistol grip, modified Monte Carlo comb and cheekpiece, sling swivels. Standard Model with arabesque engraving; Deluxe Model with hunting scenes engraved on action. Currently manufactured.

Standard Model .... **$ 900**
Deluxe Model **$1,000**

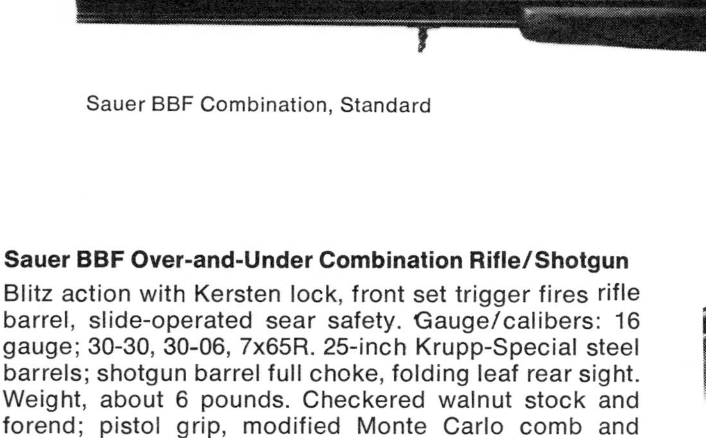

Sauer BBF Combination, Standard

Sauer BBF Over-and-Under Combination Rifle/Shotgun

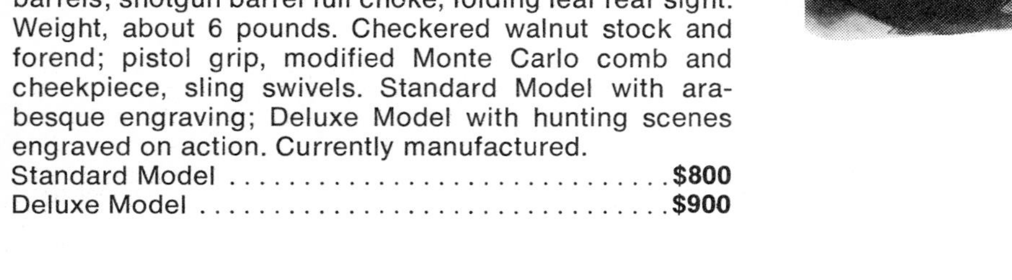

Blitz action with Kersten lock, front set trigger fires rifle barrel, slide-operated sear safety. Gauge/calibers: 16 gauge; 30-30, 30-06, 7x65R. 25-inch Krupp-Special steel barrels; shotgun barrel full choke, folding leaf rear sight. Weight, about 6 pounds. Checkered walnut stock and forend; pistol grip, modified Monte Carlo comb and cheekpiece, sling swivels. Standard Model with arabesque engraving; Deluxe Model with hunting scenes engraved on action. Currently manufactured.

Standard Model **$800**
Deluxe Model **$900**

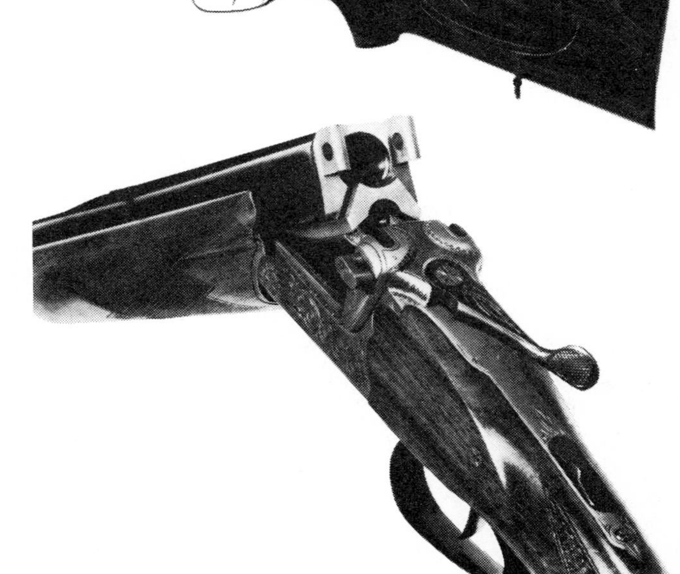

Savage Arms, Westfield, Massachusetts (formerly located at Utica, N.Y.)

Savage Model 28A Standard Grade Slide Action Repeating Shotgun $125

Hammerless. Takedown. 12 gauge. 5-shell tubular magazine. Plain barrel; lengths: 26, 28, 30, 32-inch; chokes: cylinder, modified, full. Weight, about 7½ pounds with 30-inch barrel. Plain pistol-grip stock, grooved slide handle.

Savage Model 28B $135

Raised Matted Rib; otherwise the same as Model 28A.

Savage Model 28D Trap Grade $185

Same general specifications as Model 28A except has 30-inch full choke barrel with matted rib, trap-style stock with checkered pistol-grip, checkered slide handle of selected walnut.

Savage Model 420 Over-and-Under Double Barrel Shotgun

Box lock. Hammerless. Takedown. Automatic safety. Double triggers or non-selective single trigger. Gauges: 12, 16, 20 gauge. Plain barrels; lengths: 26 to 30-inch (the latter in 12 gauge only); chokes: modified and full, cylinder and improved cylinder. Weights with 28-inch barrels: 12 gauge 7¾ pounds, 16 grauge 7½ pounds, 20 gauge 6¾ pounds. Plain pistol-grip stock and forearm. Discontinued 1942.
With double triggers **$200**
With single trigger **$250**

Savage Model 430

Same as Model 420 except has matted top barrel, checkered stock of selected walnut with recoil pad, checkered forearm. Discontinued 1942.
With double triggers **$225**
With single trigger **$275**

Savage Model 220 Single Barrel Shotgun $35

Hammerless. Takedown. Automatic ejector. Gauges: 12, 16, 20, 410. Single shot. Barrel lengths: 12 gauge—28 to 36-inch, 16 gauge—28 to 32-inch, 20 gauge—26 to 32-inch, 410 bore—26 and 28-inch. Full choke. Weight about 6 pounds. Plain pistol-grip stock and wide forearm. Made from 1947 to 1965.

Savage Model 220P $50

Same as Model 220 except has Poly Choke built integral with barrel; made in 12 gauge with 30-inch barrel, 16 gauge and 20 gauge with 28-inch barrel, not made in 410 bore; has recoil pad.

Savage Model 220AC $40

Same as Model 220 except has Savage adjustable choke.

Savage Utility Gun

See listing under "Rifles."

Savage Model 720 Standard Grade 5-Shot Autoloading Shotgun $125

Browning type. Takedown, 12 and 16 gauge. 4-shell tubular magazine. Plain barrel; lengths: 26 to 32-inch (the latter in 12 gauge only); chokes: cylinder, modified, full. Weight, about 8¼ pounds in 12 gauge with 30-inch barrel; 16 gauge about ½ pound lighter. Checkered pistol-grip stock and forearm. Made from 1930 to 1949.

Savage Model 726 Upland Sporter Grade 3-Shot Autoloading Shotgun $125

Same as Model 720 except has 2-shell magazine capacity.

Savage Model 740C Skeet Gun $150

Same as Model 726 except has special Skeet stock and full beavertail forearm, equipped with Cutts Compensator, barrel length overall with spreader tube is about 24½ inches. Discontinued 1949.

Savage Model 745 Lightweight Autoloading Shotgun $135

Three-shot or five-shot model. Same general specifications as Model 720 except has lightweight alloy receiver, 12 gauge only, 28-inch plain barrel, weighs about 6¾ pounds. Discontinued 1949.

Savage Model 755 Standard Grade Autoloading Shotgun $135

Streamlined receiver. Takedown. 12 and 16 gauge. 4-shell tubular magazine (a three-shot model with magazine capacity of two shells was also produced until 1951). Plain barrel; 30-inch full choke (12 gauge only), 28-inch full or modified, 26-inch improved cylinder. Weight, about 8¼ pounds in 12 gauge. Checkered pistol-grip stock and forearm. Manufactured from 1949 to 1958.

Savage Model 755-SC $145

Same as Model 755 except has 26-inch barrel with recoil-reducing, adjustable Savage Super Choke.

Savage Model 775 Lightweight $140

Same general specifications as Model 755 except has lightweight alloy receiver and weighs about 6¾ pounds. Discontinued 1960.

Savage Model 775-SC $150

Same as Model 775 except has 26-inch barrel with Savage Super Choke.

Savage Model 750 Automatic Shotgun $130

Browning-type autoloader. Takedown. 12 gauge. 4-shot tubular magazine. Barrels: 28-inch, full or modified choke; 26-inch, improved cylinder. Weight, about 7¼ pounds. Checkered walnut pistol-grip stock and grooved forearm. Made from 1960 to 1967.

Savage Model 750-SC $140

Same as Model 750 except has 26-inch barrel with Savage Super Choke. Made from 1962 to 1963.

Savage Model 750-AC $140

Same as Model 750 except has 26-inch barrel with adjustable choke. Made from 1964 to 1967.

Savage Model 28A

Savage Model 430

Savage Model 220

Savage Model 720

Savage Model 726

Savage Model 775

Savage Model 775-SC

Savage Model 750

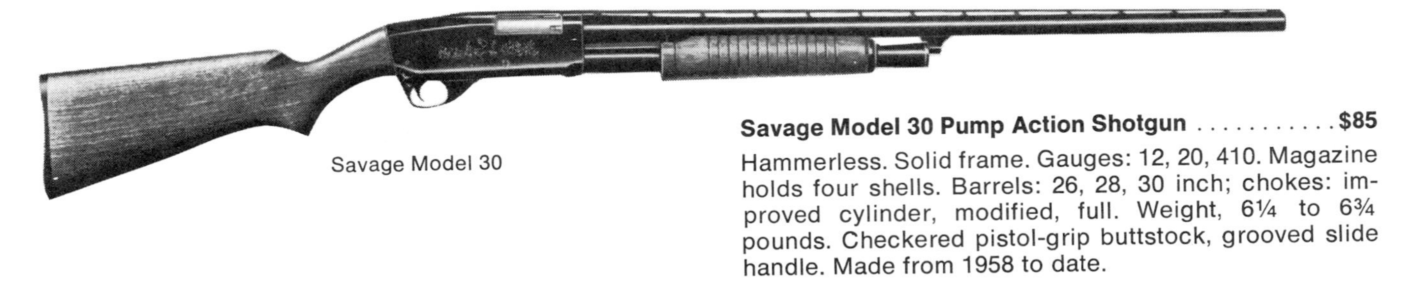

Savage Model 30

Savage Model 30 Pump Action Shotgun **$85**

Hammerless. Solid frame. Gauges: 12, 20, 410. Magazine holds four shells. Barrels: 26, 28, 30 inch; chokes: improved cylinder, modified, full. Weight, 6¼ to 6¾ pounds. Checkered pistol-grip buttstock, grooved slide handle. Made from 1958 to date.

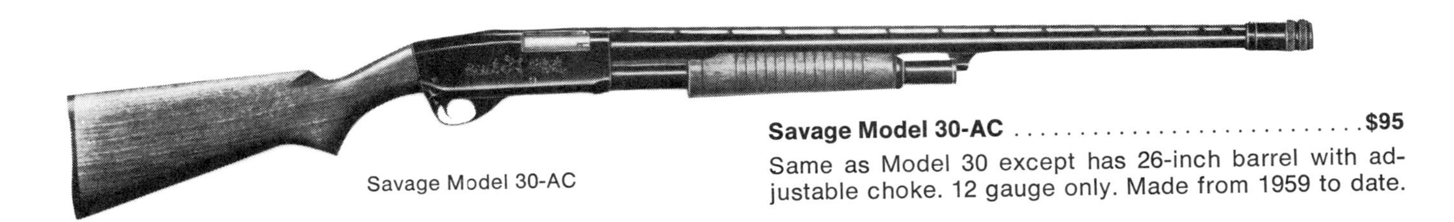

Savage Model 30-AC

Savage Model 30-AC **$95**

Same as Model 30 except has 26-inch barrel with adjustable choke. 12 gauge only. Made from 1959 to date.

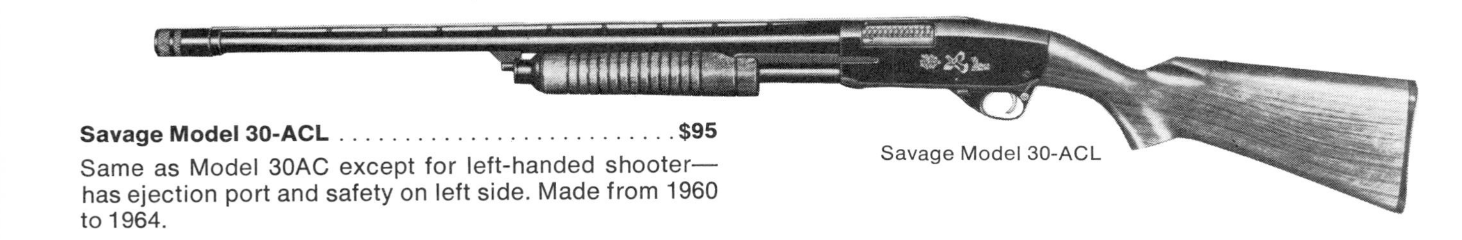

Savage Model 30-ACL

Savage Model 30-ACL **$95**

Same as Model 30AC except for left-handed shooter—has ejection port and safety on left side. Made from 1960 to 1964.

Savage Model 24

Savage Model 24 22-410 Over-and-Under Combination Gun **$65**

Same as Stevens No. 22-410, has walnut stock and forearm. Made from 1950 to 1965.

L. C. Smith Gun Co., a division of Marlin Firearms Co., New Haven, Conn. Formerly Hunter Arms Co., Fulton, N.Y.

L. C. Smith Hammerless Double Barrel Shotguns

Sidelock. Automatic ejectors standard on higher grades, extra on Field and Ideal Grades. Double triggers or Hunter single trigger (non-selective or selective). Gauges: 12, 16, 20, 410. Barrels: 26 to 32-inch, any standard boring. Weight, 6½ to 8¼ pounds in 12 gauge. Checkered stock and forend; choice of straight, half or full pistol grip, beavertail or standard-type forend. Grades differ only in quality of workmanship, wood, checkering, engraving, etc. Same general specifications apply to all. Manufacture of L. C. Smith guns was discontinued in 1951. Production of Field Grade 12 resumed 1968-1973.

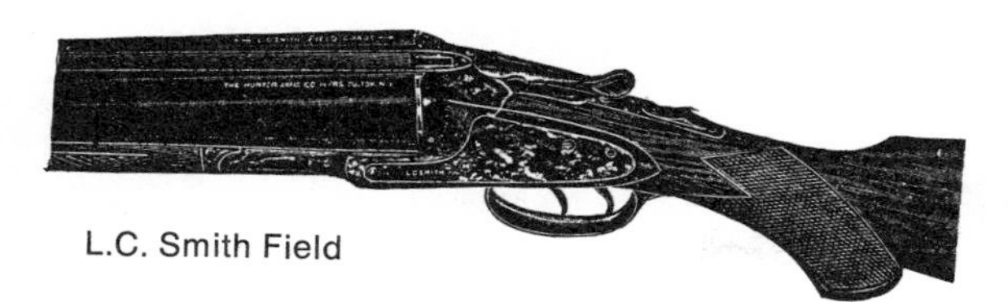

L.C. Smith Field

Field Grade, double triggers, plain extractors .. $325
Field Grade, double triggers, automatic ejectors $385
Field Grade, non-selective single trigger, plain extractors $385
Field Grade, selective single trigger, automatic ejectors $450

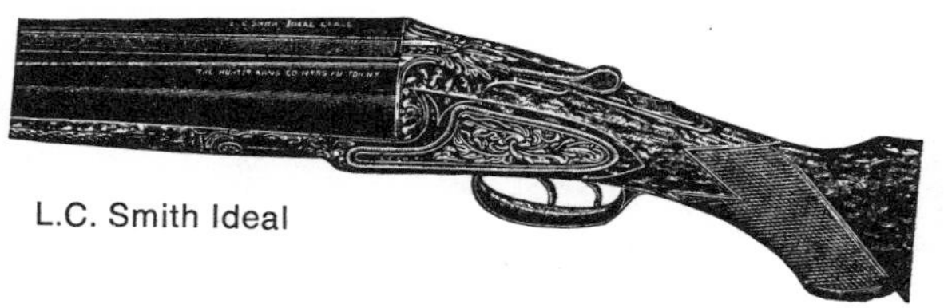

L.C. Smith Ideal

Ideal Grade, double triggers, plain extractors $400
Ideal Grade, double triggers, automatic ejectors $475
Ideal Grade, selective single trigger, automatic ejectors $550

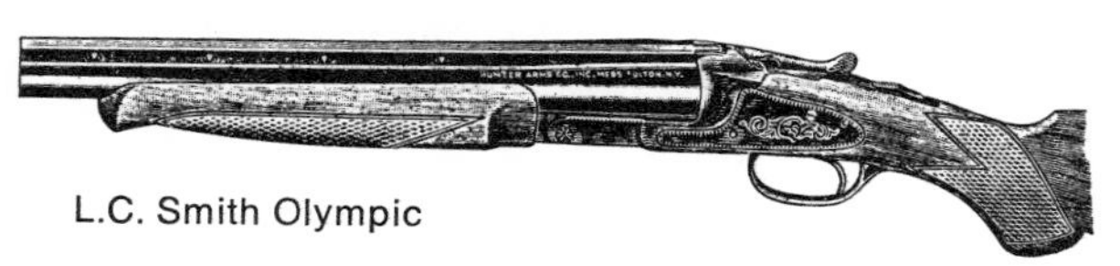

L.C. Smith Olympic

Olympic Grade, selective single trigger, automatic ejectors $600

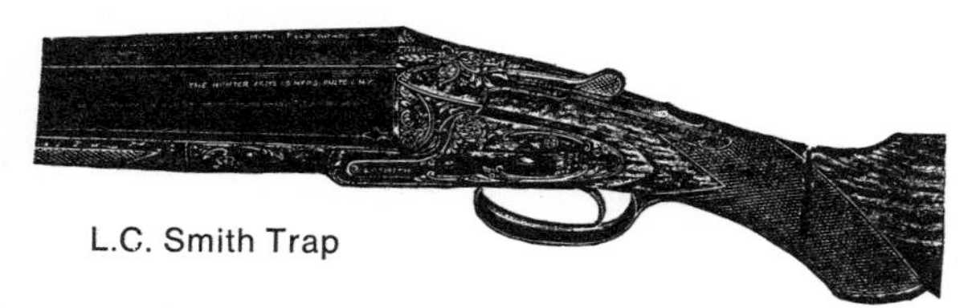

L.C. Smith Trap

Trap Grade, selective single trigger, automatic ejectors $750

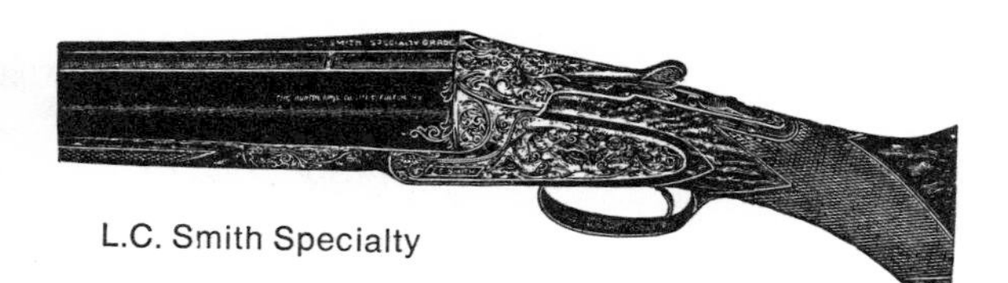

L.C. Smith Specialty

Specialty Grade, double triggers, automatic ejectors $750
Specialty Grade, selective single trigger, automatic ejectors $850

L.C. Smith Skeet

Skeet Special, non-selective single trigger, automatic ejectors $600
Skeet Special, selective single trigger, automatic ejectors $700

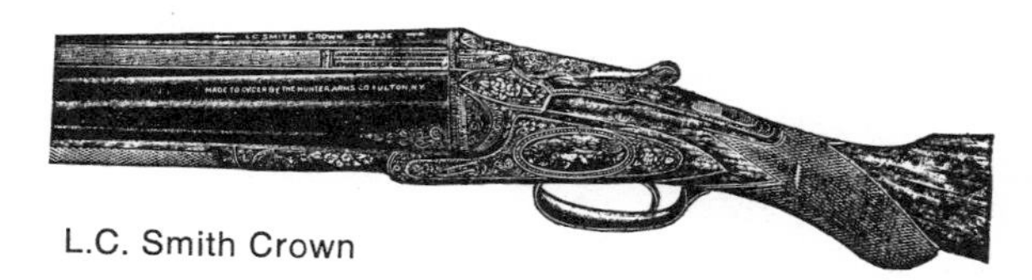

L.C. Smith Crown

Crown Grade, double triggers, automatic ejectors $1,500
Crown Grade, selective single trigger, automatic ejectors $1,600

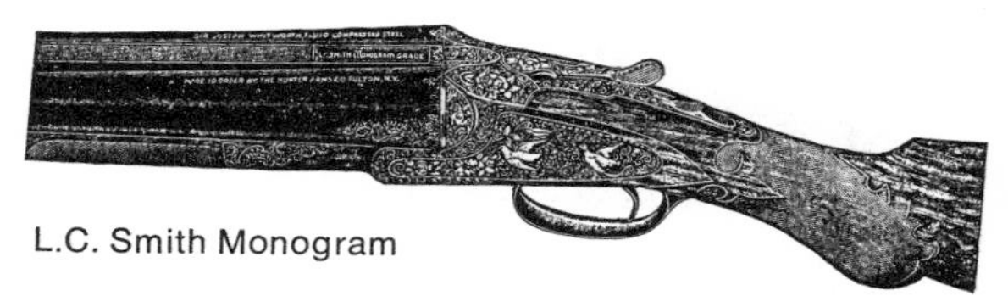

L.C. Smith Monogram

Monogram Grade, selective single trigger, automatic ejectors $2,500

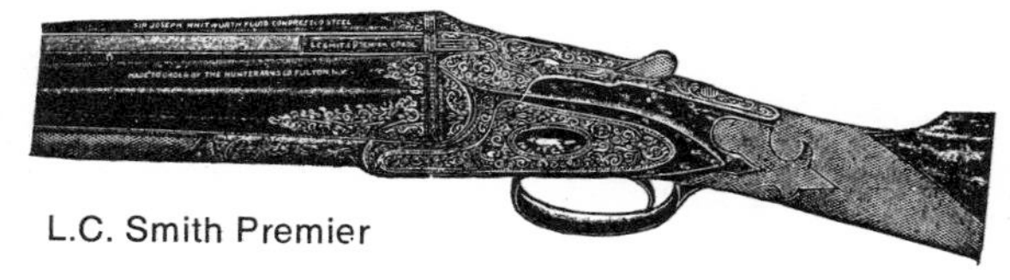

L.C. Smith Premier

Premier Grade, selective single trigger, automatic ejectors $3,500

L.C. Smith Single Barrel Trap, Olympic

L. C. Smith Single Barrel Trap Guns

Box lock. Hammerless. Automatic ejector. 12 gauge only. Barrel lengths: 32 or 34-inch. Ventilated rib. Weight, 8 to 8¼ pounds. Checkered pistol-grip stock and forend, recoil pad. The three grades vary in quality of workmanship, wood, engraving, etc.; general specifications are the same. Discontinued in 1951.

Olympic Grade ....$ 750
Specialty Grade $1,100
Crown Grade $2,000

J. Stevens Arms Company, a division of Savage Arms Corporation, Chicopee Falls, Massachusetts

Stevens Model 620 Hammerless Slide Action Repeating Shotgun $100

Takedown. Gauges: 12, 16, 20. 5-shell tubular magazine. Barrel lengths: 26, 28, 30, 32-inch; chokes: full, modified, improved cylinder, cylinder. Weights: about 7¾ pounds in 12 gauge, 7¼ in 16 gauge, 6 pounds in 20 gauge. Checkered pistol-grip stock and slide handle. Made from 1927 to 1953.

Stevens Model 621 .... $110

Same as Model 620 except has raised solid matted rib barrel. Discontinued.

Stevens Model 530 Hammerless Double Barrel Shotgun $100

Box lock. Double triggers. Gauges: 12, 16, 20, 410. Barrel lengths: 26 to 32-inch; chokes: modified and full, cylinder and modified, full and full. Weight, from 6 to 7½ pounds depending upon gauge and barrel length. Checkered pistol-grip stock and forearm, some early models were fitted with recoil pad. Made from 1936 to 1954.

Stevens Model 530ST Double Gun $120

Same as Model 530 except has non-selective single trigger. Discontinued.

Stevens Model 530M $75

Same as Model 530 except has "Tenite" (plastic) stock and forearm. Discontinued about 1947.

Stevens Model 820 Hammerless Slide Action Repeating Shotgun $90

Solid frame. 12 gauge only. 5-shell tubular magazine. 28-inch barrel; improved cylinder, modified or full choke. Weight, about 7½ pounds. Plain pistol-grip stock, grooved slide handle. Made from 1949 to 1954.

Stevens Model 820-SC $100

Same as Model 820 except has Savage Super Choke.

Stevens-Springfield Model 311 Hammerless Double Barrel Shotgun $90

Same general specifications as Stevens Model 530 except earlier production have plain stock and forearm; checkered on current guns. Originally produced as a "Springfield" gun, this model became a part of the "Stevens" line in 1948 when the "Springfield" brand name was discontinued. Made from 1931 to date.

Stevens No. 22-410 Over-and-Under Combination Gun $65

22 caliber rifle barrel over 410 bore shotgun barrel. Visible hammer. Takedown. Single trigger. 24-inch barrels, shotgun barrel full choke. Weight, about 6 pounds. Open rear sight and ramp front sight of sporting rifle type. Plain pistol-grip stock and forearm; originally supplied with walnut stock and forearm, "Tenite" (plastic) was used in later production. Made from 1938 to 1950. *Note:* This gun is now manufactured as the Savage Model 24.

Stevens Model 258

Stevens Model 58

Stevens Model 59

Stevens Model 107

Stevens Model 124

Stevens Model 77

Stevens Model 240 Over-and-Under Shotgun $150

Visible hammer. Takedown. Double triggers. 410 Gauge. 26-inch barrels, full choke. Weight, about 6 pounds. "Tenite" (plastic) pistol-grip stock and forearm; some early models may have walnut stock and forearm. Made from 1939 to 1942.

Stevens Model 258 Bolt Action Repeating Shotgun . . $40

Takedown. 20-gauge. 2-shell detachable box magazine. 26-inch barrel, full choke. Weight, about 6¼ pounds. Plain one-piece pistol-grip stock. Made from 1937 to 1965.

Stevens Model 58 Bolt Action Repeating Shotgun . . . $40

Takedown. 410 bore. 3-shell detachable box magazine. 24-inch barrel, full choke. Weight, about 5½ pounds. Plain one-piece pistol-grip stock. Made from 1937 to date.

Stevens Model 59 Bolt Action Repeating Shotgun . . . $45

Takedown. 410 bore. 5-shell tubular magazine. 24-inch barrel, full choke. Weight, about 6 pounds. Plain, one-piece pistol-grip stock. Made from 1934 to 1973.

Stevens Model 107 Single Barrel Hammer Shotgun . . $35

Takedown. Automatic ejector. Gauges: 12, 16, 20, 410. Barrel lengths: 28 and 30-inch (12 and 16 gauge), 28-inch (20 gauge), 26-inch (410 gauge); full choke only. Weight, about 6 pounds (12 gauge). Plain pistol-grip stock and forearm. Made from about 1937 to 1953.

Stevens Model 124 Cross Bolt Repeater $50

Hammerless. Solid frame. 12 gauge only. 2-shot tubular magazine. 28-inch barrel; improved cylinder, modified or full choke. Weight, about 7 pounds. Tenite stock and forearm. Made from 1947 to 1952.

Stevens Model 77 Slide Action Repeating Shotgun . $100

Solid frame. Gauges: 12, 16. 5-shot tubular magazine. Barrels: 26-inch, improved cylinder: 28-inch, modified or full choke. Weight, about 7½ pounds. Plain pistol-grip stock with recoil pad, grooved slide handle. Made from 1954 to 1971.

Stevens Model 77-AC $110

Same as Model 77 except has Savage Super Choke.

Valmet Oy, Helsinki, Finland

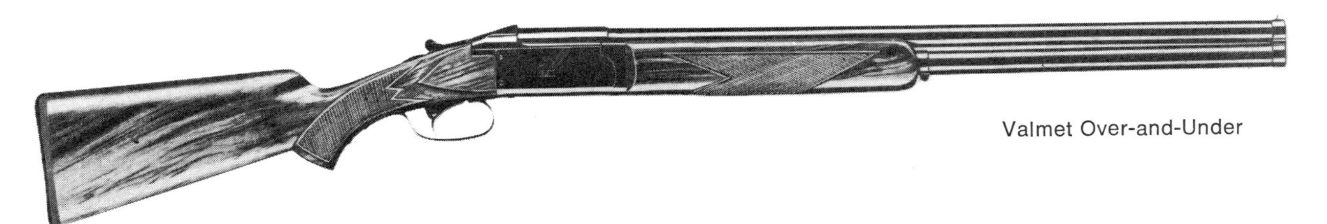
Valmet Over-and-Under

Valmet Over-and-Under Shotgun **$250**

Box lock. Single selective trigger. Plain extractors. 12 gauge only. Barrels: 26-inch, improved cylinder and modified; 28-inch, modified and full; 30-inch, modified and full, full and full. Weight, about 7 pounds. Checkered pistol-grip stock and forearm. Made from 1947 to 1968.

Western Arms Corp., a division of Ithaca Gun Co., Ithaca, N.Y.

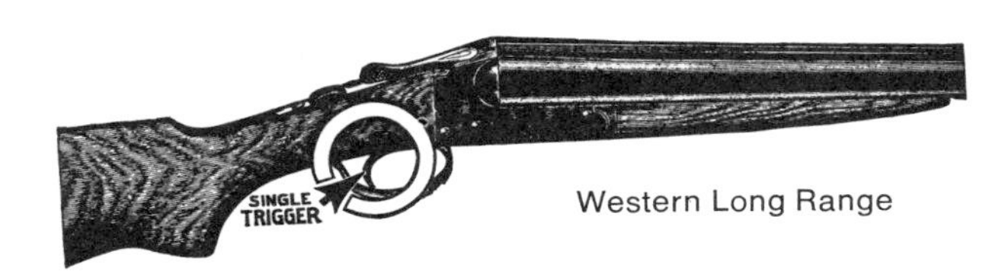

Western Long Range

Western Long Range Hammerless Double Barrel Shotgun

Box lock. Plain extractors. Double triggers or single trigger. Gauges: 12, 16, 20, 410. Barrels: 26 to 32-inch, modified and full choke standard. Weight, about 7½ pounds in 12 gauge. Plain pistol-grip stock and forend. Discontinued 1942.
With double triggers **$150**
With single trigger **$185**

Westley Richards & Co., Ltd., London, England

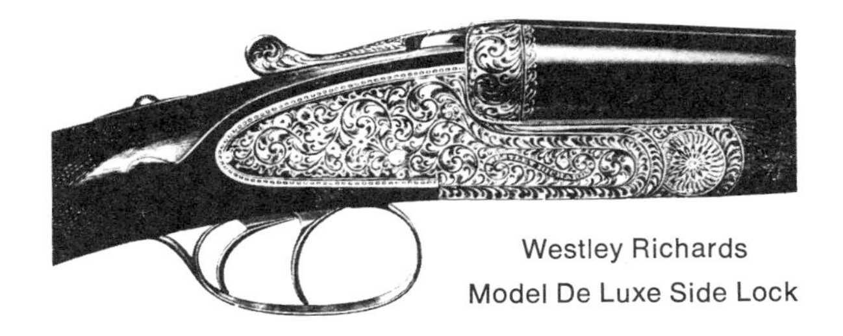
Westley Richards
Model De Luxe Side Lock

Westley Richards Modele De Luxe Quality Sidelock Hammerless Double Barrel Shotgun

Hand detachable side locks. Selective ejectors. Double triggers or selective single trigger. Gauges: 12, 16, 20. Barrel lengths and boring to order. Weight, from 5½ to 6¼ pounds depending upon gauge and barrel length. Checkered stock and forend, straight or half-pistol grip. Also supplied in Pigeon and Wildfowl Model at same price. Currently manufactured.
With double triggers **$5,500**
With selective single trigger **$6,000**

Westley Richards Best Quality Hammerless Double Barrel Shotgun

Box lock. Hand detachable locks and hinged coverplate. Selective ejectors. Double triggers or selective single trigger. Gauges: 12, 16, 20. Barrel lengths and boring to order. Weight, from 5½ to 6¼ pounds depending upon gauge and barrel length. Checkered stock and forend, straight or half-pistol grip. Currently manufactured, guns of this type have been produced by Westley Richards & Co. since 1899.
With double triggers **$3,000**
With selective single trigger **$3,500**

Westley Richards Best Quality Hammerless Double Barrel Shotgun, Pigeon and Wildfowl Model

Same general specifications as the standard Best Quality gun except for extra strength and treble bolting, chambered for 12 gauge 2¾ or 3-inch shells, 28 or 30-inch full choke barrels, weights from 7¼ pounds. Currently manufactured.
With double triggers **$3,500**
With selective single trigger **$4,000**

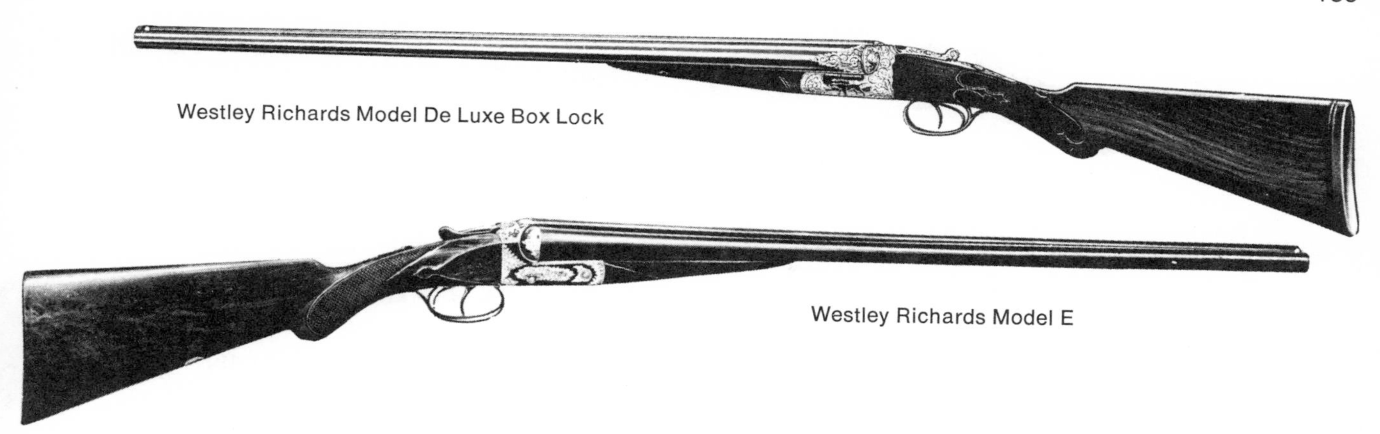

Westley Richards Model De Luxe Box Lock

Westley Richards Model E

Westley Richards Modele De Luxe Quality Hammerless Double Barrel Shotgun

Box lock. Same general specifications as standard Best Quality gun except higher quality throughout, has Westley Richards top-projection and treble-bite lever-work, hand detachable locks. Also supplied in Pigeon and Wildfowl Model at same price. Currently manufactured.
With double triggers **$5,000**
With selective single trigger **$5,500**

Westley Richards Model E Hammerless Double Barrel Shotgun

Anson & Deeley-type box lock action. Selective ejector or non-ejector. Double triggers. Gauges: 12, 16, 20. Barrel lengths and boring to order. Weight, from 5½ to 7¼ pounds depending upon type, gauge and barrel length. Checkered stock and forend, straight or half pistol grip. Also supplied in Pigeon and Wildfowl Model at same price. Currently manufactured.
Ejector model **$2,000**
Non-ejector model **$1,700**

Westley Richards Ovundo (Over-and-Under) Shotgun **$7,000**

Hammerless. Box lock. Hand-detachable locks. Dummy sideplates. Selective ejectors. Selective single trigger. 12 gauge. Barrel lengths and boring to order. Checkered stock and forend, straight or half-pistol grip. Manufactured prior to World War II.

Winchester-Western Div., Olin Corp. (formerly Winchester Repeating Arms Co.), New Haven, Conn.

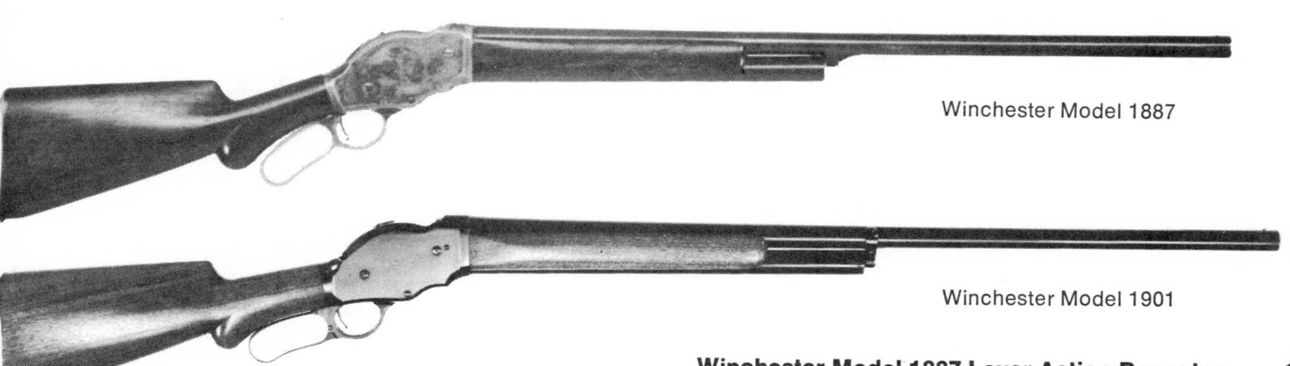

Winchester Model 1887

Winchester Model 1901

Note: Models 1887 and 1901 lever action shotguns were not designed for modern smokeless powder shot shells, their use with modern loads is hazardous.

Winchester Model 1887 Lever Action Repeater **$350**

Solid frame. Gauges: 10 and 12. 4-shot tubular magazine. Plain barrel; 30 and 32-inch, full choke. Plain pistol-grip stock and forend. Weights: 9 pounds in 10 ga., 8 pounds in 12 ga. (*Note:* This model was also offered in De Luxe Grade with Damascus barrel, checkered stock and forend.) Made from 1887 to 1901.

Winchester Model 1901 Lever Action Repeater **$325**

Same general specifications as Model 1887 of which this is a redesigned version. 10 gauge only. Made from 1901 to 1920.

Winchester Model 97

Winchester Model 1911

Winchester Model 12 Standard

Winchester Model 97 Visible Hammer Slide Action Repeating Shotgun. $185

Standard Grade. Takedown or solid frame. Gauges: 12 and 16. 5-shell tubular magazine. Plain barrel; lengths: 26 to 32 inches (the latter made in 12 gauge only); chokes: full to cylinder. Weight, about 7¾ pounds (12 gauge with 28-inch barrel). Plain pistol-grip stock, grooved slide handle. Made from 1897 to 1957.

Winchester Model 97 Riot Gun $185

Takedown or solid frame. Same general specifications as standard Model 97 except 12 gauge only, 20-inch cylinder bore barrel. Made from 1897 to 1957.

Winchester Model 97 Trench Gun $275

Solid frame. Same as Model 97 Riot Gun except has handguard and is equipped with a bayonet. World War I government issue, 1917-18.

Winchester Model 97 Trap, Tournament and Pigeon Grade Guns

These higher grade models, no longer produced, differ from the standard grade in type and forearm and higher general quality. Discontinued in 1939.

Trap Gun **$300**
Tournament Grade **$375**
Pigeon Grade **$600**

Winchester Model 1911 Autoloading Shotgun $200

Hammerless. Takedown. 12 gauge only. 4-shell tubular magazine. Barrels: plain, 26 to 32-inch, standard borings. Weight, about 8½ pounds. Plain or checkered pistol-grip stock and forearm. Made from 1911 to 1925.

Winchester Model 12 Standard Slide Action Repeating Shotgun $275

Hammerless. Takedown. Gauges: 12, 16, 20, 28. 6-shell tubular magazine. Plain barrel: lengths: 26 to 32 inches; chokes: full to cylinder. Weights: about 7½ pounds in 12 gauge 30-inch, about 6½ pounds in other gauges with 28-inch barrel. Plain pistol-grip stock, grooved slide handle. Made from 1912 to 1964.

Winchester Model 12 Featherweight $225

Same as Plain Barrel Model 12 Standard, except has alloy guard, modified takedown. 12 gauge only. Barrels: 26-inch, improved cylinder; 28-inch, modified or full; 30-inch, full choke. Weight, about 6¾ pounds. Made from 1959 to 1962.

Winchester Model 12 Standard Grade, Matted Rib Barrel $300

Same general specifications as Plain Barrel Model 12 Standard except has solid raised matted rib. Discontinued after World War II.

Winchester Model 12 Standard Grade, Ventilated Rib Barrel $350

Same general specifications as Plain Barrel Model 12 Standard except has ventilated rib. 26¾ or 30-inch barrel, 12 gauge only. Discontinued after World War II.

Winchester Model 12 Riot Gun $200

Same general specifications as Plain Barrel Model 12 Standard except has 20-inch cylinder bore barrel, 12 gauge only. Made from 1918 to 1963.

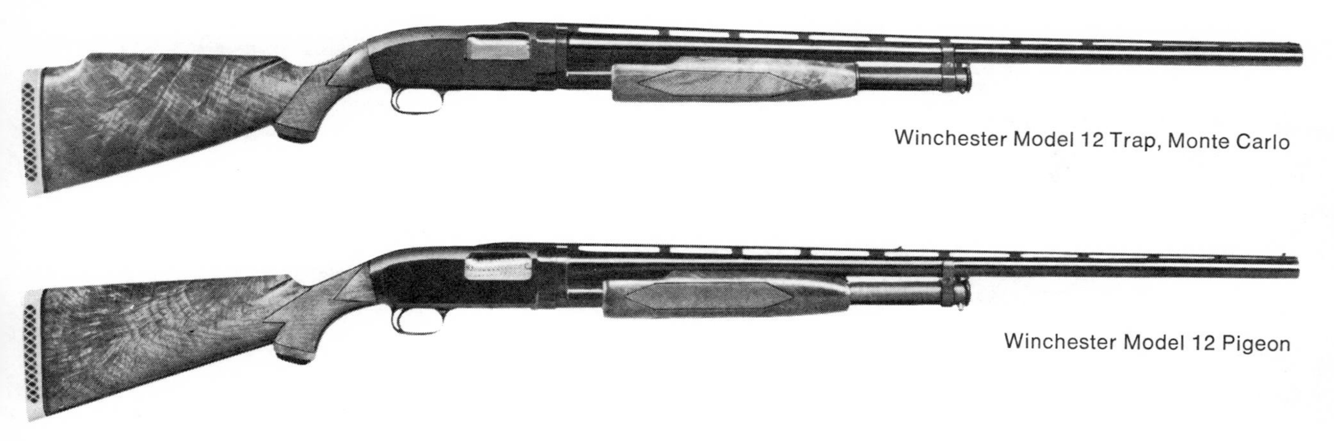

Winchester Model 12 Trap, Monte Carlo

Winchester Model 12 Pigeon

Winchester Model 12 Heavy Duck Gun $325

12 gauge only, chambered for 3-inch shells. Same general specifications as Standard Grade except 30 or 32-inch plain full choke barrel only, 3-shot magazine, recoil pad, weighs about 8¾ pounds. Discontinued in 1964.

Winchester Model 12 Heavy Duck Gun, Matted Rib Barrel $350

Same as Plain Barrel Model 12 Heavy Duck Gun except has solid raised matted rib. Discontinued in 1959.

Winchester Model 12 Skeet Gun $350

Gauges: 12, 16, 20, 28. 5-shot tubular magazine. 26-inch matted rib barrel, skeet choke. Weights: about 7¾ pounds in 12 gauge, about 6¾ pounds in other gauges. Bradley red or ivory bead front sight. Winchester 94B middle sight. Checkered pistol-grip stock and extension slide handle. Discontinued after World War II.

Winchester Model 12 Skeet Gun, Ventilated Rib Barrel $400

Same general specifications as Standard Model 12 Skeet Gun except has 26-inch barrel with ventilated rib, 12 and 20 gauge. Discontinued in 1965.

Winchester Model 12 Skeet Gun, Plain Barrel $325

Same general specifications as Standard Model 12 Skeet Gun except has plain barrel. Made from 1937 to 1947.

Winchester Model 12 Skeet Gun, Cutts Compensator $350

Same general specifications as standard Model 12 Skeet Gun, except has plain barrel fitted with Cutts Compensator, 26-inches overall. Discontinued in 1954.

Winchester Model 12 Trap Gun $350

Same general specifications as standard Model 12, except has straighter stock, checkered pistol-grip and extension slide handle, recoil pad, 30-inch matted rib barrel, full choke, 12 gauge only. Discontinued after World War II.

Winchester Model 12 Trap Gun, Ventilated Rib Barrel $400

Same as Standard Model 12 Trap Gun except has ventilated rib. Discontinued in 1965.

Winchester Model 12 Trap Gun, Monte Carlo Stock $450

Same as Model 12 Ventilated Rib Trap Gun except has Monte Carlo stock. Discontinued in 1965.

Winchester Model 12 Pigeon Grade

De Luxe versions of the regular Model 12 Standard or Field Gun, Duck Gun, Skeet Gun and Trap Gun made on special order. This grade has finer finish throughout, hand-smoothed action, engine-turned breech bolt and carrier, stock and extension slide handle of high grade walnut, fancy checkering, stock dimensions to individual specifications. Engraving and carving available at extra cost ranging from about $35 to over $200. Discontinued in 1965.

Field Gun, plain barrel **$400**
Field Gun, ventilated **$550**
Skeet Gun, matted rib **$550**
Skeet Gun, ventilated rib **$700**
Skeet Gun, Cutts Compensator **$575**
Trap Gun, matted rib **$600**
Trap Gun, ventilated rib **$750**

Winchester Model 12 Super Pigeon Grade $1,000

Custom version of Model 12 with same general specifications as standard models. 12 gauge only. 26, 28, or 30 inch ventilated rib barrel, any standard choke. Engraved receiver. Hand smoothed and fitted action. Full fancy walnut stock and forearm made to individual order. Made from 1965 to date.

Note: In 1972, production of the Model 12 was resumed in Field Gun, Skeet Gun, and Trap Gun models. Current prices range from $460 up.

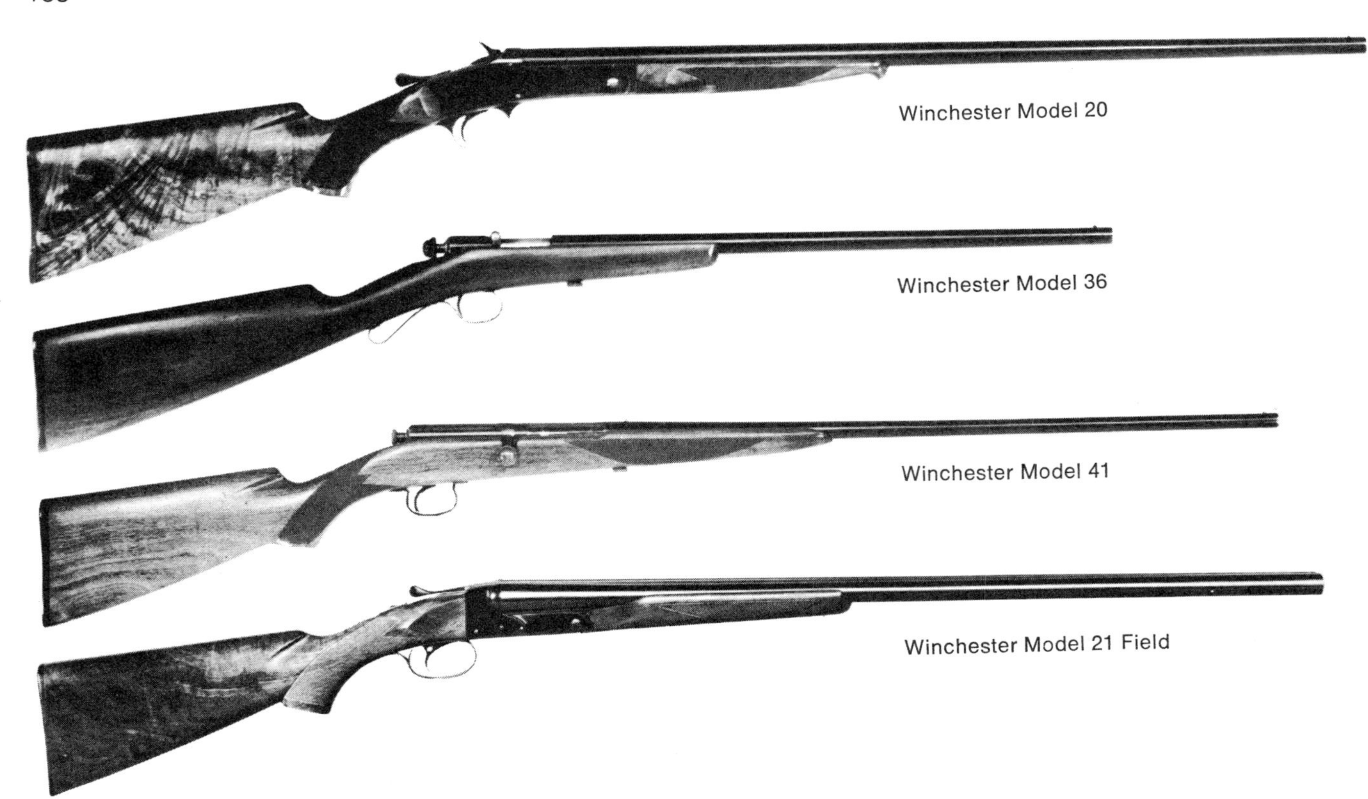
Winchester Model 20
Winchester Model 36
Winchester Model 41
Winchester Model 21 Field

Winchester Model 20 Single Shot Hammer Gun . . . $175

Takedown. 410-2½″. 26-inch barrel, full choke. Checkered pistol-grip stock and forearm. Weight, about 6 pounds. Made from 1919 to 1924.

Winchester Model 36 Single Shot Bolt Action Shotgun $100

Takedown. Uses 9mm Short or Long shot or ball cartridges interchangeably. 18-inch barrel. Plain stock. Weight, about 3 pounds. Made from 1920 to 1927.

Winchester Model 41 Single Shot Bolt Action Shotgun $125

Takedown. 410-2½″ (chambered for 3″ shells after 1932. 24-inch barrel, full choke. Plain straight stock standard. Made from 1920 to 1934.

Winchester Model 21 Double Barrel Field Gun

Hammerless. Box lock. Automatic safety. Double triggers or selective single trigger, selective or non-selective ejection (all post-war Model 21 shotguns have selective single trigger and selective ejection). Gauges 12, 16, 20. Barrels: raised matted rib or ventilated rib; 26, 28, 30, 32-inch, the latter in 12 gauge only; full choke, improved modified, modified, improved cylinder, skeet chokes. Weights: 12 gauge with 30-inch barrel, about 7½ pounds; 16 or 20 gauge with 28-inch barrel, about 6½ pounds. Pistol-grip or straight-grip stock, regular or beavertail forend, both checkered. Made from 1930 to 1958.
With double trigger, non-selective ejection . . . . . $ 800
With double trigger, selective ejection $1,000
With selective single trigger, non-selective ejection $1,000
With selective single trigger, selective ejection . $1,200
Extra for ventilated rib . . . . $ 125

Winchester Model 21 Duck Gun

Same general specifications as Model 21 Field Gun, except chambered for 12 gauge 3-inch shells, 30 or 32-inch barrels only, full choke, selective single trigger, selective ejection, pistol-grip stock with recoil pad, beavertail forearm, both checkered. Discontinued 1958.
With matted rib barrels $1,200
With ventilated rib barrels $1,400

Winchester Model 21 Skeet Gun

Same general specifications as Model 21 Standard, except has 26 or 28-inch barrels only, Skeet chokes No. 1 and 2, Bradley red bead front sight, selective single trigger, selective ejection, non-automatic safety, checkered pistol-grip or straight-grip stock without buttplate or pad (wood butt checkered), checkered beavertail forearm. Discontinued in 1958.
With matted rib barrels $1,200
With ventilated rib barrels $1,400

Winchester Model 21 Trap Gun

Same general specifications as Model 21 Standard, except has 30 or 32-inch barrels only, full choke, selective single trigger, selective ejection, non-automatic safety, checkered pistol-grip or straight-grip stock with recoil pad, checkered beavertail forearm. Discontinued in 1958.
With matted rib barrels $1,200
With ventilated rib barrels $1,400

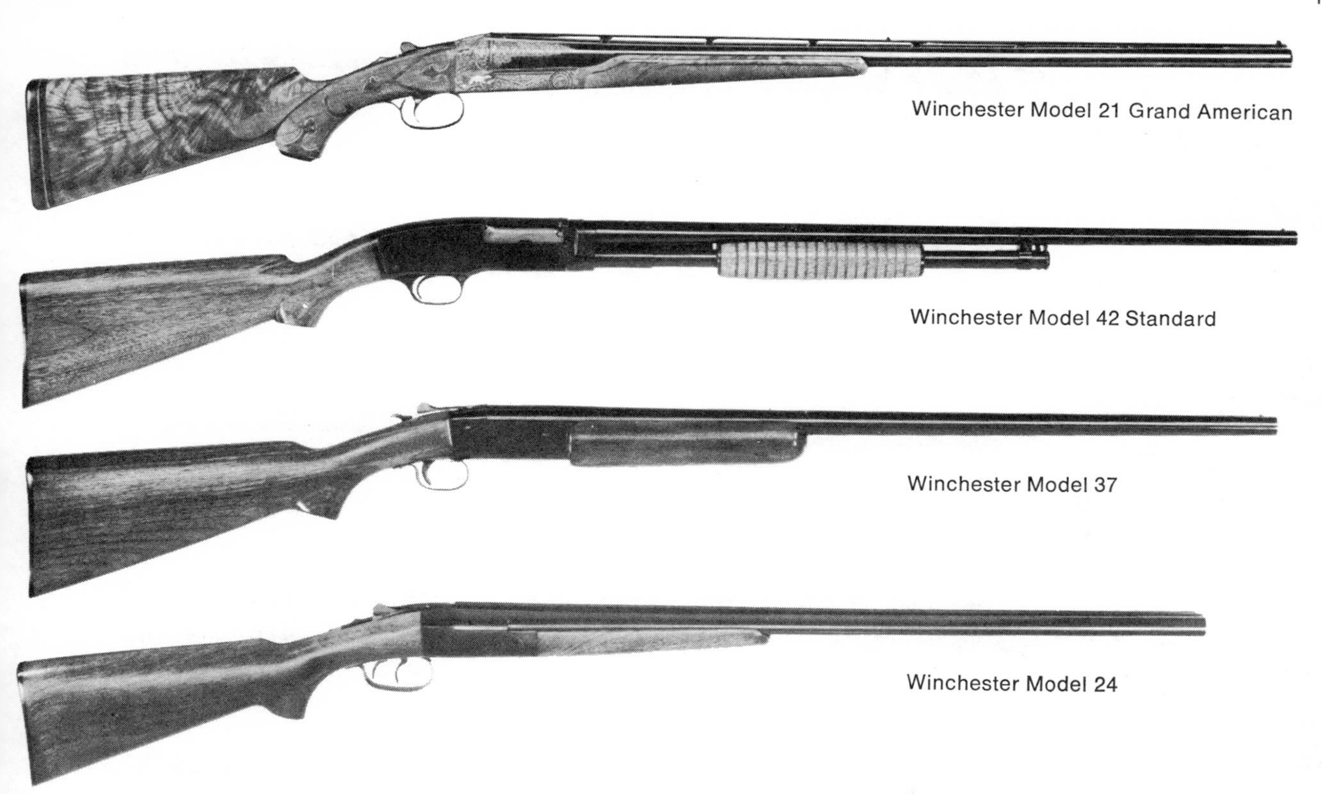
Winchester Model 21 Grand American

Winchester Model 42 Standard

Winchester Model 37

Winchester Model 24

Winchester Model 21 Custom, Pigeon, Grand American

Since 1959, the Model 21 has been offered only in deluxe models: Custom, Pigeon, Grand American—on special order. General specifications same as for Model 21 standard models except these custom guns have full fancy American walnut stock and forearm with fancy checkering, finely polished and hand-smoothed working parts, etc.; engraving inlays, carved stocks and other extras are available at additional cost. Currently manufactured.
Custom Grade **$2,000**
Pigeon Grade **$3,000**
Grand American **$4,000**

Winchester Model 42 Standard Slide Action Repeating Action $300

Hammerless. Takedown. 410 Bore (3 or 2½-inch shell). Tubular magazine holds five 3-inch or six 2½-inch shells. 26 or 28-inch plain barrel; cylinder bore, modified or full choke. Weight, about 6 pounds. Plain pistol-grip stock; grooved slide handle. Made from 1933 to 1963.

Winchester Model 42 Standard Grade, Matted Rib Barrel **$325**

Same general specifications as Plain Barrel Model 42 except has solid raised matted rib. Discontinued in 1963.

Winchester Model 42 Skeet Gun **$475**

Same general specifications as Model 42 Standard except has checkered straight-grip or pistol-grip stock and extension slide handle, 26 or 28-inch matted rib barrel, skeet choke. *Note:* Some Model 42 Skeet Guns are chambered for 2½-inch shells only. Discontinued in 1963.

Winchester Model 42 De Luxe **$650**

Same general specifications as the Model 42 Standard except has ventilated rib finer finish throughout, hand-smoothed action, engine turned breech bolt and carrier, stock and extension slide handle of high grade walnut, fancy checkering, stock dimensions to individual specifications. Engraving and carving were offered at extra cost. Made from 1933 to 1963.

Winchester Model 37 Single Shot Gun **$60**

Semi-hammerless. Automatic ejection. Takedown. Gauges: 12, 16, 20, 28, 410. Barrel lengths: 28, 30, 32-inch in all gauges except 410, 26 or 28-inch in 410; all barrels plain and full choke. Weight, about 6½ pounds in 12 gauge. Made from 1937 to 1963.

Winchester Model 24 Hammerless Double Barrel Shotgun **$200**

Box lock. Double triggers. Plain extractors. Automatic safety. Gauges: 12, 16, 20. Barrels: 26-inch improved cylinder and modified, 28-inch modified and full (also improved cylinder and modified in 12 gauge only), 30-inch modified and full in 12 gauge only. Weight, about 7½ pounds in 12 gauge. Metal bead front sight. Plain pistol grip-stock, semi-beavertail forearm. Made from 1939 to 1957.

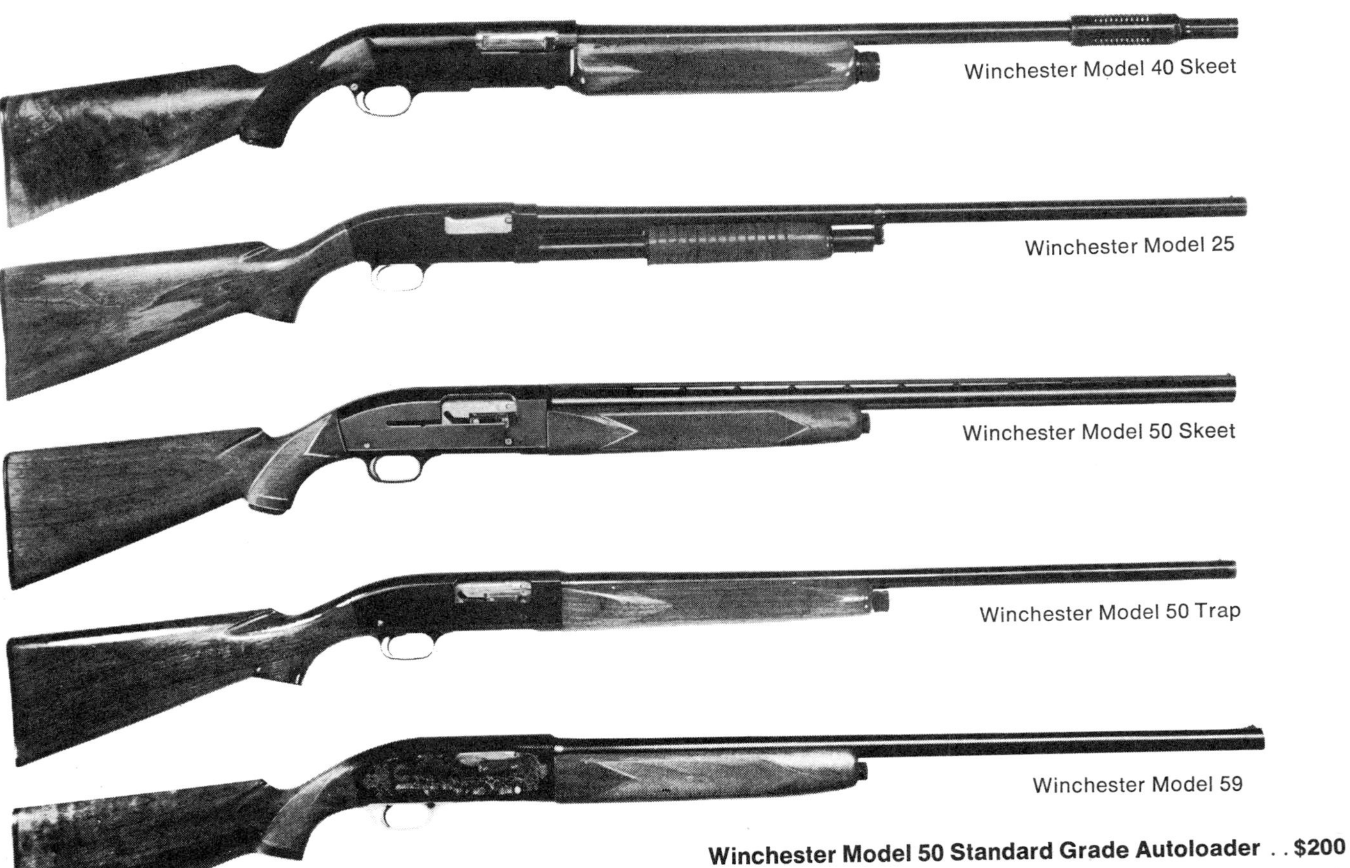

Winchester Model 40 Standard Autoloading Shotgun **$200**

Streamlined receiver. Hammerless. Takedown. 12 gauge only. 4-shell tubular magazine. 28 or 30-inch barrel; modified or full choke. Weight, about 8 pounds. Bead sight on ramp. Plain pistol-grip stock, semi-beavertail forearm. Made from 1940 to 1941.

Winchester Model 40 Skeet Gun **$250**

Same general specifications as Model 40 Standard, except has 24-inch plain barrel with Cutts Compensator, checkered forearm and pistol-grip, grip cap. Made from 1940 to 1941.

Winchester Model 25 Slide Action Repeating Shotgun **$170**

Hammerless. Solid frame. 12 gauge only. 4-shell tubular magazine. 28-inch plain barrel; improved cylinder, modified or full choke. Weight, about 7½ pounds. Metal bead front sight. Plain pistol-grip stock, grooved slide handle. Made from 1949 to 1955.

Winchester Model 25 Riot Gun **$140**

Same as Model 25 Standard except has 20-inch cylinder bare barrel, 12 gauge only. Made from 1949 to 1955.

Winchester Model 50 Standard Grade Autoloader . . **$200**

Non-recoiling barrel and independent chamber. Gauges: 12 and 20. 2-shot tubular magazine. Barrels: 12 ga.—26, 28, 30-inch; 20 ga.—26, 28-inch; improved cylinder, Skeet choke, modified, full choke. Checkered pistol-grip stock and forearm. Weight, about 7¾ pounds. Made from 1954 to 1961.

Winchester Model 50 Field Gun, Ventilated Rib . . . **$235**

Same as Model 50 Standard, except has ventilated rib.

Winchester Model 50 Skeet Gun **$250**

Same as Model 50 Standard, except has 26″ ventilated rib barrel with Skeet choke, Skeet-style stock of selected walnut.

Winchester Model 50 Trap Gun **$275**

Same as Model 50 Standard, except 12 gauge only, has 30-inch ventilated rib barrel with full choke, Monte Carlo stock of selected walnut.

Winchester Model 59 Autoloading Shotgun **$250**

12 gauge. Magazine holds two shells. Alloy receiver. Win-Lite steel and fiberglass barrel: 26-inch improved cylinder, 28-inch modified or full choke, 30-inch full choke; also furnished with 26-inch barrel with Versalite choke (interchangeable full, modified, improved cylinder tubes; one supplied with gun). Weight, about 6-12 pounds. Checkered pistol-grip stock and forearm. Made from 1959 to 1965.

Winchester Model 101 Field

Winchester Model 1200 Field

Winchester Model 1200 Field with Winchoke

Winchester Model 1200 Field Magnum

Winchester Model 101 Over-and-Under Field Gun

Box lock. Engraved receiver. Automatic ejectors. Single selective trigger. Combination barrel selector and safety. Gauges: 12 and 28—2¾″ chambers, 20 and 410—3″ chambers. Ventilated rib barrels: 30 (12 ga. only) and 28 inch, modified and full; 26 (12 ga. only) and 26½ inch, improved cylinder and modified. Weights: 6¼ to 7¾ pounds depending upon gauge and barrel length. Hand-checkered French walnut stock and forearm. Made in Japan by Olin-Kodensha Co. from 1963 to date (gauges other than 12 introduced in 1966).
12 and 20 gauge **$375**
28 and 410 gauge **$395**

Winchester Model 101 Magnum Field Gun **$385**

Same as Model 101 Field Gun, except chambered for 12 or 20 ga. 3″ magnum shells only, 30-inch barrels (full and full or modified and full), recoil pad. Made from 1966 to date.

Winchester Model 101 Skeet Gun

Same as Model 101 Field Gun, except Skeet-style stock and forearm; barrels: 12 ga., 26-inch; 20 ga., 26½ inch; 28 and 410 ga., 28-inch; all skeet choked. Made from 1966 to date.
12 and 20 gauge **$400**
28 and 410 gauge **$425**

Winchester Model 101 Over-and-Under Trap Gun

Same as Model 101 Field Gun, except trap-style stock—straight or Monte Carlo—with recoil pad; 12 gauge only; 30 or 32-inch barrels, improved modified and full or full and full. Weight, about 8 pounds. Made from 1966 to date.
With straight stock **$450**
With Monte Carlo stock **$455**

Winchester Model 1200 Slide Action Field Gun

Front-locking rotary bolt. Takedown. 4-shot magazine. Gauges: 12, 16, 20 (2¾″ chamber). Barrel: plain or ventilated rib; 26, 28, 30 inch; improved cylinder, modified, full choke, or with Winchoke (interchangeable tubes IC-M-F). Weights: 6½ to 7¼ pounds. Checkered pistol-grip stock and forearm (slide handle), recoil pad; also available 1966-70 with Winchester Recoil Reduction System (Cycolac stock). Made from 1964 to date.
With plain barrel . . . . **$ 95**
With ventilated rib barrel **$110**
Add for Winchoke . . . . **$ 5**
Add for Winchester Recoil Reduction System . . . . . **$ 50**

Winchester Model 1200 Field Gun—Magnum

Same as standard Model 1200, except chambered for 3-inch 12 and 20 gauge magnum shells; plain or ventilated rib barrel, 28 or 30 inch, full choke; weight, 7⅜ to 7⅞ pounds. Made from 1964 to date.
With plain barrel **$105**
With ventilated rib barrel **$120**
Add for Winchester Recoil Reduction System . . . . . **$ 50**

Winchester Model 1200 Deer Gun **$100**

Same as standard Model 1200, except has special 22-inch barrel, with rifle-type sights, for rifled slug or buckshot; 12 gauge only; weight, 6½ pounds. Made from 1965 to 1974.

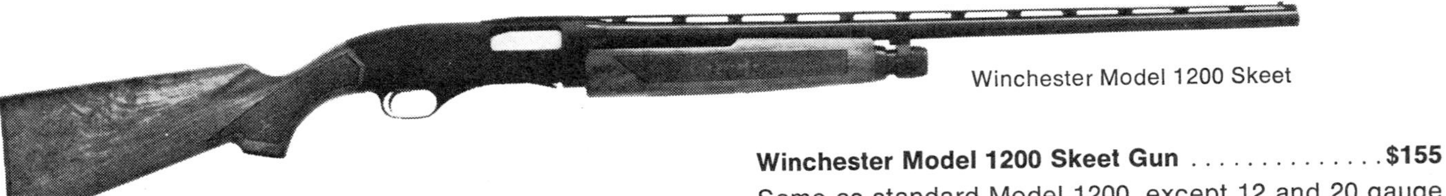

Winchester Model 1200 Skeet

Winchester Model 1200 Skeet Gun **$155**

Same as standard Model 1200, except 12 and 20 gauge only; has 2-shot magazine, specially tuned trigger, 26-inch ventilated rib barrel—skeet choke, semi-fancy walnut stock and forearm; also available 1966-70 with Winchester Recoil Reduction System (add $50 to value); weight, 7¼ to 7½ pounds. Made from 1965 to 1973.

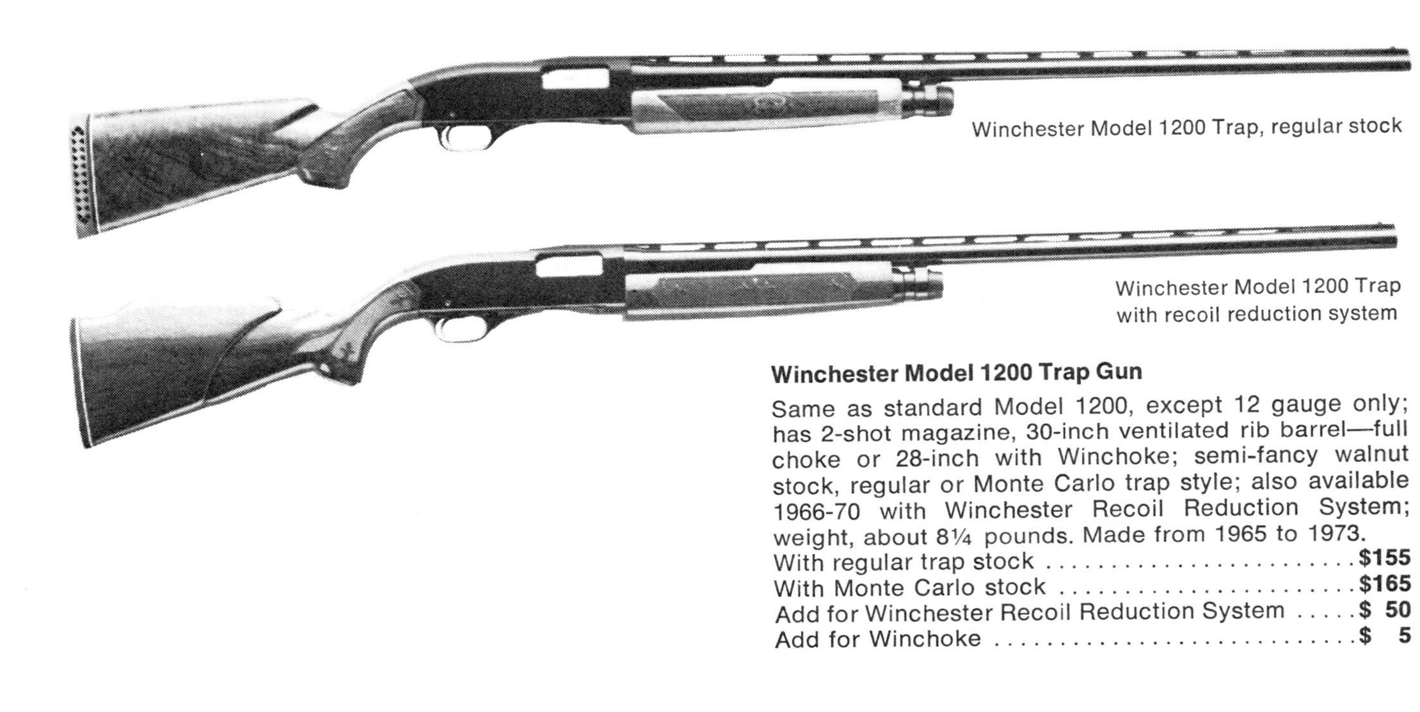

Winchester Model 1200 Trap, regular stock

Winchester Model 1200 Trap with recoil reduction system

Winchester Model 1200 Trap Gun

Same as standard Model 1200, except 12 gauge only; has 2-shot magazine, 30-inch ventilated rib barrel—full choke or 28-inch with Winchoke; semi-fancy walnut stock, regular or Monte Carlo trap style; also available 1966-70 with Winchester Recoil Reduction System; weight, about 8¼ pounds. Made from 1965 to 1973.

With regular trap stock **$155**
With Monte Carlo stock **$165**
Add for Winchester Recoil Reduction System . . . . . **$ 50**
Add for Winchoke . . . . **$ 5**

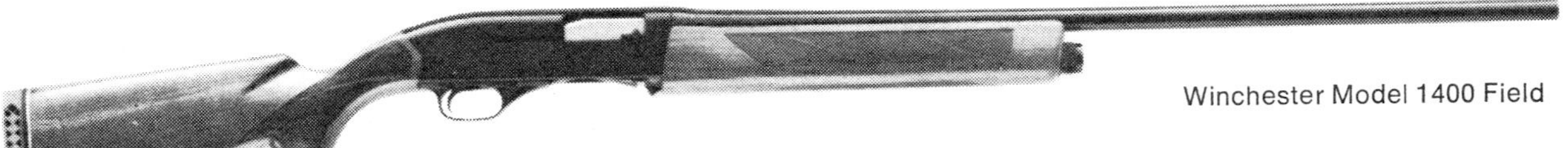

Winchester Model 1400 Field

Winchester Model 1400 Automatic Field Gun

Gas-operated. Front-locking rotary bolt. Takedown. 2-shot magazine. Gauges: 12, 16, 20 (2¾" chamber). Barrel: plain or ventilated rib; 26, 28, 30 inch; improved cylinder, modified, full choke, or with Winchoke (interchangeable tubes IC-M-F). Weights: 6½ to 7¼ pounds. Checkered pistol-grip stock and forearm, recoil pad; also available with Winchester Recoil Reduction System (Cycolac stock). Made from 1964 to 1968. (*Note:* Model 1400 was replaced by Model 1400 Mark II, essentially the same gun but with push-button carrier release and restyled stock and forearm.)

With plain barrel **$100**
With ventilated rib barrel **$120**
Add for Winchoke . . . . **$ 5**
Add for Winchester Recoil Reduction System . . . . . **$ 50**

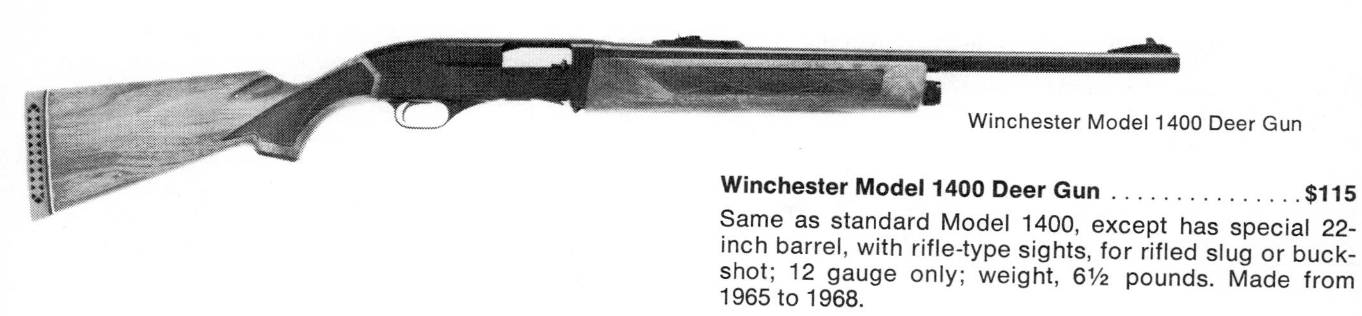
Winchester Model 1400 Deer Gun

Winchester Model 1400 Deer Gun **$115**

Same as standard Model 1400, except has special 22-inch barrel, with rifle-type sights, for rifled slug or buckshot; 12 gauge only; weight, 6½ pounds. Made from 1965 to 1968.

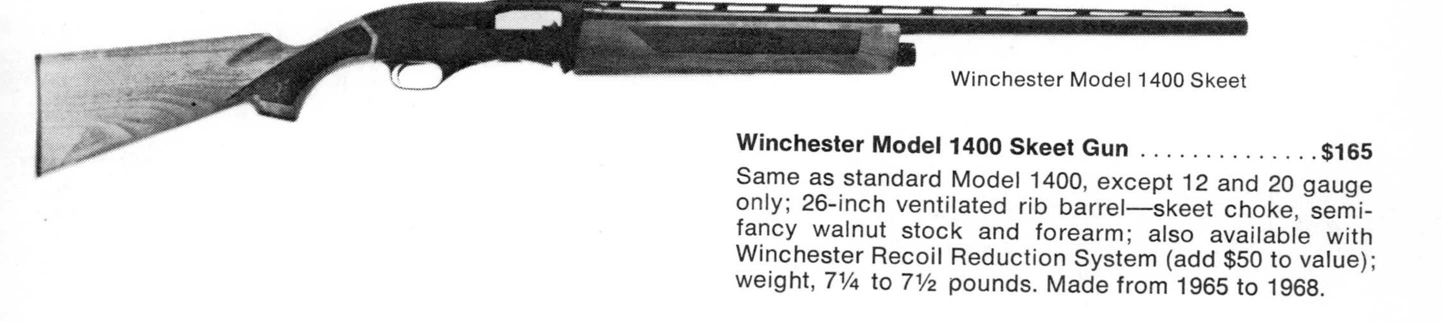
Winchester Model 1400 Skeet

Winchester Model 1400 Skeet Gun **$165**

Same as standard Model 1400, except 12 and 20 gauge only; 26-inch ventilated rib barrel—skeet choke, semi-fancy walnut stock and forearm; also available with Winchester Recoil Reduction System (add $50 to value); weight, 7¼ to 7½ pounds. Made from 1965 to 1968.

Winchester Model 1400 Trap, Monte Carlo

Winchester Model 1400 Trap Gun

Same as standard Model 1400, except 12 gauge only, 30-inch ventilated rib barrel—full choke; semi-fancy walnut stock, regular or Monte Carlo trap style; also available with Winchester Recoil Reduction System; weight, about 8¼ pounds. Made from 1965 to 1968.

With regular trap stock **$165**
With Monte Carlo stock **$175**
Add for Winchester Recoil Reduction System . . . . . **$ 50**

James Woodward & Sons, London, England. The business of this firm was acquired by James Purdey & Sons after World War II

Woodward Best Quality Hammerless Double Barrel Shotgun

Side lock. Automatic ejectors. Double triggers or single trigger. Built to order in all standard gauges, barrel lengths, boring and other specifications; made as a field gun, pigeon and wildfowl gun, skeet gun or trap gun. Manufactured prior to World War II.

With double triggers **$5,000**
With single trigger **$5,500**
Extra pair of barrels with forend **$1,500**

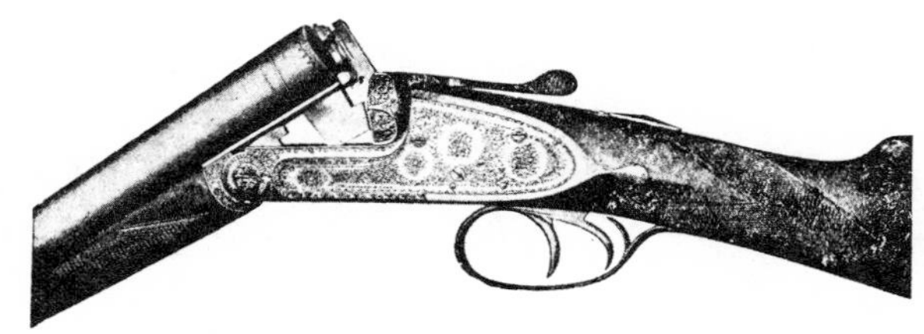
Woodward Best Quality Double Barrel

Woodward Best Quality Under-and-Over Shotgun

Side lock. Automatic ejectors. Double triggers or single trigger. Built to order in all standard guages, barrel lengths, boring and other specifications, including Special Trap Grade with ventilated rib. Woodward introduced this type of gun in 1908. Made until World War II. See listing of Purdey Over-and-Under Gun.
With double triggers **$10,000**
Single trigger, extra . . . . **$ 600**
Extra pair of barrels without forend . . . . **$ 2,500**

Woodward Best Quality Single Barrel Trap Gun . . $10,000

Sidelock. Mechanical features of the Under & Over Gun. Ventilated rib barrel. 12 gauge only. Built to customers' specifications. Made prior to World War II.

NOTES ON FOREIGN SHOTGUNS

The gunmakers whose products are included herein are those best known in the United States. There are—or were, prior to World War II—a great number of other British and European shotgun manufacturers, many of whose guns are of the same type and quality as those listed. While gunmakers in Austria, Czechoslovakia, France, Sweden, Switzerland and other countries also produce such arms, these have never been exported to the U.S. in large enough quantities to warrant inclusion in this volume.

Since the bulk of British and European shotgun production consists of side-by-side double guns built on either the Anson & Deeley or Holland & Holland system with minor variations, in general, values shown may be considered as applicable to comparable models of other makers, particularly those of the same nationality. British shotguns usually bring higher prices than similar European arms.

Many of the guns listed have been produced with very little change for over 75 years—this is especially true of the British doubles. The earlier models lack ejectors, unless fitted in later years, and quite frequently will be found to lack Nitro Proof mark. Non-ejector guns are usually worth about one-quarter to one-third less than the ejector models for which values are shown. Older guns without Nitro Proof marks have about one-half the values indicated.

Proof marks, by the way, serve as an excellent means of determining the approximate age of English shotguns. Most high grade guns produced after 1906 were given the Nitro Proof test and are marked accordingly. Barrels made after 1925 are marked with cartridge case length as well as the usual markings for Definitive Proof, Nitro Proof, etc.

Section III
HANDGUNS

American
.25 Automatic

American Firearms Manufacturing Co., Inc. San Antonio, Texas

American 25 Automatic Pistol

Caliber, 25 Automatic. 8-shot magazine. 2.1-inch barrel. 4.4 inches overall. Weight, 14½ ounces. Fixed sights. Stainless steel or blued ordnance steel. Walnut grips. Made from 1966 to date.
Stainless Steel Model **$60**
Blued Steel Model **$50**

Astra
Model 200

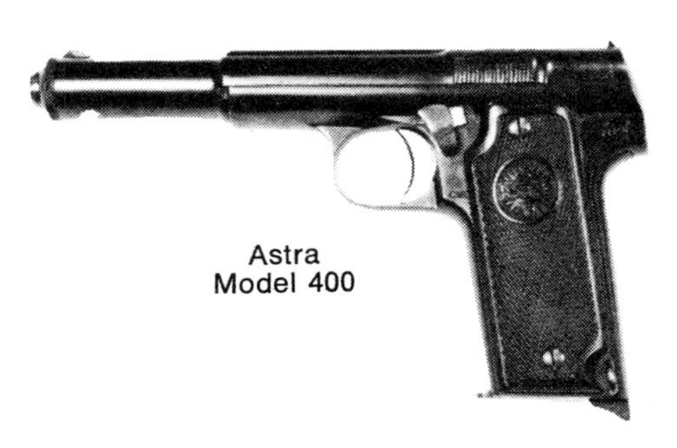
Astra
Model 400

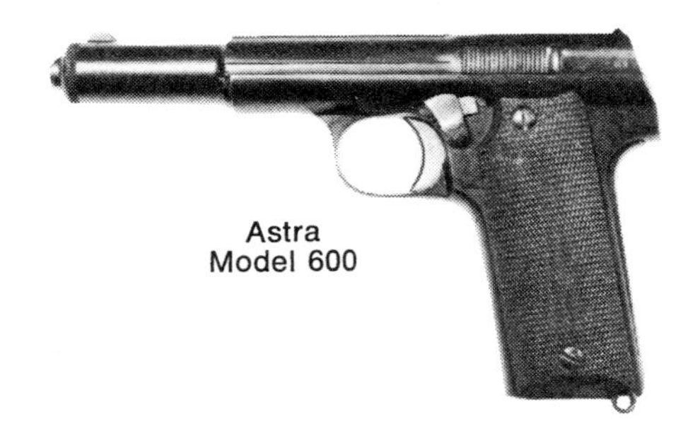
Astra
Model 600

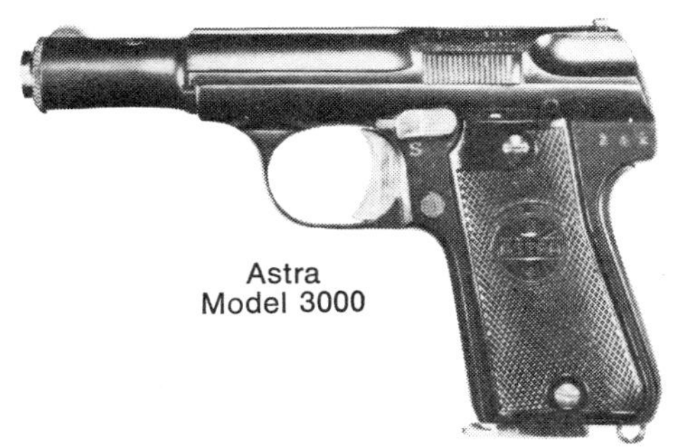
Astra
Model 3000

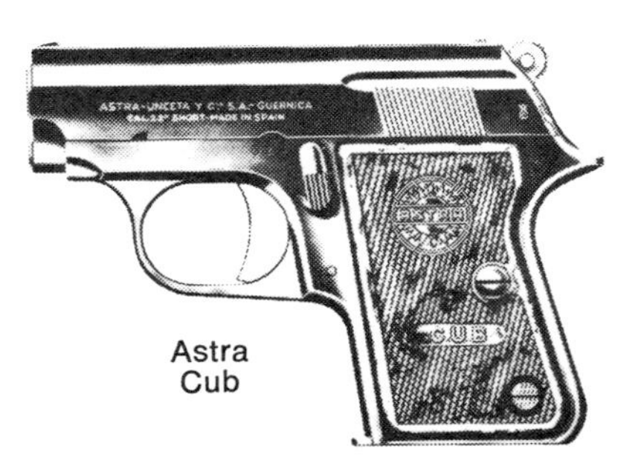

Astra
Cub

Astra Pistols manufactured by Unceta y Compania, Guernica, Spain

Astra Model 200 Firecat Vest Pocket Automatic Pistol $75

Caliber, 25 Automatic (6.35mm). 6-shot magazine. 2¼-inch barrel. 4⅜ inches overall. Weight, 11¾ ounces. Fixed sights. Blued finish. Plastic stocks. Made from 1920 to date; U.S. importation discontinued in 1968.

Astra Model 400 Automatic Pistol $125

Caliber, 9mm Bayard Long (38ACP, 9mm Browning Long, 9mm Glisenti, 9mm Luger and 9mm Steyr cartridges may be used interchangeably in this pistol because of its chamber design). 9-shot magazine. 6-inch barrel. 10-inches overall. Weight, 35 ounces. Fixed sights. Blued finish Plastic stocks. *Note:* This pistol, as well as Astra Models 600 and 3000, is a modification of the Browning Model 1912. Made from 1922 to 1945.

Astra Model 600 Military & Police Type Automatic Pistol $75

Calibers: 32 Automatic (7.65mm), 9mm Luger, 10-shot magazine (32 cal.), 8-shot (9mm). 5¼-inch barrel. 8-inches overall. Weight, about 33 ounces. Fixed sights. Blued finish. Plastic stocks. Made from 1944 to 1945.

Astra Model 3000 Pocket Automatic Pistol $75

Calibers: 22 Long Rifle, 32 Automatic (7.65mm), 380 Automatic (9mm Corto). 10-shot magazine (22 cal.), 7-shot (32 cal.), 6-shot (380 cal.), 4-inch barrel. 6⅜ inches overall. Weight, about 22 ounces. Fixed sights. Blued finish. Plastic stocks. Made from 1947 to 1956.

Astra Cub Pocket Automatic Pistol $85

Calibers: 22 Short, 25 Auto. 6-shot magazine, 2⅛-inch barrel. 4½ inches overall. Weight, about 13 ounces. Fixed sights Blued or chromed finish. Plastic stocks. Currently manufactured, but U.S. importation discontinued in 1968.

Bayard Pistols manufactured by Anciens Etablissements Pieper, Herstal, Belgium

Bayard Model 1908 Pocket Automatic Pistol $80

Calibers: 25 Automatic (6.35mm), 32 Automatic (7.65mm), 380 Automatic (9mm). 6-shot magazine. 2¼-inch barrel. 4⅞ inches overall. Weight, about 16 ounces. Fixed sights. Blued finish. Hard rubber stocks.

Bayard Model 1923 Pocket Automatic Pistol $80

Caliber, 25 Automatic (6.35mm). 2⅛-inch barrel. 4-5/16 inches overall. Weight, 12 ounces. Fixed sights. Blued finish. Checkered hard rubber stocks.

Bayard Model 1923 Pocket Automatic Pistol $100

Calibers: 32 Automatic (7.65mm), 380 Automatic (9mm). 6-shot magazine. 3-5/16-inch barrel. 5½ inches overall. Weight, about 19 ounces. Fixed sights. Blued finish. Checkered hard rubber stocks.

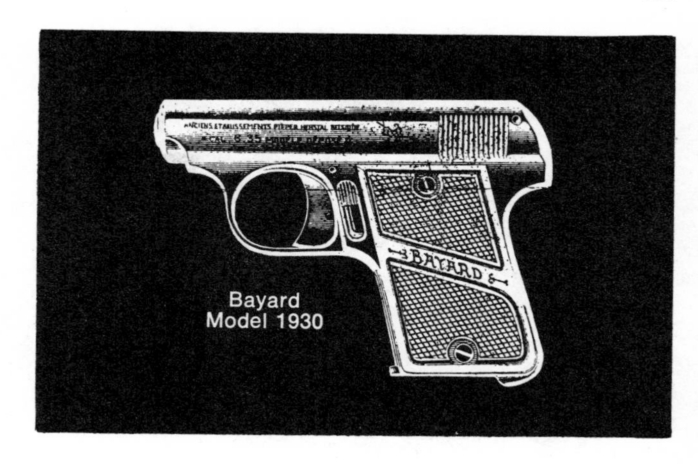

Bayard Model 1930

Bayard Model 1930 Pocket 25 Automatic Pistol . . . $100

A modification of the Model 1923 which it closely resembles.

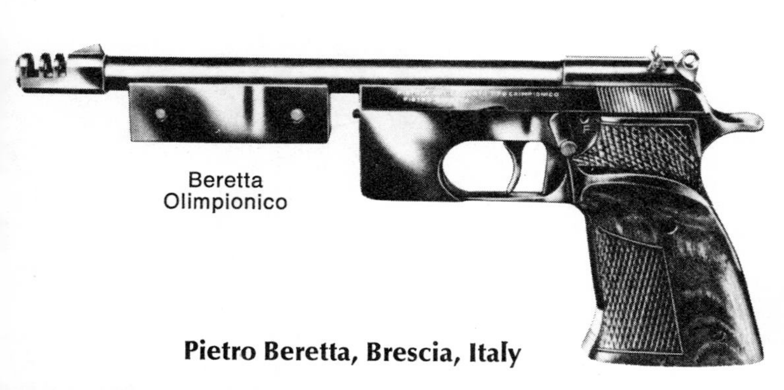

Beretta Olimpionico

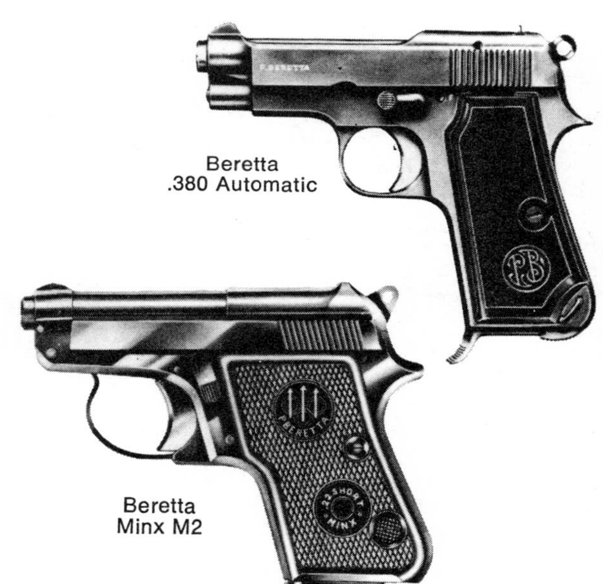

Beretta .380 Automatic

Beretta Minx M2

Pietro Beretta, Brescia, Italy

Beretta 32 Automatic Pistol

Caliber, 32 Automatic (7.65mm). 8-shot magazine. 3½-inch barrel. 5¾ inches overall. Weight, 24 ounces. Fixed sights, Blued finish. Plastic stocks. Originally introduced in 1919 and modified several times. A roughly finished version of this pistol was produced during World War II.

Commercial Model $90
War Model $70

Beretta 380 Automatic Pistol

Caliber, 380 Automatic (9mm Corto). 7-shot magazine. 3⅜-inch barrel. 5⅞ inches overall. Weight, 24 ounces. Fixed sights. Blued finish. Plastic stocks. Generally referred to as Model 1934 (date introduced), this is the official pistol of the Italian armed forces; war-time production is not as well made and finished as either prewar or current ("Cougar") commercial models.

Commercial Model $90
War Model $75

Beretta 25 Automatic Pistol $80

Caliber, 25 Automatic (6.35mm). 8-shot magazine. 2½-inch barrel. 4½ inches overall. Weight, 14 ounces. Fixed sights. Blued finish. Plastic stocks. Discontinued.

Beretta Featherweight 22 Automatic Pistol $90

Dural frame. Caliber, 22 Long Rifle, 9-shot magazine. 3 5/16-inch barrel. 5⅞ inches overall. Weight, 17 ounces. Fixed sights. Blued finish. Plastic stocks. Discontinued.

Beretta Olimpionico Automatic Pistol $225

Caliber, 22 Short. 5-shot magazine. 8¾-inch barrel. 12½ inches overall. Weight, 38 ounces Target sights. Adjustable barrel weight. Muzzle brake. Checkered walnut stocks with thumb rest. Discontinued.

Beretta Minx M2 Automatic Pistol $85

Caliber, 22 Short. 6-shot magazine. Hinged, 2⅜-inch barrel. 4¾ inches overall. Weight, 11 ounces. Fixed sights. Blued finish. Plastic stocks. Discontinued.

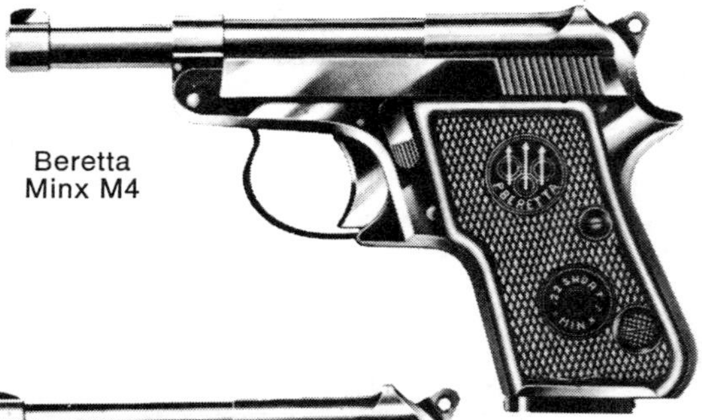

Beretta
Minx M4

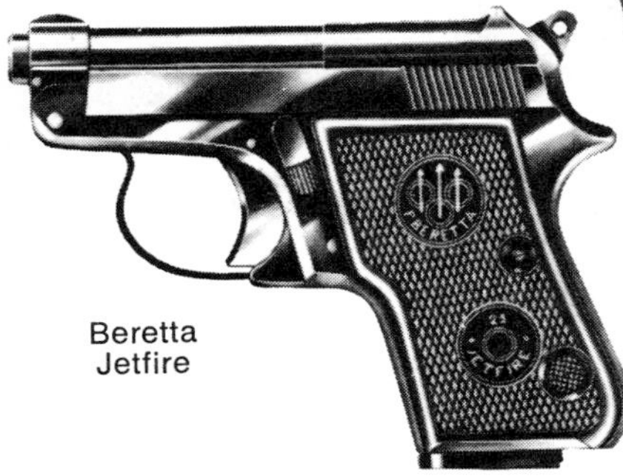

Beretta
Jetfire

Beretta
Jaguar Plinker

Beretta
Puma

Beretta Minx M4 Automatic Pistol $85

Same general specifications as M2, except has 4-inch barrel. Discontinued.

Beretta Jetfire Automatic Pistol $85

Same general specifications as Minx M2, except caliber 25 Auto, has 7-shot magazine. Discontinued.

Beretta Jaguar Plinker Automatic Pistol $105

Caliber, 22 Long Rifle. 8-shot magazine. 3½ or 6-inch barrel. 6½ or 8¾ inches overall. Weight, 15 or 18 ounces. Fixed sights. Plastic stocks. Discontinued.

Beretta Puma Automatic Pistol $90

Caliber, 32 Auto. 7-shot magazine. 3½-inch barrel. 6½ inches overall. Weight, 15 ounces. Fixed sights. Plastic stock. Discontinued.

Vincenzo Bernardelli, Gardone V. T., Italy

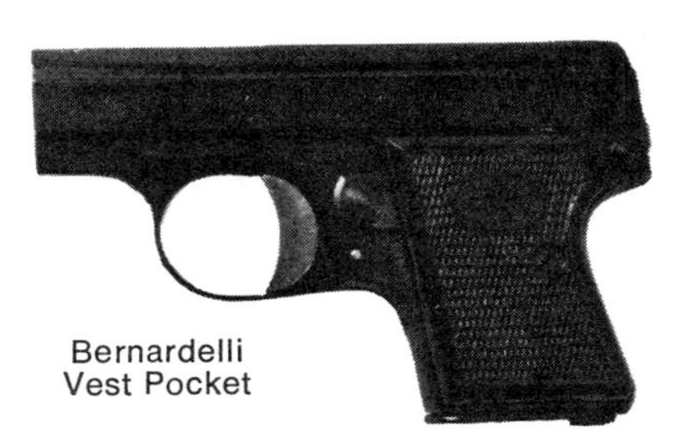

Bernardelli
Vest Pocket

Bernardelli Vest Pocket Automatic Pistol $85

Calibers: 22 Long Rifle, 25 Automatic (6.35mm). 6-shot magazine (22 cal.), 5-shot (standard magazine, 25 cal.), 8-shot (extension magazine, 25 cal.) 2⅛-inch barrel. 4⅛ inches overall. Weight, 9 ounces. Fixed sights. Blued finish. Bakelite stocks. Currently manufactured; U. S. importation discontinued in 1968.

Bernardelli
Pocket

Bernardelli Pocket Automatic Pistol $90

Calibers: 22 Long Rifle, 32 Auto (7.65mm), 380 Auto (9mm Corto). 10-shot magazine (22 cal.), 8-shot (32 cal.), 7-shot (380 cal.). 3½-inch barrel. 6⅜ inches overall. Weight, about 25 ounces. Fixed sights. Blued finish. Bakelite stocks. Currently manufactured; U. S. importation discontinued in 1968.

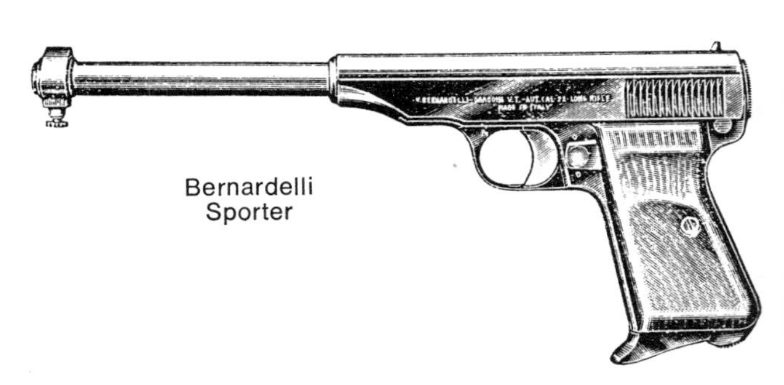

Bernardelli
Sporter

Bernardelli "Sporter" Automatic Pistol $100

Caliber, 22 Long Rifle. 10-shot magazine. Barrel lengths: 6, 8 and 10-inch. 13 inches overall with 10-inch barrel. Weight, about 30 ounces with 10-inch barrel. Target sights. Blued finish. Walnut stocks. Currently manufactured.

Browning
.25 Automatic

Browning
Renaissance
Cased Set

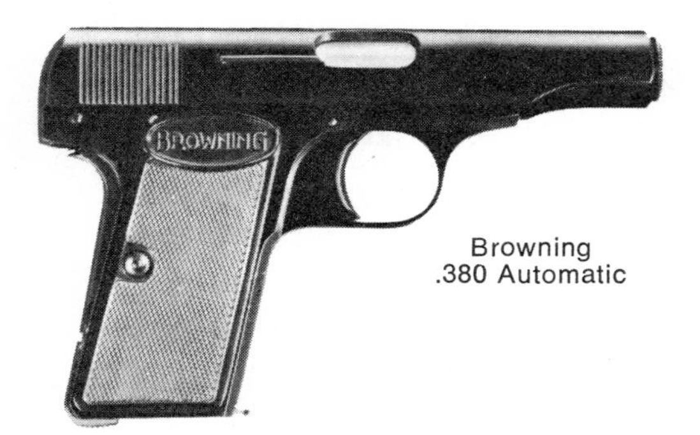

Browning
.380 Automatic

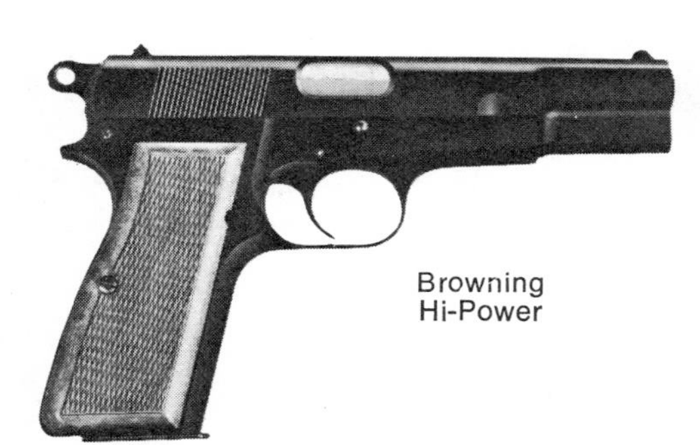

Browning
Hi-Power

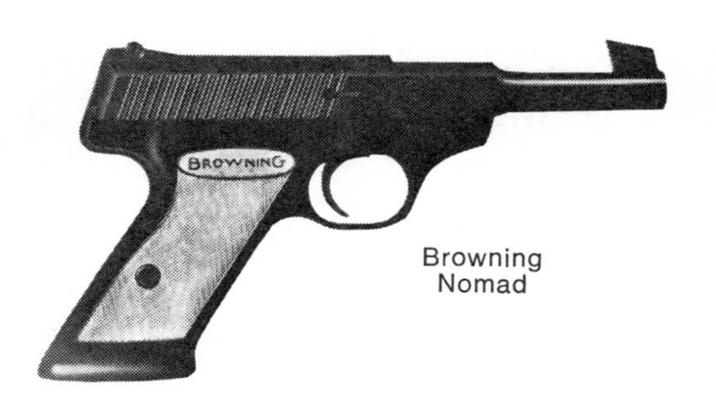

Browning
Nomad

Browning Automatic Pistols manufactured by Fabrique Nationale D'Armes de Guerre, Herstal, Belgium, and imported by Browning, Morgan, Utah. Introduced in the United States in 1954.

Browning 25 Automatic Pistol

Same general specifications as FN Browning Baby. Standard Model, Blued finish, hard rubber grips. Lightweight Model, nickel-plated, Nacrolac pearl grips. Renaissance Engraved Model, nickel-plated, Nacrolac pearl grips. Made from 1954 to 1968.

Standard Model . . . . **$ 90**
Lightweight Model **$135**
Renaissance Model **$250**

Browning 380 Automatic Pistol

Same general specifications as FN Browning 380 Pocket Auto. Standard Model, Renaissance Engraved Model, as furnished in 25 Automatic. Made from 1954 to 1968.

Standard Model **$100**
Renaissance Model **$360**

Browning Hi-Power 9mm Automatic Pistol

Same general specifications as FN Browning Model 1935 (13-shot, fixed sights). Standard Model, blued finish, checkered walnut stocks. Renaissance Engraved Model, chrome plated, Nacrolac pearl stocks. Made from 1954 to date.

Standard Model **$175**
Renaissance Model **$560**

Browning Renaissance Engraved Models, Cased Set **$1,300**

One pistol of each of the three models in a special walnut carrying case. Made from 1954 to 1968.

Browning Nomad Automatic Pistol **$90**

Caliber, 22 Long Rifle. 10-shot magazine. Barrel lengths: 4½ and 6¾ inch. 8-15/16 inches overall with 4½-inch barrel. Weight, 34 ounces with 4½-inch barrel. Removable blade front sight, screw adjustable rear sight. Blued finish. Plastic stocks. Made from 1963 to 1973.

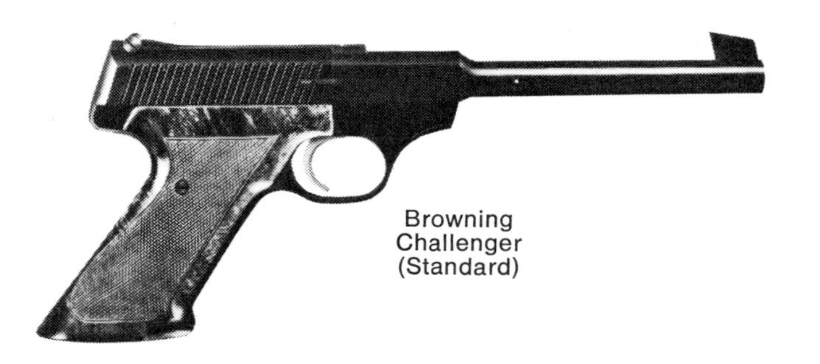

Browning Challenger (Standard)

Browning Challenger Automatic Pistol

Caliber, 22 Long Rifle. 10-shot magazine. Barrel lengths: 4½ and 6¾ inch. 11-7/16 inches overall with 6¾-inch barrel. Weight, 38 ounces with 6¾-inch barrel. Removable blade front sight, screw adjustable rear sight. Standard finish, blue; also furnished gold-inlaid (Gold Model) and engraved and chrome-plated (Renaissance Model). Checkered walnut stocks; finely figured and carved stocks on Gold and Renaissance Models. Standard Made from 1963 to 1974, higher grades introduced in 1971.

Standard Model **$115**
Gold Model **$260**
Renaissance Model **$300**

Browning Challenger (Gold Model)

Browning Medalist Automatic Target Pistol

Caliber, 22 Long Rifle. 10-shot magazine. 6¾-inch barrel with ventilated rib. 11-15/16 inches overall. Weight, 46 ounces. Removable blade front sight, click-adjustable micrometer rear sight. Standard finish, blue; also furnished gold inlaid (Gold Model) and engraved and chrome plated (Renaissance Model). Checkered walnut stocks with thumb rest (for right or left handed shooter); finely figured and carved stocks on Gold and Renaissance Models. Made from 1963 to 1974, higher grades introduced in 1971.

Standard Model **$195**
Gold Model **$350**
Renaissance Model **$385**

Ceska Zbrojovka-Narodni Podnik, Strakonice, Czechoslovakia (formerly Bohmische Waffenfabrik A. G.)

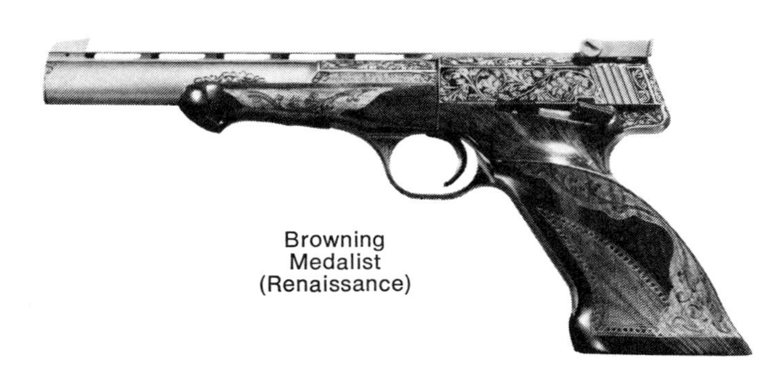

Browning Medalist (Renaissance)

CZ Model 27 Automatic Pistol $90

Caliber, 32 Automatic (7.65mm). 8-shot magazine. 4-inch barrel. 6 inches overall. Weight, 23½ ounces. Fixed sights. Blued finish. Plastic stocks.

CZ Model 1938 Double Action Automatic Pistol $90

Caliber, 380 Automatic (9mm). 9-shot magazine. 3¾-inch barrel. 7 inches overall. Weight, 26 ounces. Fixed sights. Blued finish. Plastic stocks.

CZ Double Action Pocket Automatic Pistol $90

Caliber, 25 Automatic (6.35mm). 8-shot magazine. 2½-inch barrel. 5 inches overall. Weight, 15 ounces. Fixed sights. Blued finish. Plastic stocks. Currently manufactured; U. S. importation discontinued.

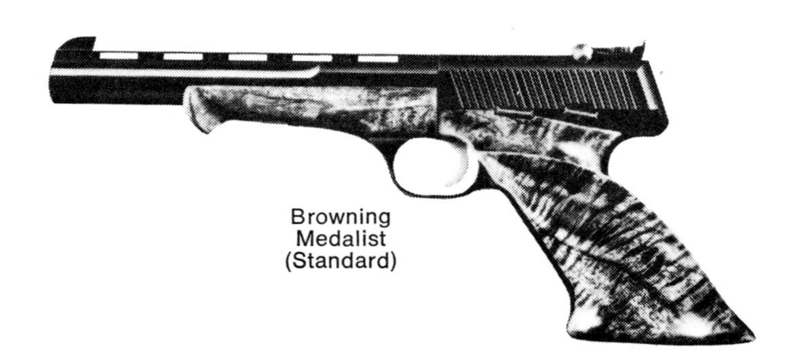

Browning Medalist (Standard)

CZ New Model .006 Double Action Automatic Pistol $125

Caliber, 32 Automatic (7.65mm). 8-shot Magazine. 3⅛-inch barrel. 6½ inches overall. Weight, 24 ounces. Fixed sights. Blued finish. Plastic stocks. Currently manufactured; U. S. importation discontinued.

CZ "Duo" Pocket Automatic Pistol $80

Caliber, 25 Automatic (6.35mm). 6-shot magazine. 2⅛-inch barrel. 4½ inches overall. Weight, 14½ ounces. Fixed sights. Blued or nickel finish. Plastic stocks. Currently manufactured; U. S. importation discontinued.

CZ
Model 27

CZ
Model 1938

CZ
Double Action

CZ
New Model .006

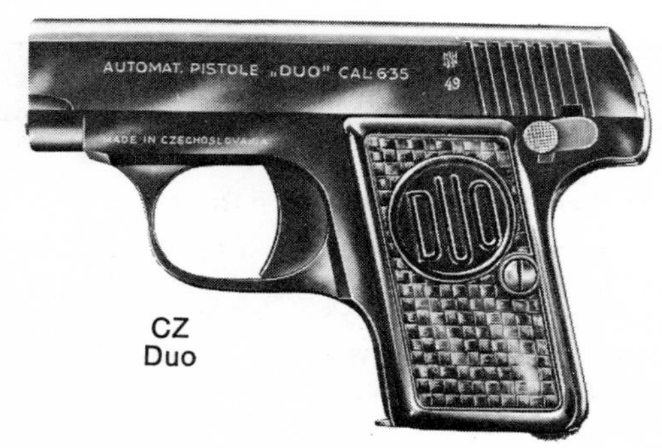

CZ
Duo

Charter Arms Corporation
Stratford, Connecticut

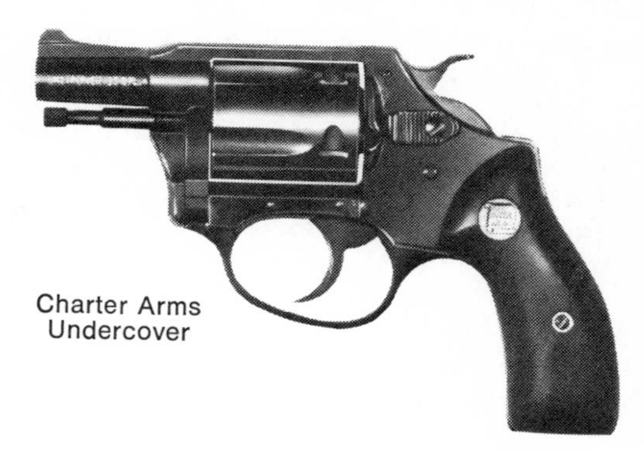

Charter Arms
Undercover

Charter Arms Undercover Double Action Revolver

Caliber, 38 Special. 5-shot cylinder. Barrel lengths: 2 and 3-inch. 6¼ inches overall with 2-inch barrel and regular grips. Weight, 16 ounces, with 2-inch barrel. Fixed sights. Blued or nickel-plated finish. Plain walnut regular grips or checkered Bulldog grips. Made from 1965 to date.

With regular grips **$65**
Add for Bulldog grips .... **$ 5**
Add for nickel finish .... **$ 7**

Colt's Firearms Division, Hartford, Connecticut

COLT REVOLVERS and SINGLE SHOT PISTOLS

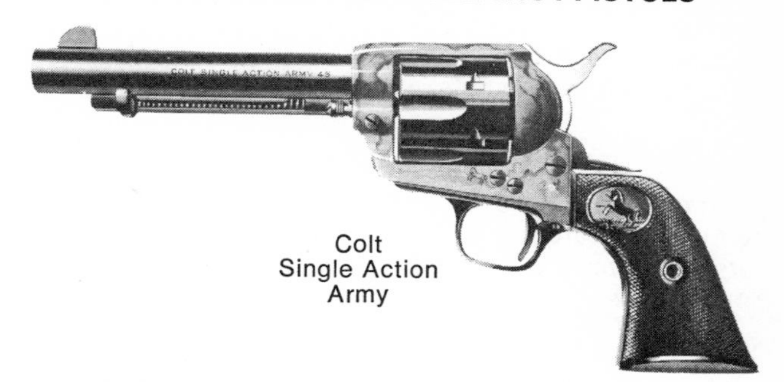

Colt
Single Action
Army

Colt Single Action Army Revolver

Also called "Frontier Six Shooter" and "Peacemaker." Calibers: 22 Rimfire (Short, Long, Long Rifle), 22 W.R.F., 32 Rimfire, 32 Colt, 32 S&W, 32-20, 38 Colt, 38 S&W, 38 Special, 357 Magnum, 38-40, 41 Colt, 44 Rimfire, 44 Russian, 44 Special, 44-40, 45 Colt, 45 Auto, 450 Boxer, 450 Eley, 455 Eley, 476 Eley. 6-shot cylinder. Barrel lengths: 4¾, 5½ and 7½-inch with ejector; 3 and 4-inch without ejector. 10¼ inches overall with 4¾-inch barrel. Weight, 36 ounces in 45 caliber with 4¾-inch barrel. Fixed sights. Also made in Target Model with flat top strap and target sights. Blued finish with case-hardened frame or nickel-plated. One-piece smooth walnut or checkered black rubber stocks. S.A. Army Revolvers with serial numbers above 165,000 (circa 1896) are adapted to smokeless powder; cylinder pin screw was changed to spring catch at about the same time. Made from 1873 to 1942; production resumed in 1955 with serial number 1001SA. Current calibers: 357 Magnum, 45 Long Colt.

U.S. Cavalry Model, .45 Colt, 7½" bbl. .... $ 650
U.S. Artillery Model, .45 Colt, 5½" bbl. .... $ 650
Frontier Six-Shooter, .44-40 .... $ 500
Storekeeper's Model, 3"-4" bbl., w/o ejector ... $ 700
Target Model, flat top strap, target sights, .22 .... $1,800
Other calibers .... $ 800
(Above values apply only to original models, not to similar S.A.A. Revolvers of recent manufacture.)
Standard Model, pre-1942 .... $375
Standard Model, current production $175

Colt Sheriff's Model 45

Limited edition of replica of "Storekeeper's Model" in caliber 45 Colt, made exclusively for Centennial Arms Corp., Chicago, Ill. Numbered from "1SM". Blued finish with case-hardened frame or nickel-plated. Walnut stocks. 478 were produced in blue, 25 in nickel. Made in 1961.
Blued finish .... $ 750
Nickel finish $3,250

Colt Buntline Special 45 .... $300

Same as standard Single Action Army, except has 12-inch barrel, caliber 45 Long Colt. Made from 1957 to 1975. *Note:* Although other similarly long-barreled "Peacemakers" were produced on special order circa 1880, a true "Buntline Special" would be one of five such revolvers with detachable shoulder stocks of walnut, reportedly made about 1876 for dime novel author Ned Buntline, said to have presented these weapons to Dodge City, Kansas, lawmen including Wyatt Earp and Bat Masterson. Properly authenticated, one of the genuine "Buntline Specials" is worth upward of $15,000.

Colt New Frontier Single Action Army Revolver ... $210

Same as Single Action Army, except has flat-top frame, adjustable target rear sight, ramp front sight, smooth walnut grips. 5½ or 7½-inch barrel. Calibers, 357 Magnum, 45 Colt. Made from 1961 to date.

Colt New Frontier Buntline Special $350

Same as New Frontier Single Action Army, except has 12-inch barrel. Made from 1962 to 1966.

Colt Single Action Army—125th Anniversary Model $325

Limited production deluxe version of Single Action Army issued in commemoration of Colt's 125th anniversary. Caliber, 45 Long Colt. 7½-inch barrel. Goldplated frame, trigger, hammer, cylinder pin, ejector rod tip, and stock medallion. Presentation case with anniversary medallion. Serial numbers from "50AM" 7,368 were produced. Made in 1961.

Colt Single Action Army Commemorative Models

Limited production versions of Single Action Army 45 issued, with appropriate inscription, to commemorate historical events.

1963 issues:
West Virginia Statehood Centennial (597 produced) $350
Arizona Territorial Centennial (1234 produced) ... $350

1964 issues:
Nevada Statehood Centennial (1688 produced) ... $325
Nevada "Battle Born" (180 produced) $750
Montana Territorial Centennial (848 produced) ... $395
New Jersey Tercentenary (250 produced) $475
St. Louis Bicentennial (200 produced) $350
Pony Express Presentation (1004 produced) $550
Chamizal Treaty (50 produced) $750
Col. Sam Colt Sesquicentennial
Presentation (4750 produced) .... $ 425
Deluxe Presentation (200 produced) .... $ 850
Special Deluxe Presentation (50 produced) ... $2,100
Wyatt Earp *Buntline* (150 produced) .... $ 850

1965 issues:
Old Fort Des Moines Reconstruction (100 produced) $400
Appomattox Centennial (250 produced) $350

1966 issues:
General Meade (200 produced) $425
Abercrombie & Fitch Trailblazer—New York (200 produced) $850
California Gold Rush (130 produced) $500
Abercrombie & Fitch Trailblazer—Chicago (100 produced) $895
Abercrombie & Fitch Trailblazer—San Francisco (100 produced) $895

1967 issues:
Lawman Series—Bat Masterson (500 produced) .. $395
Alamo (750 produced) $350

1968 issue:
Lawman Series—Pat Garrett (500 produced) $395

1969 issues:
Lawman Series—Wild Bill Hickock (500 produced) $395

1970 issues:
Texas Ranger (1000 produced) $850
Missouri Sesquicentennial (500 produced) $325
Lawman Series—Wyatt Earp (500 produced) $750

1971 issues:
NRA Centennial, 357 or 45 (5000 produced) $325

Note: Values indicated are for revolvers in new condition.

Colt Bisley Model Single Action Revolver

Variation of the Single Action Army, developed for target shooting; grips, trigger and hammer changed. Calibers, general specifications same as Single Action Army. Also made in Target Model with flat-topped frame and target sights. Made from 1896 to 1912.
Standard Model $400
Target Model $800

Colt
New Frontier
S.A.A.

Colt
Buntline
Special

Colt
New Frontier
Buntline Special

Colt New Double Action Self-Cocking Central Fire Six Shot Revolver $250

Also called "Lightning Model." Calibers: 38 and 41 Centerfire. Barrel lengths: 2½, 3½, 4½ and 6-inch without ejector, 4½ and 6-inch with ejector. 8½ inches overall with 3½-inch barrel. Weight, 38 caliber with 3½-inch barrel, 23 ounces. Fixed sights. Blued or nickel finish. Hard rubber birdshead grips. Made from 1877 to 1912.

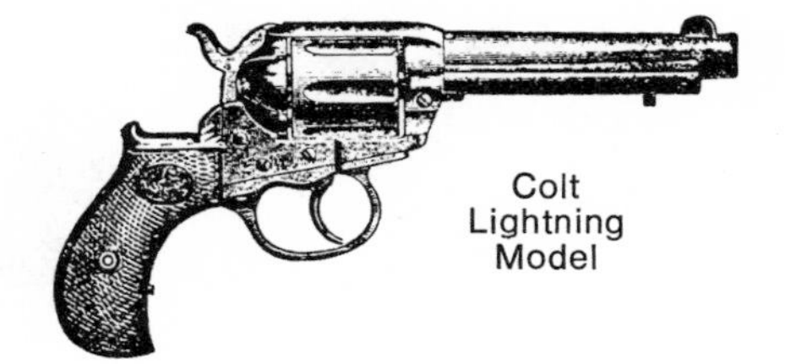

Colt
Lightning
Model

Colt Double Action Army Revolver $275

Also called "Double Action Frontier." Similar in appearance to the smaller "Lightning Model," but has heavier frame of different shape, round disc on left side of frame, lanyard loop in butt. Calibers: 38-40, 44-40, 45 Colt. 6-shot cylinder. Barrel lengths: 3½ and 4-inch without ejector; 4¾, 5½ and 7½-inch with ejector. 12½ inches overall with 7½-inch barrel. Weight, 45 caliber with 7½-inch barrel, 39 ounces. Fixed sights. Hard rubber birdshead grips. Blued or nickel finish. Made from 1877 to 1905.

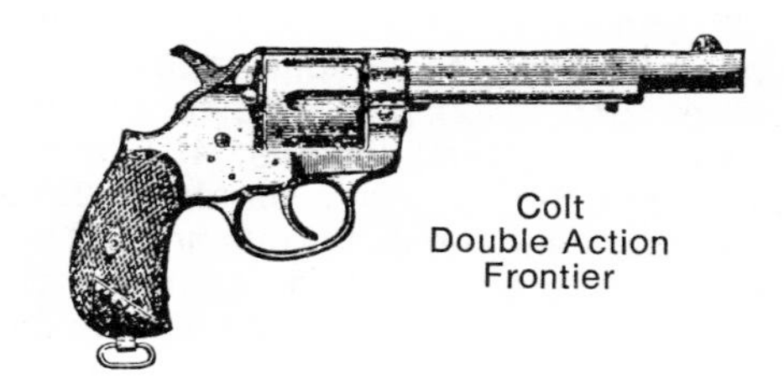

Colt
Double Action
Frontier

Colt New Navy Double Action Self-Cocking Revolver $200

Also called "New Army." First Issue. Calibers: 38 Short & Long Colt, 41 Short & Long Colt. 6-shot cylinder, left revolution. Barrel lengths: 3, 4½ and 6-inch. 11¼ inches overall with 6-inch barrel. Weight 32 ounces, with 6-inch barrel. Fixed sights, knife-blade and V-notch. Blued or nickel-plated finish. Walnut or hard rubber grips. Made from 1889 to 1892. *Note:* This model, which was adopted by both the Army and Navy, was Colt's first revolver of the solid frame, swing-out cylinder type. It lacks the cylinder-locking notches found on later models made on this .41 frame; ratchet on the back of the cylinder is held in place by a double projection on the hand.

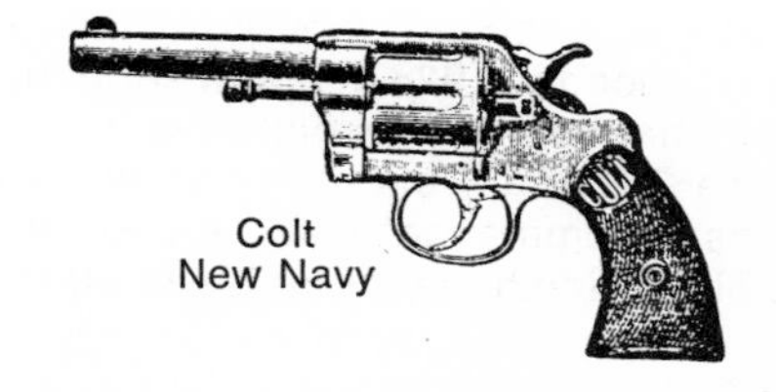

Colt
New Navy

Colt New Navy Double Action Revolver $175

Also called "New Army." Second Issue. General specifications same as First Issue, except this model has double cylinder notches and double locking bolt. Caliber 38 Special added in 1904 and 32-20 in 1905. Made from 1892 to 1908. *Note:* The heavy 38 Special High Velocity loads should not be used in 38 Special arms of this model.

Colt Marine Corps Model Double Action Revolver . . $350

General specifications same as "New Navy" Second Issue, except this model has round butt, was supplied only in 38 caliber (38 Short & Long Colt, 38 Special) and with 6-inch barrel. Made from 1905 to 1910.

Colt Army Special Double Action Revolver $175

41-caliber frame. Calibers: 32-20, 38 Special (41 Colt). 6-shot cylinder, right revolution. Barrel lengths: 4, 4½, 5 and 6-inch. 9¼ inches overall with 4-inch barrel. Weight, 32 ounces with 4-inch barrel. Fixed sights. Blued or nickel-plated finish. Hard rubber stocks. Made from 1908 to 1928. *Note:* This model has a somewhat heavier frame than the "New Navy" which is replaced. Serial numbers begin with 300,000. The heavy 38 Special High Velocity loads should not be used in 38 Special arms of this model.

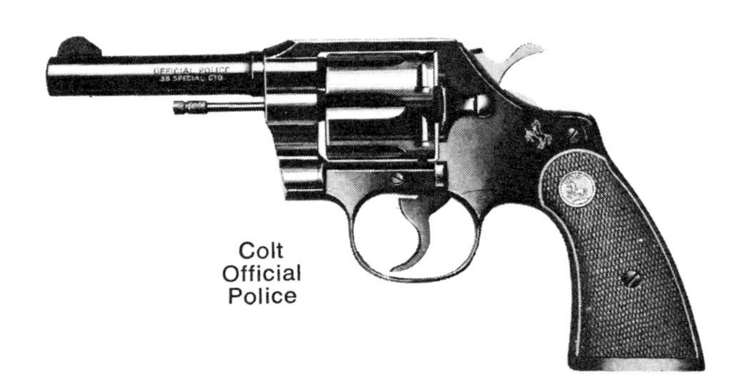

Colt Official Police

Colt Official Police Double Action Revolver

Calibers: 22 Long Rifle (introduced 1930, embedded head cylinder for high speed cartridges after 1932), 32-20 (discontinued 1942), 38 Special, 41 Long Colt (discontinued 1930). Barrel lengths: 4, 5 and 6-inch; 2-inch barrel and 6-inch heavy barrel in 38 Special only, 22 L. R. with 4 and 6-inch barrels only. 11¼ inches overall, weight—36 ounces, with standard 6-inch barrel in 38 Special. Fixed sights. Blued or nickel-plated finish. Checkered walnut stocks on all revolvers of this model except some of postwar production had checkered plastic stocks. Made from 1928 to 1969. *Note:* This model is a refined version of the "Army Special" which it replaced in 1928 at about serial number 520,000. The "Commando" 38 Special was a war-time adaptation of the "Official Police" made to Government specifications. "Commando" can be identified by its sandblasted blued finish; serial numbers start with number 1 (1942).

Commercial Model **$135**
Commando Model **$100**

Colt Officers' Model Target Double Action Revolver, First Issue $200

Caliber 38 Special. 6-inch barrel. Hand-finished action. Adjustable target sights. Checkered walnut stocks. General specifications same as "New Navy"—Second issue. Made from 1904 to 1908.

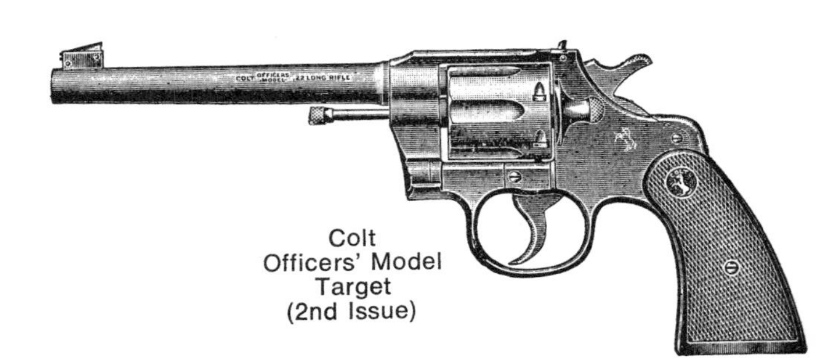

Colt Officers' Model Target (2nd Issue)

Colt Officers' Model Target, Second Issue $225

Calibers: 22 Long Rifle (introduced 1930, embedded head cylinder for high speed cartridges after 1932), 32 Police Positive (introduced 1932, discontinued 1942), 38 Special. Barrel lengths: 4, 4½, 5, 6 and 7½-inch in 38 Special; 6-inch only in 22 L. R. and 32 P. P. 11¼ inches overall with 6-inch barrel in 38 Special. Adjustable target sights. Blued finish. Checkered walnut stocks. Hand-finished action. General features same as "Army Special" and "Official Police" of same date. Made from 1908 to 1949 (with exceptions noted).

Colt Officers' Model Special $150

Target arm replacing "Officers' Model"—Second Issue; basically the same as that model, but with heavier, non-tapered barrel, redesigned hammer, ramp front sight and "Coltmaster" rear sight adjustable for windage and elevation. Calibers: 22 Long Rifle, 38 Special. 6-inch barrel. 11¼ inches overall. Weights: 39 ounces (38 cal.), 43 ounces (22 cal.). Blued finish. Checkered plastic stocks. Made from 1949 to 1953.

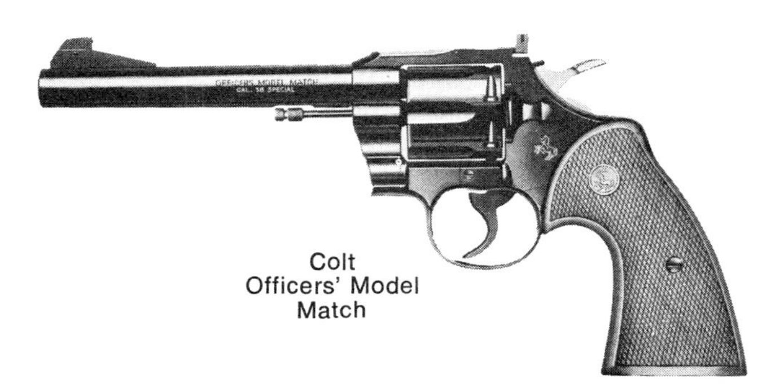

Colt Officers' Model Match

Colt Officers' Model Match $160

Same general design as previous Officers' Model revolvers, has tapered heavy barrel, wide hammer spur, Accro rear sight, ramp front sight, large target stocks of checkered walnut. Calibers. 22 Long Rifle, 38 Special. 6-inch barrel. 11¼ inches overall. Weights: 43 oz. (22 cal.), 39 oz. (38 cal.). Blued finish. Made from 1953 to 1970.

Colt Trooper Double Action Revolver

Same specifications as Officers' Model Match except has 4-inch barrel with quick draw ramp front sight, weighs 34 ounces in 38 caliber. Made from 1953 to 1969.
With standard hammer and service stocks **$150**
With wide spur hammer and target stocks **$160**

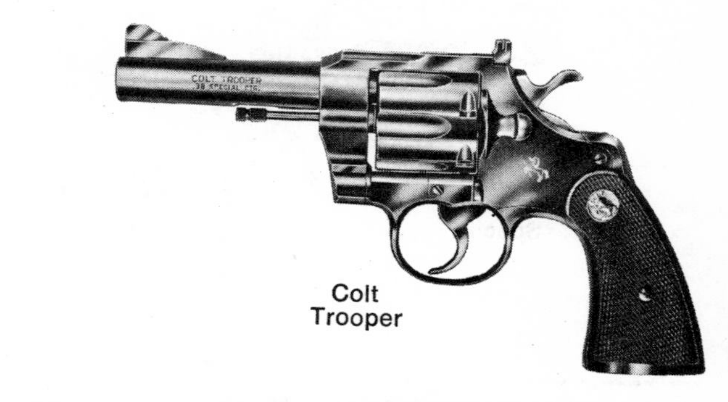

Colt
Trooper

Colt Camp Perry Model Single Shot Pistol $400

First Issue. Built on "Officers' Model" frame. Caliber, 22 Long Rifle (embedded head chamber for high speed cartridges after 1930). 10-inch barrel. 13¾ inches overall. Weight, 34½ ounces. Adjustable target sights. Handfinished action. Blued finish. Checkered walnut stocks. Made from 1926 to 1934.

Colt Camp Perry Model Single Shot Pistol $500

Second Issue. General specifications same as First Issue except this model has shorter hammer fall and 8-inch barrel. 12 inches overall. Weight, 34 ounces. Made from 1934 to 1941 (about 440 produced).

Colt
Camp Perry

Colt New Pocket Double Action Revolver $175

Caliber, 32 Short & Long Colt. 6-shot cylinder. Barrel lengths: 2½, 3½ and 6-inch. 7½ inches overall with 3½-inch barrel. Weight, 16 ounces with 3½-inch barrel. Fixed sights, knife-blade and V-notch. Blued or nickel finish. Rubber stocks. Made from 1895 to 1905.

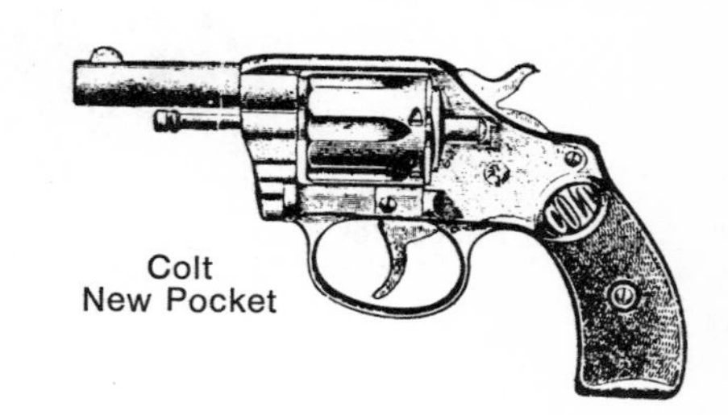

Colt
New Pocket

Colt Pocket Positive Double Action Revolver $150

General specifications same as "New Pocket" except this model has positive lock feature (see "Police Positive"). Calibers. 32 Short & Long Colt (discontinued 1914), 32 Colt New Police (32 S&W Short & Long). Fixed sights, flat top and square notch. Made from 1905 to 1940.

Colt New Police Double Action Revolver $175

Built on "New Pocket" frame but with larger grip. Calibers: 32 Colt New Police, 32 Short & Long Colt. Barrel lengths: 2½, 4 and 6-inch. 8½ inches overall with 4-inch barrel. Weight, 17 ounces with 4-inch barrel. Fixed sights, knifeblade & V-notch. Blued or nickel finish. Rubber stocks. Made from 1896 ot 1905.

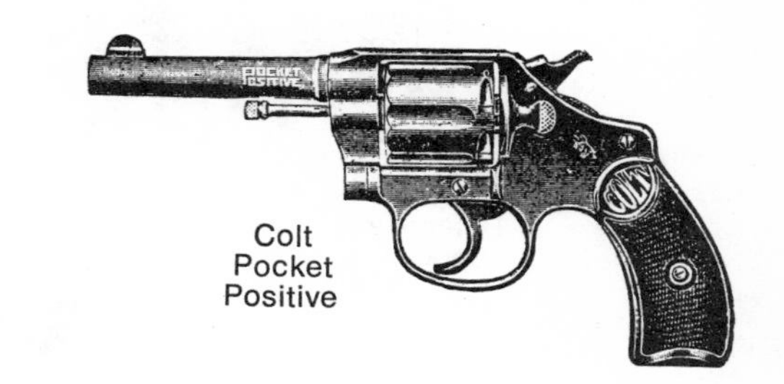

Colt
Pocket
Positive

Colt Police Positive Double Action Revolver $150

Improved version of the "New Police" with the "Positive Lock" which prevents the firing pin from coming in contact with the cartridge except when the trigger is pulled. Calibers: 32 Short & Long Colt (discontinued 1915), 32 Colt New Police (32 S&W Short & Long), 38 New Police (38 S&W). 6-shot cylinder. Barrel lengths: 2½ (32 cal. only), 4, 5 and 6-inch. 8½ inches overall with 4-inch barrel Weight, 20 ounces with 4-inch barrel. Fixed sights. Blued or nickel finish. Rubber or checkered walnut stocks. Made from 1905 to 1947.

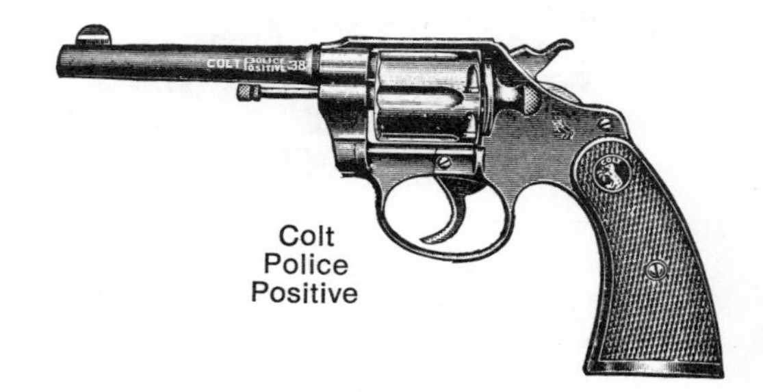

Colt
Police
Positive

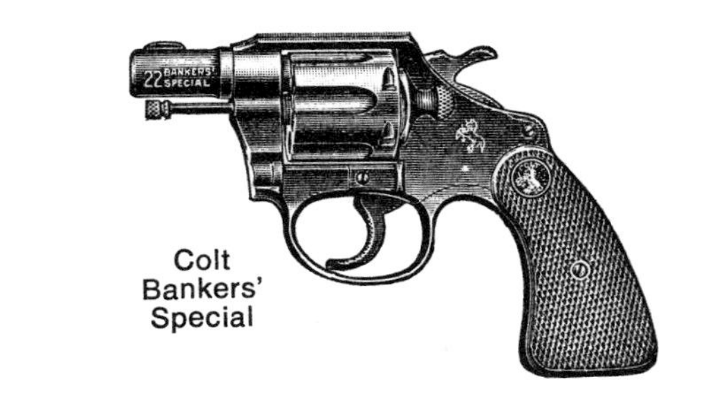

Colt Bankers' Special

Colt Bankers' Special Double Action Revolver

This is the "Police Positive" with a 2-inch barrel, otherwise specifications same as that model; rounded butt introduced in 1933. Calibers: 22 Long Rifle (embedded head cylinder for high speed cartridges introduced 1933), 38 New Police. 6½ inches overall. Weight, 23 ounces in 22 cailber, 19 ounces in 38 caliber. Made from 1926 to 1940.

38 Caliber **$250**
22 caliber **$500**

Colt New Police Target Double Action Revolver . . . $175

Target version of the "New Police" with same general specifications. Target sights. 6-inch barrel. Blued finish only. Made from 1896 to 1905.

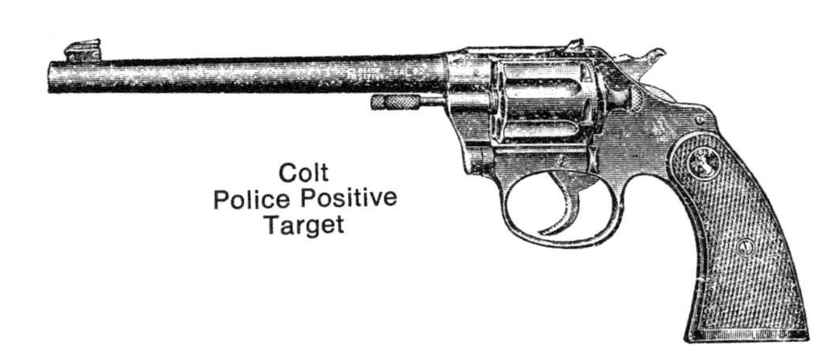

Colt Police Positive Target

Colt Police Positive Target Double Action Revolver $200

Target version of the "Police Positive." Calibers. 22 Long Rifle (introduced 1910, embedded head-cylinder for high speed cartridges after 1932), 22 W.R.F. (introduced 1910, discontinued 1935), 32 Short & Long Colt (discontinued 1915), 32 New Police (32 S&W Short & Long). 6-inch barrel, blued finish only. 10½ inches overall. Weight, 26 ounces in 22 cal. Adjustable target sights. Checkered walnut stocks. Made from 1905 to 1940.

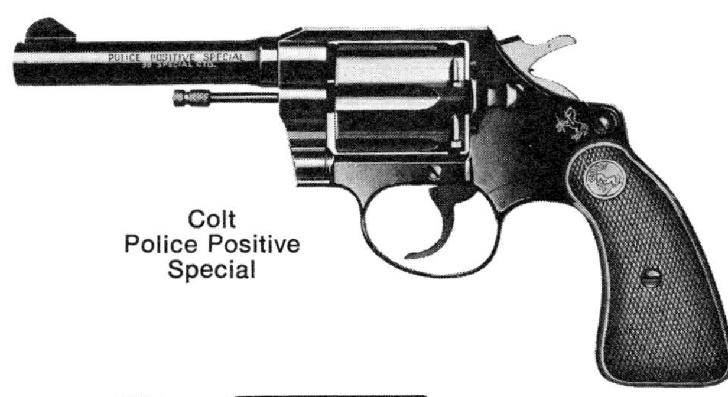

Colt Police Positive Special

Colt Police Positive Special Double Action Revolver $135

Based on the "Police Positive" with frame lengthened to permit longer cylinder. Calibers: 32-20 (discontinued 1942), 38 Special, 32 New Police and 38 New Police (introduced 1946). 6-shot cylinder. Barrel lengths: 4 (only length in current production), 5 and 6-inch. 8¾ inches overall with 4-inch barrel. Weight, 23 ounces in 38 Special with 4-inch barrel. Fixed sights. Checkered stocks of hard rubber, plastic or walnut. Made from 1907 to 1973.

Colt Detective Special

Colt Cobra Double Action Revolver $125

Square butt, 4-inch barrel. Lightweight "Police Positive Special" with same general specifications, except has "Colt-alloy" frame. Calibers: 38 Special, 38 New Police, 32 New Police. Weight, 17 ounces in 38 caliber. Blued finish. Checkered plastic or walnut stocks. Made from 1951 to 1973.

Colt Cobra Double Action Revolver $125

Round butt. 2-inch barrel. Lightweight "Detective Special" with same general specifications as that model except with "Colt-alloy" frame. Calibers: 38 Special, 38 New Police, 32 New Police. Weight, 15 ounces in 38 caliber. Blued finish. Checkered plastic or walnut stocks. Made from 1951 to 1973.

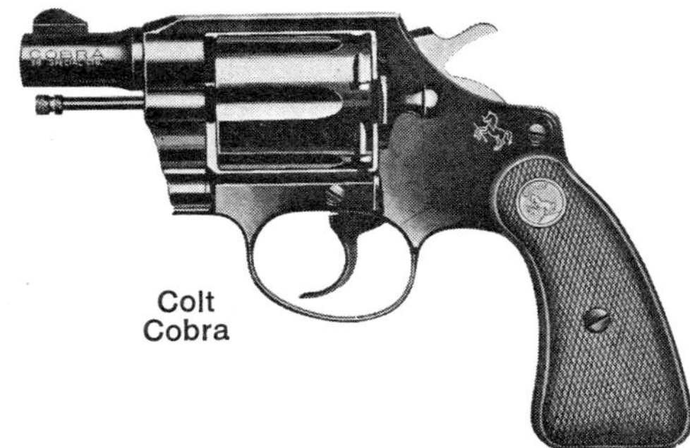

Colt Cobra

Colt Detective Special Double Action Revolver . . . $125

This is the "Police Positive Special" with a 2-inch barrel, otherwise specifications same as that model; rounded butt introduced in 1933. Originally supplied in 38 Special only, it has been made in calibers 32 New Police,, 38 New Police. Weight, 17 ounces in 38 caliber in 1946. 6¾ inches overall. Weight, 21 ounces in 38 cal. Made from 1926 to 1972.

Colt Agent Double Action Revolver **$125**

Lightweight model with short grip. Caliber, 38 Special. 2-inch barrel. 6¾ inches overall. Weight, 14 ounces. Blued finish. Checkered walnut stocks. Made from 1955 to 1973.

Colt New Service Double Action Revolver

Calibers: 38 Special, 357 Magnum (introduced 1936), 38-40, 44-40, 44 Russian, 44 Special, 45 Auto, 45 Colt, 450 Eley, 455 Eley, 476 Eley. Barrel lengths: 4, 5 and 6-inch in 38 Special and 357 Magnum; 4½, 5½ and 7½-inch in other calibers. 9¾ inches overall with 4½-inch barrel. Weight, 39 ounces in 45 caliber with 4½-inch barrel. Fixed sights. Blued or nickel finish. Checkered walnut stocks. Made from 1898 to 1942. *Note:* More than 500,000 of this model in caliber 45 Auto (designated "Model 1917 Revolver") were purchased by the U.S. Government during World War I. These arms were later sold as surplus to National Rifle Association members through the Director of Civilian Marksmanship. Price was $16.15 plus packing charge. Supply exhausted during the early 1930's.

Commercial Model **$200**
Magnum **$225**
1917 Army **$125**

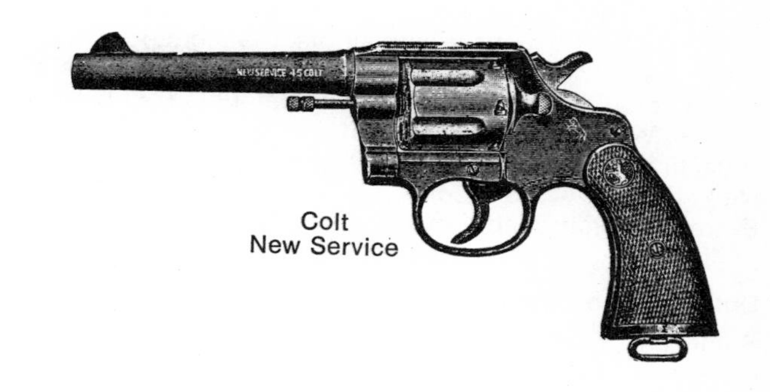

Colt
New Service

Colt New Service Target **$350**

Target version of the "New Service"; general specifications same as that model. Calibers: originally chambered for 44 Russian, 450 Eley, 455 Eley and 476 Eley; later models in 44 Special, 45 Colt and 45 Auto. Barrel lengths: 6 and 7½-inch. 12¾ inches overall with 7½-inch barrel. Weight, 42 ounces in 45 caliber with 7½-inch barrel. Adjustable target sights. Hand finished action. Blued finish. Checkered walnut stocks. Made from 1900 to 1940.

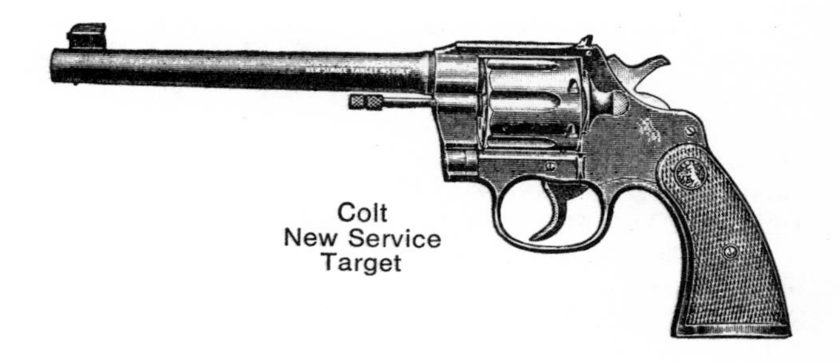
Colt
New Service
Target

Colt Shooting Master Double Action Revolver **$400**

Deluxe target arm based on the "New Service" model. Calibers. originally made only in 38 Special; 44 Special, 45 Auto and 45 Colt added in 1933 and 357 Magnum in 1936. 6-inch barrel. 11¼ inches overall. Weight, 44 ounces in 38 caliber. Adjustable target sights. Hand finished action. Blued finish. Checkered walnut stocks. Rounded butt. Made from 1932 to 1941.

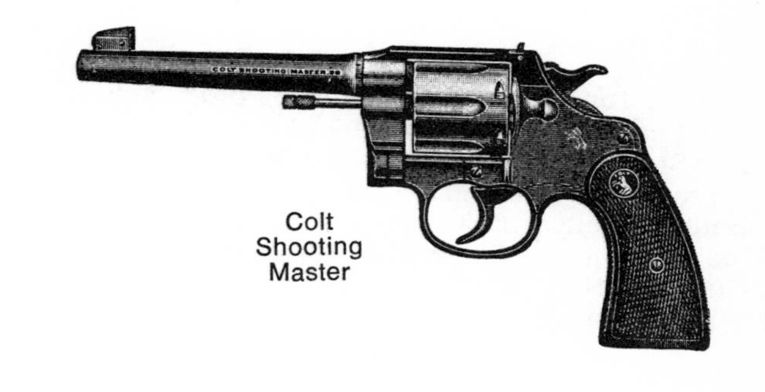
Colt
Shooting
Master

Colt Three-Fifty-Seven Double Action Revolver

Heavy frame. Caliber, 357 Magnum. 6-shot cylinder. 4 or 6-inch barrel. Quick draw ramp front sight, Accro rear sight. Blued finish. Checkered walnut stocks. 9¼ or 11¼ inches overall. Weights: 36 oz. (4" bbl.), 39 oz. (6" bbl.). Made from 1953 to 1961.

With standard hammer and service stocks **$150**
With wide spur hammer and target stocks **$160**

Colt Python Double Action Revolver **$200**

Caliber, 357 Magnum. 6-shot cylinder. Barrels: 2½, 4, 6 inch; ventilated rib. 11¼ inches overall with 6-inch barrel. Weight, 44 ounces with 6-inch barrel. Adjustable rear sight, ramp front sight. Blued or nickel plated Checkered walnut target stocks. Made from 1955 to date.

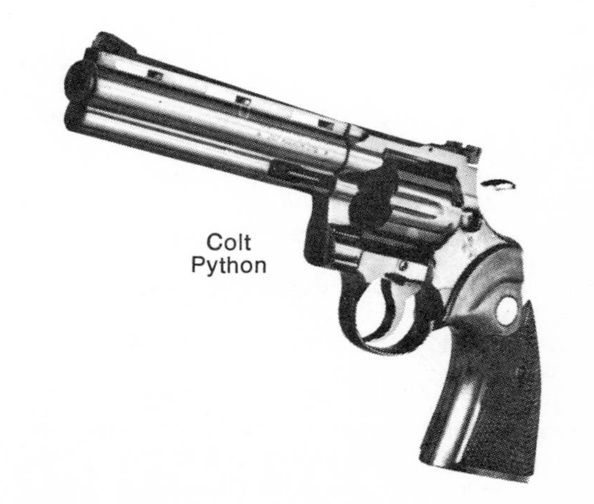
Colt
Python

Colt Frontier Scout Single Action Revolver

Single Action Army replica, 7/8 scale. Calibers: 22 Short, Long, Long Rifle; 22WRF Magnum (interchangeable cylinder available). 4¾-inch barrel. 9-15/16 inches overall. Weight, 24 ounces. Fixed sights. Plastic stocks. Originally made with bright alloy frame; since 1959 with steel frame, blue finish, also in all nickel finish with wood stocks. Made from 1958 to 1971.

Blue finish, plastic stocks **$75**
Nickel finish, wood stocks **$90**
Extra interchangeable cylinder **$10**

Colt Buntline Scout **$100**

Same as "Frontier Scout" except has 9½-inch barrel. Made from 1959 to 1971.

Colt Frontier Scout Commemorative Models

Limited production versions of "Frontier Scout" issued, with appropriate inscription, to commemorate historical events.

1961 issues:
Kansas Statehood Centennial (6201 produced) **$165**
Pony Express Centennial (1011 produced) **$350**

1962 issues:
Columbus, Ohio, Sesquicentennial (200 produced) **$425**
Fort Findlay, Ohio, Sesquicentennial (130 produced) **$425**
New Mexico Golden Anniversary (1000 produced) . . **$195**
West Virginia Statehood Centennial (3548 produced) **$165**

1963 issues:
Arizona Territorial Centennial (5355 produced) . . . **$165**
Carolina Charter Tercentenary (300 produced) . . . **$250**
Fort Stephenson, Ohio, Sesquicentennial (200 produced) **$425**
Battle of Gettysburg Centennial (1019 produced) . . **$200**
Idaho Territorial Centennial (902 produced) **$250**
Gen. John Hunt Morgan Indiana Raid (100 produced) **$575**

1964 issues:
Nevada Statehood Centennial (3988 produced) . . . **$150**
Nevada "Battle Born" (981 produced) **$150**
Montana Territorial Centennial (2230 produced) . . **$175**
Wyoming Diamond Jubilee (2343 produced) **$150**
General Hood Centennial (1503 produced). **$175**
New Jersey Tercentenary (1001 produced) **$150**
St. Louis Bicentennial (802 produced) **$150**
California Gold Rush (500 produced) **$225**
Chamizal Treaty (450 produced) **$150**

1965 issues:
Oregon Trail (1995 produced) **$150**
Forty-Niner Miner (500 produced) **$175**
Old Fort Des Moines Reconstruction (700 produced) **$175**
Appomattox Centennial (1000 produced) **$175**
General Meade Campaign (1197 produced) **$175**
St. Augustine Quadricentennial (500 produced) . . . **$225**
Kansas Cowtown Series—Wichita (500 produced) **$200**

1966 issues:
Kansas Cowtown Series—Dodge City (500 produced) **$200**
Colorado Gold Rush (1350 produced) **$150**
Oklahoma Territory (1350 produced) **$150**
Dakota Territory (1000 produced) **$150**
Kansas Cowtown Series—Abilene (500 produced) **$200**
Indiana Sesquicentennial (1500 produced) **$150**

1967 issues:
Lawman Series—Bat Masterson (3000 produced) **$200**
Alamo (2800 produced) **$150**
Kansas Cowtown Series—Coffeyville (500 produced) **$200**
Kansas Trail Series—Chisholm Trail (500 produced) **$175**

1968 issues:
Nebraska Centenniel (7001 produced) **$150**
Kansas Trail Series—Pawnee Trail (501 produced) **$175**
Lawman Series—Pat Garrett (3000 produced) **$200**

1969 issues:
Gen. Nathan Bedford Forrest (3000 produced) **$150**
Kansas Trail Series—Santa Fe Trail (501 produced) **$175**
Alabama Sesquicentennial (3001 produced) **$175**
Golden Spike (11000 produced) **$150**
Kansas Trail Series—Shawnee Trail (501 produced) **$175**
Arkansas Territory Sesquicentennial (3500 produced) **$135**
Lawman Series—Wild Bill Hickock (3000 produced) **$195**
California Bicentennial (5000 produced) **$150**

1970 issues:
Kansas Fort Series—Ft. Larned (500 produced) . . . **$150**
Kansas Fort Series—Ft. Hays (500 produced) **$150**
Maine Sesquicentennial (3000 produced) **$150**
Missouri Sesquicentennial (3000 produced) **$150**
Kansas Fort Series—Ft. Riley (500 produced) **$150**
Lawman Series—Wyatt Earp (3000 produced) **$195**

1971 issue:
Kansas Fort Series—Ft. Scott (500 produced) **$150**

Note: Values indicated are for revolvers in new condition.

Colt Deringer No. 4

Replica of Deringer No. 3 (1872). Single shot with sideswing barrel. Caliber, 22 Short. 2½-inch barrel. 4-15/16 inches overall. Weight, 7¾ ounces. Fixed sights. Gold-finished frame, blued barrel, walnut grips; also available nickel-plated with simulated ivory grips. Cased. Made from 1959 to 1963.

Single pistol . . . . **$ 50**
Pair with consecutive serial numbers **$125**

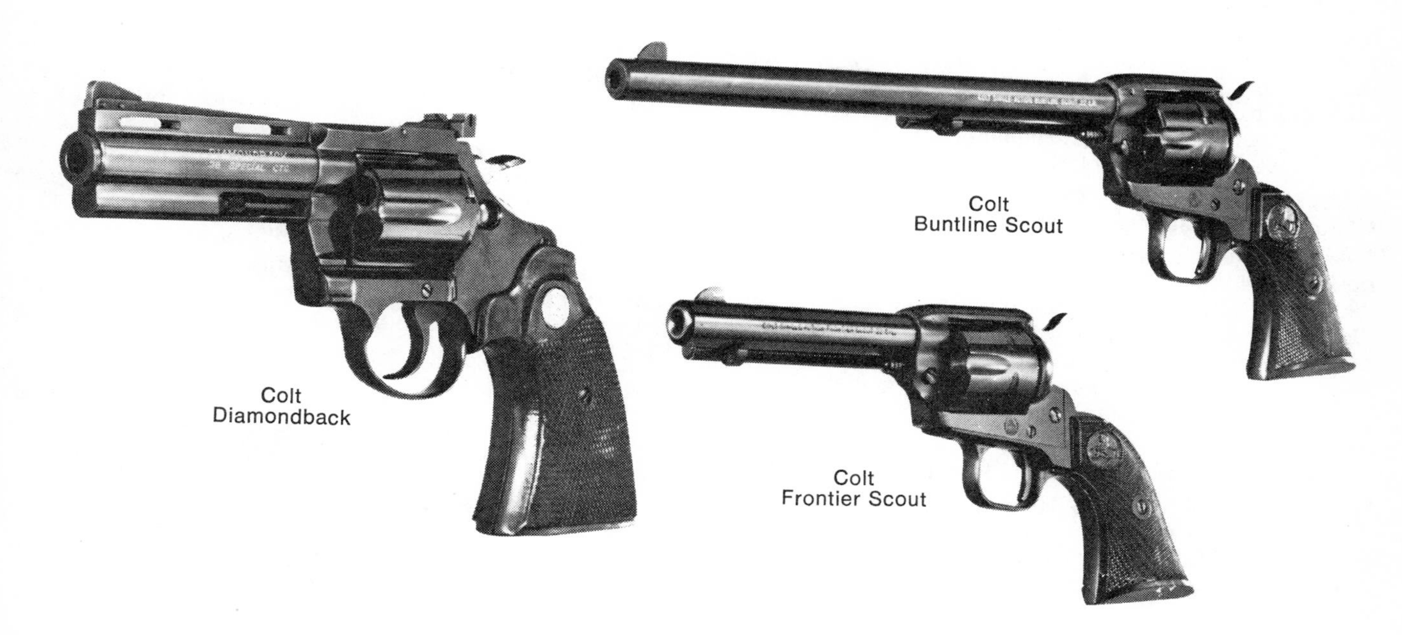

Colt
Diamondback

Colt
Buntline Scout

Colt
Frontier Scout

Colt Deringer No. 4 Commemorative Models

Limited production versions of 22 Deringer issued, with appropriate inscription, to commemorate historical events.

1961 issue:
Geneseo, Ill., 125th Anniversary (104 produced) . . **$325**

1962 issue:
Fort McPherson, Neb., Centennial (300 produced) **$150**
Note: Values indicated are for commemorative deringers in new condition.

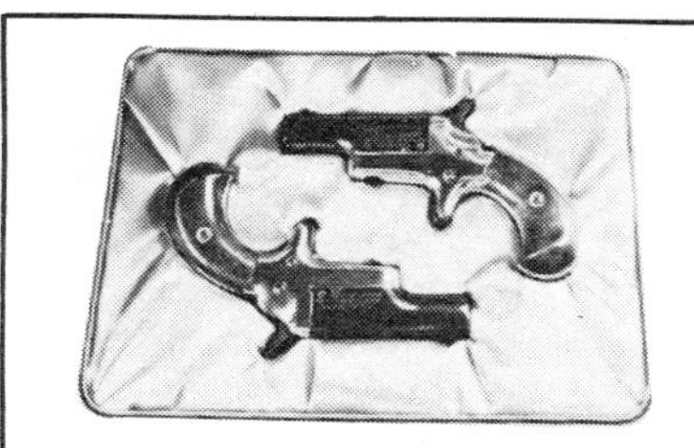

Colt
Deringer No. 4
(Cased Pair)

Colt Civil War Centennial Model Pistol

Single shot replica, 7/8 scale, of Colt Model 1860 Army Revolver. Caliber, 22 Short. 6-inch barrel. Weight, 22 ounces. Blued finish with gold-plated frame, grip frame, and trigger guard, walnut grips. Cased. 24,114 were produced. Made in 1961.
Single pistol . . . . **$ 60**
Pair with consecutive serial numbers **$125**

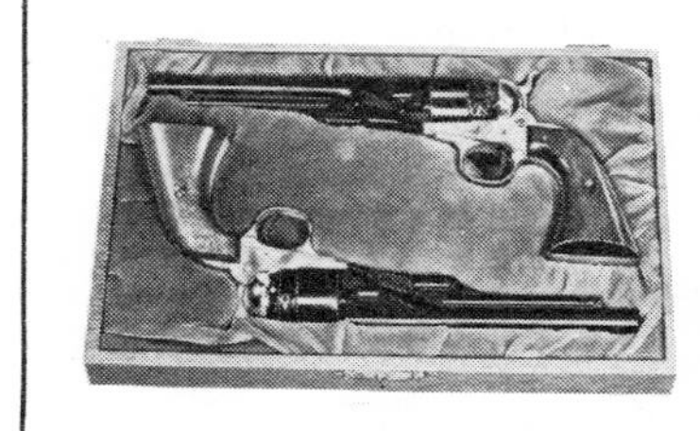

Colt
Civil War Centennial
(Cased Pair)

Colt Rock Island Arsenal Centennial Pistol $125

Limited production (550 pieces) version of Civil War Centennial Model single shot 22 pistol, made exclusively for Cherry's Sporting Goods, Geneseo, Ill., to commemorate the centennial of the Rock Island Arsenal in Illinois. Made in 1962.

Colt Diamondback Double Action Revolver $125

Calibers: 22 Long Rifle, 38 Special. 6-shot cylinder. Barrels: 2½, 4 inch; ventilated rib. 9 inches overall with 4-inch barrel. Weights (with 4-inch barrel): 22, 31¾ ounces; 38, 28½ ounces. Adjustable rear sight, ramp front sight. Blued or nickel finish. Checkered walnut stocks. Made from 1966 to date.

Colt Automatic Pistols

Colt Model 1900 38 Automatic Pistol $350

Caliber, 38 ACP (modern high velocity cartridges should not be used in this pistol). 7-shot magazine. 6-inch barrel. 9 inches overall. Weight, 35 ounces. Fixed sights. Blued finish. Plain walnut stocks. Sharp spur hammer. Combination rear sight and safety. Made from 1900 to 1902.

Colt Sporting 38 Automatic Pistol, Model 1902 . . . . $300

Caliber, 38 ACP (modern high velocity cartridges should not be used in this pistol). 7-shot magazine. 6-inch barrel. 9 inches overall. Weight, 35 ounces. Fixed sights, Knife blade and V-notch. Blued finish. Checkered hard rubber stocks. Round back hammer. No safety. Made from 1902 to 1907.

Colt Military 38 Automatic Pistol Model 1902 . . . . . $350

Caliber, 38 ACP (modern high velocity cartridges should not be used in this pistol). 8-shot magazine. 6-inch barrel. 9 inches overall. Weight, 37 ounces. Fixed sights, knife blade and V-notch. Blued finish. Checkered hard rubber stocks. Round back hammer, changed to spur type in 1908. No safety. Made from 1902 to 1928.

Colt Pocket 38 Automatic Pistol Model 1903 . . . . . . $200

Caliber, 38 ACP (modern high velocity cartridges should not be used in this pistol). Similar to Sporting 38 Model 1902, but with 4½-inch barrel. 7½ inches overall. Weight, 31 ounces. Fixed sights, knife-blade and V-notch. Blued finish. Checkered hard rubber stocks. Round back hammer, changed to spur type in 1908. No safety. Made from 1903 to 1928.

Colt Military Model 45 Automatic Pistol $500

Model of 1905. Caliber, 45 Automatic. 7-shot magazine. 5-inch barrel. 8 inches overall. Weight, 32½ ounces. Fixed sights, knife-blade and V-notch. Blued finish. Checkered walnut stocks. Similar to Model 1902 38 Automatic Pistols. Made from 1905 to 1911.

Colt Pocket Model 32 Automatic Pistol $165

First Issue. Caliber, 32 Auto. 8-shot magazine. 4-inch barrel. 7 inches overall. Weight, 23 ounces. Fixed sights. Blued finish. Checkered hard-rubber stocks. Hammerless. Slide lock and grip safeties. Barrel-lock bushing similar to that on Government Model 45 Auto. Made from 1903 to 1911.

Colt Pocket Model 380 Automatic Pistol $165

First Issue. Same as Pocket 32 Auto—First Issue, except chambered for caliber 380 Auto, 7-shot magazine. Made from 1908 to 1911.

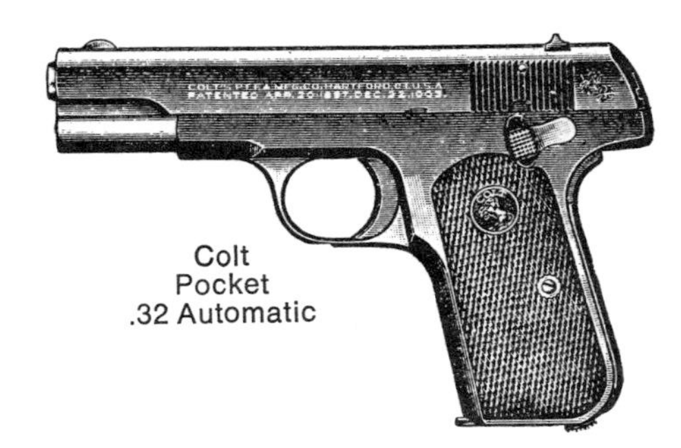

Colt Pocket .32 Automatic

Colt Pocket Model 32 Automatic Pistol $165

Second Issue. Same as First Issue but without barrel-lock bushing. Made from 1911 to 1926.

Colt Pocket Model 380 Automatic Pistol $165

Second Issue. Same as Pocket 32 Auto—Second Issue, except chambered for 380 Auto, 7-shot magazine. Made from 1911 to 1926.

Colt Pocket Model 32 Automatic Pistol $175

Third Issue. Caliber, 32 Auto. Similar to First and Second Issues, but has safety disconnector on all pistols above No. 468097 which prevents firing of cartridge in chamber if magazine is removed. 3¾-inch barrel. 6¾ inches overall. Weight, 24 ounces. Fixed sights. Blued or nickel finish. Checkered walnut stocks. Made from 1926 to 1942.

Colt Pocket Model 380 Automatic Pistol $175

Third Issue. Same as Pocket 32 Auto—Third Issue, except chambered for 380 Auto, 7-shot magazine. Safety disconnector on all pistols above No. 92,894. Made from 1926 to 1942

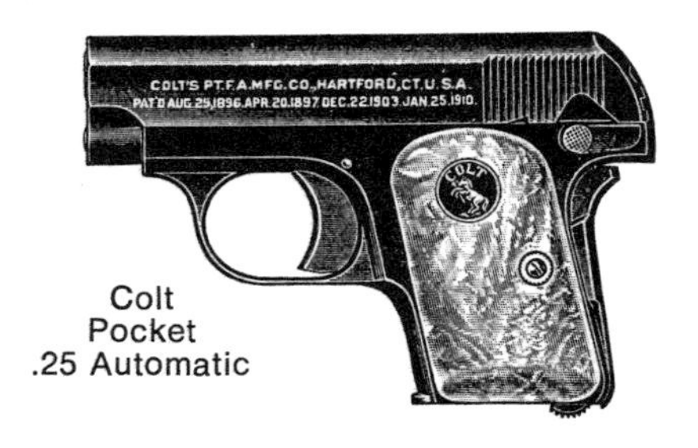

Colt Pocket .25 Automatic

Colt Pocket Model 25 Automatic Pistol $200

Caliber, 25 Automatic. 6-shot magazine. 2-inch barrel. 4½ inches overall. Weight, 13 ounces. Flat top front, square notch, rear sight in groove. Blued or nickel finish. Checkered hard rubber stocks on early models, checkered walnut on later type. Disconnector added in 1916 at pistol No. 141000. Made from 1908 to 1947.

Colt Government Model .45

Colt Government Model Automatic Pistol

U.S. Models 1911 and 1911A1. Caliber, 45 Automatic. 7-shot magazine. 5-inch barrel. 8½ inches overall. Weight, 39 ounces. Fixed sights. Blued finish on "Commercial Model," Parkerized or similar finish on most military pistols. Checkered walnut stocks formerly furnished, plastic grips on later production. Checkered arched mainspring housing and longer grip safety spur added after World War I (M/1911A1 has these features). Made from 1911 to 1970. Letter "C" precedes or follows serial number on "Commercial Model" 45's. *Note:*

During both World Wars, Colt licensed other firms to make these pistols under government contract; they include: Ithaca Gun Co., North American Arms Co. Ltd. (Canada), Remington Arms Co., Remington-Rand Co., Singer Sewing Machine Co., and Union Switch & Signal Co.

Commercial Model $175
U.S. Model 1911 or 1911A1 . . . . $150

Colt
World War II
Commemorative .45

Colt
World War I
Commemorative .45

Colt World War I 50th Anniversary Commemorative Series 45 Auto

Limited production replica of Model 1911 45 Auto engraved with battle scenes, commemorating Battles at Chateau Thierry, Belleau Wood, Second Battle of the Marne, Meuse Argonne. In special presentation display cases. Production: 7400 standard model, 75 deluxe, 25 special deluxe grade. Match numbered sets offered. Made in 1967, 1968, 1969.

Standard grade . . . . $ 220
Deluxe grade . . . . $ 650
Special deluxe grade $1,250

Colt World War II Commemorative 45 Auto $250

Limited production replica of Model 1911A1 45 Auto engraved with respective names of locations where historic engagements occurred during World War II, as well as specific issue and theater identification. European model has oak leaf motif on slide; palm leaf design frames the Pacific issue. 11,500 of each model were produced. Made in 1970.

Note: Values indicated for commemorative 45 Autos in new condition.

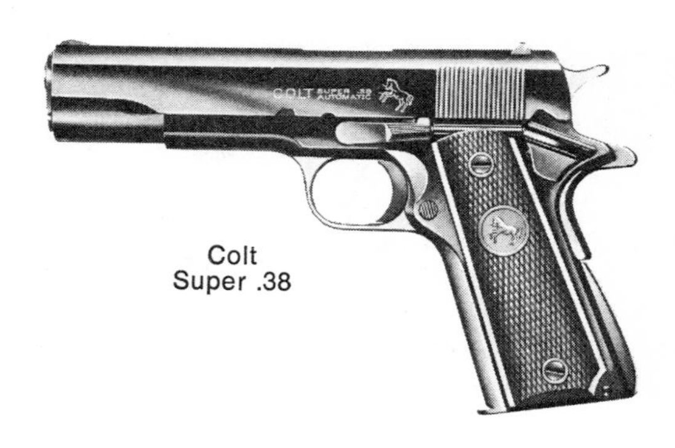

Colt
Super .38

Colt Super 38 Automatic Pistol $175

Identical with Government Model 45 Auto, except for caliber and magazine capacity. Caliber, 38 Automatic, 9-shot magazine. Made from 1928 to 1970.

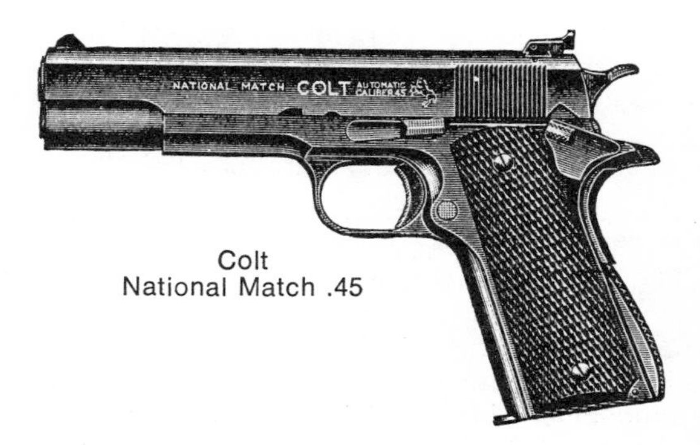

Colt
National Match .45

Colt National Match Automatic Pistol $300

Identical with the Government Model 45 Auto, but with hand-honed action, match grade barrel, adjustable rear sight and ramp front sight. Made from 1932 to 1940.

Same, with fixed sights $225

Colt
Gold Cup
National Match .45

Colt Gold Cup National Match 45 Auto **$200**

Match version of Government Model 45 Automatic with same general specifications, except: match grade barrel with new design bushing, flat mainspring housing, long wide trigger with adjustable stop, hand-fitted slide with improved ejection port, adjustable rear sight, target front sight, checkered walnut grips with gold medallions; weight, 37 ounces. Made from 1957 to 1970.

Colt Gold Cup Mark III National Match 38 Special . . **$250**

Similar to Gold Cup National Match 45 Auto, except chambered for 38 Special mid-range. Made from 1961 to 1974.

Colt Super Match Automatic Pistol **$275**

Identical with Super 38 Auto, but with hand-honed action, match grade barrel, adjustable rear sight and ramp front sight. Made from 1933 to 1940.
Same, with fixed sights **$225**

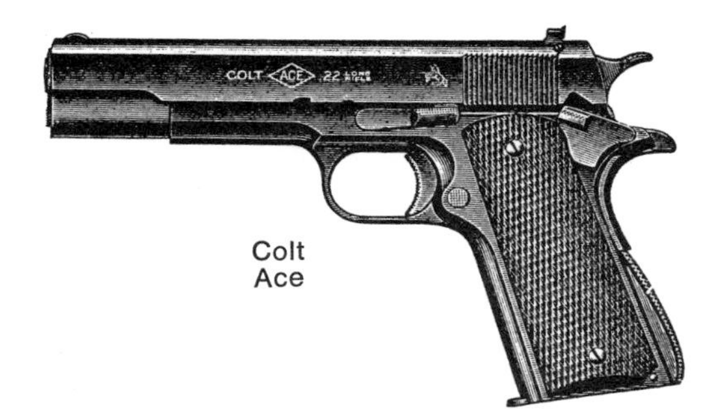
Colt
Ace

Colt Ace Automatic Pistol **$325**

Caliber, 22 Long Rifle (regular or high speed). Built on the same frame as the Government Model 45 Auto, with same safety features, etc. Hand-honed action, target barrel, adjustable rear sight. 4¾-inch barrel. 8¼ inches overall. Weight, 38 ounces. Made from 1930 to 1940.

Colt Service Model Ace Automatic Pistol **$450**

Identical with National Match Model 45 Auto, except for caliber, magazine capacity and weight; has "floating chamber" amplifying recoil to four times that normal in a 22. Caliber, 22 Long Rifle (regular or high speed). 10-shot magazine. Weight, 42 ounces. Made from 1938 to 1942.

Colt 22-45 Conversion Unit **$65**

Converts Government Model 45 Auto to a 22 L. R. target pistol. Unit consists of slide assembly, barrel, floating chamber (as in Service Ace), bushing, ejector, recoil spring, recoil spring guide and plug, magazine and slide stop. Made from 1938 to date. *Note:* Now designated "22 Conversion Unit," post-war model of this unit is also adaptable to the Super 38 pistols.

Colt 45-22 Conversion Unit **$125**

Converts Service Ace 22 to National Match 45 Auto. Unit consists of match grade slide assembly and barrel, bushing, recoil spring, recoil spring guide and plug, magazine and slide stop. Made from 1938 to 1942.

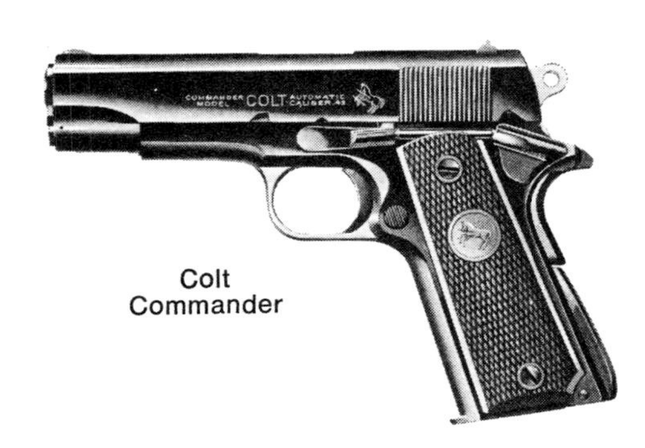
Colt
Commander

Colt Commander Lightweight Automatic Pistol . . . **$125**

Same basic design as Government Model, but shorter and lighter in weight; receiver and mainspring housing are forged from a special lightweight metal, "Coltalloy." Calibers: 45 Automatic, 38 Super Auto, 9mm Luger. 7-shot magazine in 45 Cal., 9-shot in 38 Auto and 9mm Luger. 4¼-inch barrel. 8 inches overall. Weight, 26½ ounces. Fixed sights. Round spur hammer. Improved safety lock. Blued finish. Checkered plastic stocks. Made from 1951 to date.

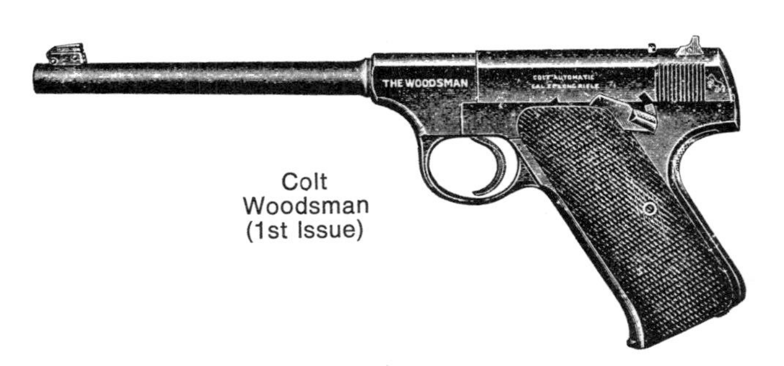

Colt
Woodsman
(1st Issue)

Colt Woodsman Target Model Automatic Pistol . . . **$175**

First Issue. Caliber, 22 Long Rifle (regular velocity). 10-shot magazine. 6½-inch barrel. 10½ inches overall. Weight, 28 ounces. Adjustable sights. Blued finish. Checkered walnut stocks. Made from 1915 to 1932. *Note:* The mainspring housing of this model is not strong enough to permit safe use of high speed cartridges. Change to a new heat treated mainspring housing was made at pistol No. 83,790. Many of the old models were converted by installation of new housings. The new housing may be distinguished from the earlier type by the checkering in the curve under the breech; new housing is grooved straight across, while the old type bears a diagnoally checkered oval.

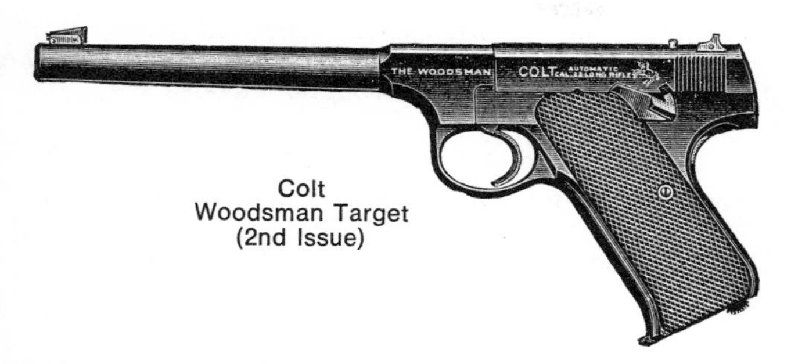

Colt
Woodsman Target
(2nd Issue)

Colt Woodsman Target Model Automatic Pistol . . . $200

Second Issue. Caliber, 22 Long Rifle (regular or high speed). Same as original model except has heavier barrel and high speed mainspring housing. See note under Woodsman—First Issue. Weight, 29 ounces. Made from 1932 to 1948.

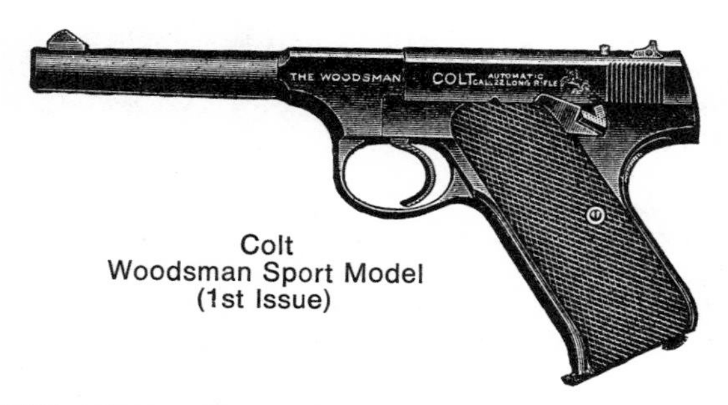

Colt
Woodsman Sport Model
(1st Issue)

Colt Woodsman Sport Model Automatic Pistol $225

First Issue. Caliber, 22 Long Rifle (regular or high speed). Same as Target Woodsman—Second Issue, except has 4½-inch barrel. Adjustable rear sight, fixed or adjustable front sight. Weight, 27 ounces. 8½ inches overall. Made from 1933 to 1948.

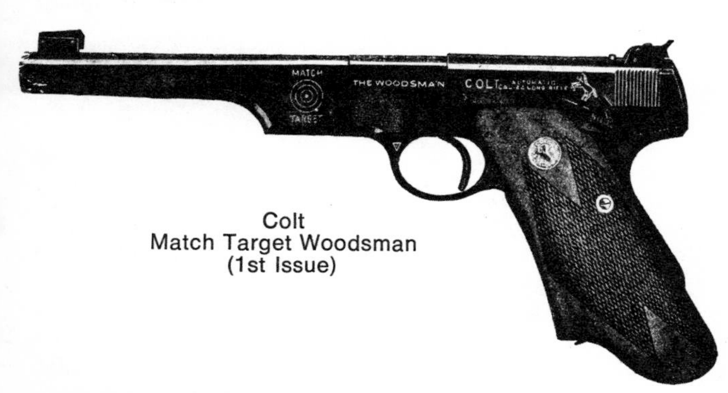

Colt
Match Target Woodsman
(1st Issue)

Colt Match Target Woodsman Automatic Pistol $400

First Issue. Same basic design as other Woodsman models. Caliber, 22 Long Rifle. 10-shot magazine. 6½-inch barrel, slightly tapered with flat sides. 11 inches overall. Weight, 36 ounces. Adjustable rear sight. Blued finish. Checkered walnut stock, one-piece design with extended sides. Made from 1938 to 1942.

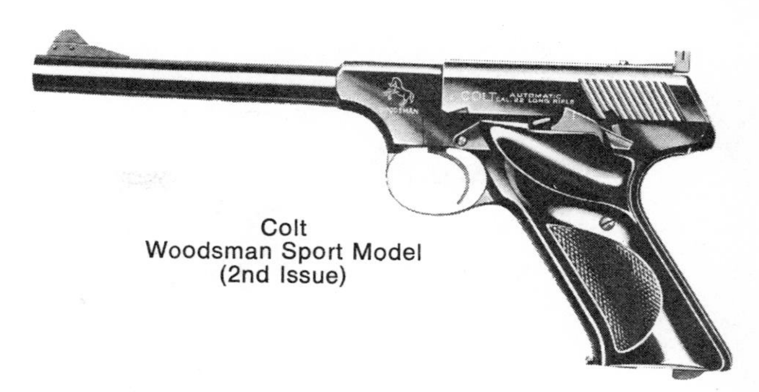

Colt
Woodsman Sport Model
(2nd Issue)

Colt Woodsman Target Model Automatic Pistol . . . $100

Third Issue. Same basic design as previous Woodsman pistols, but with these changes: longer grip, magazine catch on left side as on Government Model 45, larger thumb safety, slide stop, slide stays open on last shot, magazine disconnector, thumb rest stocks. Caliber, 22 Long Rifle (regular or high speed). 10-shot magazine. 6-inch barrel. 10½ inches overall. Weight, 32 ounces. Click adjustable rear sight, ramp front sight. Blued finish. Checkered plastic or walnut stocks. Made from 1948 to date.

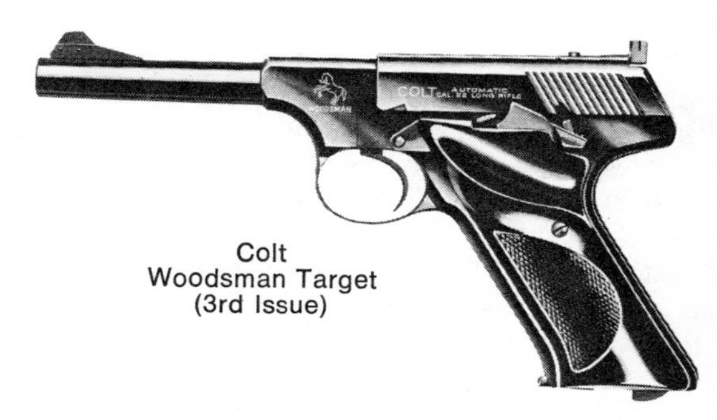

Colt
Woodsman Target
(3rd Issue)

Colt Woodsman Sport Model Automatic Pistol $100

Second Issue. Same as Target Woodsman—Third Issue, but with 4½-inch barrel. 9 inches overall. Weight, 30 ounces. Made from 1948 to date.

Colt Woodsman Targetsman $85

Similar to "Woodsman Target" but has "economy" adjustable rear sight, lacks automatic slide stop. Made from 1959 to date.

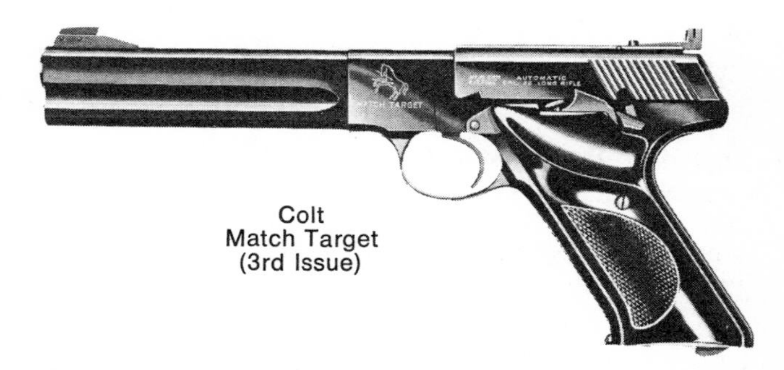
Colt
Match Target
(3rd Issue)

Colt Match Target Automatic Pistol $115

Second Issue. Same basic design as Target Woodsman—Third Issue. Caliber, 22 Long Rifle (regular or high

Colt Huntsman

Junior Colt

speed). 10-shot magazine. 6-inch flat-sided heavy barrel. 10½ inches overall. Weight, 40 ounces. Click adjustable rear sight, ramp front sight. Blued finish. Checkered plastic or walnut stocks. Made from 1948 to date.

Colt Match Target "4½" Automatic Pistol $115

Same as Match Target—Second Issue, except has a 4½-inch barrel. 9 inches overall. Weight, 36 ounces. Made from 1950 to date.

Colt Challenger Automatic Pistol $75

Same basic design as Target Woodsman—Third Issue, but lacks some of the refinements. Fixed sights. Magazine catch on butt as in old Woodsman. Does not stay open on last shot. Lacks magazine safety. 4½-inch or 6-inch barrel. 9 inches or 10½ inches overall, depending upon barrel length. Weights, 30 ounces (4½-inch), 31½ ounces (6-inch). Blued finish. Checkered plastic stocks. Made from 1950 to 1955.

Colt Huntsman $75

Same specifications as "Challenger." Made from 1955 to date.

Junior Colt Pocket Model Automatic Pistol $75

Made in Spain by Unceta y Cia. ("Astra"). Calibers: 22 Short, 25 Auto. 6-shot magazine 2¼-inch barrel. 4¾ inches overall. Weight, 12 ounces. Fixed sights. Checkered walnut grips. Made from 1958 to 1968.

Note: Data on Commemorative Colts supplied by Mr. Robert E. P. Cherry, Cherry's Sporting Goods, Geneseo, Ohio.

Dreyse Pistols manufactured by Rheinische Metallwaren und Maschinenfabrik ("Rheinmetall"), Sommerda, Germany

Dreyse Model 1907 Automatic Pistol $75

Caliber, 32 Automatic (7.65mm). 8-shot magazine. 3½-inch barrel. 6¼ inches overall. Weight, about 24 ounces. Fixed sights. Blued finish. Hard-rubber stocks.

Dreyse Vest Pocket Automatic Pistol $75

Conventional Browning type. Caliber, 25 Automatic (6.35mm). 6-shot magazine. 2-inch barrel. 4½ inches overall. Weight, about 14 ounces. Fixed sights. Blued finish. Hard rubber stocks.

Deutsche Waffen-und-Munitionsfabriken, Berlin, Germany

DWM Pocket Automatic Pistol $80

Similar to the F N Browning Model 1910. Caliber, 32 Automatic (7.65mm). 3½-inch barrel. 6 inches overall. Weight, about 21 ounces. Blued finish. Hard rubber stocks.

Enfield Revolver manufactured by Royal Small Arms Factory, Enfield Lock, Middlesex, England

Enfield (British Service) No. 2 Mark I Revolver $75

Webley pattern. Hinged frame. Double action. Caliber, 380 British Service (38 S&W with 200-grain bullet). 6-shot cylinder. 5-inch barrel. 10½ inches overall. Weight, about 27½ ounces. Fixed sights. Blued finish. Vulcanite stocks. *Note:* This model was also produced with spurless hammer for Commando use; this variation is designated MARK I*.

Erma Waffenfabrik, Erfurt, Germany

Erma Automatic Target Pistol $70

Caliber, 22 Long Rifle. 10-shot magazine. Interchangeable barrels: 8-3/16 and 11¾-inch. Overall length with 8-3/16-inch barrel, 12½ inches. Weight, 35 ounces. Adjustable target sights. Blued finish. Checkered plastic stocks.

Erma Luger Conversion Unit $55

Converts Luger Pistol to caliber 22 Long Rifle. Consists of insert barrel, sleeve and locking screws, breechblock, 6-shot magazine. Made for all Lugers, 7.65mm and 9mm, with 3⅝, 4½, 6 or 8-inch barrel.

Fabrique Nationale D'Armes de Guerre, Liege, Belgium

FN Browning 6.35mm Pocket Model Automatic Pistol **$150**

Same specifications as Colt Pocket Model 25 Automatic Pistol.

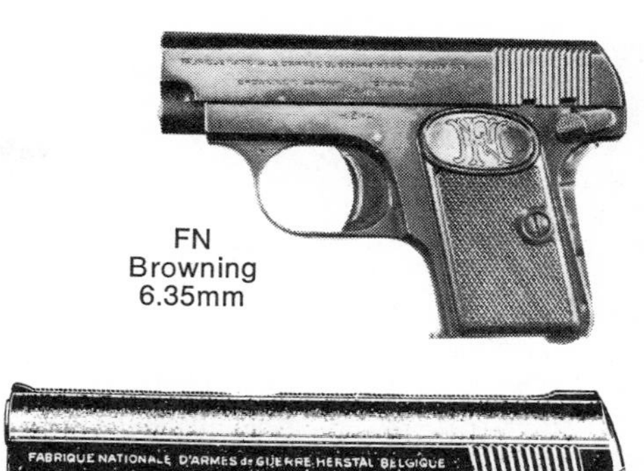

FN Browning 6.35mm

FN Browning Baby Automatic Pistol **$100**

Caliber, 25 Automatic (6.35mm). 6-shot magazine. 2⅛-inch barrel. 4 inches overall. Weight, 10 ounces. Fixed sights. Blued finish. Hard rubber stocks. Made from 1940 to date.

FN Browning Baby

FN Browning Model 1900 Pocket Automatic Pistol . . **$90**

Caliber, 32 Automatic (7.65mm). 7-shot magazine. 4-inch barrel. 6¾ inches overall. Weight, 22 ounces. Fixed sights. Blued finish. Hard rubber stocks. Made from 1899 to 1910.

FN Browning Model 1910 Pocket Automatic Pistol . **$100**

Calibers: 32 Automatic (7.65mm), 380 Automatic (9mm). 7-shot magazine (32 cal.), 6-shot (380 cal.). 3½-inch barrel 6 inches overall. Weight, 20½ ounces. Fixed sights. Blued finish. Hard rubber stocks. Made from 1910 to date.

FN Browning Model 1910

FN Browning Military Model 1903 Automatic Pistol . **$115**

Caliber, 9mm Browning Long. 7-shot magazine. 5-inch barrel. 8 inches overall. Weight, 32 ounces. Fixed sights. Blued finish. Hard rubber stocks. *Note:* Aside from size, this pistol is of the same basic design as the Colt Pocket 32 and 380 Automatic Pistols. Made from 1903 to 1939.

FN Browning Police & Military Model 1922 Automatic Pistol **$100**

Calibers: 32 Automatic (7.65mm), 380 Automatic (9mm). 9-shot magazine (32 cal.), 8-shot (380 cal.). 4½-inch barrel. 7 inches overall. Weight, 25 ounces. Fixed sights. Blued finish. Hard rubber stocks. Made from 1922 to date.

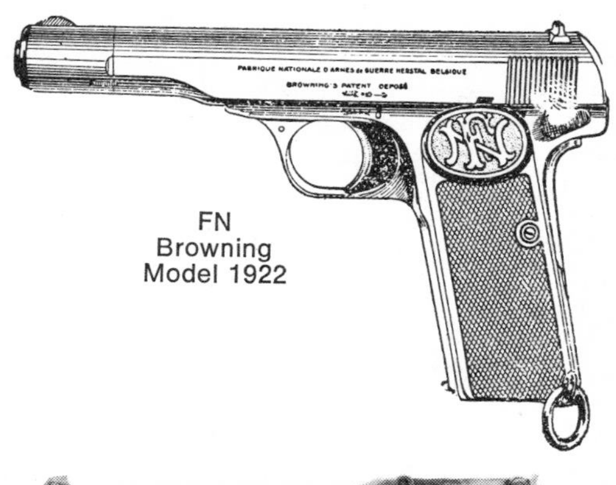

FN Browning Model 1922

FN Browning Military Model 1935 Hi-Power Automatic Pistol

Variation of the Browning-Colt 45 Auto design. Caliber, 9mm Luger. 13-shot magazine. 4⅝-inch barrel. 7¾ inches overall. Weight, about 35 ounces. Adjustable rear sight and fixed front sight or both fixed Blued finish (Canadian manufacture Parkerized). Checkered walnut or plastic stocks. *Note:* Above specifications, in general, apply to both the original FN production and the pistols made by John Inglis Company of Canada for the Chinese Government. A smaller version, with shorter barrel and slide and 10-shot magazine, was made by FN for the Belgian and Rumanian Governments from about 1937 to 1940. Both types were made at the FN plant during the German Occupation of Belgium.

With adjustable rear sight **$350**
FN manufacture, with fixed rear sight **$225**
Inglis manufacture, with fixed rear sight **$425**

FN Browning Model 1935 Hi-Power

Fiala Outfitters, Inc., New York City

Fiala Repeating Pistol **$225**

Despite its appearance, which closely resembles that of the early Colt Woodsman and Hi-Standard, this arm is not an automatic pistol. It is hand-operated by moving the slide to eject, cock and load. Caliber, 22 Long Rifle. 10-shot magazine. Barrel lengths: 3, 7½ and 20 inch. 11¼ inches overall with 7½-inch barrel. Weight, 31 ounces with 7½-inch barrel. Target sights. Blued finish. Plain wood stocks. Shoulder stock was originally supplied for use with 20-inch barrel. Made for a few years shortly after World War I. Value shown is for pistol with one barrel

Forehand & Wadsworth, Worcester, Massachusetts

Forehand & Wadsworth Revolvers

See listings of similar Harrington & Richardson and Iver Johnson models for values.

Frommer, Budapest, Hungary

Frommer Stop Pocket Automatic Pistol **$90**

Locked-breech action, outside hammer. Calibers: 32 Automatic (7.65mm), 380 Automatic (9mm short). 7-shot magazine (32 cal.), 6-shot (380 cal.). 3⅞-inch barrel. 6½ inches overall. Weight, about 21 ounces. Fixed sights. Blued finish. Hard rubber stocks. Introduced c.1912.

Frommer Baby Pocket Automatic Pistol **$110**

Similar to "Stop" model except has 2-inch barrel, is about 4¾ inches overall, weighs about 17½ ounces, magazine capacity is one round less. Introduced shortly after World War I.

Industria Armi Galesi, Brescia, Italy

Galesi Model 9 Pocket Automatic Pistol

Calibers. 25 Auto, 32 Auto. 8-shot magazine. Barrel lengths: 2¼-inch in 25 cal., 3¼-inch in 32 cal. Overall lengths: 4⅜ inches in 25 cal., 5⅞ inches in 32 cal. Weights: 11 ounces in 25 cal., 21 ounces in 32 cal. Fixed sights. Blued finish. Plastic grips.
25 Caliber **$70**
32 Caliber **$55**

Siderurgica Glisenti, Turin, Italy

Glisenti Model 1910 Italian Service Automatic Pistol **$125**

Caliber, 9mm Glisenti. 7-shot magazine. 4-inch barrel. 8½ inches overall. Weight, about 32 ounces. Fixed sights. Blued finish. Army model has checkered wood stocks, Navy model has hard rubber or plastic stocks bearing Italian Navy insignia. Made from 1910 through World War II.

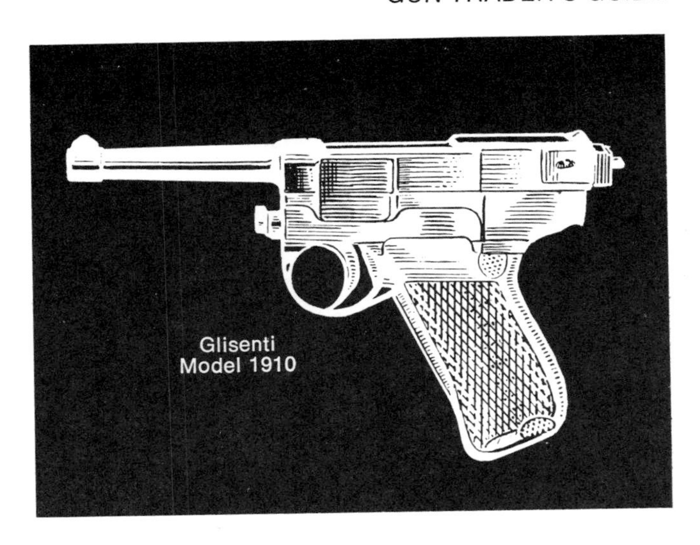
Glisenti Model 1910

Great Western Arms Co., No. Hollywood, California

Great Western Single Action Frontier Revolver **$175**

Replica of the Colt Single Action Army Revolver. Calibers: 22 Long Rifle, 357 Magnum, 38 Special, 44 Special, 44 Magnum, 45 Colt. 6-shot cylinder. Barrel lengths: 4¾, 5½ and 7½ inches. Weight, in 22 cal. with 5½" bbl., 40 ounces. Length overall, with 5½" bbl., 11⅛ inches. Fixed sights. Blued finish. Imitation stag grips. Made from 1951 to 1962. *Note:* Value shown is for improved late model revolvers; early Great Westerns are variable in quality and should be evaluated accordingly. It should also be noted that, beginning about July 1956, these revolvers were also offered in "do-it-yourself" kit form; values of guns assembled from these kits will, in general, be lower than for factory-completed weapons.

Great Western Double Barrel Derringer **$75**

Replica of Remington Double Derringer. Caliber, 38 S&W. Double barrels (superposed), 3-inch. Overall length, 5 inches. Fixed sights. Blued finish. Checkered black plastic grips. Made from 1953 to 1962.

Great Western Single Action

Haemmerli-Walther Olympia

Haemmerli Model 100

Haemmerli Jagd und Sportwaffen-Fabrik A. G., Lenzburg, Switzerland

Haemmerli Model 100 Free Pistol

System Martini action. Caliber, 22 Long Rifle. Single Shot. 11½-inch barrel. 15 inches overall. Weight, 42 ounces. Target sights, micrometer rear. Blued finish. Walnut stock and forearm. Discontinued.

With standard stock and forearm **$400**
With deluxe carved stock and forearm illustrated . . **$475**

Haemmerli-Walther Olympia Model 200 Automatic Pistol **$400**

See Walther Olympia Funfkampf Model for general specifications. Discontinued 1956.

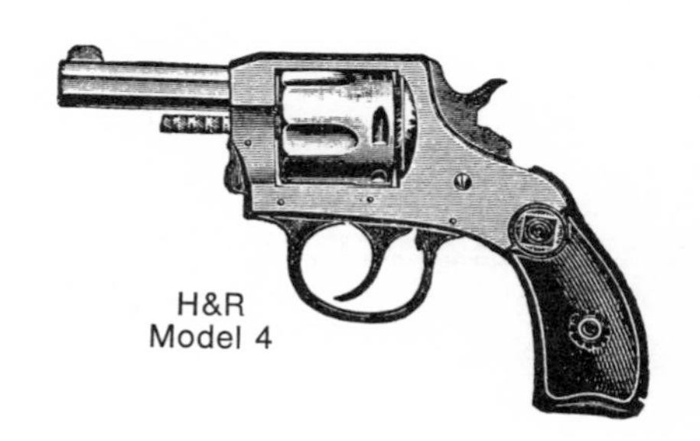

H&R Model 4

Harrington & Richardson Arms Co., Worcester, Massachusetts

Harrington & Richardson Model 4 (1904) Double Action Revolver **$50**

Solid frame. Calibers: 32 S&W Long, 38 S&W. 6-shot cylinder (32 cal.), 5-shot (38 cal.). Barrel lengths: 2½, 4½ and 6-inch. Weight, about 16 ounces in 32 caliber. Fixed sights. Blued or nickel finish. Hard rubber stocks.

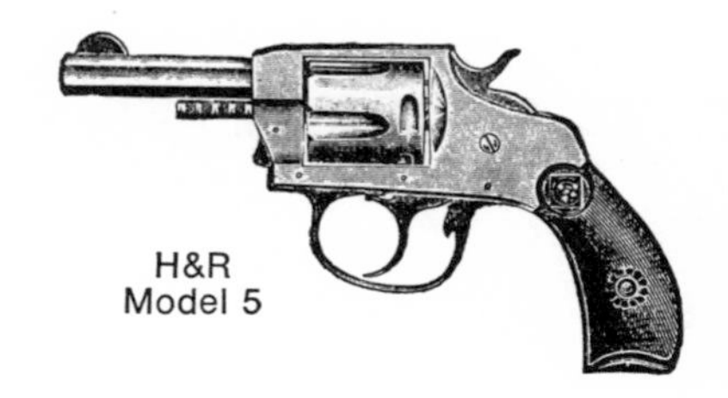

H&R Model 5

Harrington & Richardson Model 5 (1905) Double Action Revolver **$50**

Solid frame. Caliber, 32 S&W. 5-shot cylinder. Barrel lengths: 2½, 4½ and 6-inch. Weight, about 11 ounces. Fixed sights. Blued or nickel finish. Hard rubber stocks.

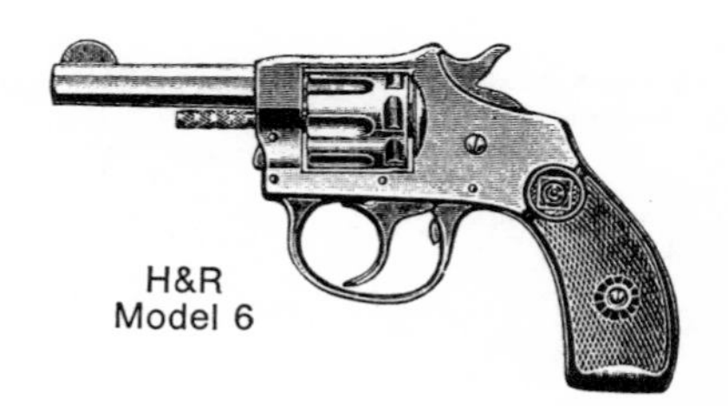

H&R Model 6

Harrington & Richardson Model 6 (1906) Double Action Revolver **$50**

Solid frame. Caliber, 22 Long Rifle. 7-shot cylinder. Barrel lengths. 2½, 4½ and 6-inch. Weight, about 10 ounces. Fixed sights. Blued or nickel finish. Hard rubber stocks.

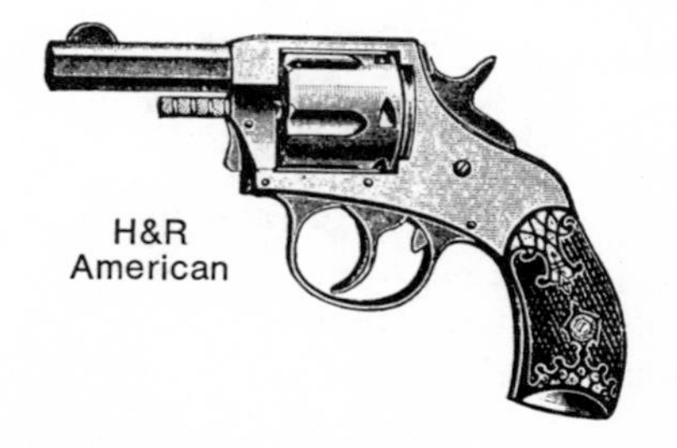

H&R American

Harrington & Richardson American Double Action Revolver **$50**

Solid frame. Calibers: 32 S&W Long, 38 S&W. 6-shot cylinder (32 cal.), 5-shot (38 cal.). Barrel lengths: 2½, 4½ and 6-inch. Weight, about 16 ounces. Fixed sights. Blued or nickel finish. Hard rubber stocks.

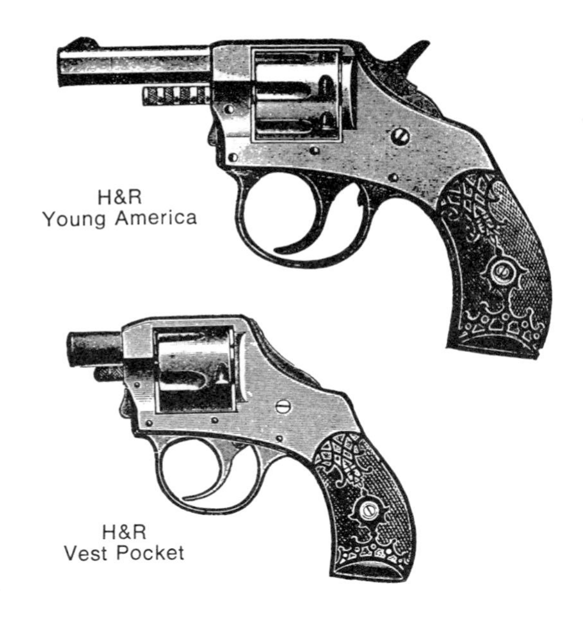

H&R
Young America

H&R
Vest Pocket

Harrington & Richardson Young America Double Action Revolver **$50**

Solid frame. Calibers: 22 Long, 32 S&W. 7-shot cylinder (22 Cal.), 5-shot (32 Cal.). Barrel lengths: 2, 4½ and 6-inch. Weight, about 9 ounces. Fixed sights. Blued or nickel finish. Hard rubber stocks.

Harrington & Richardson Vest Pocket Double Action Revolver **$50**

Solid frame. Spurless hammer. Calibers: 22 Rimfire, 32 S&W 7-shot cylinder, (22 cal.), 5-shot (32 cal.). 1⅛-inch barrel. Weight, about 9 ounces. Blued or nickel finish. Hard rubber stocks.

Harrington & Richardson Hunter Model Double Action Revolver **$60**

Solid frame. Caliber, 22 Long Rifle. 9-shot cylinder. 10-inch octagon barrel. Weight, 26 ounces. Fixed sights. Blued finish. Checkered Walnut stocks. Safety cylinder on later models. *Note:* An earlier "Hunter Model" was built on the smaller 7-shot frame.

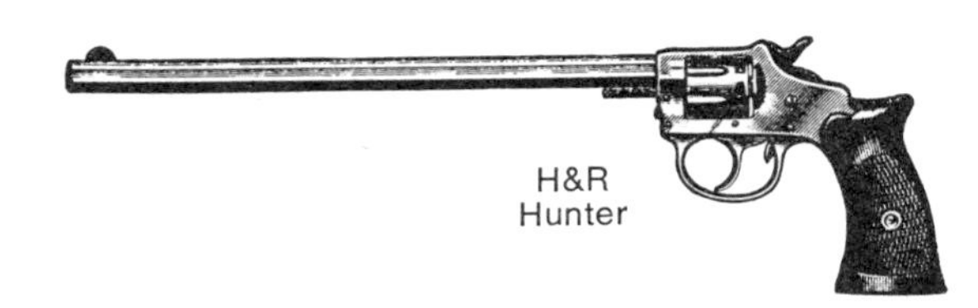

H&R
Hunter

Harrington & Richardson Trapper Model Double Action Revolver **$60**

Solid frame. Caliber, 22 Long Rifle. 7-shot cylinder. 6-inch octagon barrel. Weight, 12¼ ounces. Fixed sights. Blued finish. Checkered walnut stocks. Safety cylinder on later models.

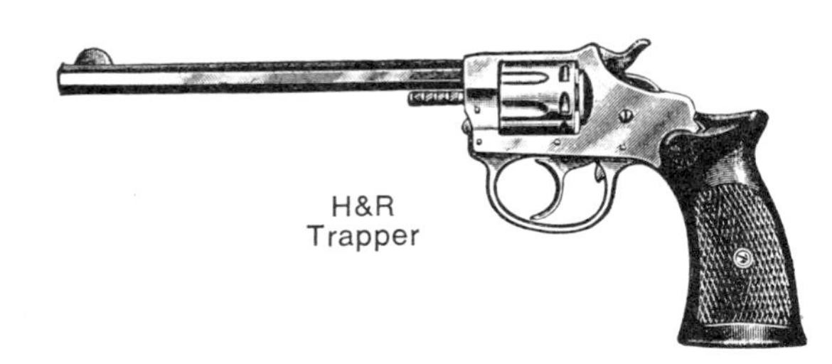

H&R
Trapper

Harrington & Richardson Model 922 Double Action Revolver **$60**

Solid frame. Caliber, 22 Long Rifle. 9-shot cylinder. Barrel lengths: 4 or 6-inch on late production, formerly available with 10-inch barrel. Weight, with 6″ bbl., 26 ounces. Fixed sights. Blued or chrome finish. Checkered walnut or Tenite stocks. Safety cylinder and round barrel on later models, earlier production had octagon barrel. Recent model incorporates a few changes such as redesigned hammer and push-pin extractor, Tenite stocks. *Note:* Model 923 is same except chrome finish. Discontinued in 1961.

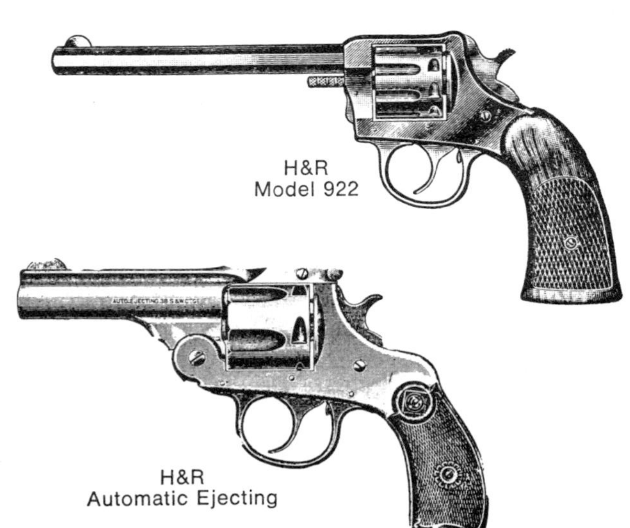

H&R
Model 922

H&R
Automatic Ejecting

Harrington & Richardson Model 922 Bantamweight .. **$60**

Same as standard Model 922 except has 2½-inch barrel, round butt stocks and weighs 20 ounces.

Harrington & Richardson Automatic Ejecting Double Action Revolver **$70**

Hinged frame. Calibers: 32 S&W Long, 38 S&W. 6-shot cylinder (32 cal.), 5-shot (38 cal.). Barrel lengths: 3¼, 4, 5 and 6-inch. Weights: about 16 ounces (32 cal.), 15 ounces (38 cal.). Fixed sights. Blued or nickel finish. Black hard rubber stocks.

Harrington & Richardson Premier Double Action Revolver **$50**

Small hinged frame. Calibers: 22 Long Rifle, 32 S&W 7-shot cylinder (22 cal.), 5-shot (32 cal.). Barrel lengths: 2, 3, 4, 5 and 6-inch. Weights: 13 ounces (22 cal.), 12 ounces (32 cal.). Fixed sights. Blued or nickel finish. Black hard rubber stocks. Discontinued 1941.

Harrington & Richardson Hammerless Double Action Revolver **$60**

Small hinged frame model. Calibers: 22 Long Rifle, 32 S&W. 7-shot cylinder (22 cal.), 5-shot (32 cal.). Barrel lengths: 2, 3, 4, 5 and 6-inch. Weight, about 13 ounces. Fixed sights. Blued or nickel finish. Hard rubber stocks.

Harrington & Richardson Hammerless Double Action Revolver **$60**

Large hinged frame model. Calibers: 32 S&W Long, 38 S&W. 6-shot cylinder (32 cal.), 5-shot (38 cal.). Barrel lengths: 3¼, 4, 5 and 6-inch. Weight, about 17 ounces. Fixed sights. Blued or nickel finish. Hard rubber stocks.

Harrington & Richardson Target Model Double Action Revolver **$60**

Small hinged frame. Calibers: 22 Long Rifle, 22 W.R.F. 7-shot cylinder. 6-inch barrel. Weight, 16 ounces. Fixed sights. Blued finish. Checkered walnut stocks.

Harrington & Richardson 22 Special Double Action Revolver **$70**

Heavy hinged frame. Calibers: 22 Long Rifle, 22 W.R.F. 9-shot cylinder. 6-inch barrel. Weight, 23 ounces. Fixed sights, front gold-plated. Blued finish. Checkered walnut stocks. Recessed safety cylinder on later models for high speed ammunition. Discontinued 1941.

Harrington & Richardson Expert Model Double Action Revolver **$70**

Same specifications as "22 Special" except has 10-inch barrel. Weight, 28 ounces.

Harrington & Richardson No. 199 Sportsman Single Action Revolver **$75**

Hinged frame. Caliber, 22 Long Rifle. 9-shot cylinder. 6-inch barrel. 11 inches overall. Weight, 30 ounces. Adjustable target sights. Blued finish. Checkered walnut stocks. Discontinued 1951.

Harrington & Richardson No. 999 Sportsman Double Action Revolver **$60**

Hinged frame. Calibers: 22 Long Rifle, 22 W.R.F. Same specifications as Sportsman Single Action. Still manufactured, 22 Long Rifle only, current model has redesigned hammer, ventilated-rib barrel.

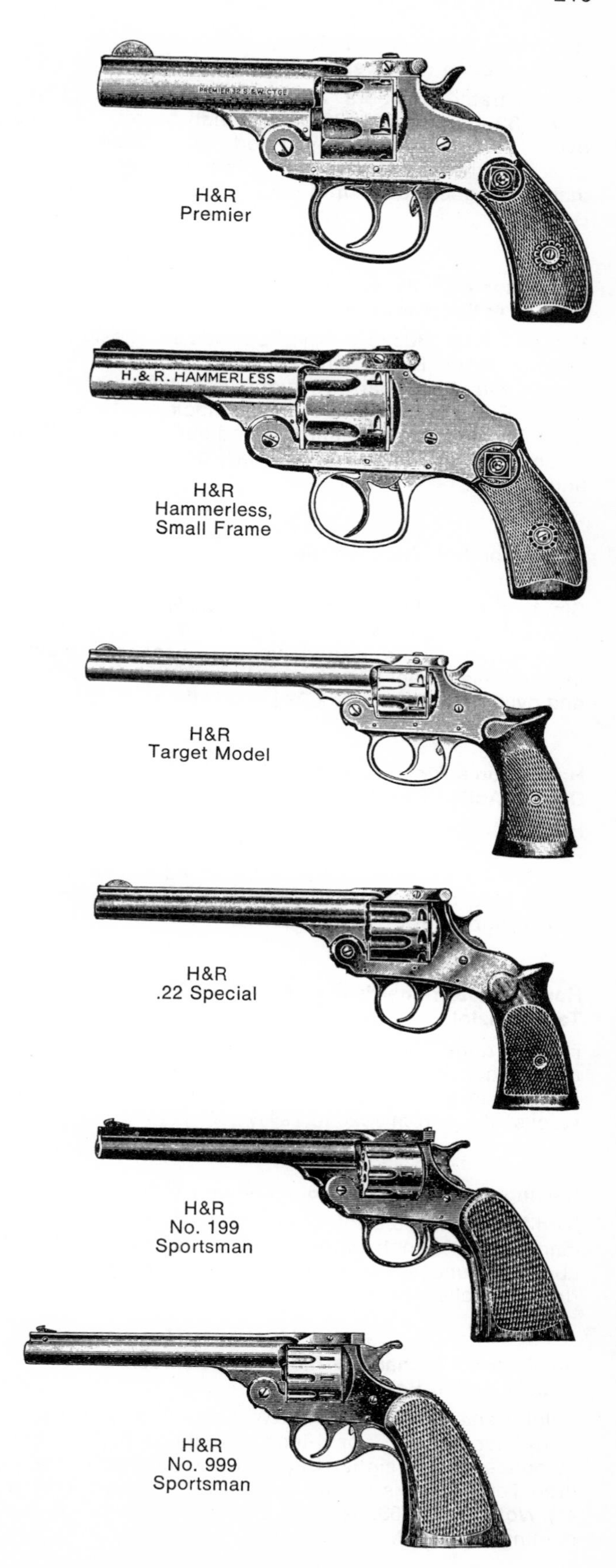

H&R Premier

H&R Hammerless, Small Frame

H&R Target Model

H&R .22 Special

H&R No. 199 Sportsman

H&R No. 999 Sportsman

Harrington & Richardson Bobby Double Action Revolver **$75**

Hinged frame. Calibers: 32 S&W, 38 S&W. 6-shot cylinder (32 cal.), 5-shot (38 cal.). 4-inch barrel. 9 inches overall. Weight, 23 ounces. Fixed sights. Blued finish. Checkered walnut stocks. *Note:* This revolver was originally designed and produced for use by London's Bobbies.

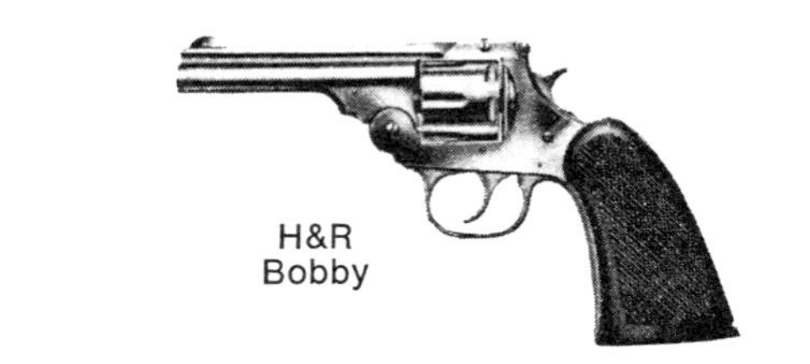
H&R
Bobby

Harrington & Richardson Defender 38 Double Action Revolver **$75**

Hinged frame. Based on the "Sportsman" design. Caliber: 38 S&W. Barrel lengths: 4 and 6-inch. 9 inches overall with 4-inch barrel. Weight, 25 ounces with 4-inch barrel. Fixed sights. Blued finish. Black plastic stocks. *Note:* This model was manufactured during World War II as an arm for plant guards, auxiliary police, etc. Discontinued 1946.

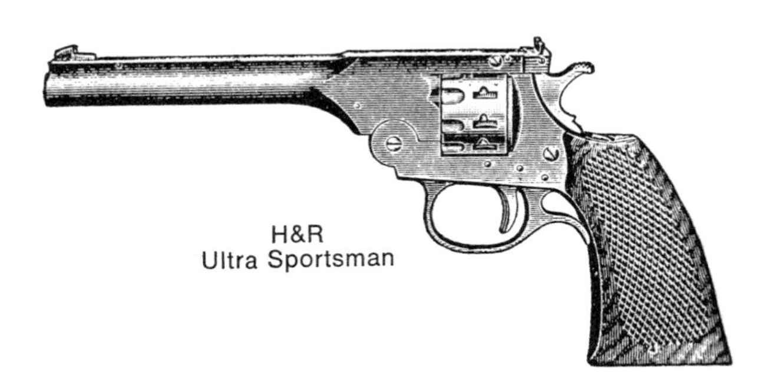
H&R
Ultra Sportsman

Harrington & Richardson Ultra Sportsman Revolver **$90**

Single action. Hinged frame. Caliber, 22 Long Rifle. 9-shot cylinder. 6-inch barrel. Weight, 30 ounces. Adjustable target sights. Blued finish. Checkered walnut stocks. This model has short action, wide hammer spur and cylinder is length of a 22 Long Rifle cartridge.

H&R
New Defender

Harrington & Richardson New Defender Double Action Revolver **$90**

Hinged frame. Caliber, 22 Long Rifle. 9-shot cylinder. 2-inch barrel. 6¼ inches overall. Weight, 23 ounces. Adjustable sights. Blued finish. Checkered walnut stocks, round butt. *Note:* Basically, this is the Sportsman D.A. with a short barrel.

Harrington & Richardson USRA Model Single Shot Target Pistol **$200**

Hinged frame. Caliber, 22 Long Rifle. Barrel lengths: 7, 8 and 10-inch. Weight, 31 ounces, with 10-inch barrel. Adjustable target sights Blued finish. Checkered walnut stocks. Made from 1928 to 1941.

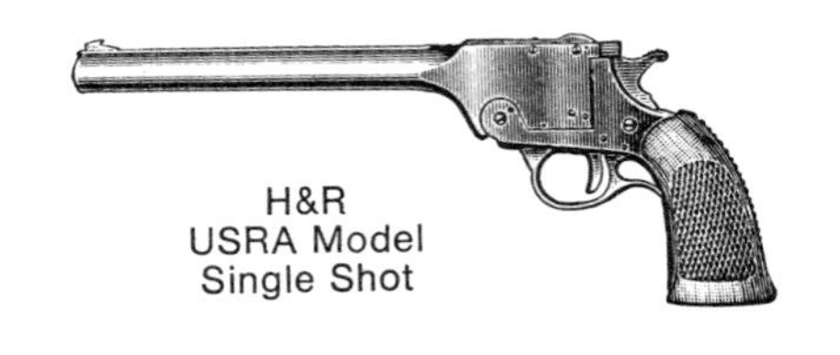
H&R
USRA Model
Single Shot

Harrington & Richardson Self Loading Pistol **$175**

Modified Webley & Scott design. Caliber, 32 Auto. 8-shot magazine. 3½-inch barrel. 6½ inches overall. Weight about 20 ounces. Fixed sights. Blued finish. Black hard rubber stocks. Also made in caliber 25 Auto.

Harrington & Richardson Model 632 Guardsman Double Action Revolver **$40**

Solid frame. Caliber, 32 S&W Long. 6-shot cylinder. Barrel lengths: 2½ or 4-inch. Weight, with 2½" bbl., 19 ounces. Fixed sights. Blued or chrome finish. Checkered Tenite stocks (round butt on 2½", square butt on 4"). *Note:* Model 633 is same except chrome finish. Discontinued in 1957.

H&R
Model 632

H&R Model 732

H&R Model 939

H&R Model 949

H&R Model 900

H&R Model 925

Harrington & Richardson Model 929 Side-Kick Double Action Revolver **$40**

Solid frame, swing-out cylinder. Caliber, 22 Long Rifle. 9-shot cylinder. Barrel lengths: 2½, 4, 6-inch. Weight, with 4″ bbl., 24-ounces. Fixed sights. Blued finish. Checkered plastic stocks. Made from 1956 to date.

Harrington & Richardson Model 622 Double Action Revolver **$35**

Solid frame. Caliber, 22 Short, Long, Long Rifle. 6-shot cylinder. Barrel lengths: 2½, 4, 6 inch. Weight, with 4″ bbl., 26 ounces. Fixed sights. Blued finish. Plastic stocks. Made from 1957 to date. *Note:* Model 623 (discontinued in 1963). is same except chrome finish.

Harrington & Richardson Model 732 Double Action Revolver **$40**

Solid frame, swing-out cylinder. Caliber, 32 S&W, 32 S&W Long. 6-shot cylinder. Barrel lengths: 2½, 4-inch. Weight, with 4″ bbl., 26 ounces. Fixed sights (windage adjustable rear on 4″ bbl. model). Blued finish. Plastic stocks. Made from 1958 to date. *Note:* Model 733 (2½″ bbl. only) is same except nickel finish.

Harrington & Richardson Model 939 Ultra Sidekick Double Action Revolver **$55**

Solid frame, swing-out cylinder. Safety lock. Caliber, 22 Short, Long, Long Rifle. 9-shot cylinder. 6-inch barrel with ventilated rib. Weight, 33 ounces. Adjustable rear sight, ramp front sight. Blued finish. Checkered walnut stocks. Made from 1958 to date.

Harrington & Richardson Model 949 Forty-Niner Double Action Revolver **$40**

Solid frame. Side loading and ejection. Caliber, 22 Short, Long, Long Rifle. 9-shot cylinder. 5½-inch barrel. Weight, 31 ounces. Adjustable rear sight, blade front sight. Blue or nickel finish. One-piece, Western-style walnut grip. Made from 1960 to date.

Harrington & Richardson Model 900 Double Action Revolver **$40**

Solid frame, snap-out cylinder. Caliber, 22 Short, Long, Long Rifle. 9-shot cylinder. Barrel lengths: 2½, 4, 6 inch. Weight, with 6″ bbl., 26 ounces Fixed sights. Blued finish. Blade Cycolac stocks. Made from 1962 to 1973. *Note:* Model 901 (discontinued in 1963) is the same except chrome-plated, has white Tenite stocks.

Harrington & Richardson Model 925 Defender Double Action Revolver **$50**

Hinged frame. Caliber, 38 S&W. 5-shot cylinder. 2½-inch barrel. Weight, 22 ounces. Adjustable rear sight, fixed front sight. Blued finish. One-piece wrap-around grip. Made from 1964 to date.

Hartford Arms & Equipment Co., Hartford, Connecticut

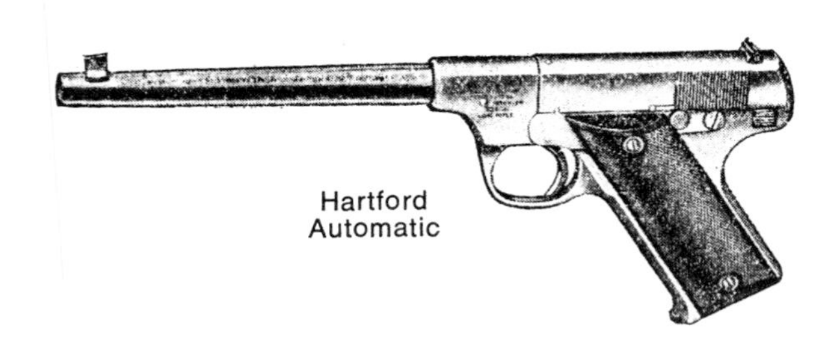
Hartford Automatic

Hartford Automatic Target Pistol $200

Caliber, 22 Long Rifle. 10-shot magazine. 6¾-inch barrel. 10¾ inches overall. Weight, 31 ounces. Target sights. Blued finish. Black rubber stocks. This arm closely resembles the early Colt Woodsman and Hi-Standard pistols. Made from 1929 to 1930.

Hartford Repeating Pistol $175

Same general design as the automatic pistol of this manufacture, but this model is a hand-operated repeating pistol on the order of the Fiala. Made from 1929 to 1930.

Hartford Single Shot Target Pistol $175

Similar in appearance to the Hartford Automatic. Caliber, 22 Long Rifle. 6¾-inch barrel. 10¾ inches overall. Weight, 38 ounces. Target sights. Mottled frame and slide, blued barrel. Black rubber or walnut stocks. Made from 1929 to 1930.

High Standard Mfg. Co., Hamden, Connecticut

Hi-Standard Model B Automatic Pistol $85

Hammerless. Caliber, 22 Long Rifle. 10-shot magazine. Barrel lengths: 4½ and 6¾-inch. 10¾ inches overall with 6¾-inch barrel. Weight, 33 ounces with 6¾-inch barrel. Fixed sights. Blued finish. Hard rubber stocks. The original Hi-Standard pistol introduced about 1930, discontinued 1942.

Hi-Standard Model SB Automatic Pistol $85

Same as Model B, except smoothbore, made for use with 22 Long Rifle Shot cartridges. 6¾-inch barrel only. Discontinued 1942.

Hi-Standard Model H-B Automatic Pistol $85

Same as Model B but with visible hammer, no thumb safety. Discontinued 1942.

Hi-Standard Model C Automatic Pistol $100

Same as Model B except chambered for 22 Short. Discontinued 1942.

Hi-Standard Model A Automatic Pistol $100

Hammerless. Caliber, 22 Long Rifle. 10-shot magazine. Barrel lengths: 4½ and 6¾-inch. 11½ inches overall with 6¾-inch barrel. Weight, 36 ounces with 6¾-inch barrel. Adjustable target sights. Blued finish. Checkered walnut stocks Made from 1936 to 1942.

Hi-Standard Model H-A Automatic Pistol $100

Same as Model A but with visible hammer, no thumb safety. Discontinued 1942.

Hi-Standard Model D Automatic Pistol $110

Same general specifications as Model A, but with heavier barrel. Weight, 40 ounces with 6¾-inch barrel. Discontinued in 1942.

Hi-Standard Model H-D Automatic Pistol $110

Same as Model D but with visible hammer, no thumb safety. Discontinued 1942.

Hi-Standard Model H-DM Automatic Pistol $125

Also called H-D Military. Same as Model H-D but with thumb safety. Made from 1946 to 1951.

Hi-Standard Model E Automatic Pistol $135

Same general specifications as Model A, but with extra heavy barrel and thumb rest stocks. Weight, 42 ounces with 6¾-inch barrel. Discontinued 1942.

Hi-Standard Model H-E Automatic Pistol $150

Same as Model E but with visible hammer, no thumb safety. Discontinued 1942.

Hi-Standard Model G-380 Automatic Pistol $175

Take down. Visible hammer. Thumb safety. Caliber, 380 Automatic. 6-shot magazine. 5-inch barrel. Weight: 40 ounces. Fixed sights. Blued finish. Checkered plastic stocks. Made from 1947 to 1950.

Hi-Standard Model G-B Automatic Pistol

Takedown. Hammerless. Interchangeable barrels. Caliber, 22 Long Rifle. 10-shot magazine. Barrel lengths: 4½ and 6¾-inch. 10¾ inches overall with 6¾-inch barrel. Weight, 36 ounces with 6¾-inch barrel. Fixed sights. Blued finish. Checkered plastic stocks. Made from 1949 to 1951.
With one barrel . . . . $ 85
With both barrels $100

Hi-Standard Model G-D Automatic Pistol

Takedown. Hammerless. Interchangeable barrels. Caliber, 22 Long Rifle. 10-shot magazine. Barrel lengths: 4½ and 6¾-inch. 11½ inches overall with 6¾-inch barrel. Weight, 41 ounces with 6¾-inch barrel. Target sights. Blued finish. Checkered walnut stocks. Made from 1949 to 1951.
With one barrel $110
With both barrels $125

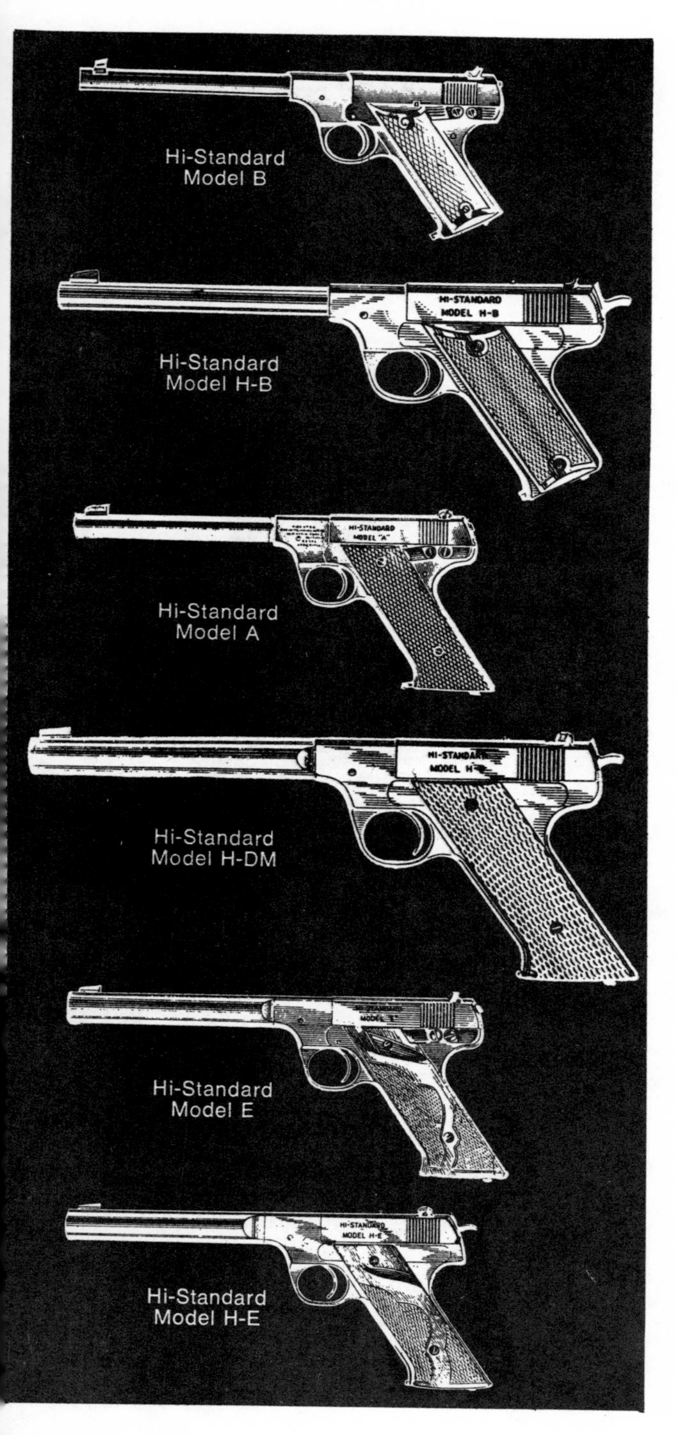

Hi-Standard Model B

Hi-Standard Model H-B

Hi-Standard Model A

Hi-Standard Model H-DM

Hi-Standard Model E

Hi-Standard Model H-E

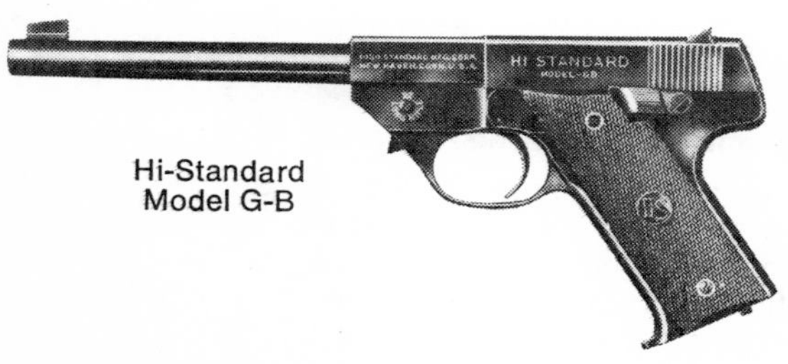

Hi-Standard Model G-B

Hi-Standard Model G-E Automatic Pistol

Same general specifications as Model G-D, but with extra heavy barrel and thumb-rest stocks. Weight, 44 ounces with 6¾-inch barrel. Made from 1949 to 1951.

With one barrel **$135**
With both barrels **$155**

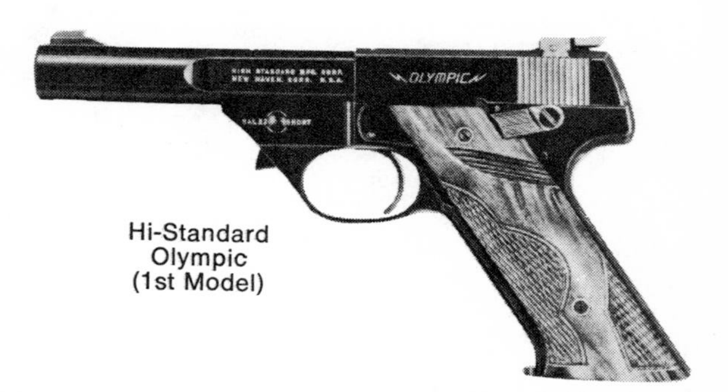

Hi-Standard Olympic (1st Model)

Hi-Standard Olympic Automatic Pistol—First Model

Same general specifications as Model G-E, but chambered for 22 Short, has light alloy slide. Made from 1950 to 1951.

With one barrel **$200**
With both barrels **$225**

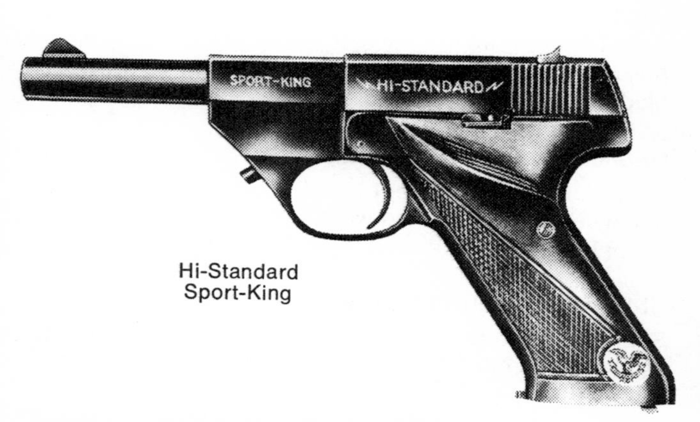

Hi-Standard Sport-King

Hi-Standard Sport-King Automatic Pistol

Takedown. Hammerless. Interchangeable barrels. Caliber, 22 Long Rifle. 10-shot magazine. Barrel lengths: 4½ and 6¾-inch. 11½ inches overall, with 6¾-inch barrel. Weight, 39 ounces with 6¾-inch barrel. Fixed sights. Blued finish. Checkered plastic thumb-rest stocks. Made from 1951 to 1958.

With one barrel **$75**
With both barrels **$90**

Hi-Standard Flite-King Automatic Pistol

Same general specifications as Sport-King, except caliber 22 short, has aluminum alloy frame and slide, weighs 26 ounces with 6½″ bbl. Made from 1953 to 1958.

With one barrel **$75**
With both barrels **$90**

Hi-Standard Lightweight Sport-King

Same as standard Sport-King except has forged aluminum alloy frame, weighs 30 ounces with 6¾″ barrel. Made from 1954 to 1965.
With one barrel **$75**
With both barrels **$90**

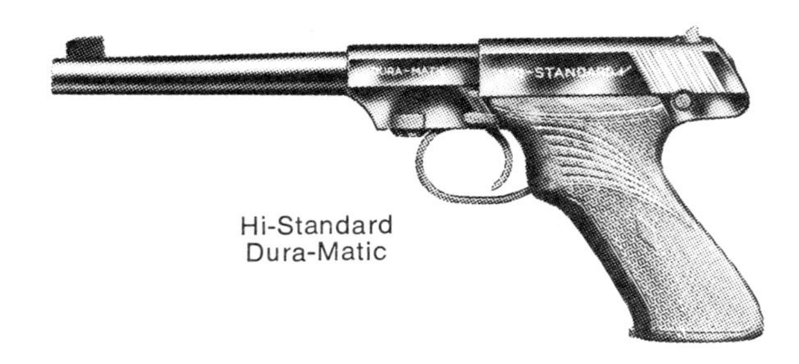

Hi-Standard Dura-Matic

Hi-Standard Dura-Matic Automatic Pistol $55

Takedown. Caliber, 22 Long Rifle. 10-shot magazine. Barrels. 4½ or 6½-inch, interchangeable. Overall length, with 6½″ bbl., 10⅞ inches. Weight, with 6½″ bbl., 35 ounces. Fixed sights. Blued finish. Checkered grips. Made from 1955 to 1969.

Hi-Standard Sentinel Double Action Revolver $55

Solid frame, swing-out cylinder. Caliber, 22 Long Rifle. 9-shot cylinder. Barrels: 3, 4 or 6-inch. Overall length, with 4″ bbl., 9 inches. Weight, with 4″ bbl., 19 ounces. Fixed sights. Blued or nickel finish. Checkered grips. Made from 1955 to 1956.

Hi-Standard Sentinel Imperial $60

Same as Sentinel, except has onyx-black or nickel finish, two-piece checkered walnut grips, ramp front sight. Made from 1962 to 1965.

Hi-Standard Sentinel Deluxe $60

Same as Sentinel, except 4″ and 6″ barrels only; has wide trigger, movable rear sight, two-piece square-butt grips. Made from 1957 to 1974.

Hi-Standard Sentinel Snub $60

Same as Sentinel Deluxe, except 2⅜″ barrel (7¼″ overall, weight 15 oz.), checkered birdshead-type grips. Made from 1957 to 1974.

Hi-Standard Double-Nine Double Action Revolver . . $60

Western style version of Sentinel Aluminum frame. Blued or nickel finish with simulated ivory, ebony or stag grips. 5½-inch barrel. 11 inches overall. Weight, 27¼ ounces. Made from 1959 to 1971.

Hi-Standard Posse $60

Similar to Double-Nine, except 3½-inch barrel (9″ overall, weight 23¼ ounces), blued finish, brass-grip frame and trigger guard, walnut grips. Made from 1961 to 1966.

Hi-Standard Sentinel

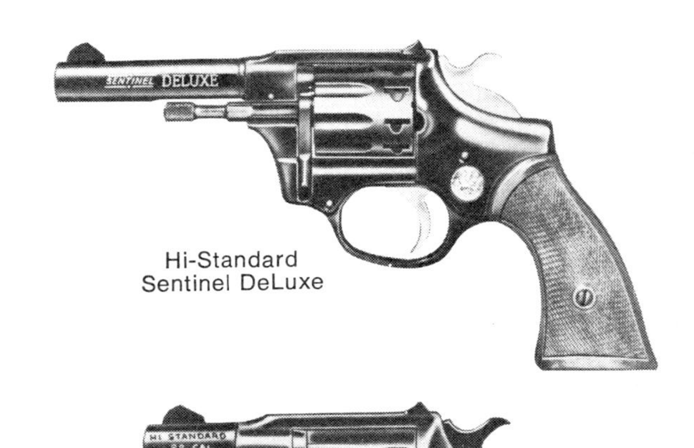

Hi-Standard Sentinel DeLuxe

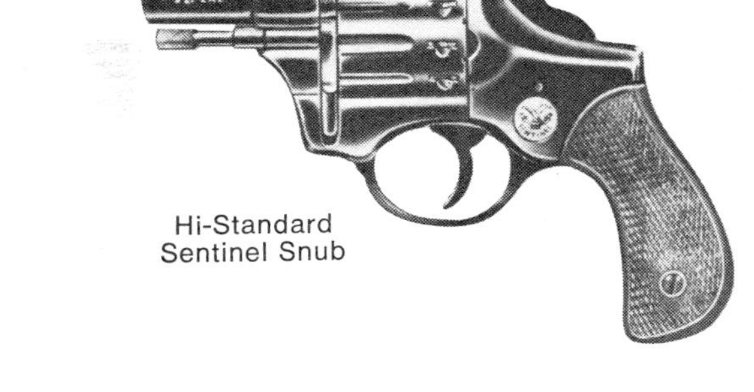

Hi-Standard Sentinel Snub

Hi-Standard Natchez $60

Similar to Double-Nine, except 4½-inch barrel (10″ overall, weight 25¼ ounces), blued finish, simulated ivory birdshead grips. Made from 1961 to 1966.

Hi-Standard Longhorn

Similar to Double-Nine. Aluminum frame. Longhorn hammer spur. Blued finish 4½-inch barrel with simulated pearl grips; 5½-inch, simulated stag grips; 9½-inch walnut grips. Latter model made from 1960 to 1971 others made from 1961 to 1966.
With 4½ or 5½ inch barrel **$6**
With 9½ inch barrel **$7**

Hi-Standard Field-King Automatic Pistol

Same general specifications as Sport-King, but with heavier barrel and target sights. Late model 6¾-inch barrels have recoil stabilizer feature. Weight, 43 ounces with 6¾-inch barrel. Made from 1951 to 1958.
With one barrel **$8**
With both barrels **$9**

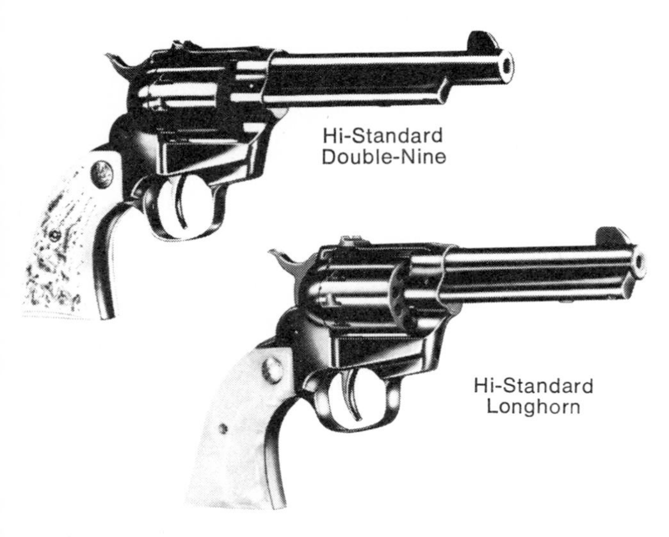

Hi-Standard Double-Nine

Hi-Standard Longhorn

Hi-Standard Supermatic Automatic Pistol

Takedown. Hammerless. Interchangeable barrels. Caliber, 22 Long Rifle. 10 shot magazine. Barrel lengths: 4½ and 6¾-inch. Late model 6¾-inch barrels have recoil stabilizer feature. Weight, with 6¾″ bbl., 43 ounces. 11½ inches overall with 6¾″ bbl. Target sights. Elevated serrated rib between sights Adjustable barrel weights add 2 or 3 ounces. Blued finish. Checkered plastic thumbrest stocks. Made from 1951 to 1958.
With one barrel **$110**
With both barrels **$125**

Hi-Standard Olympic Automatic Pistol—Second Model

Same general specifications as Supermatic, but chambered for 22 Short, has light alloy slide. Weight, 39 ounces with 6¾-inch barrel. Made from 1951 to 1958.
With one barrel **$140**
With both barrels **$160**

Hi-Standard Sport-King Automatic Pistol
Second Model **$55**

All-steel. Caliber, 22 Long Rifle. 10-shot magazine. Barrels: 4½ or 6¾ inch, interchangeable. 11¼ inches overall with 6¾″ bbl. Weight, with 6¾″ bbl., 42 ounces. Fixed sights. Blued finish. Checkered grips Made from 1958 to 1970.

Hi-Standard Flite-King Automatic Pistol
Second Model **$65**

Same as Sport-King Second Model, except caliber 22 Short and weight 2 ounces lighter. Made from 1958 to 1966.

Hi-Standard Supermatic Tournament
Automatic Pistol **$110**

Takedown. Caliber, 22 Long Rifle. 10-shot magazine. Barrels (interchangeable): 5½-inch bull, 6¾-inch straight notched and drilled for stabilizer and weights. 10 inches overall with 5½″ bbl. Weight, with 5½″ bbl., 44 ounces. Click adjustable rear sight, undercut ramp front sight. Blued finish. Checkered grips. Made from 1958 to 1963.

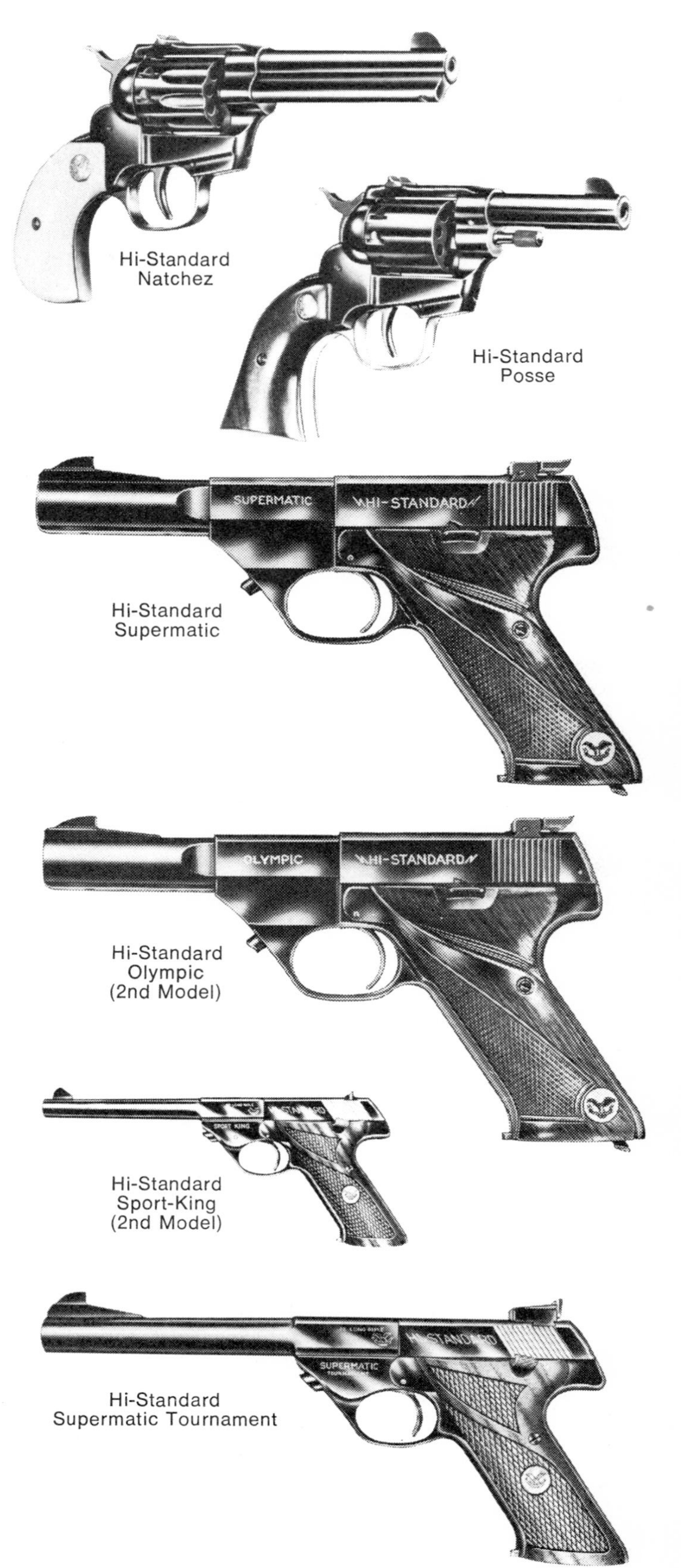

Hi-Standard Natchez

Hi-Standard Posse

Hi-Standard Supermatic

Hi-Standard Olympic (2nd Model)

Hi-Standard Sport-King (2nd Model)

Hi-Standard Supermatic Tournament

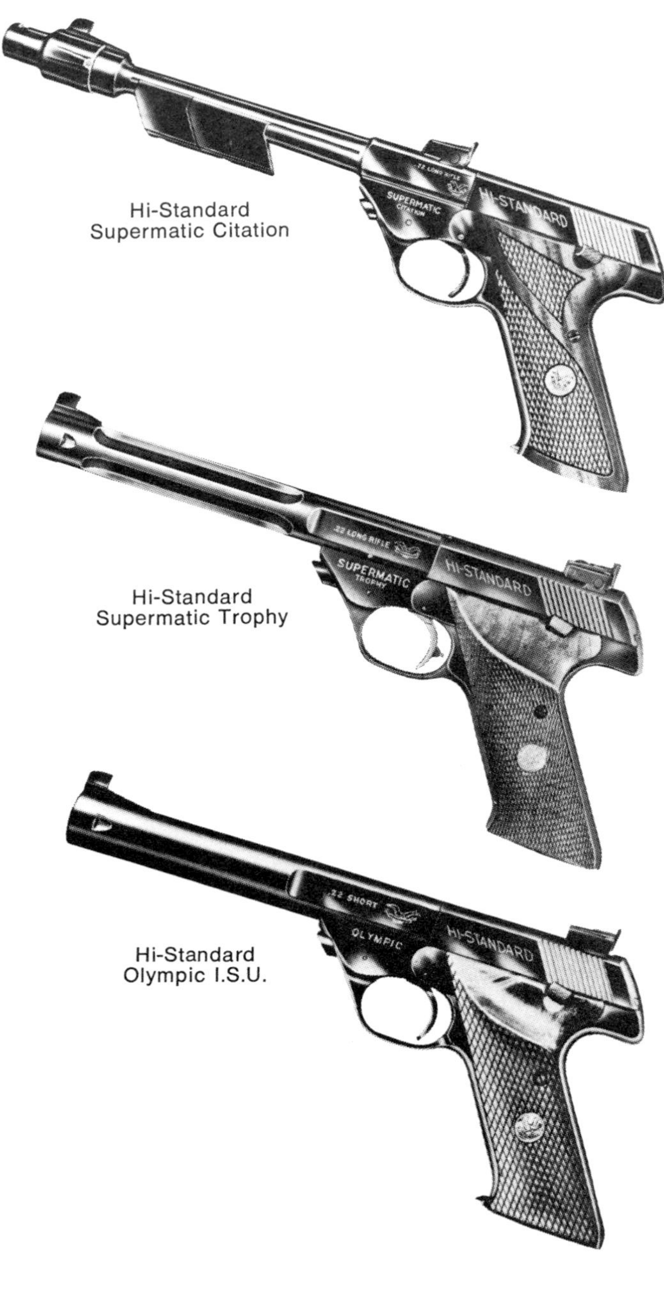

Hi-Standard
Supermatic Citation

Hi-Standard
Supermatic Trophy

Hi-Standard
Olympic I.S.U.

Hi-Standard
Derringer

Hi-Standard Supermatic Citation

Same as Supermatic Tournament, except: barrels—6¾, 8, 10 inch—tapered and with stabilizer and two removable weights; also furnished with Tournament's 5½″ bull barrel; adjustable trigger pull; recoil-proof click adjustable rear sight; (barrel-mounted on 8″ and 10″ barrels) checkered walnut thumb-rest grips on bull barrel Model. Made from 1958 to 1966.

With bull barrel $115
With tapered barrel $120

Hi-Standard Supermatic Trophy $130

Same as Supermatic Citation, except: 5½″ bull barrel or 7¼″ fluted barrel with detachable stabilizer and weights; extra magazine; high-lustre blued finish; checkered walnut thumb-rest grips. Made from 1963 to 1966.

Hi-Standard Olympic I.S.U. $135

Same as Supermatic Citation, except: caliber 22 Short; 5½″ bull barrel, 6¾″ and 8″ tapered barrels with stabilizer, detachable weights. Bull barrel model made from 1963 to 1966; 8″ barrel made from 1958 to 1964; 6¾″ barrel made from 1958 to date.

Hi-Standard Derringer

Hammerless, double action, double barrel (over/under). Calibers. 22 Short, Long, Long Rifle; 22 Magnum Rimfire. 2-shot. 3½-inch barrels. 5 inches overall. Weight, 11 ounces. **Standard** model has blued or nickel finish, plastic grips; presentation model is gold plated, comes in walnut case. Standard model made from 1963 (22 S-L-LR) and 1964 (22 MRF) to date; gold model made from 1965 to 1966.

Gold presentation, one derringer $105
Gold presentation, matched pair, consecutive
numbers $235
Standard model . . . .$ 50

Hopkins & Allen Arms Co., Norwich, Connecticut

Hopkins & Allen Revolvers

See listings of comparable Harrington & Richardson and Iver Johnson models for values.

Iver Johnson's Arms & Cycle Works, Fitchburg, Massachusetts

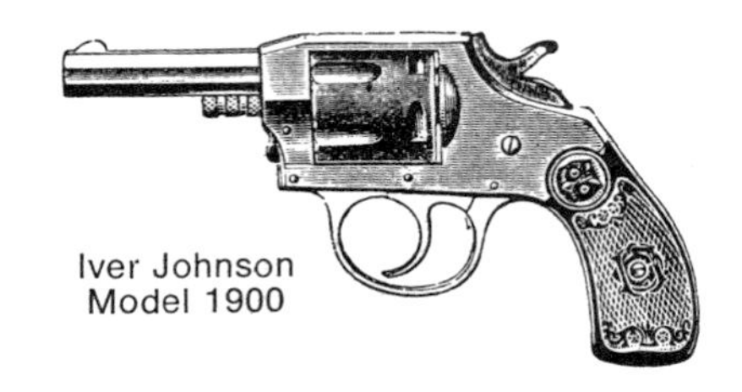

Iver Johnson
Model 1900

Iver Johnson Model 1900 Double Action Revolver . . $40

Solid frame. Calibers: 22 R. F., 32 S&W, 32 S&W Long, 38 S&W. 7-shot cylinder (22 cal.), 6-shot (32 S&W), 5-shot (32 S&W Long, 38 S&W). Barrel lengths: 2½, 4½ and 6-inch. Weight, 12 ounces (32 S&W with 2½-inch barrel). Fixed sights. Blued or nickel finish. Hard rubber stocks. Made from 1900 to 1947.

Iver Johnson Model 1900 Target Double Action Revolver $50

Solid frame. Caliber, 22 Long Rifle, 7-shot cylinder. Barrel lengths: 6 and 9½-inch. Fixed sights. Blued finish. Checkered walnut stocks. This earlier model does not have counterbored chambers as in the Target Sealed 8. Made from 1925 to 1942.

Iver Johnson Target Sealed 8

Iver Johnson Target Sealed 8 Double Action Revolver $60

Solid frame. Caliber, 22 Long Rifle. 8-shot cylinder. Barrel lengths: 6 and 10-inch. 10¾ inch overall, with 6-inch barrel. Weight, 24 ounces with 6-inch barrel. Fixed sights. Blued finish. Checkered walnut stocks. Made from 1931 to 1957.

Iver Johnson Target 9 Shot Double Action Revolver $50

Same as Target Sealed 8 except this model has nine chambers, not counterbored. Made from 1929 to 1946.

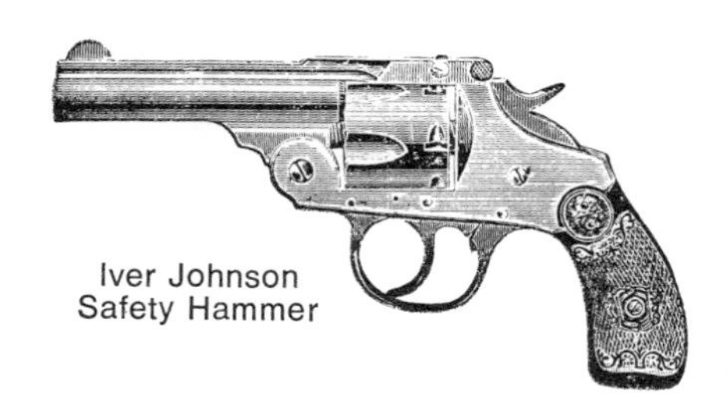

Iver Johnson Safety Hammer

Iver Johnson Safety Hammer Double Action Revolver $50

Hinged frame. Calibers: 22 Long Rifle, 32 S&W, 32 S&W Long, 38 S&W. 7-shot cylinder (22 cal.), 6-shot (32 S&W Long), 5-shot (32 S&W, 38 S&W). Barrel lengths: 2, 3, 3¼, 4, 5 and 6-inch. Weights with 4-inch barrel: 15 ounces (22, 32 S&W), 19½ ounces (32 S&W Long), 19 ounces (38 S&W). Fixed sights. Blued or nickel finish. Hard rubber stocks, round butt; square butt rubber and walnut stocks available. *Note:* 32 S&W Long and 38 S&W models built on heavy frame. Made from 1892 to 1950.

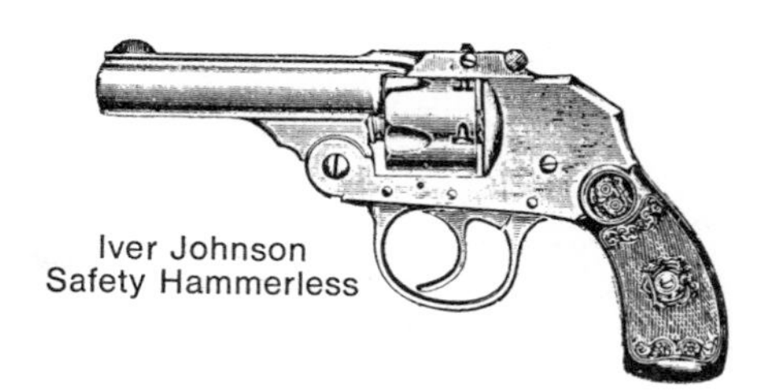

Iver Johnson Safety Hammerless

Iver Johnson Safety Hammerless Double Action Revolver $60

Hinged frame. Calibers: 22 Long Rifle, 32 S&W, 32 S&W Long, 38 S&W. 7-shot cylinder (22 cal.), 6-shot (32 S&W Long), 5-shot (32 S&W, 38 S&W). Barrel lengths: 2, 3, 3¼, 4, 5 and 6-inch. Weights with 4-inch barrel: 15 ounces (22, 32 S&W), 20½ ounces (32 S&W Long), 20 ounces (38 S&W). Fixed sights. Blued or nickel finish. Hard rubber stocks, round butt. Square butt rubber and walnut stocks available. *Note:* 32 S&W Long & 38 S&W models built on heavy frame. Made from 1895 to 1950.

Iver Johnson 22 Supershot Double Action Revolver $50

Hinged frame. Caliber, 22 Long Rifle. 7-shot cylinder. 6-inch barrel. Fixed sights. Blued finish. Checkered walnut stocks. This earlier model does not have counterbored chambers as in the Supershot Sealed 8. Made from 1929 to 1949.

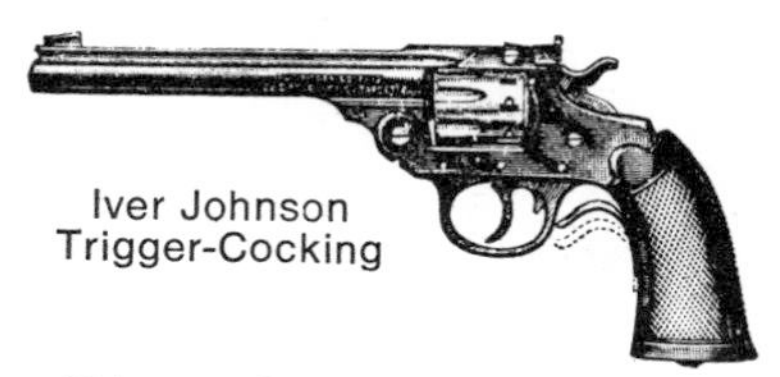

Iver Johnson Trigger-Cocking

Iver Johnson Trigger-Cocking Single Action Target Revolver $70

Hinged frame. First pull on trigger cocks hammer, second pull releases hammer. Caliber, 22 Long Rifle. 8-shot cylinder, counterbored chambers. 6-inch barrel. 10¾ inches overall. Weight, 24 ounces. Adjustable target sights. Blued finish. Checkered walnut stocks. Made from 1940 to 1947.

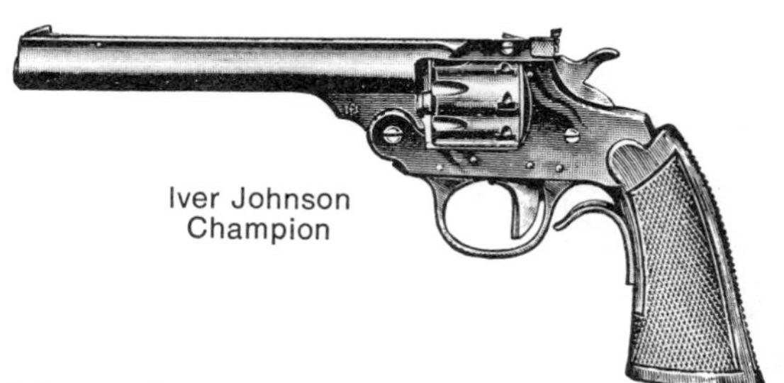

Iver Johnson Champion

Iver Johnson Champion 22 Target Single Action Revolver $70

Hinged frame. Caliber, 22 Long Rifle. 8-shot cylinder. Counterbored chambers as in Sealed 8 models. 6-inch barrel. 10¾ inches overall. Weight, 28 ounces. Adjustable target sights. Blued finish. Checkered walnut stocks, adjustable finger rest. Made from 1938 to 1948.

Iver Johnson Supershot Sealed 8

Iver Johnson Supershot Sealed Eight Double Action Revolver **$75**

Hinged frame. Caliber, 22 Long Rifle. 8-shot cylinder. 6-inch barrel. 10¾ inches overall. Weight, 24 ounces. Adjustable target sights. Blued finish. Checkered walnut stocks. Post-war model does not have adjustable finger rest found on earlier version. Made from 1931 to 1957.

Iver Johnson Supershot 9-Shot Double Action Revolver **$60**

Same as Supershot Sealed Eight except this model has nine chambers, not counterbored. Made from 1929 to 1949.

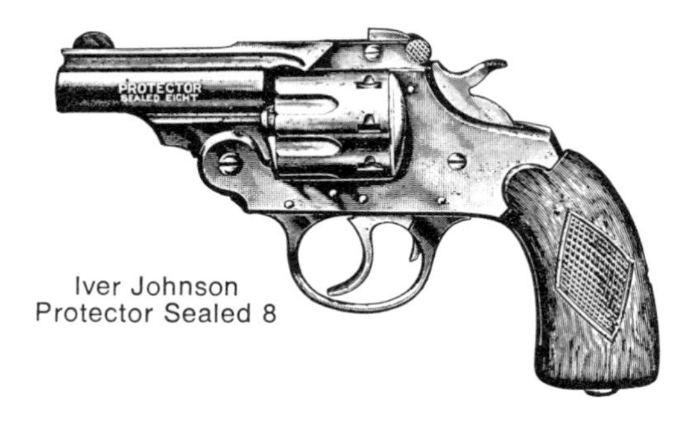

Iver Johnson Protector Sealed 8

Iver Johnson Protector Sealed Eight Double Action Revolver **$80**

Hinged frame. Caliber, 22 Long Rifle. 8-shot cylinder. 2½-inch barrel. 7¼ inches overall. Weight, 20 ounces. Fixed sights. Blued finish. Checkered walnut stocks. Made from 1933 to 1949.

Iver Johnson Supershot Model 844 Double Action Revolver **$60**

Hinged frame. Caliber, 22 Long Rifle. 8-shot cylinder. Barrel lengths: 4½ or 6-inch. Overall length, with 4½" bbl., 9¼ inches. Weight, with 4½" bbl., 27 ounces. Adjustable sights. Blued finish. Checkered walnut one-piece grip. Made from 1955 to 1956.

Iver Johnson Armsworth Model 855 Single Action Revolver **$70**

Hinged frame. Caliber, 22 Long Rifle. 8-shot cylinder. Barrel length, 6-inch. Overall length, 10¾ inches. Weight, 30 ounces. Adjustable sights. Blued finish. Checkered walnut one-piece grip. Adjustable finger rest. Made from 1955 to 1957.

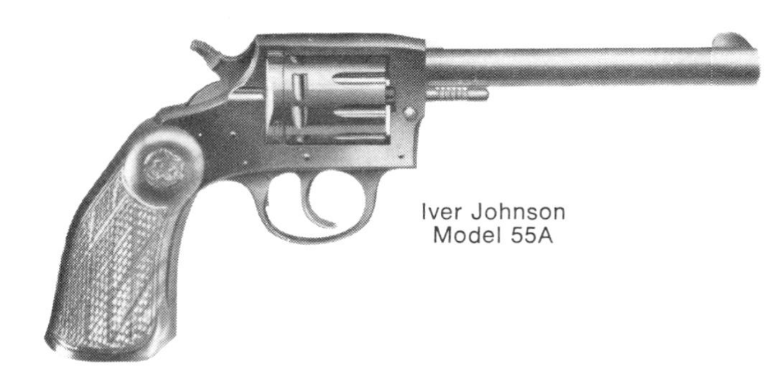
Iver Johnson Model 55A

Iver Johnson Model 55A Target Double Action Revolver **$35**

Solid frame. Caliber, 22 Short, Long, Long Rifle. 8-shot cylinder. Barrel lengths: 4½, 6 inch. 10¾ inches overall (6" bbl.). Weight. 30½ ounces (6" bbl.). Fixed sights. Blued finish. Walnut stocks. Made from 1955 to date. *Note:* Original model designation was 55, changed to 55A when loading gate was added in 1961.

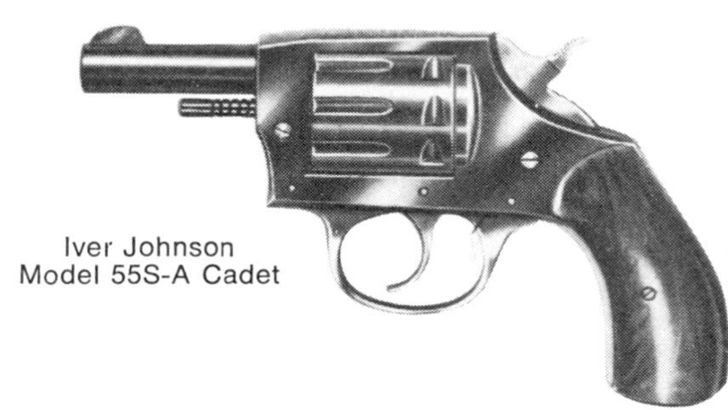
Iver Johnson Model 55S-A Cadet

Iver Johnson Model 55S-A Cadet Double Action Revolver **$35**

Solid frame. Calibers: 22 Short, Long, Long Rifle; 32 S&W; 38 S&W. 8-shot cylinder in 22; 5-shot in 32 and 38. 2½-inch barrel. 7 inches overall. Weight, 24 ounces. Fixed sights. Blued finish. Small plastic grip. Made from 1955 to date. *Note:* Original model designation was 55S, changed to 55S-A when loading gate was added in 1961.

Iver Johnson Model 57A Target

Iver Johnson Model 57A Target Double Action Revolver **$38**

Solid frame. Caliber, 22 Short, Long, Long Rifle. 8-shot cylinder. Barrel lengths: 4½, 6 inch. 10¾ inches overall (6" bbl.). Weight, 30½ ounces (6" bbl.). Adjustable sights. Blued finish. Walnut stocks. Made from 1956 to date. *Note:* Original model designation was 57, changed to 57A when loading gate was added in 1961.

Iver Johnson
Model 66 Trailsman

Iver Johnson Model 66 Trailsman
Double Action Revolver **$40**

Hinged frame. Rebounding hammer. Caliber, 22 Short, Long, Long Rifle. 8-shot cylinder. 6-inch barrel. 11 inches overall. Weight, 34 ounces. Adjustable sights. Blued finish. Walnut stocks. Made from 1958 to date.

Iver Johnson
Model 50A Sidewinder

Iver Johnson Model 50A Sidewinder
Double Action Revolver **$35**

Solid frame. Frontier style. Caliber, 22 Short, Long, Long Rifle. 8-shot cylinder. 6-inch barrel. 11¼ inches overall. Weight, 31 ounces. Fixed sights. Blued finish. "Staghorn" plastic stocks. Made from 1961 to date.

Iver Johnson
Model 67 Viking

Iver Johnson Model 67 Viking
Double Action Revolver **$45**

Hinged frame. Caliber, 22 Short, Long, Long Rifle. 8-shot cylinder. Barrel lengths: 4½ and 6-inch. 11 inches overall with 6-inch barrel. Weight, with 6-inch barrel, 34 ounces. Adjustable sights. Walnut stocks with thumb rest. Made from 1964 to date.

Iver Johnson
Model 67S Viking Snub

Iver Johnson Model 67S Viking Snub
Double Action Revolver **$45**

Hinged frame. Calibers: 22 Short, Long, Long Rifle; 32 S&W Short and Long; 38 S&W. 8-shot cylinder in 22; 5-shot in 32 and 38 calibers. 2¾-inch barrel. Weight, 25 ounces. Adjustable sights. Tenite grips. Made from 1964 to date.

Japanese Military Pistols manufactured by Government plant at Tokyo, Japan

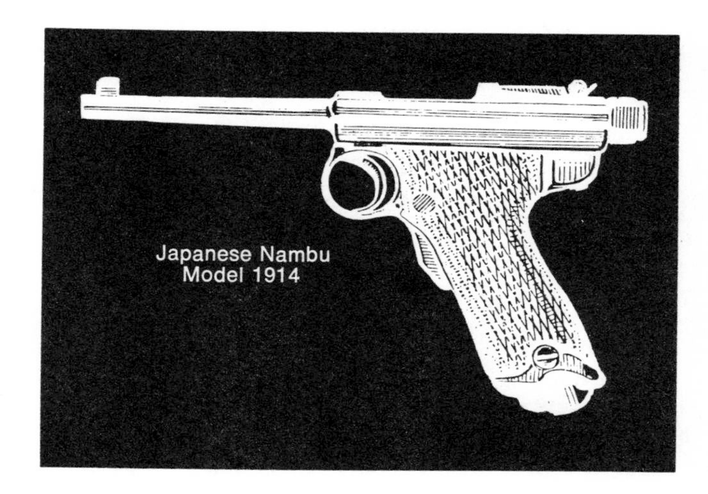

Japanese Nambu
Model 1914

Japanese Nambu Model 1914 Automatic Pistol . . . **$125**

Original Japanese service pistol, resembles Luger in appearance and Glisenti in operation. Caliber, 8mm Nambu. 7-shot magazine, 4½-inch barrel. 9 inches overall. Weight, about 30 ounces. Fixed front sight, adjustable rear sight. Blued finish. Checkered wood stocks. Made from 1914 to 1925.

Japanese Model 14 (1925) Automatic Pistol **$100**

Modification of the Nambu Model 1914, changes chiefly intended to simply mass production. Either standard round trigger guard or oversize guard to permit firing while wearing glove. Caliber, 8mm Nambu. 8-shot magazine. 4¾-inch barrel. 9 inches overall. Weight, about 29 ounces. Fixed sights. Blued finish. Grooved wood stocks. Introduced 1925, manufactured through World War II.

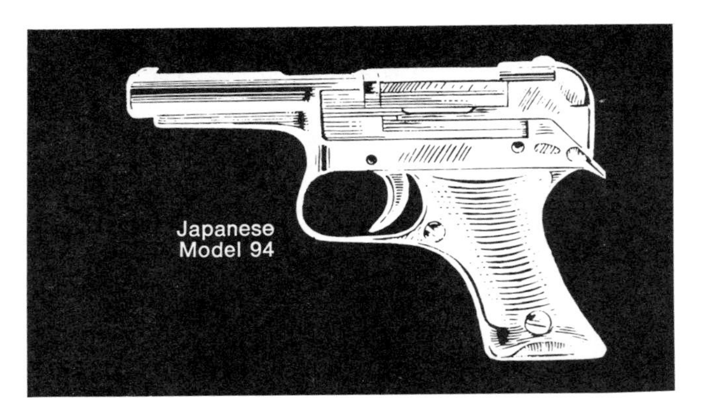
Japanese Model 94

Japanese Model 94 (1934) Automatic Pistol $125

This weapon is of extremely poor design and construction; the sear is exposed on the left side and the pistol can be fired by pressure on this part. Caliber, 8mm Nambu. 6-shot magazine. 3⅛-inch barrel. 7⅛ inches overall. Weight, about 27 ounces. Fixed sights. Blued finish. Hard rubber or wood stocks. Introduced in 1934, principally for export to Latin American countries. Production was continued through World War II.

Lahti Pistols manufactured by Husqvarna Vapenfabriks A. B. in Sweden, Valtion Kivaar Tedhas ("VKT") in Finland

Lahti, Swedish Model

Lahti Automatic Pistol

Caliber, 9mm Luger, 8-shot magazine. 4¾-inch barrel. Weight, about 46 ounces. Fixed sights. Blued finish. Plastic stocks. Specifications given are those of the Swedish Model 40 but also apply in general to the Finnish Model L-35 which differs only slightly. A considerable number of Swedish "Lahti" pistols were imported and sold in the U.S. a few years ago; the Finnish Model, which is somewhat better made, is a rather rare modern pistol.
Finnish model **$400**
Swedish model **$150**

Le Francais Pistols manufactured by Societe Francaise d'Armes et Cycles de St. Etienne, France

Le Francais Policeman Model Automatic Pistol $70

Double-action. Hinged barrel. Caliber, 25 Automatic (6.35mm). 7-shot magazine. 3½-inch barrel. 6 inches overall. Weight, about 12 ounces. Fixed sights. Blued finish. Hard rubber stocks. Introduced prior to World War I.

Le Francais Staff Officer Model Automatic Pistol . . . $70

Caliber, 25 Automatic. Similar to the "Policeman" Model except does not have cocking-piece head, barrel is about an inch shorter and weight is an ounce less.

Le Francais Army Model Automatic Pistol $70

Similar in operation to the Le Francais 25 Automatics. Caliber, 9mm Browning Long. 8-shot magazine, 5-inch barrel. 7¾ inches overall. Weight, about 34 ounces. Fixed sights. Blued finish. Checkered walnut stocks. First manufactured about 1928.

Aktien-Gesellschaft "Lignose" Abteilung, Suhl, Germany

**Lignose Einhand Model 2A
Pocket Automatic Pistol $100**

As the name implies, this pistol is designed for one-hand operation; pressure on a "trigger" at the front of the guard retracts the slide. Caliber, 25 Automatic (6.35mm). 6-shot magazine. 2-inch barrel. 4¾ inches overall. Weight, about 14 ounces. Blued finish. Hard rubber stocks.

Lignose Einhand Model 3A

**Lignose Einhand Model 3A
Pocket Automatic Pistol $100**

Same as the Model 2A except has longer grip, 9-shot magazine, weighs about 16 ounces.

Lignose Model 2 Pocket Automatic Pistol $60

Conventional Browning type. Same general specifications as Model 2A "Einhand" but lacks the one-hand operation feature. Early models marked "Bergmann" after inventor Theodore Bergmann.

Llama Pistols manufactured by Gabilondo y Cia., Vitoria, Spain

Llama Model IIIA Automatic Pistol $85

Caliber, .380 Automatic. 7-shot magazine. 3$^{11}/_{16}$-inch barrel. 6½ inches overall. Weight, 23 ounces. Adjustable target sights. Blued finish. Plastic grips. Made from 1951 to date.

Llama Model IIIA

Llama Model XA Automatic Pistol $85

Same as Model IIIA except caliber .32 Automatic, 8-shot magazine.

Llama Model XV Automatic Pistol $85

Same as Model XA except caliber .22 Long Rifle.

Llama Model VIII

Llama Model VIII Automatic Pistol $105

Caliber, .38 Super. 9-shot magazine. 5-inch barrel. 8½ inches overall. Weight, 40 ounces. Fixed sights. Blued finish. Checkered walnut grips. Made from 1952 to date.

Llama Model IXA Automatic Pistol $105

Same as Model VIII except caliber .45 Automatic, 7-shot magazine.

Llama Model XI

Llama Model XI Automatic Pistol $105

Caliber, 9mm Luger. 8-shot magazine. 4⅞-inch barrel. 8 inches overall. Weight, 34 ounces. Fixed sights. Blued finish. Plastic grips. Made from 1951 to 1975.

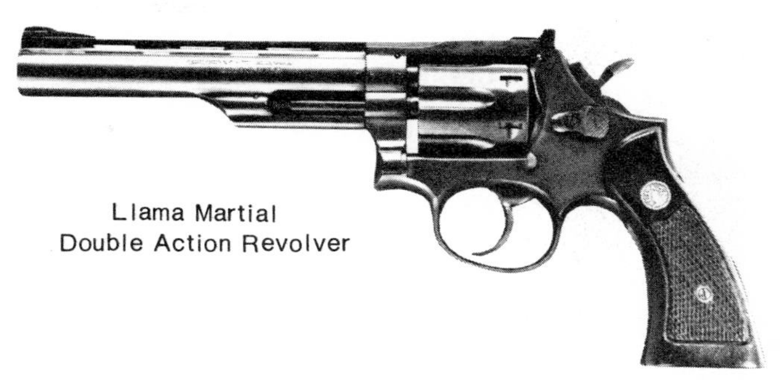
Llama Martial
Double Action Revolver

Llama Martial Double Action Revolver $90

Calibers: .22 Long Rifle, .22 Magnum Rim Fire, .38 Special. 6-shot cylinder. Barrel lengths: 4-inch (.38 Special only), 6-inch. 11¼ inches overall with 6-inch barrel. Weight, with 6-inch barrel, 32 ounces. Target sights. Blued finish. Checkered walnut grips. Made from 1969 to date.

Luger Pistol manufactured by Deutsche Waffen-und Munitionsfabriken (D.W.M.) in Berlin; also by Erfurt Arsenal, Simson & Co., Vickers Ltd., Waffenfabrik Bern, Heinrich Krieghoff Waffenfabrik prior to and during World War I; after the war, production was resumed at the Mauser Works at Oberndorf

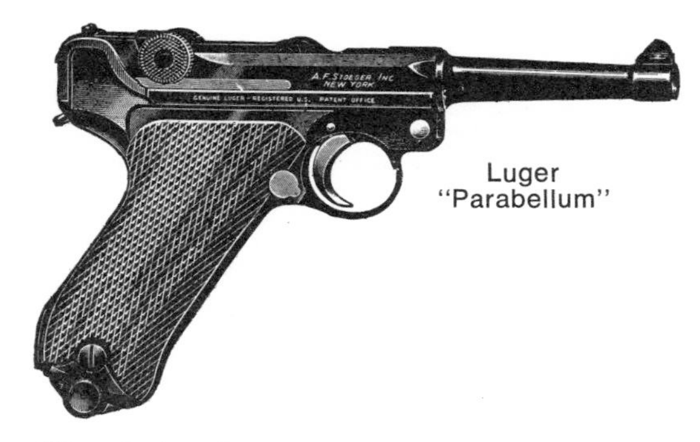
Luger
"Parabellum"

Luger "Parabellum" Automatic Pistol $275

Calibers: 7.65mm Luger, 9mm Luger. 8-shot magazine. Barrel lengths: 3⅝, 4½, 6-inch (7.65mm); 4, 6, 8-inch (9mm). Overall length with 4-inch barrel, 8¾ inches. Weight, with 4-inch barrel, 30 ounces. Fixed sights, adjustable rear sight on long barrel models. Blued finish. Checkered walnut stocks. Lugers manufactured prior to 1908 have a flat mainspring and a number of other parts differ from later models, early pistols have grip safety (not found on later production, except for export to Switzerland), some pre-World War I models lack the shoulder stock lug found on most Lugers. German Service Lugers bear a year stamp on the receiver, not found on the commercial models, which are also better finished. Pistols made for export to the United States were generally stamped with an American Eagle on receiver or bleechblock; those imported by A. F. Stoeger, Inc. after World War I bear that firm's name. Made from 1900 to 1942; production resumed in 1971 by Mauser (current model retails for $299). Specialist collectors recognize a great many Luger variations with a wide range of values. Price shown is for the common military model P.08 9mm Luger.

Waffenfabrik Mauser or Mauser-Werke A. G., Oberndorf, Germany

Mauser Military Model Automatic Pistol $400

Model of 1898. Caliber, 7.63mm Mauser. Box magazine, 10-shot. 5¼-inch barrel. 12 inches overall. Weight, 45 ounces. Adjustable rear sight. Blued finish. Walnut stocks. *Note:* This pistol was also chambered for 9mm Luger (marked with a large red "9" in the stocks) and 9mm Mauser; the latter is the rather rare "Export" Mauser.

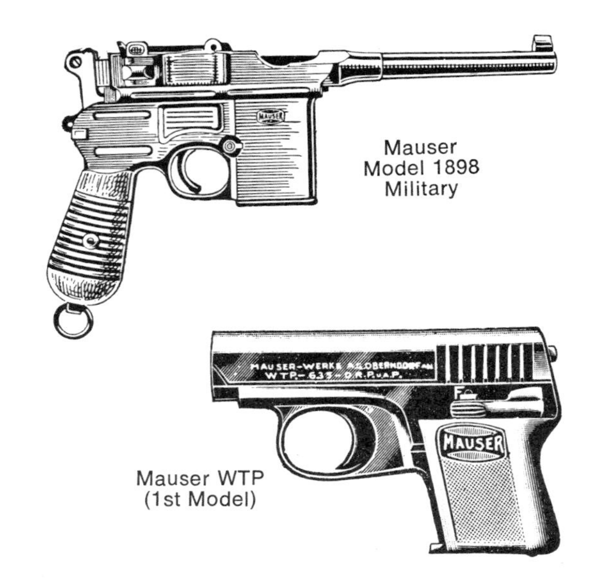

Mauser Model 1898 Military

Mauser WTP (1st Model)

Mauser WTP Model Automatic Pistol $125

"Westentaschen-Pistole" (Vest Pocket Pistol). First Model. Caliber, 25 Automatic (6.35mm). 6-shot magazine. 2½-inch barrel. 4½ inches overall. Weight, 11½ ounces. Blued finish. Hard rubber stocks.

Mauser WTP Model Automatic Pistol $150

Second Model. Similar to the earlier First Model but smaller and lighter. Caliber, 25 Automatic (6.35mm). 6-shot magazine. 2-inch barrel. 4 inches overall. Weight, 9½ ounces. Blued finish. Hard rubber stocks.

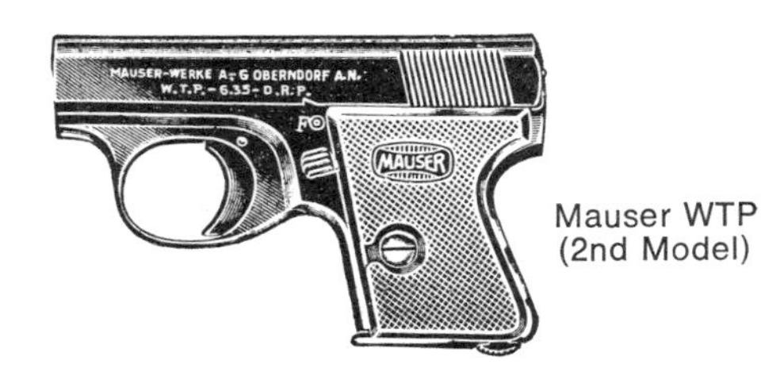

Mauser WTP (2nd Model)

Mauser Automatic Pocket Pistol $125

Calibers: 25 Automatic (6.35mm), 32 Automatic (7.65mm). 9-shot magazine (25 cal.), 8-shot (32 cal). Barrel lengths: 3 1/16 inches (25 cal.), 3½ inches (32 cal.). Overall lengths: 5⅜ inches (25 cal.), 5⅞ inches (32 cal.). Weights: 15¼ ounces (25 cal.), 20¾ ounces (32 cal.). Fixed sights. Blued finish. Checkered walnut or hard rubber stocks.

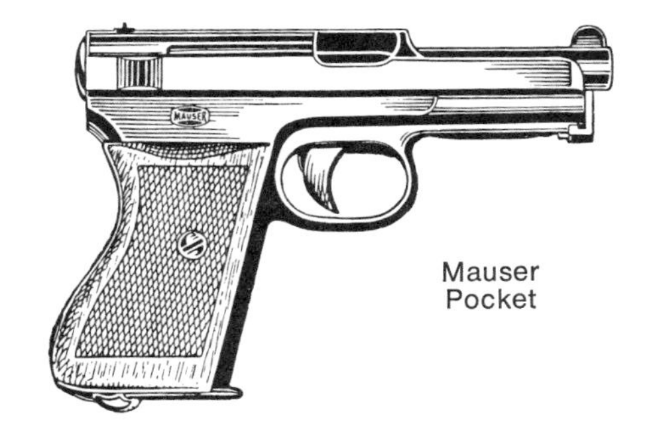

Mauser Pocket

Mauser Model HSc Pocket Automatic Pistol $140

Double action. Caliber, 32 Automatic (7.65mm). 8-shot magazine. 3⅜-inch barrel. 6½ inches overall. Weight, 20½ ounces. Fixed sights. Blued finish. Checkered walnut stocks. Currently manufactured.

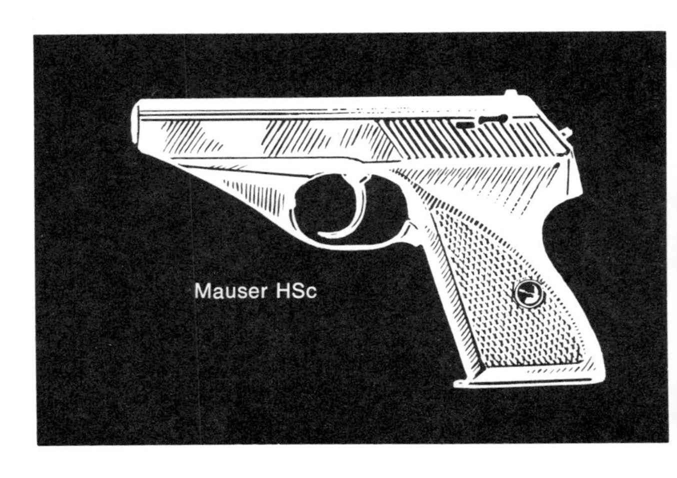

Mauser HSc

Meriden Fire Arms Co., Meriden, Connecticut

Meriden Revolvers

See listings of comparable Harrington & Richardson and Iver Johnson models for values.

Ortgies Pistols manufactured by Deutsche Werke A. G., Erfurt, Germany

Ortgies Pocket Automatic Pistol $85

Caliber, 25 Automatic (6.35mm). 6-shot magazine. 2¾-inch barrel. 5-3/16 inches overall. Weight, 13½ ounces. Fixed sights. Blued finish. Plain walnut stocks.

Ortgies Pocket Automatic Pistol $85

Calibers: 32 Automatic (7.65mm), 380 Automatic (9mm). 7-shot magazine (380 cal.), 8-shot (32 cal.). 3¼-inch barrel. 6½ inches overall. Weight, 22 ounces. Fixed sights. Blued finish. Plain walnut stocks.

Phoenix, Lowell, Massachusetts

Phoenix Pocket Automatic Pistol $150

Similar to the Browning Model 1900. Calibers: 25 Auto, 32 Auto. Made c. 1920.

Radom Pistol manufactured by Polish Arsenal et Radom

Radom P-35 Automatic Pistol $150

Variation of the Colt Government Model 45 Auto. Caliber, 9mm Luger. 8-shot magazine. 4¾-inch barrel. 7¾ inches overall. Weight, 29 ounces. Fixed sights. Blued finish. Plastic stocks. Made from 1935 through World War II.

Record-Match Pistols manufactured by Udo Anschutz, Zella-Mehlis, Germany

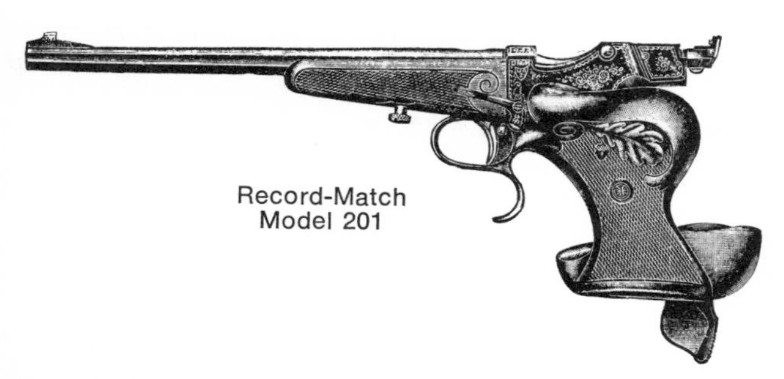
Record-Match Model 201

Record-Match Free Pistol Model 201 . . . . $1,000

System Martini action, set trigger with button release. Caliber 22 Long Rifle. Single shot. 11-inch barrel. Weight, 46 ounces. Target sights, micrometer rear. Blued finish. Carved and checkered walnut stock and forearm, adjustable hand base. Also made with dural action; weight of this model 35 ounces.

Record-Match Free Pistol Model 200 . . . . $500

Basically the same as Model 210 except plainer, with different stock design and conventional set trigger, spur trigger guard.

Reising Arms Co., Hartford, Connecticut

Reising Automatic Pistol $200

Hinged frame. Outside hammer. Caliber, 22 Long Rifle. 12-shot magazine. 6½-inch barrel. Fixed sights. Blued finish. Hard rubber stocks. Made for a few years during the early 1920's.

Remington Arms Company, Ilion, N. Y.

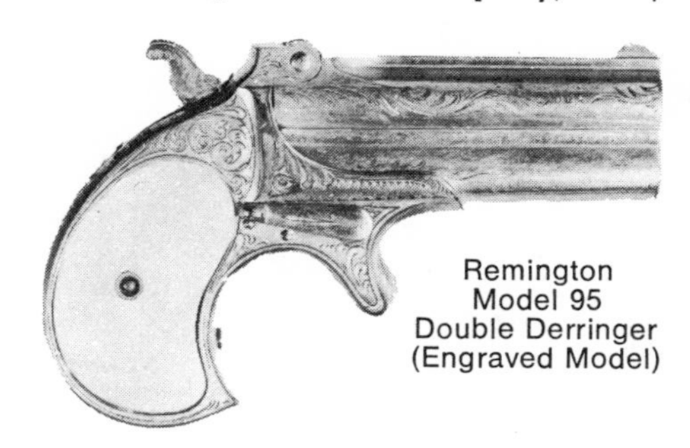
Remington Model 95 Double Derringer (Engraved Model)

Remington Model 95 Double Derringer

Single action. Caliber, 41 Short Rimfire. Double barrels (superposed), 3-inch. 4⅞ inches overall. Early models have long hammer spur and two-armed extractor; later production have short hammer spur and sliding extractor (a few have no extractor). Fixed sights: front blade integral with barrels, rear groove. Finishes: all blued, blued with nickel-plated frame, fully nickel plated; also furnished with factory engraving. Grips: walnut, checkered hard rubber, pearl, ivory. Weight, 11 ounces. Made from 1866 to 1935. Approximately 150,000 were manufactured. *Note:* During the seventy years of its production, serial numbering of this model was repeated two or three times. Therefore, aside from hammer and extractor differences between the earlier model and the later type, the best clue to the age of a Double Derringer is the stamping of the company's name on the top of the barrel or side-rib. Prior to 1888, derringers were stamped "E. Remington & Sons"; from 1888 to 1910, "Remington Arms Co."; from 1910 to 1935, "Remington Arms-U.M.C. Co."

Plain model $250
Factory-engraved model with ivory or pearl grips $400

Remington New Model Single Shot Target Pistol . . . $200

Also called Model 1901 Target. Rolling-block action. Calibers: 22 Short, 22 Long Rifle, 44 S&W Russian. 10-inch barrel, half-octagon. 14 inches overall. Weight, 45 ounces (22 cal.). Target sights. Blued finish. Checkered walnut grips and forearm. Made from 1901 to 1909.

Remington Model 51

Remington Model 51 Automatic Pistol $175

Calibers: 32 Auto, 380 Auto. 7-shot magazine. 3½-inch barrel. 6⅝ inches overall. Weight, 21 ounces. Fixed sights. Blued finish. Hard rubber stocks. Made from 1918 to 1934.

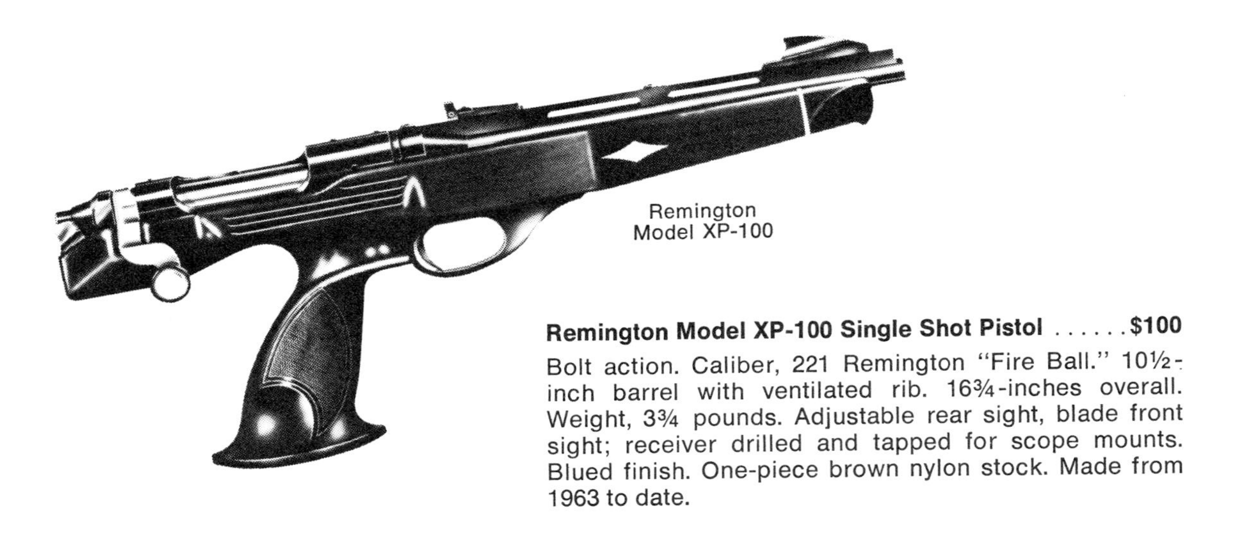

Remington Model XP-100

Remington Model XP-100 Single Shot Pistol $100

Bolt action. Caliber, 221 Remington "Fire Ball." 10½-inch barrel with ventilated rib. 16¾-inches overall. Weight, 3¾ pounds. Adjustable rear sight, blade front sight; receiver drilled and tapped for scope mounts. Blued finish. One-piece brown nylon stock. Made from 1963 to date.

Sturm, Ruger & Co., Southport, Connecticut

Ruger Standard Model Automatic Pistol $50

Caliber, 22 Long Rifle. 9-shot magazine. 4¾ or 6-inch barrel. 8¾ inches overall with 4¾″ bbl. Weight, with 4¾″ bbl. Weight, with 4¾″ bbl., 36 ounces. Fixed sights. Blued or chrome finish. Butaprene-type hard rubber stocks. Made from 1949 to date.

Ruger Mark I Target Automatic Pistol $60

Caliber, 22 Long Rifle, 9-shot magazine. 5¼-inch or 6⅞-inch heavy barrel. 10⅞ inches overall, weight 42 ounces, with 6⅞-inch barrel. Target sights, Micro rear. Blued or chrome finish. Butaprene-type hard rubber stocks. Made from 1951 to date.

Ruger Single-Six Revolver $60

Single action. Calibers: 22 Long Rifle, 22 Win. Magnum Rimfire. 6-shot cylinder. Barrel lengths: 4⅝, 5½, 6½, 9½ inches. Overall length with 5½″ bbl., 10⅞ inches. Weight, about 35 ounces. Fixed sights. Blued finish. Checkered hard rubber or smooth walnut grips. Made from 1953 to 1972.

Ruger Lightweight Single Six $75

Same general specifications as Single Six except: 4⅝-inch barrel, 10 inches overall length, weighs 23 ounces; cylinder, cylinder frame and grip frame of lightweight alloy. Made from 1955 to 1958.

Ruger Convertible Super Single Six Revolver $65

Same general specifications as Single Six except: ramp front sight, click-adjustable rear sight with protective ribs integral with frame; 5½ or 6½-inch barrel only; two interchangeable cylinders, 22 LR and 22 WMR. Made from 1964 to 1972.

Ruger Blackhawk 357 Magnum Single Action Revolver $115

Caliber, 357 Magnum. 6-shot cylinder. Barrel lengths: 4⅝, 6½ inch. 12 inches overall (6½″ bbl.). Weight, 40 ounces (6½″ bbl.). Click adjustable rear sight, ramp front sight. Blued finish. Checkered hard rubber or smooth walnut stocks. Made from 1955 to 1972.

Ruger Blackhawk 41 Magnum $115

Same general specifications as 357 Blackhawk, except caliber 41 Magnum. Made from 1965 to 1972.

Ruger Blackhawk 44 Magnum Revolver $200

Single action with heavy frame and cylinder. Caliber, 44 Magnum. 6-shot cylinder. 6½-inch barrel. Overall length, 12⅛ inches. Weight, 40 ounces. Adjustable rear sight, ramp front sight. Blued finish. Smooth walnut stocks. Made from 1956 to 1963.

Ruger Super Blackhawk Single Action Revolver . . $115

Caliber, 44 Magnum. 6-shot cylinder. 7½-inch barrel. 13⅜ inches overall. Weight, 48 ounces. Click adjustable rear sight, ramp front sight. Blued finish. Steel or brass grip frame. Smooth walnut stocks. Made from 1959 to 1972.

Ruger Bearcat Single Action Revolver $125

Caliber, 22 Short, Long, Long Rifle. 6-shot cylinder. 4-inch barrel. 8⅞ inches overall. Fixed sights. Blued finish. Smooth walnut stocks. Made from 1958 to 1971.

Ruger Hawkeye Single Shot Pistol $350

Single action; cylinder replaced by rotating breechblock; chamber is in barrel. Caliber, 256 Magnum. 8½-inch barrel. 14½ inches overall. Weight, 45 ounces. Blued finish. Click adjustable rear sight, ramp front sight. Smooth walnut stocks. Made from 1963 to 1964.

Ruger
Standard Model

Ruger
Mark I Target

Ruger
Convertible
Super Single Six

Ruger
Blackhawk 357

Ruger
Blackhawk 44

Ruger
Hawkeye

Ruger
Super Blackhawk

Ruger
Bearcat

Russian Service Pistol manufactured by Government plants at Tula and elsewhere

Russian Tokarev

Russian Tokarev Service Automatic Pistol **$125**

Modified Colt-Browning type. Caliber, 7.62mm Russian Automatic (also uses 7.63mm Mauser Automatic cartridge). 8-shot magazine. 4½-inch barrel. 7¾ inches overall. Weight, about 29 ounces. Fixed sights. First manufactured about 1930.

J. P. Sauer & Sohn, Suhl, Germany

Sauer Pocket Automatic Pistol **$100**

Model of 1913. Caliber, 32 Automatic (7.65mm). 7-shot magazine. 3-inch barrel. 5⅞ inches overall. Weight, 22 ounces. Fixed sights. Blued finish. Black hard rubber stocks. Made from 1913 to 1930.

Sauer Pocket 25 Automatic Pistol **$100**

Smaller version of Model of 1913, issued about same time as 32 caliber model. Caliber, 25 Automatic (6.35mm). 7-shot magazine. 2½-inch barrel, 4¼-inches overall. Weight, 14½ ounces. Fixed sights. Blued finish. Black hard rubber stocks.

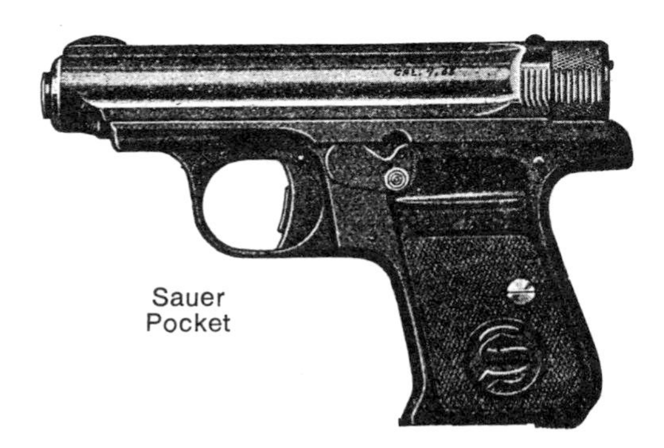
Sauer Pocket

Sauer Pocket Automatic Pistol **$135**

Model of 1930 or Authority Model (Behorden-Modell). Successor to Model of 1913, has improved grip and safety. Caliber, 32 Automatic (7.65mm). 7-shot magazine. 3-inch barrel. 5¾ inches overall. Weight, 22 ounces. Fixed sights. Blued finish. Black hard rubber stocks. *Note:* Some pistols of this model have indicator pin showing when cocked. Also manufactured with dural slide and receiver; this type weighs about 1/3 less than the standard model.

Sauer Model H

Sauer Model H Double Action Automatic Pistol ... **$135**

Calibers: 25 Auto (6.35mm), 32 Auto (7.65mm), 380 Auto (9mm). Specifications shown are for 32 Auto model. 7-shot magazine. 3¼-inch barrel. 6¼ inches overall. Weight, 20 ounces. Fixed sights. Blued finish. Black plastic stocks. Also made in dural model weighing about 1/3 less. *Note:* This pistol, designated Model 38, was manufactured during World War II for military use. These war-time models are inferior to the earlier production, some lack safety lever.

Savage Arms Co., Utica, N. Y.

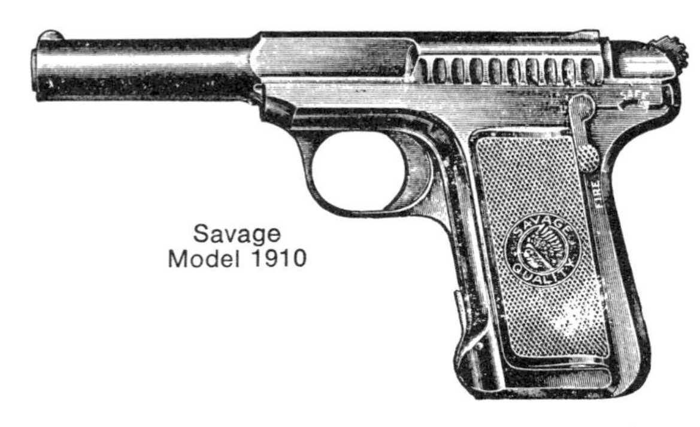
Savage Model 1910

Savage Model 1910 Automatic Pistol **$150**

Calibers: 32 Auto, 380 Auto. 10-shot magazine (32 cal.), 9-shot (380 cal.), 3¾-inch barrel (32 cal.), 4½-inch (380 cal.), 6½-inch overall (32 cal.), 7-inch (380 cal.). Weight, about 23 ounces. Fixed sights. Blued finish. Hard rubber stocks. *Note:* This model was made in hammerless type with grip safety as well as with exposed hammer spur. Made from 1910 to 1917.

Savage Model 1917 Automatic Pistol **$150**

Same specifications as 1910 Model, except has spur-type hammer and redesigned heavier grip. Made from 1917 to 1928.

R. F. Sedgley, Inc., Philadelphia, Pennsylvania

Sedgley Baby Hammerless Ejector Double Action Revolver $75

Solid frame. Folding trigger. Caliber, 22 Long. 6-shot cylinder. 4 inches overall. Weight, 6 ounces. Fixed sights. Blued or nickel finish. Rubber stocks.

Sheridan Products, Inc., Racine, Wisconsin

Sheridan Knocabout

Sheridan Knocabout Single Shot Pistol $60

Tip-up type. Caliber, 22 Long Rifle, Long, Short. 5-inch barrel. 6¾ inches overall. Weight, 24 ounces. Fixed sights. Checkered plastic stocks. Blued finish. Made from 1953 to 1960.

Smith & Wesson, Inc., Springfield, Massachusetts

Smith & Wesson 38 Double Action Revolver $150

Hinged frame. Caliber, 38 S&W. 5-shot cylinder. Barrel lengths: 3¼, 4, 5, and 6-inch. Fixed sights. Blued or nickel finish. Hard rubber stocks. Made from 1880 to 1911. Various minor changes.

Smith & Wesson Perfected Model 38 Double Action Revolver $150

Hinged frame. Similar to earlier 38 Double Action Model, but heavier frame, side latch as in solid frame models, improved lockwork. Caliber, 38 S&W. 5-shot cylinder. Barrel lengths: 3¼, 4, 5 and 6-inch. Fixed sights. Blued or nickel finish. Hard rubber stocks. Made from 1909 to 1920.

Smith & Wesson 32 Double Action Revolver $150

Hinged frame. Caliber, 32 S&W. 5-shot cylinder. Barrel lengths: 3, 3½ and 6-inch. Fixed sights. Blued or nickel finish. Hard rubber stocks. Made from 1880 to 1919. Various minor changes.

Smith & Wesson No. 3 Single Action (New Model) Revolver $375

Hinged frame. 6-shot cylinder. Caliber, 44 S&W Russian. Barrel lengths: 4, 5, 6, 6½, 7½ and 8-inch. Fixed or target sights. Blued or nickel finish. Round butt stocks, hard rubber or checkered walnut. Made from 1878 to 1908.

Smith & Wesson No. 3 Single Action (Frontier) Revolver $450

Caliber, 44-40 Winchester. Barrel lengths: 4, 5, and 6½-inch. Fixed or target sights. Blued or nickel finish. Round butt stocks, hard rubber or checkered walnut. Made from 1885 to 1908.

Smith & Wesson No. 3 Single Action Target Revolver $425

Hinged frame. 6-shot cylinder. Calibers: 32/44 S&W, 38/44 S&W Gallery & Target. 6½-inch barrel only. Fixed or target sights. Blued or nickel finish. Round butt stocks, hard rubber or checkered walnut. Made from 1887 to 1910.

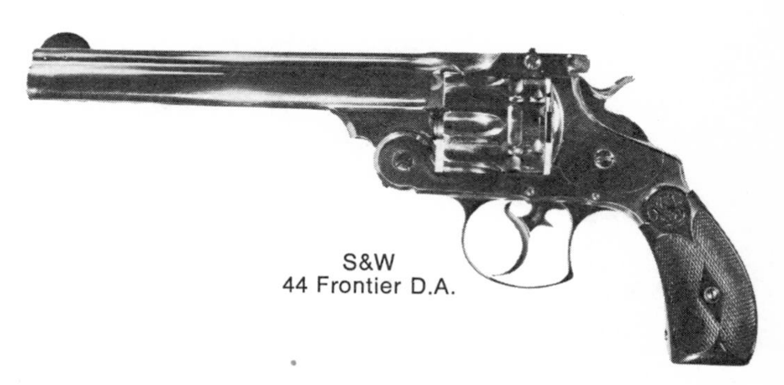
S&W 44 Frontier D.A.

Smith & Wesson 44 Double Action Revolver $200

Also called "Wesson Favorite" (lightweight model), "Frontier" (caliber 44-40). Hinged frame. 6-shot cylinder. Calibers: 44 S&W Russian, 38-40, 44-40. Barrel lengths: 4, 5, 6, and 6½-inch. Weight, with 6½-inch barrel, 37½ ounces. Fixed sights. Blued or nickel finish. Hard rubber stocks. Made from 1881 to 1913, except "Frontier" which was discontinued in 1910.

S&W Safety Hammerless

Smith & Wesson Safety Hammerless Revolver $225

Also called "New Departure" Double Action. Hinged frame. Calibers: 32 S&W, 38 S&W. 5-shot cylinder. Barrel lengths: 32 cal.—2, 3 and 3½-inch; 38 cal.—2, 3¼, 4, 5 and 6-inch. Length overall: 32 cal. with 3-inch barrel—6¾ inches; 38 cal. with 3¼-inch barrel—7½ inches. Weights: 32 cal. with 3-inch barrel—14¼ ounces; 38 cal. with 3¼-inch barrel—18¼ ounces. Fixed sights. Blued or nickel finish. Hard rubber stocks. 32 cal. made from 1888 to 1937, 38 cal. from 1887 to 1941. Various minor changes.

Smith & Wesson Model 1891 Single Action Revolver

Hinged frame. Caliber, 38 S&W. 5-shot cylinder. Barrel lengths: 3¼, 4, 5, and 6-inch. Fixed sights. Blued or nickel finish. Hard rubber stocks. Made 1891 to 1911.

Note: Until 1906, an accessory single shot target barrel (see Model 1891 Single Shot Target Pistol) was available for this revolver.

Revolver only **$200**
Set with 22 single shot barrel **$400**

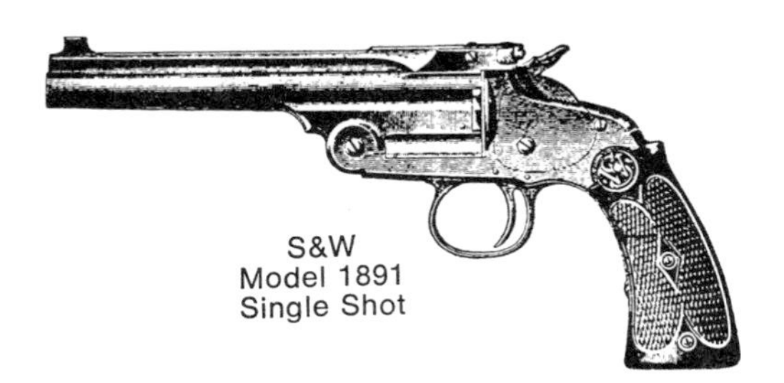

S&W Model 1891 Single Shot

Smith & Wesson Model 1891 Single Shot Target Pistol

First Model. Hinged frame. Calibers: 22 Long Rifle, 32 S&W, 38 S&W. Barrel lengths: 6, 8 and 10-inch. Approximately 13½ inches overall with 10-inch barrel. Weight, about 25 ounces. Target sights, barrel catch rear sight adjustable for windage and elevation. Blued finish. Square butt, hard rubber stocks. Made from 1893 to 1905. *Note:* This model was available also as a combination arm with accessory 38 revolver barrel and cylinder to convert the single shot target pistol to a pocket revolver. It has the frame of the 38 Single Action Revolver Model 1891 with side flanges, hand and cylinder stop slots.
Single shot pistol only **$250**
Combination set, revolver and S. S. pistol **$575**

Smith & Wesson Model 1891 Single Shot Target Pistol **$250**

Second Model. Basically the same as the First Model, except side flanges, hand and stop slots eliminated, cannot be converted to revolver, redesigned rear sight. Caliber, 22 Long Rifle only. 10-inch barrel only. Made from 1905 to 1909.

Smith & Wesson Perfected Single Shot Target Pistol

Also called "Olympic Model" (see note below). Similar to 1891 Single Shot Second Model except has double action lockwork. Caliber, 22 Long Rifle only. 10-inch barrel. Checkered walnut stocks, extended square butt target type. Made from 1909 to 1923. *Note:* In 1920 and thereafter, pistols of this model were made with barrels having bore diameter of .223 instead of .226 and tight, short chambering. The first of these pistols were produced for the U.S. Olympic Team of 1920 and, therefore, the designation "Olympic Model" was adopted.
Pre-1920 Type **$250**
Olympic Model **$400**

S&W Model I

Smith & Wesson Model "I" Hand Ejector Double Action Revolver **$130**

First Model. Forerunner of the current "32 Hand Ejector" and "Regulation Police" models, this was the first S&W revolver of the solid-frame, swing-out cylinder type. Top strap of this model is longer than later models and it lacks the usual S&W cylinder latch. Caliber, 32 S&W Long. Barrel lengths: 3¼, 4¼ and 6-inch. Fixed sights. Blued or nickel finish. Round butt, hard rubber stocks. Made from 1896 to 1903.

S&W Model 30

Smith & Wesson Model 30 32 Hand Ejector Double Action Revolver **$70**

2 (introduced 1949), 3, 4 and 6-inch. 8-inches overall with 4-inch barrel. Weight, 18 ounces with 4-inch barrel. Fixed sights. Blued or nickel finish. Checkered walnut or hard rubber stocks, round butt. Made from 1903 to date. Numerous changes, mostly minor, as in M & P model.

S&W Model 31

Smith & Wesson Models 31 & 33 Regulation Police Double Action Revolver **$70**

2 (introduced 1949), 3, 4 and 6-inch in 32 cal.; 4-inch only in 38 cal. 8½ inches overall with 4-inch barrel. Weights: 18 ounces in 38 cal. with 4-inch barrel, 32 cal. ¾-ounce heavier. Fixed sights. Blued or nickel finish. Checkered walnut stocks. Made from 1917 to date.

S&W Regulation Police Target

Smith & Wesson Regulation Police Target Double Action Revolver **$125**

Target version of the "Regulation Police" with standard features of that model. Caliber, 32 S&W Long. 6-inch barrel. 10¼-inches overall. Weight, 20 ounces. Adjustable target sights. Blued finish. Checkered walnut stocks. Made from about 1917 to 1940.

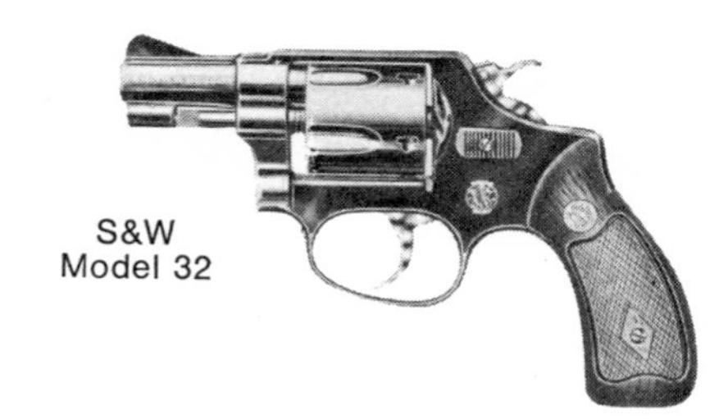

S&W Model 32

Smith & Wesson Model 32 Terrier Double Action Revolver **$100**

Caliber, 38 S&W. 5-shot cylinder. 2-inch barrel. 6¼ inches overall. Weight, 17 ounces. Fixed sights. Blued or nickel finish. Checkered walnut or hard rubber stocks. Built on "32 Hand Ejector" frame. Made from 1936 to 1974.

S&W Model 36

Smith & Wesson Model 36 Chiefs Special Double Action Revolver **$80**

Based on 32 Hand Ejector with frame lengthened to permit longer cylinder necessary for 38 Special cartridge. Caliber, 38 Special. 5-shot cylinder. Barrel lengths: 2 or 3-inch. Overall length, with 2″ bbl., 6½ inches. Weight, 19 ounces. Fixed sights. Blued or nickel finish. Checkered walnut stocks, round or square butt. Made from 1952 to date.

Smith & Wesson Model 37 Airweight Chiefs Special $80

Same general specifications as standard Chiefs Special, except has light alloy frame, weighs 12½ ounces with 2″ bbl., blued finish only. Made from 1954 to date.

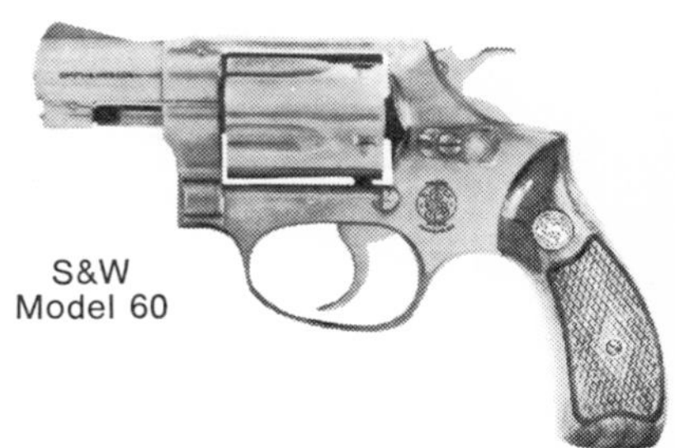

S&W Model 60

Smith & Wesson Model 60 38 Chiefs Special Stainless **$100**

Same as standard Chiefs Special, except satin-finished stainless steel; 2-inch barrel only. Made from 1965 to date.

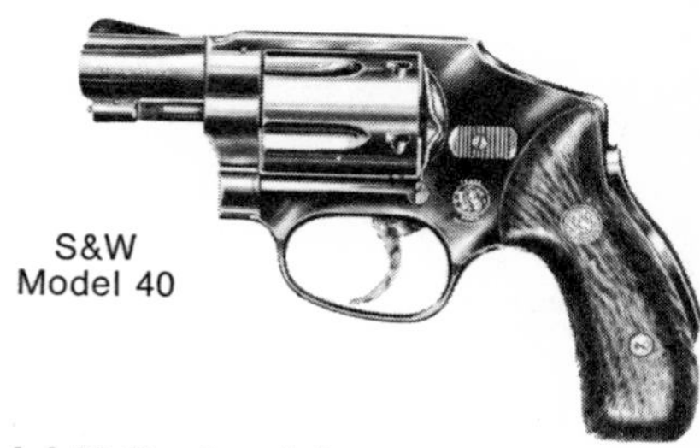

S&W Model 40

Smith & Wesson Model 40 Centennial Double Action Hammerless Revolver **$100**

Similar to Chiefs Special, but has Safety Hammerless type mechanism with grip safety. 2-inch barrel. Weight, 19 ounces. Made from 1953 to 1974.

Smith & Wesson Model 42 Centennial Airweight . . . $100

Same as standard Centennial model except has light alloy frame, weighs 13 ounces. Made from 1954 to 1974.

S&W Model 38

Smith & Wesson Model 38 Bodyguard Airweight Double Action Revolver **$80**

"Shrouded" hammer. Light alloy frame. Caliber, 38 Special. 5-shot cylinder. 2-inch barrel. 6⅜-inches overall. Weight, 14½ ounces. Fixed sights. Blued or nickel finish. Checkered walnut stocks. Made from 1955 to date.

Smith & Wesson Model 49 Bodyguard $80

Same as Model 38 Bodyguard Airweight, except has steel frame, weighs 20½ ounces. Made from 1959 to date.

S&W
22/32 Target

Smith & Wesson 22/32 Target Double Action Revolver $150

Also known as the "Bekeart Model." Design based upon "32 Hand Ejector." Caliber, 22 Long Rifle (recessed head cylinder for high speed cartridges introduced 1935). 6-shot cylinder. 6-inch barrel. 10½ inches overall. Weight, 23 ounces. Adjustable target sights. Blued finish. Checkered walnut stocks. Made from 1911 to 1953.

S&W
Model 35

Smith & Wesson Model 35 1953 22/32 Target $120

Same general specifications as previous model 22/32 Target, except has new micrometer click rear sight, Magna-type target stocks, weighs 25 ounces. Made from 1953 to 1974.

S&W
22/32 Kit Gun

Smith & Wesson 22/32 Kit Gun $150

Same as "22/32 Target" except has 4-inch barrel and round butt stocks. 8 inches overall. Weight, 21 ounces. Made from 1935 to 1953.

S&W
Model 34

Smith & Wesson Model 34 1953 22/32 Kit Gun $90

Same general specifications as previous model Kit Gun, except furnished in choice of 2-inch or 4-inch barrel and round or square butt stocks, blue or nickel finish. Made from 1953 to date.

S&W
Model 43

Smith & Wesson Model 43 1955 22/32 Kit Gun Airweight $100

Same as Model 34 Kit Gun, except has light alloy frame, furnished with 3½-inch barrel only, weighs 14¼ ounces, square butt stock. Made from 1954 to 1974.

S&W
Model 51

Smith & Wesson Model 51 1960 22/32 Kit Gun M.R.F. $110

Same as Model 34 Kit Gun, except chambered for 22 Winchester Magnum Rim Fire; has 3½-inch barrel, weighs 24 ounces. Made from 1960 to 1974.

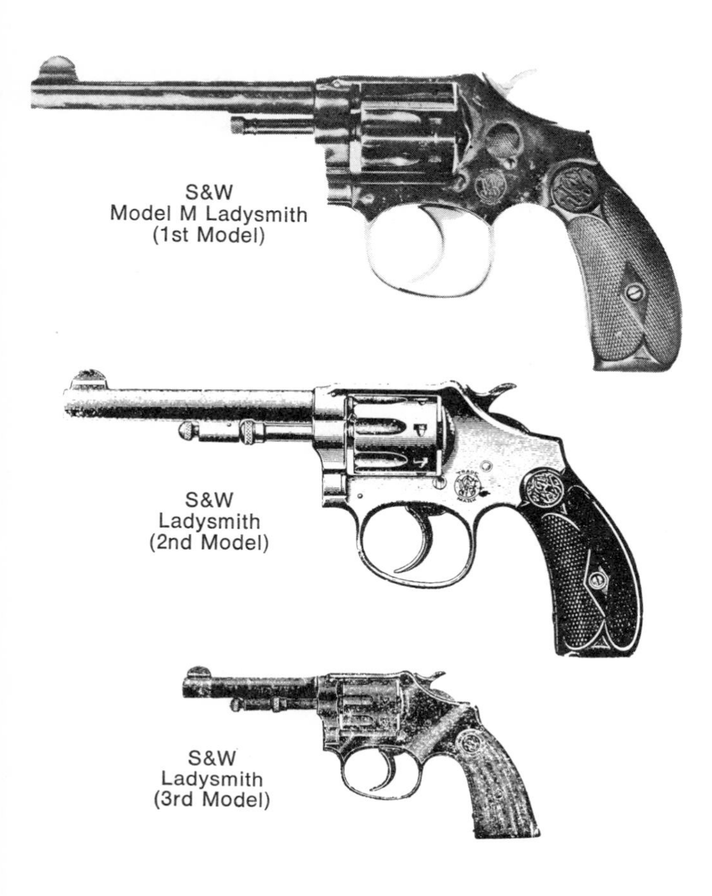

S&W
Model M Ladysmith
(1st Model)

S&W
Ladysmith
(2nd Model)

S&W
Ladysmith
(3rd Model)

Smith & Wesson Model "M" Hand Ejector Double Action Revolver $425

Also called "Ladysmith." Caliber, 22 Long Rifle. 7-shot cylinder. Barrel lengths: 2¼ (First Model only), 3, 3½ and 6-inch (Third Model only). Approximately 7 inches overall with 3½-inch barrel. Weight, about 9½ ounces. Fixed sights, adjustable target sights were available on Third Model. Blued or nickel finish. Round butt, hard rubber stocks on First and Second Model; Checkered walnut or hard rubber square butt stocks on Third Model. First Model—1902 to 1906: cylinder locking bolt operated by button on left side of frame, no barrel lug and front locking bolt. Second Model—1906 to 1911: rear cylinder latch eliminated, has barrel lug, forward cylinder lock with draw-bolt fastening. Third Model—1911 to 1921: same as Second Model except has square butt stocks, target sights and 6-inch barrel available.

Smith & Wesson Model 38 Hand Ejector Double Action Revolver $125

"Military & Police"—First Model. Resembles Colt "New Navy" in general appearance, lacks barrel lug and locking bolt common to all later S&W hand ejector models. Caliber, 38 Long Colt. 6-shot cylinder. Barrel lengths: 4, 5, 6 and 6½-inch. 11½ inches overall with 6½-inch barrel. Fixed sights. Blued or nickel finish. Checkered walnut or hard rubber stocks, round butt. Made from 1899 to 1902.

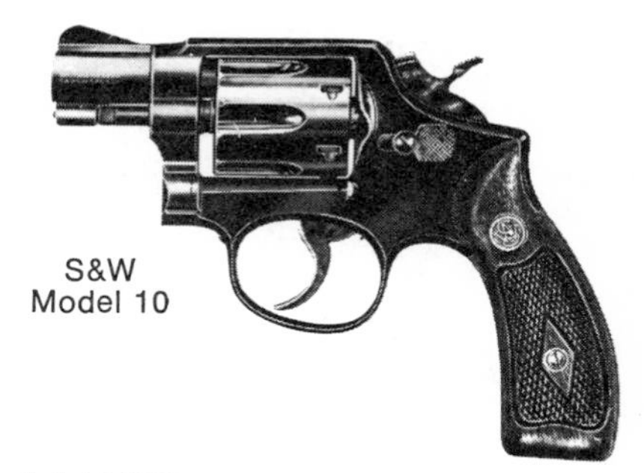

S&W
Model 10

Smith & Wesson Model 10 Military & Police Double Action Revolver

Also called "Hand Ejector Model 1902," "Hand Ejector Model 1905," "Model K." Manufactured in substantially its present form since 1902, this model has undergone numerous changes, most of them minor. Both round and square butt models available, the latter introduced in 1904. Caliber, 38 Special. 6-shot cylinder. Barrel lengths: 2 (introduced 1933), 4, 5, 6 and 6½-inch (latter discontinued 1915). 11⅛ inches overall in square butt model with 6-inch barrel. Weight, 31 ounces in square butt model with 6-inch barrel. Round butt model is ¼-inch shorter, weighs about ½ ounce less. Fixed sights. Blued or nickel finish. Checkered walnut stocks, hard rubber available in round butt style. Current production has short action. Made from 1902 to date. *Note:* S&W Victory Model, war time version of the M & P 38, was produced for the U.S. Government from 1940 to the end of the war. A similar revolver, designated "38/200 British Service Revolver" was produced for the British Government during the same period. These arms have either brush-polish or sand-blast blue finish and most of them have plain smooth walnut stocks and lanyard swivels.

Standard Model **$75**
Victory Model or 38/200 British **$90**

S&W
Model 12

Smith & Wesson Model 12 38 Military & Police Airweight $80

Same as standard Military & Police, except has light alloy frame, furnished with 2-inch barrel only, weighs 18 ounces. Made from 1952 to date.

Smith & Wesson Military & Police—Winchester 32-20 Double Action Revolver $125

Same as "M & P 38," except chambered for 32-20 cartridge. First introduced in the 1899 model, M & P Revolvers were produced in this caliber until about 1940.

Smith & Wesson 38 Military & Police Target Double Action Revolver **$135**

Target version of the Military & Police with standard features of that model. Caliber, 38 Special. 6-inch barrel. Weight, 32¼ ounces. Adjustable target sights. Blued finish. Checkered walnut stocks. Discontinued 1941.

Smith & Wesson K-32 Target Double Action Revolver **$175**

Same as "38 Military & Police Target," except chambered for 32 S&W Long cartridge, slightly heavier barrel. Weight 34 ounces. Manufactured 1940.

Smith & Wesson K-22 Outdoorsman Double Action Revolver **$175**

Design based upon the "38 Military & Police Target." Caliber, 22 Long Rifle. 6-shot cylinder barrel. 11⅛ inches overall. Weight, 35 ounces. Adjustable target sights. Blued finish. Checkered walnut stock. Made from 1931 to 1940.

Smith & Wesson K-22 Masterpiece Double Action Revolver **$175**

First Issue. Improved version of "K-22 Outdoorsman" with same specifications but with micrometer click rear sight, short action and anti-backlash trigger. Manufactured 1940.

Smith & Wesson Models 17 (K22), 48 (K22-MRF), 16 (K32) and 14 (K38) Masterpiece Double Action Revolvers **$100**

Calibers: 22 Long Rifle, 22 Magnum Rim Fire, 32 S&W Long, 38 Special. 6-shot cylinder. Barrel lengths: 4 (22 MRF only), 6, 8⅜ inch (latter not available in K32). 11⅛ inches overall (6" bbl.). Weight, 38½ ounces (6" bbl.). Click adjustable rear sights, Patridge front sight. Blued finish. Checkered walnut stocks. Made from 1947 to date. (Model 16 discontinued 1974).

Smith & Wesson K32 and K38 Heavy Masterpiece Double Action Revolvers **$100**

Same as K32 and K38 Masterpiece but with heavy weight barrel. Weight, 38½ ounces. Made from 1949 to date.

Smith & Wesson Combat Masterpiece 22 and 38 Double Action Revolvers **$95**

Same as K22 and K38 Masterpiece but with 4-inch barrel and Baughman quick draw front sight. 9⅛ inches overall. Weight, 34 ounces in 38 cal. Made from 1950 to date.

Smith & Wesson New Century Model Hand Ejector Double Action Revolver **$400**

Also called "Triple Lock" because of its third cylinder lock at the crane. 6-shot cylinder. Calibers: 44 S&W Special, 450 Eley, 455 Mark II. Barrel lengths: 4, 5, 6½ and 7½-inch. Weight, with 6½-inch barrel, 39 ounces. Fixed sights. Blued or nickel finish. Checkered walnut stocks. Made from1907 to 1915.

Smith & Wesson 44 Hand Ejector Second Model Double Action Revolver **$250**

Basically the same as "New Century" except crane lock ("Triple Lock" feature) and extractor rod casing eliminated. Calibers: 44 S&W Special, 44-40 Winchester, 45 Colt. Barrel lengths: 4, 5, 6½ and 7½-inch. 11¾ inches overall with 6½-inch barrel. Weight, 38 ounces with 6½-inch barrel. Fixed sights. Blued or nickel finish. Checkered walnut stocks. Made from 1915 to 1937.

Smith & Wesson 1917 Army Double Action Revolver

Caliber, 45 Automatic (using 3-cartridge half moon clip, 45 Auto Rim without clip). 6-shot cylinder. 5½-inch barrel. 10¾ inches overall. Weight, 36¼ ounces. Fixed sights. Blued finish (blue-black finish on commercial model, brush polish on military). Checkered walnut stocks (commercial model, smooth on military). Made under U.S. Government contract from 1917 to 1919; produced commercially from 1919 to 1941. *Note:* About 175,000 of these revolvers were produced during World War I. The DCM sold these to NRA members during the 1930's at $16.15 each.

Commercial model **$200**
Military model **$175**

Smith & Wesson Model 22 1950 Army Double Action Revolver **$175**

Post-war version of the 1917 Army. Same specifications as that model. Redesigned hammer. Made from 1950 to 1967.

Smith & Wesson 1926 Model 44 Military Double Action Revolver **$250**

Basically the same as the early "New Century" model, having the extractor rod casing but lacking the "Triple Lock" feature. Caliber, 44 S&W Special. 6-shot cylinder. Barrel lengths: 4, 5 and 6½-inch. 11¾ inches overall with 6½-inch barrel. Weight, 39½ ounces with 6½-inch barrel. Fixed sights. Blued or nickel finish. Checkered walnut stocks. Made from 1926 to 1941.

Smith & Wesson Model 21 1950 44 Military Double Action Revolver **$200**

Post-war version of the 1926 Model 44 Military. Same specifications as that model. Redesigned hammer. Made from 1950 to 1967.

Smith & Wesson 1926 Model 44 Target Double Action Revolver **$300**

Target version of the 1926 Model 44 Military. 6½-inch barrel only. Target sights. Blued finish only. Made from 1926 to 1941.

Smith & Wesson Model 24 1950 44 Target Double Action Revolver **$225**

Post-war version of the 1926 Model 44 Target with same general specifications except has redesigned hammer, ribbed barrel, micrometer click rear sight. Made from 1950 to 1967.

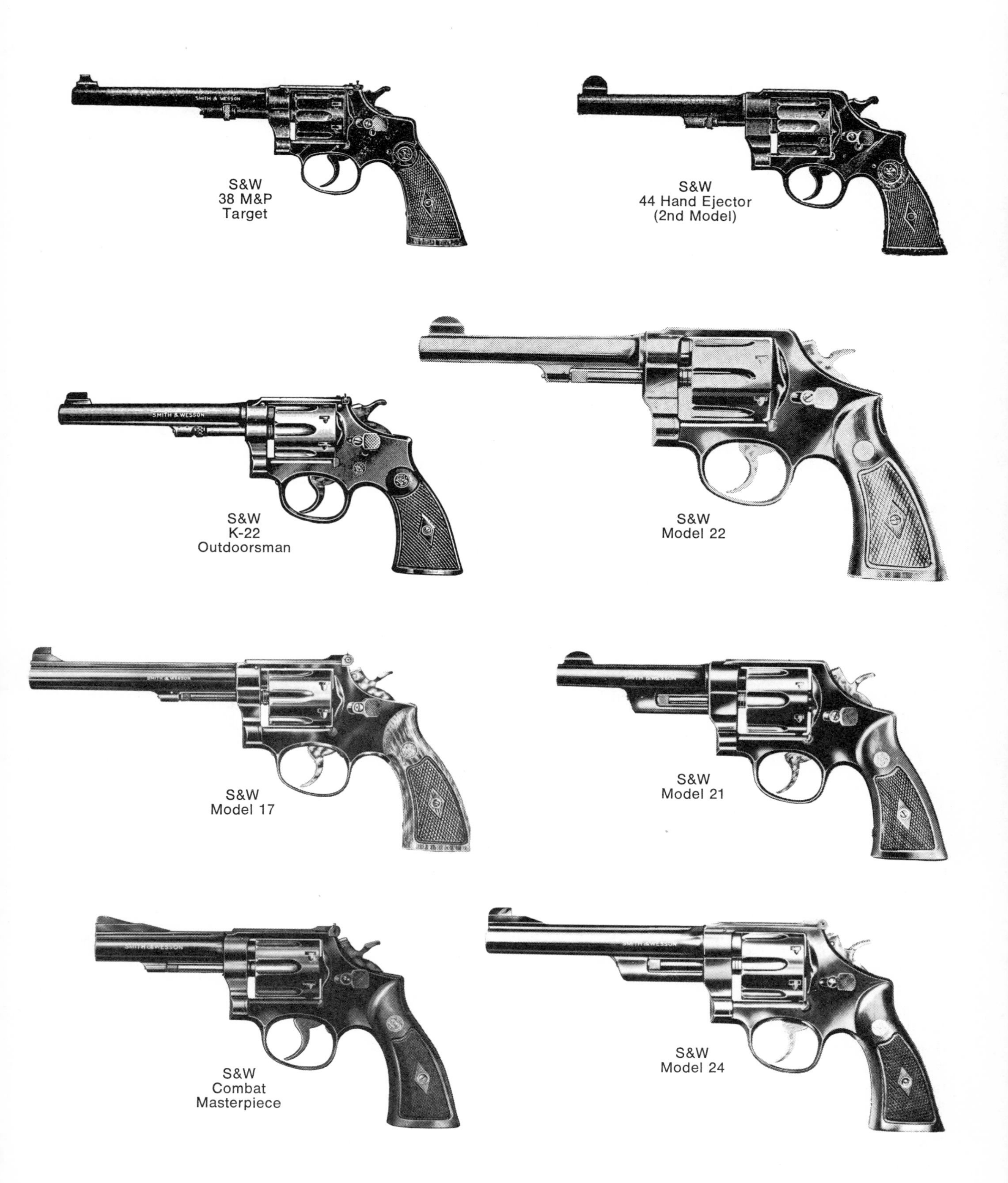

S&W
38 M&P
Target

S&W
44 Hand Ejector
(2nd Model)

S&W
K-22
Outdoorsman

S&W
Model 22

S&W
Model 17

S&W
Model 21

S&W
Combat
Masterpiece

S&W
Model 24

Smith & Wesson Model 25 1950 45 Target Double Action Revolver **$160**

Same as 1950 Model 44 Target but chambered for 45 Automatic cartridge. Made from 1950 to date.

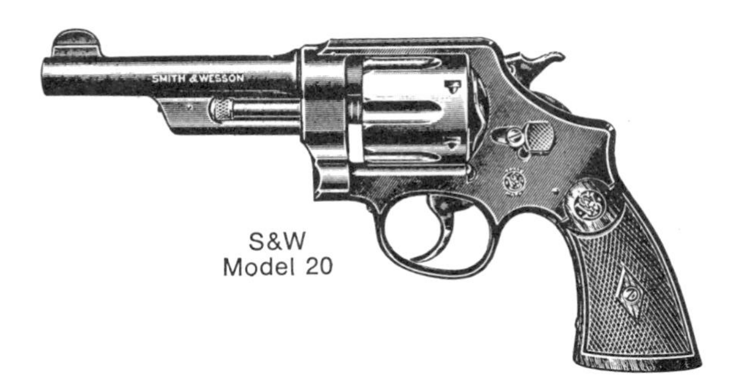

S&W Model 20

Smith & Wesson Model 20 38/44 Heavy Duty Double Action Revolver **$200**

Caliber, 38 Special (especially designed for high speed ammunition). 6-shot cylinder. Barrel lengths: 4, 5 and 6½-inch. 10⅜ inches overall with 5-inch barrel. Weight, 40 ounces with 5-inch barrel. Fixed sights. Blued or nickel finish. Checkered walnut stocks. Current production has short action. Made from 1930 to 1967.

S&W Model 23

Smith & Wesson Model 23 38/44 Outdoorsman Double Action Revolver **$225**

Target version of the 38/44 Heavy Duty. 6½-inch barrel only. Weight, 41¾ ounces. Target sights, micrometer click rear on post-war models. Blued finish only. Current production has ribbed barrel, redesigned hammer. Made from 1930 to 1967.

Smith & Wesson Model 27 357 Magnum Double Action Revolver

Caliber, 357 S&W Magnum. 6-shot cylinder. Barrel lengths 3½, 5, 6 and 6½-inch. 11⅜ inches overall with 6-inch barrel. Weight, 44 ounces with 6-inch barrel. Adjustable target sights, Baughman quick draw ramp front sight on 3½-inch barrel. Blued or nickel finish. Checkered walnut stocks. Made from 1935 to date. *Note:* Until 1938 the 357 Magnum was custom made in any

S&W Model 27

barrel length from 3½-inch to 8¾-inch; each of these revolvers was accompanied by a registration certificate and has its registration number stamped on the inside of the yoke. Post-war Magnums have a redesigned hammer with shortened fall and the new S&W micrometer click rear sight.

Prewar registered model **$500**
Prewar model without registration number **$300**
Current model **$145**

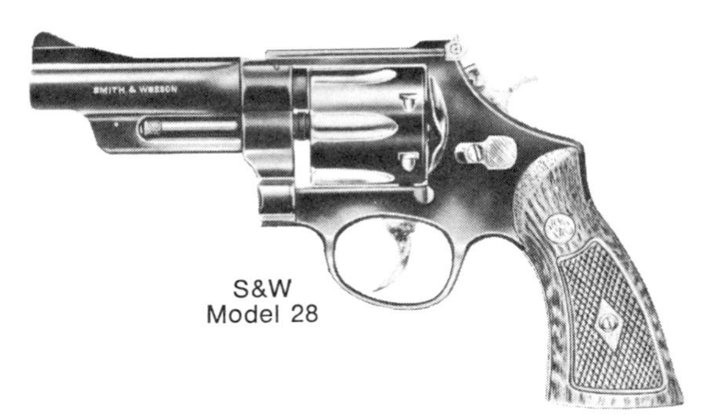

S&W Model 28

Smith & Wesson Model 28 Highway Patrolman Double Action Revolver **$100**

Caliber, 357 Magnum. 6-shot cylinder. Barrel lengths: 4 or 6-inch. Overall length, with 6″ bbl., 11¼ inches. Weight with 6″ bbl., 44 ounces. Adjustable rear sight, ramp front sight. Blued finish. Checkered walnut stocks, Magna or target type. Made from 1954 to date.

S&W Model 19

Smith & Wesson Model 19 357 Combat Magnum Double Action Revolver **$125**

Caliber, 357 Magnum. 6-shot cylinder. Barrel lengths: 4, 6 inch. 9½ inches overall (4″ bbl.). Weight, 35 ounces (4″ bbl.). Click adjustable rear sight, ramp front sight. Blued or nickel finish. Target stocks of checkered Goncalo Alves. Made from 1956 to date.

S&W
Model 29

Smith & Wesson Model 29 44 Magnum Double Action Revolver $175

Caliber, 44 Magnum. 6-shot cylinder. Barrel lengths: 4, 6½, 8⅜ inch. 11⅞ inches overall (6½" bbl.). Weight, 47 ounces (6½" bbl.). Click adjustable rear sight, ramp front sight. Blued or nickel finish. Target stocks of checkered Goncalo Alves. Made from 1956 to date.

S&W
Model 53

Smith & Wesson Model 53 22 Magnum Double Action Revolver $250

Caliber, 22 Remington Jet C.F. Magnum. 6-shot cylinder (inserts permit use of 22 Short, Long, or L.R. cartridges). Barrel lengths: 4, 6, 8⅜ inches. Overall length (with 6-inch barrel), 11¼ inches. Weight (with 6-inch barrel), 40 ounces. Micrometer click rear sight, ramp front sight. Checkered walnut stocks. Made from 1960 to 1974.

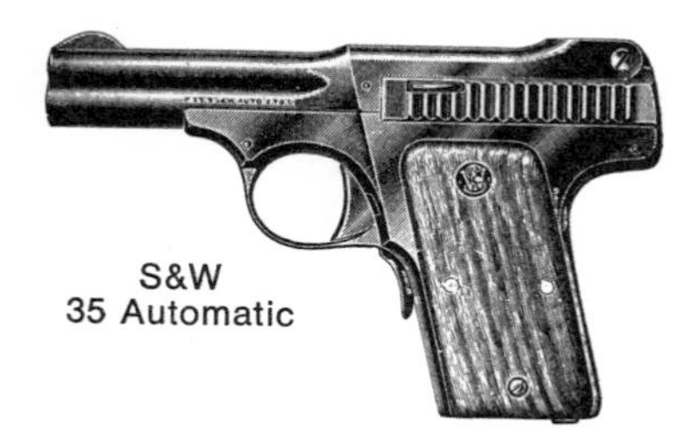
S&W
35 Automatic

Smith & Wesson 35 Automatic Pistol $250

Caliber, 35 S&W Automatic. 7-shot magazine. 3½-inch barrel (hinged to frame). 6½ inches overall. Weight, 25 ounces. Fixed sights. Blued or nickel finish. Plain walnut stocks. Made from 1913 to 1921.

S&W
Model 57

Smith & Wesson Model 57 41 Magnum Double Action Revolver $175

Caliber, 41 Magnum. 6-shot cylinder. Barrel lengths: 4, 6, 8⅜ inches. Overall length (with 6-inch barrel), 11⅜ inches. Weight (with 6-inch barrel), 40 ounces. Micrometer click rear sight, ramp front sight. Target stocks of checkered Goncalo Alves. Made from 1964 to date.

S&W
32 Automatic

Smith & Wesson 32 Automatic Pistol $400

Caliber, 32 Automatic. Same general specifications as 35 caliber model, but barrel is fastened to the receiver instead of hinged. Made from 1924 to 1937.

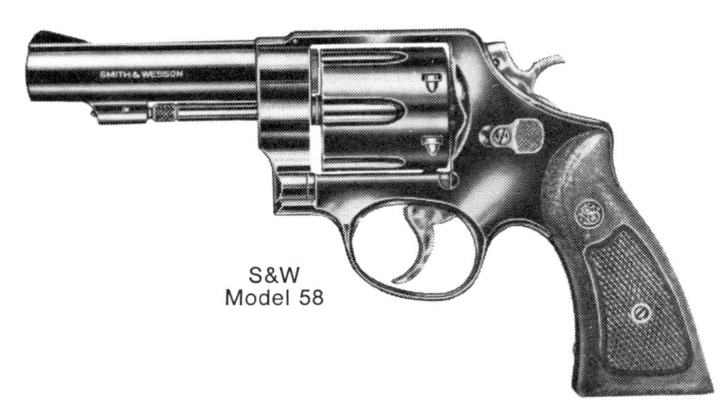

S&W
Model 58

Smith & Wesson Model 58 41 Military & Police Double Action Revolver $95

Caliber, 41 Magnum. 6-shot cylinder. 4-inch barrel. Overall length, 9¼ inches. Weight, 41 ounces. Fixed sights. Checkered walnut stocks. Made from 1964 to date.

S&W
Model 39

Smith & Wesson Model 39 9mm Double Action Automatic Pistol

Caliber, 9mm Luger. 8-shot magazine. 4-inch barrel. Overall length, 7-7/16 inches. Weight, 26½ ounces. Click adjustable rear sight, ramp front sight. Checkered walnut stocks. Made from 1954 to date.
Note: Between 1954 and 1966, 927 pistols of this model were made with steel, instead of alloy, frames.
With steel frame **$500**
With alloy frame **$105**

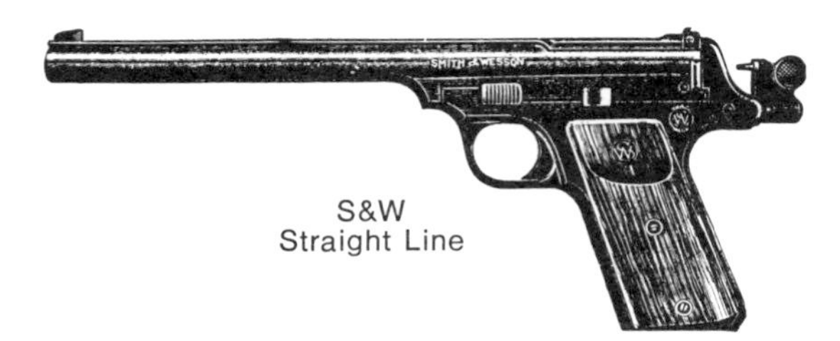

S&W
Straight Line

Smith & Wesson Straight Line Single Shot Target Pistol $400

Frame shaped like that of an automatic pistol, barrel swings to the left on pivot for extracting and loading, straight line trigger and hammer movement. Caliber, 22 Long Rifle. 10-inch barrel. Approximately 11¼ inches overall. Weight, 34 ounces. Target sights. Blued finish. Smooth walnut stocks. Supplied in metal case with screwdriver and cleaning rod. Made from 1925 to 1936.

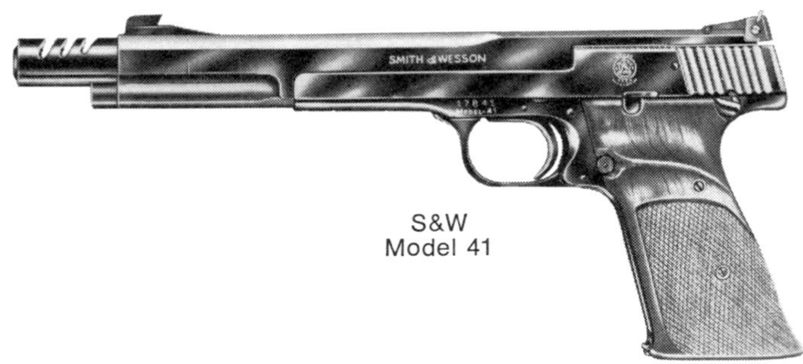

S&W
Model 41

Smith & Wesson Model 41 22 Automatic Pistol $120

Caliber: 22 Long Rifle, 22 Short (not interchangeably). 10-shot magazine. Barrel lengths: 5, 7⅜ inch; latter has detachable muzzle brake. 12 inches overall (7⅜" bbl.). Weight, 43½ ounces (7⅜" bbl.). Click adjustable rear sight, undercut Patridge front sight. Blued finish. Checkered walnut stocks with thumb-rest. Made from 1957 to date.

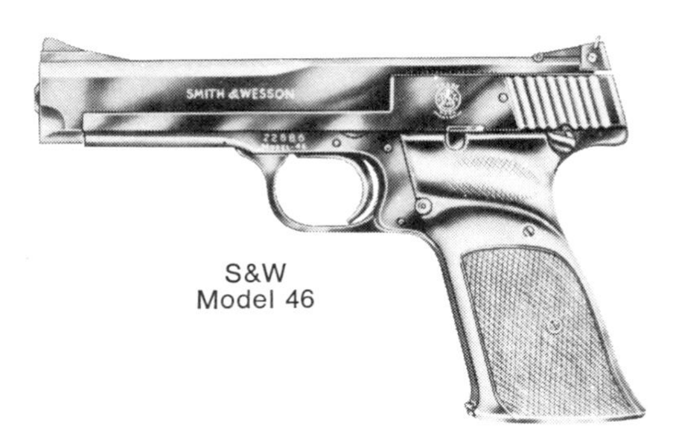

S&W
Model 46

Smith & Wesson Model 46 22 Automatic Pistol $100

Caliber, 22 Long Rifle. 10-shot magazine. Barrel lengths: 5, 7 inch. 10-9/16 inches overall (7" bbl.). Weight, 42 ounces (7" bbl.). Click adjustable rear sight, undercut Patridge front sight. Blue finish. Molded nylon stocks with thumb-rest. Made from 1957 to 1966.

S&W
Model 52

Smith & Wesson Model 52 38 Master Automatic Pistol $200

Caliber, 38 Special (mid-range wadcutter only). 5-shot magazine. 5-inch barrel. Overall length, 8⅝ inches. Weight, 41 ounces. Micrometer click rear sight, Patridge front sight on ramp base. Checkered walnut stocks. Made from 1961 to date.

Star, Bonifacio Echeverria, S. A., Eibar, Spain

Star Model CO Pocket Automatic Pistol $85

Caliber, 25 Automatic (6.35mm). 2¾-inch barrel. 4½ inches overall. Weight, 13 ounces. Fixed sights. Blued finish. Plastic stocks.

Star Model HN Automatic Pistol $85

Caliber, 380 Automatic (9mm Corto). 6-shot magazine. 2¾-inch barrel. 5-9/16 inches overall. Weight, 20 ounces. Fixed sights. Blued finish. Plastic stocks.

Star Model H Automatic Pistol $85

Same as Model HN except caliber 32 Automatic (7.65mm). 7-shot magazine. Weight, 20 ounces.

Star Police Model I Automatic Pistol $85

Caliber, 32 Automatic (7.65mm). 9-shot magazine. 4-13/16-inch barrel. 7½ inches overall. Weight, 24 ounces. Fixed sights. Blued finish. Plastic stocks.

Star Police Model IN Automatic Pistol $85

Same as Model I, except caliber 380 Automatic (9mm Corto), 8-shot magazine, weighs 24½ ounces.

Star Military Model A Automatic Pistol $100

Modification of the Colt Government Model 45 Auto which it closely resembles. Calibers: 9mm Bergmann, 38 ACP, 9mm Luger. 8-shot magazine. 5-inch barrel. 8 inches overall. Weight, 35 ounces. Fixed sights. Blued finish. Checkered stocks.

Star Military Model M Automatic Pistol $100

Modification of the Colt Government Model 45 Auto which is closely resembles. Calibers: 9mm Bergmann, 38 ACP, 9mm Luger. 8-shot magazine. 5-inch barrel. magazine, except 7-shot in 45 caliber. 5-inch barrel. 8½ inches overall. Weight, 36 ounces. Fixed sights. Blued finish. Checkered stocks.

Star Model SI Automatic Pistol $100

Reduced-size modification of the Colt Government Model 45 Auto. Caliber, 32 Automatic (7.65mm). 8-shot magazine. 4-inch barrel. 6½ inches overall. Weight, 20 ounces. Fixed sights. Blued finish. Plastic stocks.

Star Model S Automatic Pistol $100

Same as Model SI except caliber 380 Automatic (9mm), 7-shot magazine, weighs 19 ounces.

Star Model Super SI & Super S Automatic Pistols . $100

Same general specifications as the regular Model SI & S except with improvements described under "Super Star."

Super Star Automatic Pistol $110

Improved version of the Model "M" with same general specifications; has disarming bolt permitting easier takedown, indicator of cartridge in chamber, magazine safety, takedown magazine, improved sights with luminous spots for aiming in darkness. Calibers: 38 ACP, 45 Auto.

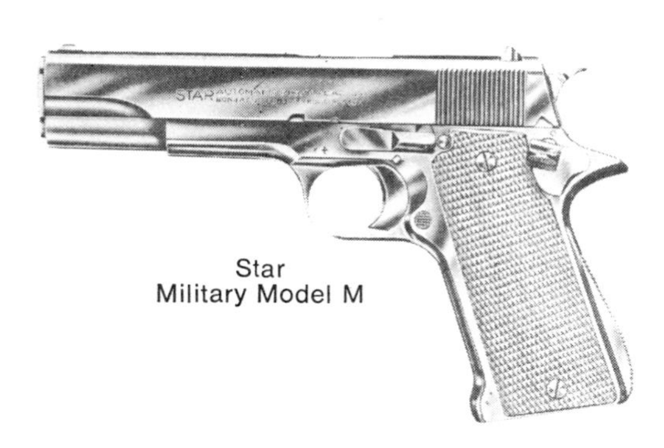

Star
Military Model M

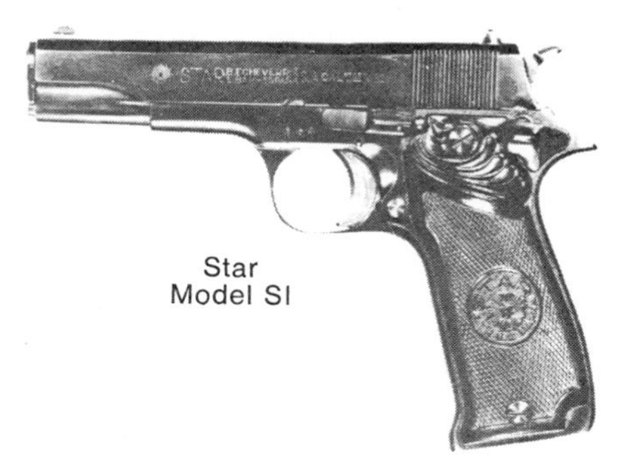

Star
Model SI

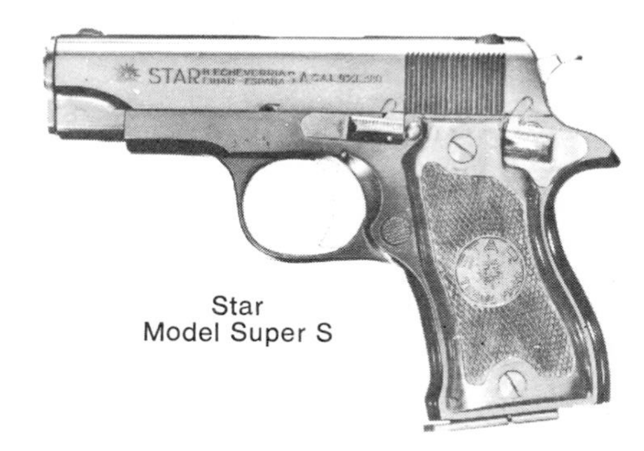

Star
Model Super S

Super Star

Super Star Target Model Automatic Pistol $125

Same as regular "Super Star" except with adjustable target rear sight.

Star Model F Automatic Pistol $80

Caliber, 22 Long Rifle. 10-shot magazine. 4½-inch barrel. 7¼ inches overall. Weight, 25 ounces. Fixed sights. Blued finish. Plastic stocks. Currently manufactured.

Star Model F Sport Automatic Pistol $90

Same as regular Model F but with 6-inch barrel and adjustable sights. Weighs, 27 ounces.

Star Model F Target Automatic Pistol $90

Same as regular Model F but with 7-inch barrel and adjustable sights. Weight, 29 ounces.

Star Olympia Rapid-Fire Automatic Pistol $125

Caliber, 22 Short. 9-shot magazine. 7-inch barrel. 11-1/16 inches overall. Weight, 52 ounces with weights). Adjustable target sight. Adjustable 3-piece barrel weight. Aluminum alloy slide. Muzzle brake. Plastic stocks.

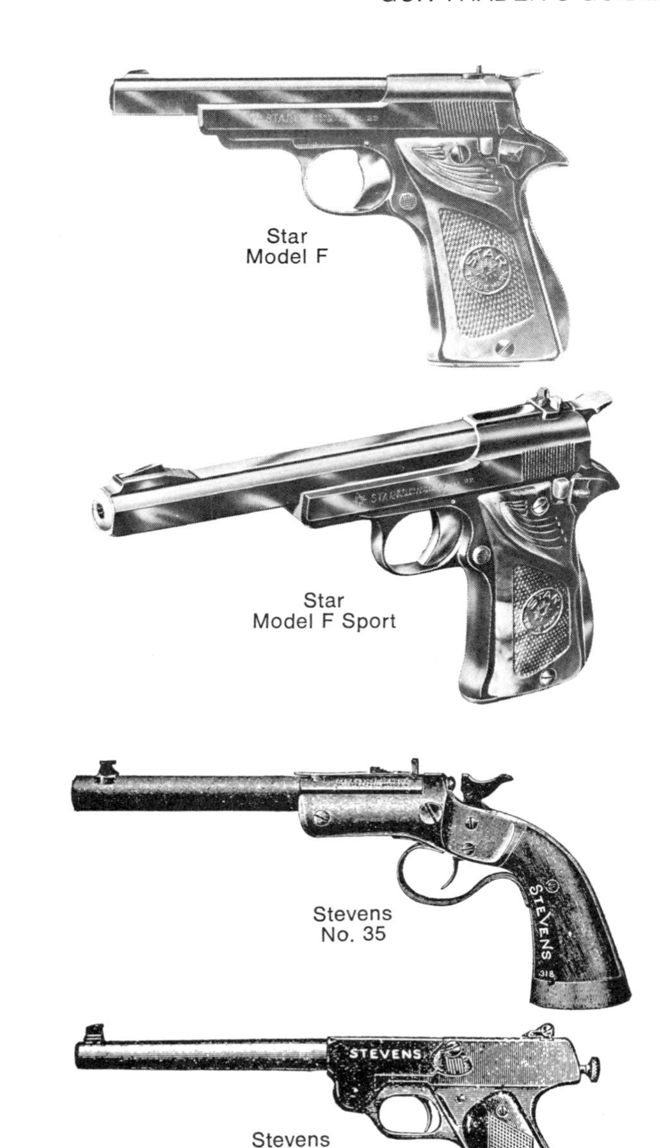

Star Model F

Star Model F Sport

Stevens No. 35

Stevens No. 10

J. Stevens Arms Co., Chicopee Falls, Massachusetts

Stevens No. 35 Offhand Model Single Shot Target Pistol $150

Tip-up action. Caliber, 22 Long Rifle. Barrel lengths: 6, 8, 10 and 12¼-inch. Weight, 24 ounces with 6-inch barrel. Target sights. Blued finish. Walnut stocks. *Note:* This pistol is similar to the earlier "Gould" model. No. 35 was also supplied chambered for 410 shotshell. Made from 1907 to 1939.

Stevens No. 10 Single Shot Target Pistol $75

Caliber, 22 Long Rifle. 8-inch barrel. 11½ inches overall. Weight, 36 ounces. Target sights. Blued finish. Hard rubber stocks. In external appearance this arm resembles an automatic pistol; it has a tip-up action.

Thompson/Center Contender

Thompson/Center Arms Rochester, New Hampshire

Thompson/Center Contender Single Shot Pistol

Break frame, underlever action. Calibers: (rimfire) 22 LR, 22 WMR, 5mm RRM; (standard centerfire) 22 Hornet, 22 Rem. Jet, 221 Fireball, 222 Rem., 256 Win. Mag., 30 M1 Carbine, 30-30, 38 Auto, 38 Special, 357 Mag, 9mm Luger, 45 Auto, 45 Colt, 44 Magnum/Hot Shot; (wildcat centerfire) 17 Ackley Bee, 17 Bumblebee, 17 Hornet, 17 K Hor-

net, 17 Mach IV, 17-222, 17-223, 22 K Hornet, 357-44 B&D. Barrel lengths: 8¾" or 10-inch; 44 Mag. barrel has detachable choke. 13½ inches overall with 10-inch barrel. Weight, with 10-inch barrel, about 43 ounces. Blued finish; receiver sides photoengraved. Ramp front sight, adjustable rear sight. Checkered walnut fore end and grips. Made from 1966 to date.
Centerfire calibers **$105**
Rimfire calibers **$100**
Extra barrel, centerfire . . . . **$ 35**
Extra barrel, rimfire . . . . **$ 30**

Union Fire Arms Co., Toledo, Ohio

Union Automatic Revolver $125

Similar in action to the Webley-Fosbery. Hinged frame. Caliber, 32 S&W. 5-shot cylinder. 3-inch barrel. 6½ inches overall. Weight, about 18 ounces. Fixed sights. Blued finish. Hard rubber stocks.

Union Pocket Automatic Pistol $125

Caliber, 32 Automatic. Bears a superficial resemblence to the Luger.

Unique Pistol made by Manufacture D'Armes Des Pyrenees Francaises, Hendaye, France

Unique Model 52 Pocket Automatic Pistol $70

External hammer. Caliber, 22 Long Rifle. 10-Shot magazine. 3¼-inch barrel. 5¾ inches overall. Weight, 24 ounces. Fixed sights. Blued finish. Plastic grips. Currently manufactured.

U. S. Revolvers manufactured by Iver Johnson's Arms & Cycle Works, Fitchburg, Massachusetts

U. S. Double Action Revolver $45

Solid frame. Calibers: 22 R.F., 32 R.F., 32 S&W, 38 S&W. 7-shot cylinder (22 cal), 5-shot cylinder (other calibers). Barrel lengths: 2½ and 4½-inch. Weights: 11 ounces (22 cal.), 12 ounces (32 cal.), 17 ounces (38 cal.). Fixed sights. Blued or nickel finish. Hard rubber stocks.

U. S. Hammerless Double Action Revolver $55

Hinged frame. Calibers: 32 S&W, 38 S&W. 5 shot cylinder. Barrel length: 3, 3¼ and 5-inch. Fixed sights. Blued or nickel finish. Hard rubber stocks.

Walther Pistols made prior to and during World War II by Waffenfabrik Walther, Zella-Mehlis (Thur.), Germany

Walther Model 1 Automatic Pistol $125

Caliber, 25 Automatic (6.35mm). 6-shot magazine. 2.1-inch barrel. 4.4 inches overall. Weight, 12.8 ounces. Fixed sights. Blued finish. Checkered hard rubber stocks. Introduced in 1908.

Walther Model 2 Automatic Pistol $125

Caliber, 25 Automatic (6.35mm). 6-shot magazine. 2.1-inch barrel. 4.2 inches overall. Weight, 9.8 ounces. Fixed sights. Blued finish. Checkered hard rubber stocks. Introduced in 1909.

Walther Model 3 Automatic Pistol $125

Caliber, 32 Automatic (7.65mm). 6-shot magazine. 2.6-inch barrel. 5 inches overall. Weight, 16.6 ounces. Fixed sights. Blued finish. Checkered hard rubber stocks. Introduced in 1910.

Walther Model 4 Automatic Pistol $135

Caliber, 32 Automatic (7.65mm). 8-shot magazine. 3.5-inch barrel. 5.9 inches overall. Weight, 18.6 ounces. Fixed sights. Blued finish. Checkered hard rubber stocks. Made from 1910 to 1918.

Walther Model 5 Automatic Pistol $125

Caliber, 25 Automatic (6.35mm). 6-shot magazine. 2.1-inch barrel 4.2 inches overall. Weight, 9.6 ounces. Fixed sights. Blued finish. Checkered hard rubber stocks. Introduced in 1913.

Walther Model 6 Automatic Pistol $175

Caliber, 9mm Luger. 8-shot magazine. 4¾-inch barrel. 8¼ inches overall. Weight, 34 ounces. Fixed sights. Blued finish. Checkered hard rubber stocks. Made from 1915 to 1917. *Note:* Powerful 9mm Luger cartridge really is too much for the simple blowback system of this pistol and firing is not recommended.

Walther Model 7 Automatic Pistol $125

Caliber, 25 Automatic (6.35mm). 8-shot magazine. 3-inch barrel. 5.3 inches overall. Weight, 11.8 ounces. Fixed sights. Blued finish. Checkered hard rubber stocks. Made from 1917 to 1918.

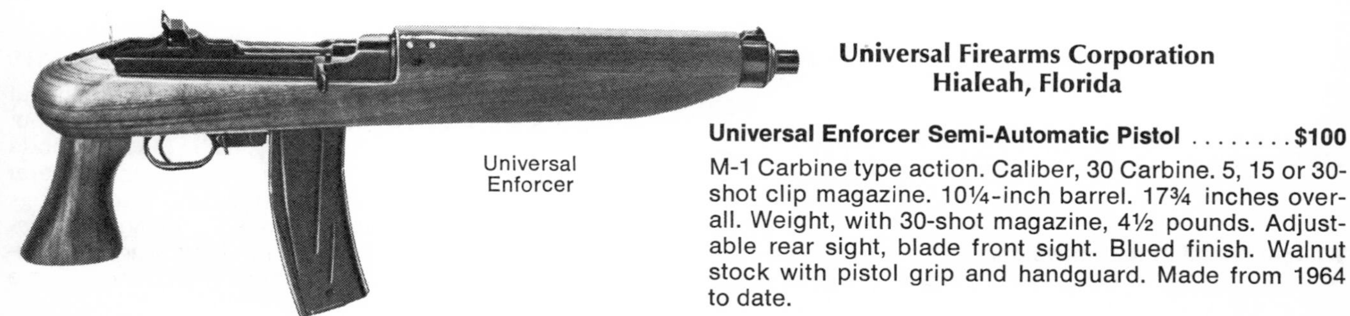

Universal Enforcer

Universal Firearms Corporation Hialeah, Florida

Universal Enforcer Semi-Automatic Pistol $100

M-1 Carbine type action. Caliber, 30 Carbine. 5, 15 or 30-shot clip magazine. 10¼-inch barrel. 17¾ inches overall. Weight, with 30-shot magazine, 4½ pounds. Adjustable rear sight, blade front sight. Blued finish. Walnut stock with pistol grip and handguard. Made from 1964 to date.

Walther Model 8 Automatic Pistol **$135**

Caliber, 25 Automatic (6.35mm). 8-shot magazine. 2⅞-inch barrel. 5⅛ inches overall. Weight, 12⅜ ounces. Fixed sights. Blued finish. Checkered plastic stocks. Made from 1920 to 1945.

Walther Model 8 Lightweight Automatic Pistol **$160**

Same as standard Model 8 except about 25% lighter due to use of aluminum alloys.

Walther Model 9 Vest Pocket Automatic Pistol **$135**

Caliber, 25 Automatic (6.35mm). 6-shot magazine. 2-inch barrel. 3-15/16 inches overall. Weight, 9 ounces. Fixed sights. Blued finish. Checkered plastic stocks. Made from 1921 to 1945.

Walther Model PP Automatic Pistol

Polizeipistole ("Police Pistol"). Caliber: 22 Long Rifle (5.6mm), 25 Automatic (6.35mm), 32 Automatic (7.65mm), 380 Automatic (9mm). 8-shot magazine. 3⅞-inch barrel. 6-5/16 inches overall. Weight, 23 ounces. Fixed sights. Blued finish. Checkered plastic stocks. *Note:* Wartime models are inferior in workmanship to prewar commercial pistols. Made from 1929 to 1945.

22 caliber, commercial model **$275**
25 caliber, commercial model **$300**
32 and 380 caliber, commercial model **$200**
Wartime model **$175**

Walther Model PP Lightweight

Same as standard Model PP except about 25% lighter due to use of aluminum alloys. Values 50% higher.

Walther Presentation Model PP 7.65mm **$400**

Made of soft aluminum alloy in green gold color, these pistols were not intended to be fired.

Walther Model PPK Automatic Pistol

Polizeipistole Kriminal ("Detective Pistol"). Calibers: 22 Long Rifle (5.6mm), 25 Automatic (6.35mm), 32 Automatic (7.65mm), 380 Automatic (9mm). 7-shot magazine. 3¼-inch barrel. 5⅞ inches overall. Weight, 19 ounces. Fixed sights. Blued finish. Checkered plastic stocks. *Note:* Wartime models are inferior in workmanship to prewar commercial pistols. Made from 1931 to 1945.

22 and 25 caliber, commercial model **$300**
32 and 380 caliber, commercial model **$225**
Wartime model **$200**

Walther Model PPK Lightweight

Same as standard Model PPK except about 25% lighter due to use of aluminum alloys. Values 50% higher.

Walther Presentation Model PPK 7.65mm **$425**

Made of soft aluminum alloy in green gold color, these pistols were not intended to be fired.

Walther Self-Loading Sport Pistol **$275**

Caliber, 22 Long Rifle. 10-shot magazine. Barrel lengths: 6 and 9-inch. 9⅞ inches overall with 6-inch barrel. Target sights. Blued finish. One-piece, wood or plastic stocks, checkered. Introduced in 1932.

Walther Olympia Sport Model Automatic Pistol **$300**

Caliber, 22 Long Rifle. 10-shot magazine. 7.4-inch barrel. 10.7 inches overall. Weight, 30½ ounces, less weights. Adjustable target sights. Blued finish. Checkered stocks. Set of four detachable weights was supplied at extra cost. Introduced about 1936.

Walther Olympia Hunting Model Automatic Pistol .. **$300**

Same general specifications as Olympia Sport Model but with 4-inch barrel. Weight, 28½ ounces.

Walther Olympia Rapid Fire Model Automatic Pistol **$400**

Caliber, 22 Short. 6-shot magazine. 7.4-inch barrel. 10.7 inches overall. Weight (without 12⅜ ounce detachable muzzleweight), 27½ ounces. Adjustable target sights. Blued finish. Checkered stocks. Introduced 1936.

Walther Olympia Funfkampf Model Automatic Pistol **$500**

Caliber, 22 Long Rifle. 10-shot magazine. 9.6-inch barrel. 13 inches overall. Weight, 33 ounces, less weight. Set of 4 detachable weights. Adjustable target sights. Blued finish. Checkered stocks.

Walther Model HP Automatic Pistol **$400**

Pre-war commercial version of the P-38. "HP" is abbreviation of "Heeres Pistole" ("Army Pistol"). Caliber, 9mm Luger. 8-shot magazine. 5-inch barrel. 8⅜ inches overall. Weight, about 34½ ounces. Fixed sights. Blued finish. Checkered wood or plastic stocks. The Model HP is distinguished by its notably fine material and workmanship. Introduced in 1937.

Walther P-38 Military Automatic Pistol **$150**

Modification of the Model HP adopted as an official German Service arm in 1938 and produced throughout World War II by Walther (code "ac"), Mauser (code "byf") and a number of other manufacturers. General specifications are the same as Model HP, but there is a vast difference in quality, the P-38 being a mass-produced military pistol; some of the late wartime models were very roughly finished and tolerances were quite loose.

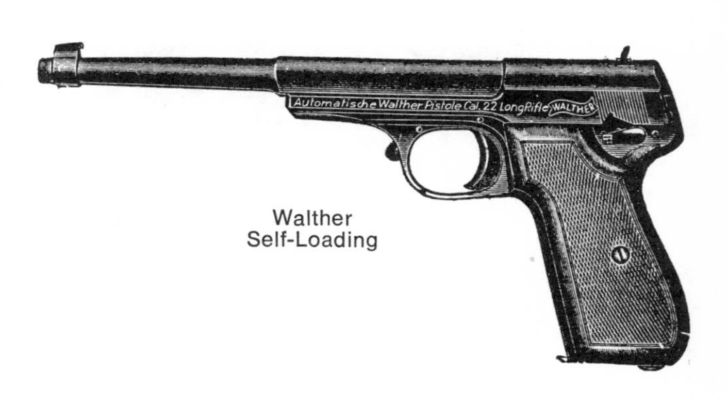

Walther
Self-Loading

Walther
Model 9

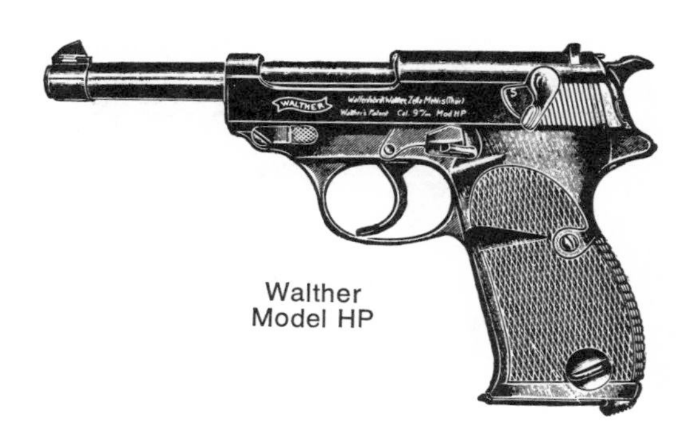

Walther
Model HP

Walther PP
(Prewar)

Walther
P-38
(WWII Model)

Walther PPK
(WWII Model)

Walther Pistols currently manufactured in West Germany by Carl Walther Waffenfabrik, Ulm/Donau.

Walther Model PP (Postwar)

Walther Model PP Automatic Pistol **$140**

Same general specifications as prewar Model PP.

Walther Model PPK (Postwar)

Walther Model PPK Automatic Pistol **$250**

Same general specifications as prewar Model PPK. Steel and lightweight alloy models. U.S. importation discontinued in 1968.

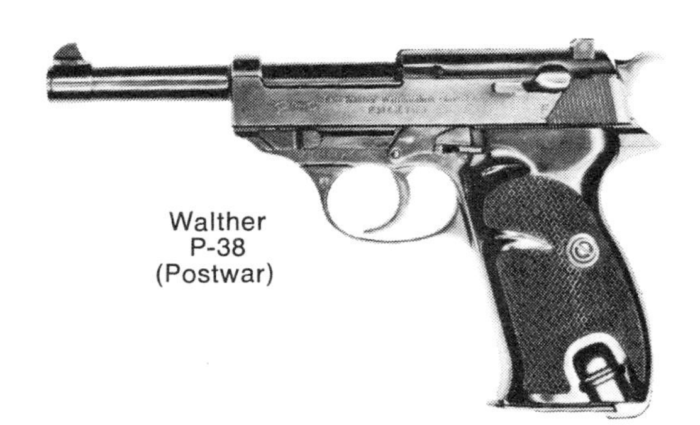

Walther P-38 (Postwar)

Walther Model P-38 Automatic Pistol Commercial . **$180**

Postwar commercial version of P-38 military pistol. Same general specifications, except lighter weight—27½ ounces—due to use of lightweight alloys.

Walther Pistols made in France, since 1953, by Manufacture De Machines Du Haut-Rhin (MANURHIN) at Mulhouse-Bourtzwiller

Walther Mark II Model PP Automatic Pistol **$125**

Same general specifications as pre-war Model PP.

Walther Mark II Model PPK Automatic Pistol **$225**

Same general specifications as pre-war Model PPK.

Walther Mark II Model PPK Lightweight **$225**

Same as standard PPK except has dural receiver. Calibers. 22 Long Rifle and 32 Auto.
Note: The designation "Mark II" is used here to distinguish between these and the pre-war models. Actually, only recent MANURHIN production bears the marking "Walther Mark II"; early (c. 1953-54) models have the MANURHIN trademark on slide and grips instead of that of Walther. U.S. importation discontinued.

Warner Arms Corporation (or "Davis-Warner Arms Co.") of Norwich, Connecticut

Warner Infallible Pocket Automatic Pistol **$125**

Similar to the Browning Model 1900. Caliber, 32 Automatic. 7-shot magazine. 3-inch barrel. 6½ inches overall. Weight about 24 ounces. Fixed sights. Blued finish. Hard rubber stocks. Made c. 1917.

Webley & Scott Ltd., London & Birmingham, England

Webley .25 Hammer Model

Webley 25 Hammer Model Automatic Pistol **$70**

Caliber, 25 Automatic. 6-shot magazine. Length overall, 4¾ inches. Weight, 11¾ ounces. No sights. Blue finish. Checkered vulcanite stocks.

Webley
.25 Hammerless

Webley 25 Hammerless Model Automatic Pistol $70

Caliber, 25 Automatic. 6-shot magazine. Length overall, 4¼ inches. Weight, 9¾ ounces. Fixed sights. Blued finish. Checkered vulcanite stocks.

Webley
Metropolitan
Police

Webley Metropolitan Police Automatic Pistol $75

Calibers: 32 Automatic, 380 Automatic. 8-shot magazine (32 cal.), 7-shot (380 cal). 3½-inch barrel. 6¼ inches overall. Weight, 20 ounces. Fixed sights. Blued finish. Checkered vulcanite stocks.

Webley
9mm Military & Police

Webley 9mm Military & Police Automatic Pistol $75

Caliber, 9mm Browning Long. 8-shot magazine. 8 inches overall. Weight, 32 ounces. Fixed sights. Blued finish. Checkered vulcanite stocks.

Webley "Semi-Automatic" Single Shot Pistol $85

Similar in appearance to the Webley Metropolitan Police Model Automatic, this pistol is "semi-automatic" in the sense that the fired case is extracted and ejected and the hammer cocked as in a blow-back automatic pistol; it is loaded singly and the slide manually operated in loading. Caliber, 22 Long. Barrel lengths: 4½ and 9-inch. Overall length with 9-inch barrel 10¾ inches. Weight with 9-inch barrel, 24 ounces. Adjustable sights. Blued finish. Checkered vulcanite stocks.

Webley
Single Shot Target

Webley Single Shot Target Pistol $90

Hinged frame. Caliber, 22 Long Rifle. 10-inch barrel. 15 inches overall. Weight, 37 ounces. Fixed sights on earlier models, current production has adjustable rear sight. Blued finish. Checkered walnut or vulcanite stocks.

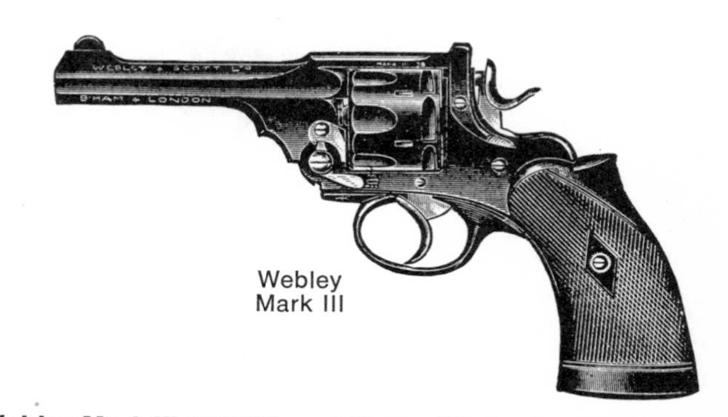

Webley
Mark III

Webley Mark III 38 Military & Police Model Revolver . $75

Hinged frame. Double action. Caliber, 38 S&W, 6-shot cylinder. Barrel lengths: 3 and 4-inch. Overall length with 4-inch barrel 9½ inches. Weight, with 4-inch barrel, 21 ounces. Fixed sights. Blued finish. Checkered walnut or vulcanite stocks.

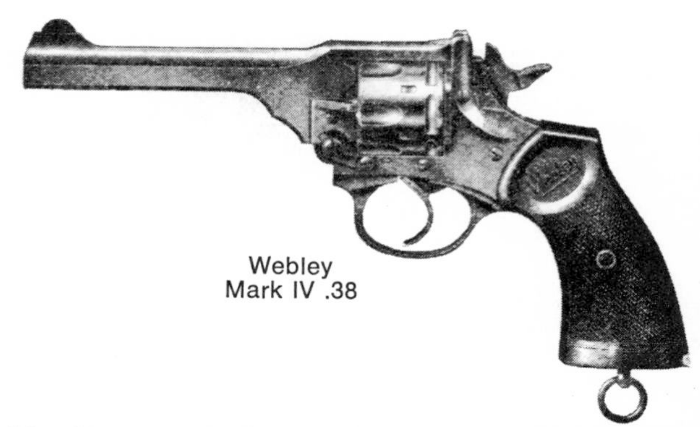

Webley
Mark IV .38

Webley Mark IV 38 Military & Police Model Revolver $75

Hinged frame. Double Action. Caliber, 38 S&W. 6-shot cylinder. Barrel lengths: 3, 4 and 5-inch. 9⅛ inches overall with 5-inch barrel. Weight with 5-inch barrel, 27 ounces. Fixed sights. Blued finish. Checkered stocks.

Webley
Mark IV .22

Webley Mark IV 22 Caliber Target Revolver **$100**

Same frame and general appearance as Mark IV 38. Caliber, 22 Long Rifle. 6-shot cylinder. 6-inch barrel. 10⅛ inches overall. Weight, 34 ounces. Target sights. Blued finish. Checkered stocks.

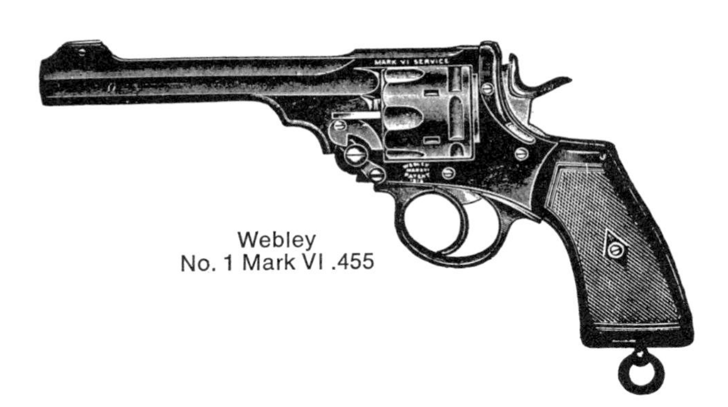

Webley
No. 1 Mark VI .455

Webley No. 1 Mark VI 455 British Service Revolver .. **$75**

Double action. Hinged frame. Caliber, 455 Webley. 6-shot cylinder. Barrel length: 4, 6 and 7½-inch. Overall length with 6-inch barrel, 11¼ inches. Weight, with 6-inch barrel, 38 ounces. Fixed sights. Blued finish. Checkered walnut or vulcanite stocks.

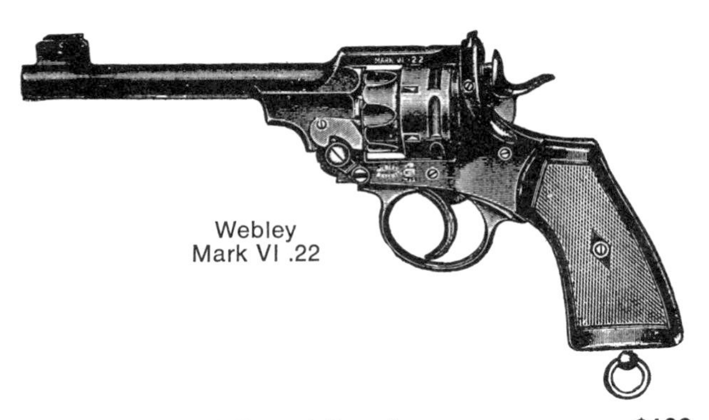

Webley
Mark VI .22

Webley Mark VI 22 Target Revolver **$100**

Same frame and general appearance as the Mark VI 455. Caliber, 22 Long Rifle. 6-shot cylinder. 6-inch barrel. 11¼ inches overall. Weight, 40 ounces. Target sights. Blued finish. Checkered walnut or vulcanite stocks.

Webley
RIC Model

Webley "RIC" Model Revolver **$85**

Royal Irish Constabulary or "Bulldog" Model. Double Action. Solid frame. Caliber, 455 Webley. 5-shot cylinder. 2¼-inch barrel. Weight, 21 ounces. Fixed sights. Blued finish. Checkered walnut or vulcanite stocks.

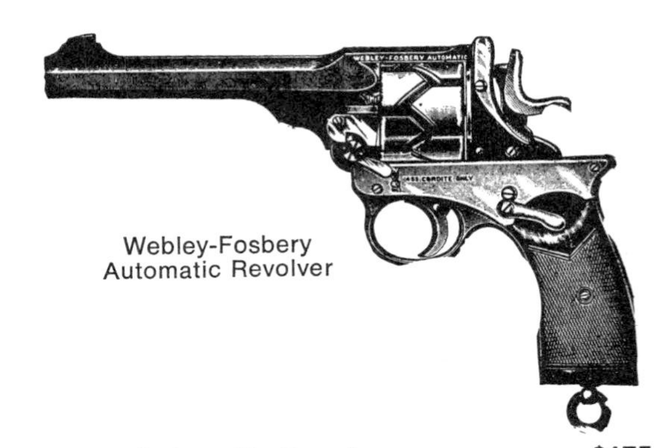

Webley-Fosbery
Automatic Revolver

Webley-Fosbery Automatic Revolver **$175**

Hinged frame. Recoil action revolves cylinder and cocks hammer. Caliber, 455 Webley. 6-shot cylinder. 6-inch barrel. 12 inches overall. Weight, 42 ounces. Fixed sights. Blued finish. Checkered walnut stocks.

NOTES ON HANDGUN VALUES

Current high demand for new pistols and revolvers (especially Colt and Smith & Wesson) at times results in shortages of some popular models. When this occurs, the price of a used handgun of such a model often becomes inflated temporarily, rising well above its *Gun Trader's Guide* value, which is normal and not low.

Advanced handgun collectors frequently recognize minor variations that can greatly affect value. Unless otherwise indicated, a value shown in this book is for the lowest-priced variety of its type.